THE PRINCIPLES OF
FOREST YIELD STUDY

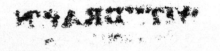

THE PRINCIPLES OF
FOREST YIELD STUDY

Studies in the Organic Production, Structure, Increment and Yield of Forest Stands

BY

Dr. ERNST ASSMANN

Professor at the University of Munich

TRANSLATED BY

SABINE H. GARDINER

ENGLISH EDITOR

P. W. DAVIS

PERGAMON PRESS

Oxford · New York · Toronto · Sydney · Braunschweig

Pergamon Press Ltd., Headington Hill Hall, Oxford
Pergamon Press Inc., Maxwell House, Fairview Park, Elmsford, New York 10523
Pergamon of Canada Ltd., 207 Queen's Quay West, Toronto 1
Pergamon Press (Aust.) Pty. Ltd., 19a Boundary Street, Rushcutters Bay,
N.S.W. 2011, Australia
Vieweg & Sohn GmbH, Burgplatz 1, Braunschweig

First English edition 1970
Library of Congress Catalog Card No. 74–114 851

This is a translation of the original German *Waldertragskunde*
© 1961 BLV Bayerischer Landwirtschaftsverlag GmbH, München

Printed in Hungary
08 006658 5

CONTENTS

FOREWORD   xiii

INTRODUCTION   1

1. Historical Development   1
2. The Place of Forest Yield Theory in Forest Science   3
3. Research Objects and Methods Employed in Forest Yield Studies   4

SECTION A   WOODY GROWTH AS PART OF THE TOTAL PRODUCE OF PLANT SOCIETIES   7

1. Soil, Climate and Plant Production   7
     Mutual interactions between soil, climate and plant cover   7
     Yields in agriculture and forestry   8
     Soil factors of primary importance in the formation of plant material   9
2. The Assimilation Process from the Point of View of Quantitative Ecology   10
     (a) The Principal Factors in the Assimilation Process   11
     The factor of light   11
     The part played by temperature   13
     The CO_2-content of the air   14
     Transpiration and water requirements   18
     The influence of nutrient supplies   20
       Mitscherlich's efficacy law   20
     (b) The Characteristic Behaviour of Different Forest Trees in the Assimilatory Process   23
     The respiration economy of our native tree species   25
     Respiration of the root system   26
     The economy of transpiration   27
     (c) Assimilation Rates and Leaf Quantities of Trees and Stands   28
     Leaf area and stocked ground area   29
     Relative performances of sun-leaves and shade-leaves   30
     Leaf quantities and increment   31
3. The Organic Production of Forest Stands and Its Components   33
     The production equation of Boysen-Jensen   34
     Foliage and increment   35
     Production spectra of Mar:Møller   36

SECTION B   TREE GROWTH AND FORM   39

1. Annual Shoot Growth and Height Increase   39
     (a) Seasonal Changes of the Annual Height Increment   40
     (b) Height Growth Related to Age   41
     Curves of total growth and increment   41
     The Backman growth law   42
     (c) Factors Influencing Height Growth   44
2. Width of Annual Rings and Diameter Increment   48
     (a) Seasonal Start, Duration and Rate of Formation of the Annual Ring   49
     (b) The Growth Rhythm of Diameter and Basal Area in Relation to Age   51
     (c) Annual Ring Width, Diameter and Sectional Area Increments at Different Stem Heights   53
     Characteristic increment distribution on the tree stem   53
     Changes of the increment distribution on the stem   55

3. The Shape of the Tree Stem   57
   (a) The Stem Profile   57
   (b) The Form of Stem Cross-sections   63
   (c) Form Factor, Volume and Assortment Tables   64
       The problem of form and form factor   64
       Stem measurement according to Hohenadl   66
       Assortment tables   70
   (d) Formation and Dimensions of the Root System   70
   (e) The Bark Fraction   73
   (f) Units of Volume and Weight employed in the Determination of Growth and Yield   75
       Festmetres of standing and felled trees   77
       Timber production in terms of dry weight; volume/weight relationships   78

4. Volume Increment   79
   Current and mean annual increment   80

SECTION C   THE CONSTITUTION AND DEVELOPMENT OF STANDS   83

I. The Social Structure of Tree Crops   83

1. Tree Classes   83
   Natural tree classes   83
   Technical and economic aspects of classification   87

2. Typical Structure of Stands according to Tree Classes and Storeys   92
   Numerical tree classes   92
   Examples of crop classification   96
   Growth comparisons among the tree classes   98

II. Growing Space and Increment   101

1. Growing Space and Ground Coverage of Individual Trees in the Stand   101
   Basal area and crown canopy   101
   Square or quadrat spacing   102
   Triangular spacing   102
   Severe breaking of canopy, extent of ground coverage and degree of disengagement   106
   The "growing-space index" of v. Seebach   108

2. Tree Crown and Increment Efficiency   111
   (a) Structure and Form of the Crown   111
       Descriptive crown measures   111
       Crown morphology   112
       Calculation of the volume and surface of tree crowns   115
       Mean needle and leaf quantities for individual trees   115
   (b) Leaf Quantities, Crown Dimensions and Increment Efficiencies   116
       (i) Factors which influence the efficiencies of given leaf quantities   116
           The influence of site, climate, age and seed origin   116
           Social position and productive capacity   117
           Vertical distribution of the radiation consumption on 7.7.1952   118
       (ii) Crown size and area-related efficiency with different structures of stands and different
            silvicultural treatment   119
            Crown size and capacity in even-aged stands   120
            The effects of thinning on crown dimensions and increment efficiency   123
            Crown size and efficiency in stands of several storeys and mixed ages   127
            Crown size and performance in selection forests   130
            Crown size and productivity in natural mixed forests   136

III. The Pattern of Development and Growth of Pure Stands in Dependence on Age and Site
     Quality   139

1. Dependence on Age   139
   The Age Problem of Our Forest Trees   139
   (a) The Development of Stem Numbers   141

(b) The Height Development   143
    Mean height—top height   143
(c) Progress of Diameter Growth   147
(d) Basal Area and Volume Increment   149
    Relationships between basal area and volume increment; the form-height   151
    The volume increment   152
    Culmination and decline of the mean annual increment of stands   155
    The course of the mean annual increment for a crop anticipates the mean annual increments
      of individual trees   155

2. Dependence on Site: Growth Performance of Tree Crops in Relation to Site   158
  (a) The Problem of Site Quality   158
    The basic relations   160
    The so-called Eichhorn's rule   161
    Gehrhardt's Norway spruce yield table of 1921   163
    Yield tables and reality   164
    Height and total crop yield   165
    Height quality class and total crop yield   168
    Peculiarities of the customary yield tables for spruce   172
    Macro-climatic and local site influences on the total crop yield   173
    Height quality classes or m.a.i. quality classes?   177
    "Static" or "dynamic" quality classification?   180
    Further development of yield tables   181
      General tables and local tables   181
      Essential corrections of commonly used yield tables   181
      Construction of local tables   185
  (b) Productive Efficiencies of Native and Exotic Tree Species on Different Sites   186
    Growth patterns and increment performances of tree species compared on a given site 187
    Growth performance of different species on European sites, as extracted from yield tables 194

3. Disturbances in the Normal Trend of Increment   196
    Climate, weather during the year, and increment   196
    Seed development and wood increment   201
    Increment reductions through pathological influences   202

4. Growth Patterns and Their Interpretation   203
    Attempts to develop mathematical formulae from yield study observations   204
    Growth laws or growth patterns?   205

SECTION D STRUCTURE, INCREMENT AND YIELD OF STANDS IN RELATION TO SILVICULTURAL TREATMENT 207

I. Concept and Scope of Cultural Measures in Stands   207
    Size restrictions upon silvicultural units   208
    Classification of cultural measures by thinning   208

II. The Research Projects of the Verein der Forstlichen Versuchsanstalten (Association of
    Forest Research Institutes)   210

1. Characterization of Thinning Methods   210
    Working plan of 1873   210
    Work project of the Association of Forest Research Institutes drawn up in 1902   211
    The kind of thinning   213
    Criteria of grading in measuring severity of thinning   214
    The mean basal area over a period (p.m.b.a.)   216
    The intensity of thinning; beginning and frequency of intervention   217
    Levels of thinning intensity   218
    Conflict between biological and technico-economic points of view   218

2. Experimental Methods and the Accuracy of Growth Determinations   219
  (a) Layout of the Experiments   219
  (b) Methods of Field Inventory and Computation   220
    Measurement of the basal area   220

Height measuring   221
Measurement of form factors   222
Calculation methods   222
(c) Accuracy of the Increment Determination   223
Is the basal area increment suitable as a criterion of performance in thinning experiments?   225
Correction and smoothing out of faulty experimental results   225

III. The Effects of Different Thinning Methods on Growth and Yield   227

1. Typical Increment Reactions to Thinning   227
The experimental Norway spruce series at Dalby, Sweden   227
Characteristic values of the basal area for different periods   229
The natural critical degree of stocking and the "optimum basal area"   231
An attempt to explain the progress of the optimum curve   232
The acceleration of growth   233

2. Typical Changes of the Average Tree Dimensions   235
The thickening of the stem   235
Reduced length of the harvested stems   236
The change in the distribution of the total production by diameter classes and grades of produce   239

3. Enlargement of Dimensions, Improvement of Timber Quality and Financial Yields   239
Timber prices and price differentials   240
Comparison of the value yields, with and without computation of future value of thinnings   241
Selective and quality-promoting effects of thinning   244

IV. Results of Thinning Experiments carried out to Date in Pure Even-aged Stands   245

1. Common Beech   245
A brief characterization of the species Common beech   245
The most important experimental thinning series   246
Outdated conclusions from former experimental results   247
(a) Volume and Value Efficiencies in Low-thinning Experiments   248
Thinning of A-grade plots, not in accordance with plans   248
Periodic mean basal areas and volume increments of some typical low-thinned series   249
Brief site-description of the research series   250
Results of the Bavarian low-thinned beech series   256
Results of Danish thinning experiments   258
Recent attempts at a total statistical evaluation   261
Optimum and critical basal areas in Common beech   262
Changes in value efficiency due to low thinning   263
Reduction in average length of harvested stem   265
Value performance in the experimental series, Rothenbuch   266
(b) Volume and Value Yields with Crown-thinning Experiments   270
Volume yield in crown-thinning experiments   270
Changes in value yield with crown thinning   270
Experimental crown-thinning series of Common beech, Dalheim 116   271
Disadvantages of the early and inflexible selection of "future stems"   277
The experimental crown-thinning series at Wieda   278
Prospects for success by treatment in the early growth and thicket stages according to
    Schädelin's doctrine   284
(c) Summarizing Conclusions about a Suitable Thinning Technique for Common Beech   286

2. Norway Spruce   287
Brief characterization of the species Norway spruce   287
The most important experimental Norway spruce thinning series and their treatments   288
(a) Volume and Value Yields of Norway Spruce under Different Thinning Régimes   290
Periodic basal area content and volume increment in the Bavarian experimental Norway
    spruce series   290
Is the total growth performance a suitable measure for comparisons?   298
The three characteristic periods of treatment of the Bavarian experimental Norway spruce
    series and their yields   298
The average percentage reduction in basal area as a quantitative measure of thinning   302

Periodic basal area and increment in experimental Norway spruce series of other countries   304
Crown thinning in pure Norway spruce stands?   309
Changes in the total volume and value production as a result of a medium early start of low thinning   312
Changes in the volume and value efficiency with early low thinning: "Rapid growth management"   313
Advantages and disadvantages of rapid-growth management   320
  (b) Summarizing Conclusions for Suitable Thinning Techniques in Norway Spruce Stands   322
3. Scots Pine   323
Brief characterization of the species Scots pine   323
Shortcomings and disturbances of Scots pine thinning experiments   324
Mean basal area and volume increment in Scots pine, based on examples   325
Thinning and value production of Scots pine   328
Summary of conclusions for a suitable thinning technique in Scots pine stands   329
4. Oak   330
Characterization of oak   330
Mean periodic basal area and volume increment of Sessile oak   331
Thinning treatments and financial production of Sessile oak stands   335

V. The Influence of Methods of Establishment and Plant Spacing on Production   338

The Norway spruce cultural trials at Wermsdorf   338
Norway spruce spacing experiment Dietzhausen 37   341
South German Norway spruce spacing experiments   342
Summary of conclusions from cultivation and spacing experiments   345

VI. Increment and Yield of Mixed Stands without Large Age Differences and in Underplanted Stands   346

1. Fundamental Problems of Growth in Mixed Species   346

2. Results of Experiments in Mixed Stands   348
  (a) Combinations of Light-demanding and Shade-tolerant Species   348
    (i) Mixed stands of oak and Common beech   348
    (ii) Mixed stands of Scots pine and Common beech   350
Scots pine open-stand thinning experiment with underplanted beech, Eberswalde 16   351
Mixed Scots pine–Common beech experiment, Eberswalde 21/22   352
The value production of the Common beech fraction   356
    (iii) Mixed stands of Scots pine–Norway spruce (Silver fir, Douglas fir)   356
    (iv) Mixed stands of larch–Common beech   358
    (v) Mixed stands of Common beech and high-grade hardwoods   359
  (b) Combinations of Shade-tolerant and Semi-shade-tolerant Species   360
    (i) Mixtures of beech and spruce   360
Financial production of mixed Common beech–Norway spruce stands; mixed stands or pure stands?   364
    (ii) Mixed stands of Silver fir–Norway spruce–Common beech   365
Characteristics of the species Silver fir (*Abies alba* Miller)   366
Growth production of Silver fir stands and mixed stands of Silver fir–Norway spruce–Common beech   366
Financial production of mixed stands of Silver fir–Norway spruce–Common beech   368

VII. Increment and Yield in Open-stand Systems and Stands which are felled in Several Cutting Operations ("Mehrhiebig")   369

1. Open-stand and High Forest with Reserves System in Common Beech   369
v. Seebach's classic open-stand system   369
  (a) Performance of the "Seebach System", based on Experimental "Seebach" Series   370
  (b) Modern Increment-felling Procedure ("Lichtwuchsbetrieb") in Common beech   374
The Lichtwuchs indicator plots of Common beech in Fabrikschleichach forest   376
Results of Lichtwuchs experiments in the Taunus, Solling and Harz   377
The effect of the Lichtwuchs system on the stem taper, specific gravity and quality of timber   379
Freist's (1960) new yield table for the Lichtwuchs treatment of Common beech   381
Financial production in the Lichtwuchs treatment of beech   382

(c) Two-storeyed High Forest and High Forest with Reserves System   384
   The beech crop under Lichtwuchs treatment in the locality of "Kleinengelein", in Hundels-
      hausen forest   384
   Two-storeyed beech high-forest system in Walkenried forest   385
   System of reserves   389
   Proportionality limit in beech; degree of disengagement and production per unit area   389

2. The Scots Pine Standards (or Reserves) System   391
   (a) Scots Pine Standards System with Pure Scots Pine in the Under Storey   391
   (b) Scots Pine Standards System with a Large Proportion of Shade-tolerant Species in the
        Under Storey   394
   Lowered production in the under storey   395
   The growth of standards   397
   Total volume production and financial production   399

3. The "Perpetual Forest" System of Bärenthoren   401

VIII. Yield Changes Consequent on Deterioration or Improvement of the Local Site Conditions   406

1. Deterioration of Yield   406
   Degradation by the cultivation of pure crops   407
   Lowering of the ground water level   408
   Edge effects   408
   Litter utilization   412

2. Yield Improvements by Amelioration and Fertilizer Treatments   413
   Amelioration and fertilizer experiments and their consequences   413
   The fertilizer experiment at Owingen   415
   The fertilizer experiment in the municipal forest of Speyer   416
   Summary of the results of forest fertilizer experiments prior to 1953   420
   Results of more recent fertilizer experiments   421
   The economic aspect of fertilizer treatment in the forest   427
   Improvement of soils after litter exploitation   428
   Fertilizer treatment of forest soils, soil biology and the living community   432

SECTION E   FOREST ORGANIZATION AND YIELD   435

I. Growth and Yield Relationships in Working Sections of the Normal High Forest   435

1. Model of the Normal Working Section   435

2. Changes in the Characteristic Values of Working Sections due to Different Grades of Thinning
    and Different Rotations   439
   The place of thinning yields in the concept of rotation   444

3. Age Divisions and Increment of Working Sections with an Irregular Structure   445

II. Growth and Output of Selection Forests   446

1. The Selection Forest as a Special Case of a Working Section   446
   (a) Diameter Distribution Curves and Height Curves for a Working Section of an Even-aged High
        Forest and for a Selection Forest   447
   The mean height curves of working sections   452
   (b) The Quality Classification of Selection Stands   454
   Flury's selection forest qualification by class heights   454
   The range of ages within diameter classes of the selection forest   455
   Mitscherlich's quality classification by the diameter increment   456
   The taper and form of trees in a high forest cut by compartments and in a selection forest 457
   Size classes, the lower limit of measurement, and recruitment   459
   The control method. Growing-stock, yield, increment and optimum stocking   459

2. Production of Selection Stands and Comparison with the Production of Normal Even-aged
    High Forest Stands   461
   Results from long-term selection experiments   461

Results of temporary (once-measured) selection-forest sample plots   471
Comparisons of production and tree age   473
Comparison of production according to Flury. Selection or normal high forest?   475

III. Structure and Increment of Natural Forest Stands   479
    Stages of development in natural forests   480
    Increment production of natural forest stands   484

IV. Organization and Production of Intensively Managed Economic Forests   487

APPENDIX 1. Hohenadl's Method   491

APPENDIX 2   492

    Conversion Table of Metric into English Measurements   492
    Dimensions of German Assortments   492
    Classification of Timber   492
    Assortments of Poles   493

REFERENCES   495

INDEX   504

FOREWORD

THE progress made during the past 15 years in the field of forest yield studies is so significant that, for the sake of forest science as well as practical forestry, a summary of the present state of knowledge appeared to be of some pressing urgency.

Effective and reliable information in this field must be sought mainly by attentiveness to the concepts of natural science. It is this fundamental attitude which has led the author to endeavour to establish closer connecting links with the natural sciences, and especially with plant physiology, soil science and meteorology.

Recent works have so successfully contributed to our awareness of the basic processes of organic production in forests—and this includes the quantitative aspects—that it is now possible to make a rough estimate of the influence and importance of the main factors. The study of forest yield is in a favourable position in this respect, because it enables the integrated result of complex individual growth processes to be assessed quantitatively. Thus it has been possible to widen the bridges built by Robert Hartig, Boysen-Jensen, Burger and Mar:Møller. The new *Handbuch der Pflanzenphysiologie*, the 16th volume of which has been published recently, conveys an idea of the extent of research in plant physiology. The subject of CO_2-assimilation alone occupies two volumes and a total of 1881 pages.

The central core of this study of forest yields appertains to the research into growing space and increment which is summarized in section C (The constitution and development of stands). In these studies, new insight is obtained into the intrinsic relationships between crown dimensions and basal area increment. In general, the hitherto commonly practised silvicultural techniques can be regarded as attempts to achieve an optimal allocation of growing space. With the help of the latest key-discoveries it has now become possible on the basis of natural laws to solve the problems of ordinary thinning (Durchforstung), heavy thinning which results in a permanently interrupted crown canopy (Lichtung) and thinning of multi-storey stands. In silviculture, therefore, one is no longer exclusively dependent on the summary results of experiments which in layout, methods and interpretation have been largely inadequate.

On this new basis it has been possible in section D (Structure, increment and yield of stands in relation to silvicultural treatment) to give a clear and indisputable interpretation of the complicated relationships and apparently contradictory results of former thinning experiments. The natural laws which have been worked out in section C have, moreover, helped to simplify the critical interpretation of experiments with mixed stands. In these, as well as in open stand systems and stands with more than one storey, new results have been discovered which are important to practical forestry.

In the chapter headed "Yield changes" the amelioration and treatment by fertilizers of forest soils are discussed from the standpoint of yield studies. The results of new fertilizer experiments open up very hopeful prospects. Not only is it possible by such methods to achieve a considerable increase in the organic production of the forest, but—by means of improved nutrition of forest trees, and a general improvement of the site—also to promote the health and security of the forests under our management.

Among the subjects discussed in the final section, headed "Forest organization and yield", a clarification of important points about selection forest systems has been given. This entailed the unavoidable disappointment of exaggerated expectations which, even now, are often attached to an uneven-aged structure of the growing stock. Sober discoveries, however, are more profitable to forestry, with its long rotations and the important consequences of early decisions, than hopeful illusions.

In all questions treated by the author, he has endeavoured to draw inferences which are sufficiently extensive for their serviceable application in silviculture, yield regulation, and practical forest management. It is hoped that it will be evident that short-sighted profit motives have not been among the determining ideas and that the diverse functions of the modern forest have been sufficiently considered. Owing to the expense of the work involved in a critical study of the extensive data hitherto published, it has, unfortunately, not been possible to give full consideration to works published in languages other than German.

If, today, the results of 80 years of research work in experimental forests and forest research institutes have made it possible to clarify numerous problems, we must remind ourselves of the large amount of selfless and patient work which has been done to produce these results. Thus for a start, thanks must be rendered to all those persons who, by laborious measurements and calculation, have compiled the data which are now susceptible of interpretation. The author's particular thanks are given to those gentlemen who have so readily contributed valuable field inventory results, namely: Prof. Dr. E. Badoux of the Eidgenössische Anstalt für das Forstliche Versuchswesen, Zürich; Prof. Ch. Carbonnier of the Swedish Forest Research Institute, Stockholm; Dr. E. Holmsgaard, Head of the Danish Forest Research Institute, Springforbi; Dr. H. A. Henriksen, Copenhagen; Dr. A. Horki, former Head of the Österreichische Bundes-Versuchsanstalt, Mariabrunn; Prof. Dr. Erteld, Eberswalde; Prof. Dr. G. Mitscherlich, Freiburg; and Landforstmeister K. Hausser, Hechingen. Sincere thanks also go to the heads of the different Landesforstverwaltungen, Oberforstdirektionen and various private forest administrations as well as to the head foresters and foresters of the different forest districts who have kindly assisted the author and his staff of fellow workers. Thanks are also due to the Deutsche Forschungsgemeinschaft who, by generous research grants, have made possible the undertaking of several research projects. Particularly sincere thanks go finally to my fellow workers, especially Dozent Dr. R. Magin, Forstmeister Dr. R. Mayer, Forstassessor R. Kennel, Ingenieur K. Balling and Fräulein E. Hodurek.

In this translation it has been possible to give consideration to some supplementary information and corrections in accordance with the latest state of research.

The author expresses his thanks to the publishers, Springer-Verlag, Berlin, and to Professor Dr. Pisek, Innsbruck, for their kind permission to reproduce some figures.

Munich

ERNST ASSMANN

INTRODUCTION

PRODUCTION techniques in forestry depend on the utilization and systematic control of growth processes. In the course of these processes, smaller or larger quantities of vegetable substance are produced, of which, in the case of a forest, we are mainly interested in the woody substance. *It is the task of yield studies to examine the quantitative extent of growth processes in the forest in relation to time, site and the economical and technical measures available to man.*

Every year, forest trees add to their volume by means of a further layer of wood. If, by measurement, we have determined the volume of an individual tree or of a whole stand at the beginning and at the end of a certain period of time, the *difference* between the two volumes represents the *increment* of that tree or stand for that particular period. Because of the central importance of increment as a measure of performance in our forest stands for a particular period, the subject is, in technical language, known as *increment theory.*

The increment produced by a forest is not identical with the yield. If we aimed at harvesting the actual annual increment we should need to detach the individual increment layers which have grown on the trees of this forest and this, of course, would be absurd. Timber harvesting in a forest requires the felling of entire trees, including their successive increments added over many years. *Yield, in the sense used in this book therefore, is the harvested growth or increment of tree stands.*[1] This explains why, even today, the double title "increment and yield theory" is often used in this special context. If we use the shorter terms "yield theory" or "yield studies", it becomes evident that, on the one hand, the subject is concerned with the growth processes and the quantitative measure of growth conditions of trees and stands, and on the other hand, it has to examine the quantities, method of formation, and dimensions of the harvested timber contributing to the yield.

1. Historical Development

Scientific endeavours in this respect are as old as planned forest management. Sustained forest management requires not only a knowledge of the existing stock of a forest but also a knowledge of the yields to be expected in the future. Thus, practically all great foresters of the eighteenth and early nineteenth centuries have themselves undertaken yield studies or have caused them to be made. As early as 1795 Oberförster J. Ch. Paulsen (1748–1825) from the Lippe province issued usable yield tables for the most important tree species. Ch. v. Seebach (1793–1865), whose name has become known for the open stand system for beech, was one of the first to study yield by systematic and scientific methods. M. R. Pressler (1815–86) created a wealth of methods and devices for the determination of the timber volume and increment of growing trees and stands. Robert Hartig's

---

[1] From the point of view of management it would be possible to visualize non-harvested yields, i.e. timber stocks which could be harvested consistently with sustained management but which, as a result of a personal decision by the forest owner, are not harvested, being conserved instead.

(1839–1901) work was a pioneering effort. We not only have to thank him for the first faultlessly constructed yield tables but we must also regard him as the founder of research which is based on plant physiology and only lately brought to fruition by Boysen-Jensen, Burger and Mar:Møller. By contrast, F. von Baur (1830–97) laid stress on the collection of extensive data for the purpose of constructing auxiliary tables for practical use.

R. Weber gave us the first summary of the theory of increment in one section of his textbook on forest management. He entitled it "Die Lehre vom Holzzuwachs" (app. 180 pages). Amongst other subjects dealt with by R. Weber is an attempt to impart mathematical formulation to the natural laws of woody growth.

v. Guttenberg supplied a short summary of increment theory in his timber mensuration studies within the framework of the well-known *Handbuch der Forstwissenschaft* (Textbook of Forest Science) by Lorey.

As a result of the extensive experimentation carried out by forest research institutes, vast quantities of data have been amassed since the seventies of the last century. These have since been partially interpreted in important publications by Schwappach, Dieterich, Flury, Wiedemann, Zimmerle and others.

In his *Einführung in die Forstliche Zuwachs- und Ertragslehre*, of which the first edition was published in 1941, Vanselow has, for the first time, treated this particular aspect separately. The 2nd edition of *Forstliche Zuwachs- und Ertragslehre* by Weck, published in 1955, gives a stimulating representation of the subject of yield studies though from a slightly biased view-point. Finally, Wiedemann, in his work *Ertragskundliche und waldbauliche Grundlagen der Forstwirtschaft*, published in 1949 (2nd edition 1955), provided a summarized interpretation of the very extensive basic material hitherto compiled by the former Prussian Research Institute. In this excellent work, a large section is given up to the discussion of silvicultural and ecological relationships and to conclusions reached in the broader field of forest economics. The precision of experiments in connection with yield studies and the inferences drawn therefrom are somewhat prejudiced by unreliable increment determinations and the summarization for statistical purposes of non-homogenous data.

A review of the development which has taken place so far in this field leads us to make the following statement: Whereas earlier yield studies were treated as a mere appendage to forest management or the theory of forest mensuration, the situation has changed with the passing of time. Forest mensuration has today become an auxiliary subject of yield study. It furnishes methods for the assessment of increment phenomena and their results. Thus an objective has been achieved which Dieterich (1935) indicated in a far-sighted thesis wherein he suggested that the principles of forest mensuration should be extended to comprise "the biological principles of forest yield or forest growth". It is on this basis that the author wishes to employ the term "principles of forest yield"[1] *(Waldertragskunde)* to define his subject. Apart from emphasizing a biological approach, this title is also intended to seize upon the concept of forest yields in their entirety. The main considerations which will determine the possible size and extent of a sustained yield will be the constitution and treatment of the forests. Both these will be taken into consideration in the course of this book.

---

[1] The term "forest yield theory" is used synonymously with this.

2. The Place of Forest Yield Theory in Forest Science

With Dieterich (1953) we start from the basic assumption that forest science must deal with an examination of the mutual relationships which exist between human society and the living community of the forest:

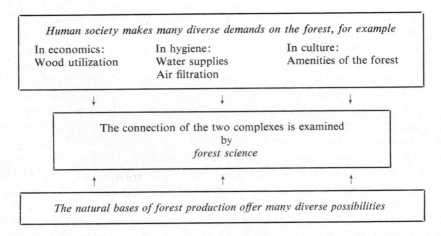

Human society makes many diverse demands on the forest, for example

In economics: In hygiene: In culture:
Wood utilization   Water supplies   Amenities of the forest
                       Air filtration

↓   ↓   ↓

The connection of the two complexes is examined
by
forest science

↑   ↑   ↑

The natural bases of forest production offer many diverse possibilities

A division of forest science into different sections on a systematic basis will show the position, confines and tasks of these respective fields (Table 1). We shall find the theory of forest yields among the "basic subjects" the task of which is to inquire into the underlying principles and methods applied in forest production. As this invokes the logical and causal coherence of facts, it merits the title of a theoretical science. In so far as it is, however, concerned with the rational application of discoveries it assumes the features

TABLE 1

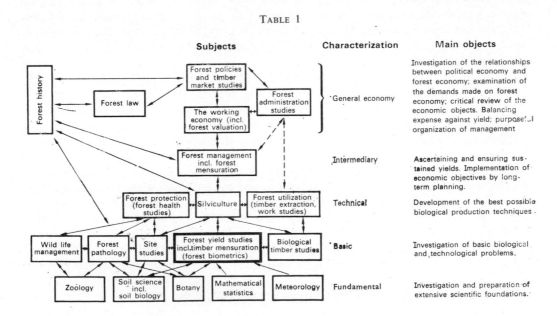

Subjects	Characterization	Main objects
Forest policies and timber market studies; Forest law; The working economy (incl. forest valuation); Forest administration studies	General economy	Investigation of the relationships between political economy and forest economy; examination of the demands made on forest economy; critical review of the economic objects. Balancing economic expense against yield; purposeful organization of management
Forest management incl. forest mensuration	Intermediary	Ascertaining and ensuring sustained yields. Implementation of economic objectives by long-term planning.
Forest protection (forest health studies); Silviculture; Forest utilization (timber extraction, work studies)	Technical	Development of the best possible biological production techniques.
Wild life management; Forest pathology; Site studies; Forest yield studies incl.timber mensuration (forest biometrics); Biological timber studies	Basic	Investigation of basic biological and technological problems.
Zoology; Soil science incl. soil biology; Botany; Mathematical statistics; Meteorology	Fundamental	Investigation and preparation of extensive scientific foundations.

of a practical science or technology, and it can safely be said that this "Janus face" characterizes forest science as a whole, which circumstance renders satisfactory systematization[1] difficult.

3. Research Objects and Methods Employed in Forest Yield Studies

The research work in this field has, until recently, been mainly the task of forest research institutes. The working methods employed in such institutes and the results which have been achieved are a warning example of the *insufficiency* of a *way of thinking which leans mainly on technical and economic considerations* and of the *short-sightedness* of the outlook entertained on such a foundation. The object of yield research should be the quantitative assessment of growth phenomena in relationship to site and silvicultural methods of treatment. However, the technical expediency cannot be examined or the economic objects discussed until the purely biological inferences of the growth processes have been clarified. A research method having as its sole object the solution of some urgent current problem in technical economics is unable to throw light on the basic biological problem. There is a danger that, owing to the length of time required for experiment, the desired solution may be found *much too late* because the development in technical operations which has taken place in the meantime has *long since outpaced* the original problem. A comprehensive multilateral attack on the problem from the biological angle would, during the same period of experimentation, have supplied answers which might serve as basis for many and varied conclusions in technical economics.

We shall therefore try to use a generalized percept of the phenomena and their conformity to law as our main point of departure. From thence, we shall be able the more successfully to enter into questions involving special forest techniques. We shall soon discover that the *production of timber represents only part of the organic accretion which goes on in a forest*. Problems and methods which are confined to an arbitrarily limited part of this production, for example the technically utilizable timber of and exceeding a certain minimum size, are unable to uncover for us the laws governing this output. Only a comprehensive and penetrating research method, as for example the one used by Boysen-Jensen in his profound work *Die Stoffproduktion der Pflanzen*, can lead to new and fundamental discoveries.

The quantitative assessment of biological processes poses a difficult task for yield research. The main complicating factor is the size of forest trees which are not—as with agricultural food plants—harvested once every year, and which cannot therefore easily be measured by weight and volume. The annual changes in dimensions are relatively small and assessable only by careful measurements. It becomes accordingly necessary to develop a special timber mensuration technique with appropriate methods of measurement. If we examine the relationships between characteristic values of biological material which are either directly or indirectly related to age, we shall meet with marked irregularities which remain even after the exclusion of errors of measurements. This is properly known as "natural variability". The organisms which we examine are, after all, living beings and are able, each one of them, to develop in their own individual ways. Moreover, a large number of factors exert their influence on the organisms, and the resultant effects induced by these are of corresponding diversity. *The resulting natural variability excludes*

---

[1] On the systematic theory of the forest economy see also H.W. Weber (1929).

the possibility of obtaining strict "functional" relationships. We must therefore be satisfied with "stochastic" relationships, i.e. those assumed on the basis of probability theory. The importance of employing precise methods for measurement and calculation which have been developed to a high degree of perfection in *mathematical statistics,* becomes evident. Thus it is possible to define the research methods used in modern yield studies simply as *biometrics,* as *biometrics applied to forestry.* This science attempts, through a method of calculation adapted to the characteristics of large numbers of living beings, to assess biological relationships, to describe hypotheses with the help of suitable statistics and on appropriate occasions to express them by approximate mathematical functions.

If we attempt an orderly assessment of the motley and multi-shaped reality of organic life in its bearing upon technico-economic relationships, we shall find ourselves unable to manage without abstractions and mental aids. One is reminded of yield tables—often scorned without reason—and the model of a normal working section. We shall attempt to make a survey of the extensive complex of biological inter-relationships and their relevance to technology and economics. If we thus strive, wherever possible, to replace hitherto predominantly subjective ideas by definite knowledge and the quantitative framing of such discoveries, we must remain aware of the fact that practical forestry cannot be expressed in purely mathematical calculations. In practice—as in real life—the professional forester will always be confronted with fresh tasks, the solution of which should never be sought without giving consideration to all those relationships which hold between human society and the living community of the forest.

WOODY GROWTH AS PART OF THE TOTAL PRODUCE OF PLANT SOCIETIES

1. Soil, Climate and Plant Production

Mutual interactions between soil, climate and plant cover

A closed plant cover cannot be developed until a weathering of the surface rocks has sufficiently progressed to promote the formation of a soil. To begin this process, the original supply of minerals must be released and made available by hydrolysis. Reactions between the products of hydrolysis result in building up the secondary *clay minerals* which, as ion-exchangers, are of decisive importance in plant nutrition. The releasing process is actively aided by secretions from the roots of plants. But it is the decomposition residues of organic products which, together with the effective co-operation of the soil fauna, are supremely responsible for the development of those *humus substances which, together with the clay minerals, are the main contributors of soil fertility.*

Under the combined effects of climate, soil and plant cover, the process of *soil maturing* takes place; the individual stages of this can be distinguished in the soil profile and are used as divisions for the different *soil types.* Under the influence of favourable climate and soil conditions, an *equilibrium* is reached between the current loss of nutrients which are leached away by drainage, and the release of further nutrients by weathering; also between the loss of humus and its renewal by a simple break-down of the fallen litter. Concurrently the locality attains its highest production level of substances from natural plant societies, without human interference.

In warm and dry climates where evaporation exceeds rainfall the maturing processes are slow. At the same time, large quantities of genuine humus substances develop. The result of these processes is the well-known black earths. Translocation proceeds more quickly under the influence of a humid climate when the soil undergoes heavy leaching. The acid end-products of organic transposition cause the top soil to become impoverished of bases. The surfaces of the secondary clay minerals lose more and more of their adsorptively bound ions and exchange them for H-ions so that the soil reaction becomes more and more acid. The products of the decaying clay minerals are translocated into the sub-soil in the form of a colloidal sol; there they are precipitated as flocs in an alkaline environment. This *break-down of clay* which is accompanied by a progressive impoverishment in the iron, aluminium and silicic acid constituents of the top-soil is, owing to the characteristic greying feature accompanying it, known as *podsolization.*

Whereas the maturing process from the raw soil stage to "Central European brown earth" or "brown forest soil" with A–(B)–C-profile and a high biological soil activity is accompanied by an increase of the plant production performance, the transition to "podsolized brown earth" or yet again, to "gleyed-podsol" sees a decrease in performance.[1] This process of soil *degradation* is, in humid climates, an apparently obligatory development for all soil types in *a level situation;* the speed of this development depends on the original mineral content and the crumb structure of the soils. The cultivation of pure conifers, for example spruce, on former hardwood sites is likely to cause a *hastening* of this process but we have so far been unable to collect indisputable evidence about the speed of such deterioration.

In localities of varied gradients, particularly *on hill slopes,* the progressive weathering of the soil, in which the plant cover actively participates, is capable of effecting a *continuous reinforcement of the nutritive elements* so that the degradation is checked and reversed. This *"recreative power of the slope"* is largely responsible for the lasting and high production capacities of our forests on mountain sites with a cool and humid climate.

Yields in agriculture and forestry

In his book *Die natürlichen Grundlagen des Pflanzenertrages in Europa*, Filzer (1951) examined the regional yields of German agriculture and made the results comparable by calculating the quantity of dry substance. He found *the highest agricultural yields in those dry regions* which are characterized by the occurrence of *black earth* or *loess soils.* Filzer considers this to be the effect of the *natural wealth of humus* and the nutrient salts of these soils. This developed during the post-Ice Age era under the influence of a warm steppe-climate and has been maintained by the still very low amounts of rainfall of approximately 500 mm per year in these dry regions.

The small precipitation in these regions, which are at present almost exclusively utilized for highly intensified agriculture, does not allow the expectation of high forest yields. The *finest growth of forest crops in Germany*, apart from the meadow forests on low alluvial soils, is found in the South German mountain forests, i.e. the Black Forest, the Bavarian Forests and most particularly in the region of the Lower Alps. There we have *moderate rainfall* (1200 mm and over per year, 500 mm and over during the vegetative period) *and adequate warmth;* furthermore, in the Lower Alps, there are many robust soils with a high base content.

Weck (1955) in his studies of growth and yield compared, as did Filzer, the dry-substance yield of agricultural crops with average values of forest produce calculated from the 1937 statistical returns. He established that the dry-substance production of forests in the central mountain ranges of the Black Forest, the Harz mountains and the slopes of the Lower Alps substantially exceeds, on average, that of agricultural areas in the same growth regions. Weck states that by contrast, the loessic loam soils of both hilly and flat regions and the dry sandy eastern plains under a continental climate produce lower yields in forest areas than in agricultural areas. However, a comparison between the yields from agriculture and forestry is, strictly speaking, only reliable if the two areas exist side by side on the same site. Such possibilities for comparison do not often occur because, as a rule, the better soils are claimed for agriculture whilst forestry must be content with those of poor quality. However, the dry-substance production of forests probably exceeds that of agricultural crops on all slopes of steep gradient where the permanent vegetation affords adequate protection against soil losses by erosion.

Weck furthermore discovered that a close correlation exists between the average yields

---

[1] Apart from this particularly common sequence there are others which also occur on forest soils. The reader is referred to the special literature on soil and site studies.

of twenty-five German forest regions and a *climatic index* which takes into account the total amounts of rainfall and the mean temperatures for the months from May to July, the rainfall frequences for the same period and the number of days in the year which are free from frost. Recently, Weck modified an index formula given by Paterson (1956) which incorporated the factors of temperature, humidity and length of the vegetative period and he found that therewith the gross forest production potentials of natural forests in various parts of the world, from the tropics to the arctic regions, can be closely correlated.

Notwithstanding the immense influence of climate upon forest production, one must not overlook the extraordinary modifications imposed, at least in temperate zones, by the soil—its type, condition, slope and local topography. Those properties of the soil[1] which are mainly instrumental in their effects on forest yield are briefly summarized below.

Soil factors of primary importance in the formation of plant material

Laatsch (1957), in his highly commendable study of forest nutrition, makes the following distinctions:

1. *Primary yield factors*

The *soil* offers to the roots:
   warmth,
   oxygen from the air,
   water.

In addition, the following nutritive elements:

Nitrogen Phosphorus Sulphur Boron	Non-metallic	Iron Manganese Copper Zinc Molybdenum	Heavy metals
Potassium Calcium Magnesium	Light metals		

2. *Nutrient storage*

Responsible for this are the *humus and the clay fractions* which hold the nutrients loosely and in easily available form ready to supply the roots.

3. *Nutrient media*

These are the *soil layers, bacteria, fungi, algae* and *soil fauna*.
They are responsible for conveying the nutrients to the tree roots.

---

[1] It seems that even today many foresters would still consider that the argument advanced by Biolley (*Forest Management by the Control Method*, 1920) was justified from the point of view of natural science: "Wood contains 45–48 per cent of carbon, approximately 42 per cent of oxygen, 6–7 per cent of hydrogen, 1–2 per cent of nitrogen and 3–5 per cent of solid substances which come from the soil. This shows that with regard to the supply of plant-building substances the air is 20 to 30 times as important to the forest as the soil."

4. *Sources* from which the yield factors originate:

(a) weathered minerals; (b) the atmosphere.

Laatsch defines the following as *limiting factors* which often fail to be available in sufficient quantities:

water and oxygen from the air,

nitrogen and phosphorus,

calcium.

This matter will be further discussed in the chapter on fertilizer treatment. But the decisive importance of *litter breakdown and humus formation* to forest productiveness must be stressed even at this early stage. We are indebted to the pioneer work of Wittich for an improved insight into these processes, in which bacteria, algae, fungi and the soil fauna play a far larger part than hitherto supposed in premises which were adduced mainly from soil chemistry.

The manufacture of plant substances derives initially from the assimilatory process of photosynthesis, which will be discussed in more detail in the following chapter.

2. The Assimilation Process from the Point of View of Quantitative Ecology

In the process of photosynthesis carbon dioxide from the atmosphere is reduced with the help of solar energy and transformed into sugar according to the formula:

$$6 \, CO_2 + 6 \, H_2O + 680,000 \, cal = C_6H_{12}O_6 + 6 \, O_2.$$

Although most of the stages which make up the whole process described in the above formula are known, some decisive factors remain to be cleared up. The structural formula for chlorophyll, the green colouring matter of leaves, shows a striking resemblance to that of the colouring matter of blood, haematin, except that the central metallic ingredient in chlorophyll is magnesium whilst in haematin it is iron. The chlorophyll carries out its function as an agent of the living plasma in plant cells. This mysterious fundamental process on which the organic life of this planet is based is fulfilled by the chlorophyll carriers, which are known as chloroplasts.

In relation to forest growth, the *quantitative* ecological approach to this process is important since it is concerned with the vital activities on which the yield ultimately depends. Whereas biological research has hitherto concentrated upon piecemeal analyses, biologists now make ever-increasing efforts to appraise the assimilatory processes in quantitative terms. This can be regarded as symptomatic of the rapid growth of the world's population, necessitating as it does, notable increases in agricultural production and the framing of numerous estimates of productive resources.[1] Thus the path is opened up for a quantitative examination of the vital productive processes. This is where the aims of plant physiology coincide with those of forest yield studies.

The process of assimilation, in which energy is utilized and stored in the shape of complex molecular combinations, is conjointly accompanied by the *process of respiration*

---

[1] It is to be hoped that, at the same time, thought will be given to the *effective conservation of productive resources*, since there are natural limitations set to any desired increase. *This would provide a parallel to the idea of sustained yield in European forestry* which arose 150 years ago under the pressure of a threat of timber shortage. Unchecked abuse of the energies of natural production, careless felling of trees, a squandering of rich natural resources and the heedless conversion of natural plant associations into plantations of single species have already caused serious damage.

in which the stored energy is partially released by oxidation. Thus, assimilation is evidenced by the *consumption* of carbon dioxide and respiration by its *release*. When actively assimilating leaves are examined experimentally these two simultaneously occurring processes cannot be readily separated. In gas-analysis experiments, the changes in carbon dioxide content are detected by an airstream passing through a closed glass container and guided past actively functioning leaves which are exposed to light. These leaves not only absorb carbon dioxide, but, at the same time, release part of the already assimilated carbon dioxide during the process of respiration. *The assimilation performance of the leaves, measured in milligrams* of consumed CO_2 per hour and per gram of leaf weight, or per square decimetre of leaf area, therefore represents a *net quantity*. To plant physiologists this is known as the "*apparent* (i.e. apparent by the consumption of carbon dioxide) *assimilation*". In order to measure the amount of respiration, the glass container enclosing the test material is covered with a black cloth. Whereas formerly the examinations were made upon cut leaves and branches, and accordingly had to be evaluated with some caution, it has lately become possible by means of IRGA (infra-red gas analyser),[1] *to observe the exchange of gases in the branches of living trees* without their previous severance from the tree. This makes it possible to measure extremely small changes in concentration[2] with safety. In a quantitative analysis of the total gas-substance exchange of trees, it is necessary to consider the large amounts of carbon dioxide which are continually released by the respiration of all the live parts of the trees, especially the roots.

(a) THE PRINCIPAL FACTORS IN THE ASSIMILATION PROCESS

The rate of apparent assimilation depends on several factors which will be considered below.

The factor of light

The *energy of solar radiation* in our latitudes, measured *in thermal units* when the air is clear, amounts to approximately *1·2 calories* per square centimetre per minute; of this approximately 0·6 calories per square centimetre per minute fall as light and warmth.

The *spectrum of solar radiation* embraces the wavelengths from 290 to 5000 mμ. Of these the wavelengths 400–750 mμ are visible to the eye and the wavelengths 320–750 mμ are photosynthetically effective. The two portions of the spectrum are nearly identical. The light which the eye perceives up to the visual purple is also photosynthetically effective. The infra-red portion of the spectrum extends beyond the 750 mμ wavelength and the ultra-violet portion begins below 400 mμ.

Measured in lux units, the solar radiation in our latitudes *reaches 40–50,000 lux in a clear summer sky*, and when reflected by light cumulus clouds, an extreme value of 70,000 lux.

The extent to which the wavelengths of the spectrum are absorbed whilst passing through green leaves varies. In Fig. 1 the leaves of a Common beech show a particularly

---

[1] In German, known as URAS ("Ultrarot—Absorptions—Schreiber")—Transl.

[2] The normal CO_2-content of the air is 0·03 per cent = 300 ppm (parts per million). Modern instruments enable the detection of differences in concentrations which are scarcely bigger than 1 ppm (!) and the automatic recording of measurements which are repeated at intervals of no more than 6 minutes.

high absorption rate of 90 per cent and over for the wave lengths around 680 mμ (red) and 500–400 mμ (blue-violet) whilst the light absorption in the region between 540–570 mμ (green-yellow) is strikingly low. This discovery, which we owe to the experiments of Seybold (1942) and his pupils, is very important to forest production. *The relatively high absorption of those wavelengths which most affect the assimilation process causes the light which has already passed through some leaves to have a lower photosynthetic effect on leaves which it later falls upon than would be indicated solely by the weakening of the total*

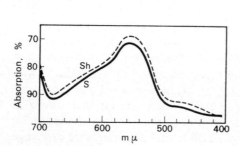 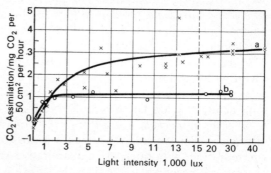

FIG. 1 *(left)*. Light absorption curves for a Common beech leaf: (S) sun-leaf and (Sh) shade-leaf *(Seybold and Weissweiler)*.

FIG. 2 *(right)*. Assimilation curves for Common beech leaves: (a) sun-leaf and (b) shade-leaf *(Boysen-Jensen)*.

light intensity, i.e. by the reduced *brightness*. Wiesner, for example, using chlorinated silver paper for his classical recordings of light intensities under forest conditions, discovered, among other things, the so-called light utilization minimum required by forest tree shade-leaves. The degree of blackening of this silver paper is caused by the light of those parts of the spectrum which are chemically effective and accordingly it is useless as evidence upon decreasing strength in the specifically effective regions of radiation. Even if the major part of the total radiation arriving at the leaf[1] is utilized, namely 30 per cent for the endothermal transpiration process and only about 1 per cent for the actual process of photosynthesis, the changed quality of the light which filters out may still be of decisive importance with respect to its exploitability for assimilation by forest tree leaves in shade.

The apparent assimilation gain of a leaf increases directly with the light intensity, measured in lux. A positive assimilation rate, which in experiments shows itself in the *consumption* of carbon dioxide, can only be achieved with a certain minimum of light below which the respiration loss, indicated by the *yield* of carbon dioxide, dominates. In Fig. 2, the light assimilation curves for sun-leaves and shade-leaves of Common beech show the ordinate values for assimilation (unit: CO_2-consumption per 50 cm^2 leaf-surface per hour) plotted against their corresponding values of light intensity (unit: 1000 lux) as abscissae. As can be seen, the zero ordinate value which indicates the *balance between assimilation gain and respiration loss* is attained by shade leaves at approximately 200 lux, but by sun-leaves

---

[1] The works of Baumgartner (1956, 1957) have introduced a whole range of new aspects into the problem of the radiation balance of forest trees. These are of the greatest importance to the potential production of forest stands, because they have shown the negative effects of many storeys and mixed ages (for example, in selection forests) on productivity. This will be further discussed in Sections C and E.

not until approximately 500 lux. This point in an assimilation curve is known as the *compensation-point*. It is generally lower for shade-leaves of forest trees than for sun-leaves. The same applies for the leaves of "shade-tolerant plants" compared with "light-demanding plants". In the following examples, the lux values for the point of compensation at a given temperature are:

for shade-leaves of Ash	approximately 150 lux
sun-leaves of Ash	700
shade-needles of Silver Fir[1]	250
sun-needles of Silver Fir[1]	550
shade-needles of N. Spruce[1]	350
sun-needles of N. Spruce[1]	1150
Wood sorrel (Oxalis) leaves	100
White mustard (Sinapis) leaves	700

With an increased supply of light, i.e. increased lux values, *the assimilation of shade-leaves very soon reaches its culmination, whilst for sun-leaves it continues to rise steeply and reaches much higher end-values.* In Fig. 2, a beech shade-leaf receiving approximately 2000 lux has nearly reached its highest performance of approximately 1·2 mg CO_2 per 50 cm^2 per hour whilst the performance of a sun-leaf at 15,000 lux is approximately 3·1 mg. From 2000 lux upwards, the sun-leaf has a superior performance.

The part played by temperature

Raising the temperature does not simply increase the assimilation gain, as one might assume. *An increase in temperature is accompanied by an increase of respiration* (i.e. breathing) *which is decidedly "temperature-controlled". As a result, the particular temperature-optimum,* i.e. that temperature giving the highest assimilation performance for a given light intensity, is lower when the light is poor than when the light is intense.

Pisek and Winkler (1958) have been successful in discovering by laboratory tests in which they used artificial lighting by Xenon lamps, the exact relationship between the temperature and assimilation rates of spruce branches for light powers of 3000, 10,000 and 30,000 lux respectively. In the particular example shown in Fig. 3 these important relationships are neatly presented in optimum curves which have been constructed from well-authenticated data. The optima of the examined branches taken from the part of the tree in full sunlight are:

for the light power of	at a temperature of
3000 lux	11°C
10,000 lux	15°C
30,000 lux	18°C

The steep increase of respiration associated with a rise in temperature makes it appear as though the optimum curves in the higher temperature ranges of 25°C and over were, so to speak, forced down so that at temperatures of 33–37°C, a balance is achieved.

[1] According to Miller (1959).

However, under natural conditions the shade branches are unable to reach their superiority in performance over the light branches which they have displayed in these laboratory tests because of the poor light conditions existing in the shaded part of the crown.

If the curve for 3000 lux were extended into the temperature range below 0°C, a balance would not be reached until −4°C. The relatively low temperature optima for low light powers are apparently of great importance for the assimilation performance of forest stands in cool climates, especially in the far North. There, the light intensity of the midnight sun, which amounts to no more than approximately 1 per cent of the midday sun can, despite the cool night temperatures, be used to achieve positive assimilation. Thus, our winter cereals are capable of achieving positive assimilation gains even at temperatures around 0°C. The same applies for evergreen conifers, as for example spruce, which only experiences a complete absence of the exchange of gases during long periods of frost (Walter, 1951; Pisek and Winkler, 1958).

The CO_2-content of the air

The carbon dioxide content of atmospheric air amounts, on the average, to no more than 0·03 per cent, i.e. only approximately $\frac{1}{2}$ mg/litre or $\frac{1}{2}$ g/m³ of air. Huber, in his plant physiology, mentions the signal misfortune which lies in the fact that four-fifths of the volume of the atmosphere is nitrogen and only 0·03 per cent carbon dioxide. One can therefore assume that the low carbon dioxide content of the air[1] represents a limiting minimum factor.

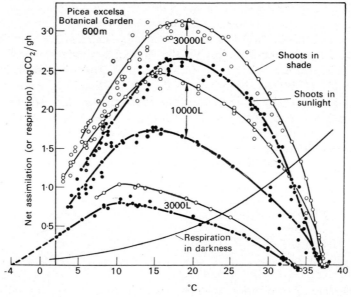

FIG. 3. Relationship between light and temperature and the net assimilation of an adult spruce (*A. Pisek* and *E. Winkler*, 1958).

---

[1] The CO_3-ions which are absorbed by the roots and carried upwards in the ascending transpiration stream supply only approximately 8 per cent of the carbon dioxide requirement of plants.

In fact, experiments by Stålfelt and Lundegårdh have shown that an increase of the carbon dioxide content of the air, with unchanged temperature and given degrees of lighting, results in improved assimilation. (See Fig. 4.)

Many foresters attach to these experimental laboratory results the hope that, by providing wind shelter to our forest stands, as by imparting a multi-storeyed structure, it should be possible to enable the trees to benefit from the carbon dioxide which continually issues from the soil. We have only a small amount of reliable data about the quantities of carbon dioxide which are continually released from forest soils by *bacterial processes*

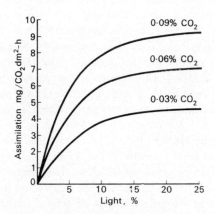

FIG. 4. Dependence of CO_2 assimilation of *Oxalis acetosella* upon light (per cent of the normal daylight) and CO_2 concentration *(Lundegårdh)*.

and as a result of *root respiration* (see Eidmann, section A, 2b). The values per hectare which were published by Lundegårdh have proved to be too large by a factor of 10. By comparison, the values for forest soils of *200–700 mg CO_2 per square metre per hour* given by Romell in 1932, are more realistic, as Walter discovered recently. More recent measurements by Haber, published by Walter and Haber (1957), gave amongst others the following values:

For a *beech forest* near Waiblingen between April and May 1952	407 mg CO_2/m²/hour
For a *spruce forest* on the same site with loessic loam	220 mg CO_2/m²/hour
For *spruce forests in the south-east of the Black Forest* at 900–1000 metres above sea level, between August and September 1954	
1. on shell limestone (Rendzina soils, brown loam)	431 mg CO_2/m²/hour
2. on bunter-sandstone (brown podsolic forest soil)	360 mg CO_2/m²/hour
3. the same (impeded gley soils with deep raw humus surface layer)	264 mg CO_2/m²/hour
In the "Nockgebirge" north of Klagenfurt, 500–650 metres above sea level, loamy soils with some gravel, in summer 1956	
in a *spruce forest* with abundant ground flora	228 mg CO_2/m²/hour
in a mixed *black alder–spruce forest*	241 mg CO_2/m²/hour
For a mixed *oak–hornbeam–ash forest* without ground vegetation, on heavy alluvial loam near Datteln in Westphalia	
between April and June 1954	240 mg CO_2/m²/hour
between October and November 1954	273 mg CO_2/m²/hour
For a *cultivated meadow* on loamy soil near Münster in Westphalia	
between April and July 1955	623 mg CO_2/m²/hour
between November and December 1955	156 mg CO_2/m²/hour

The soil respiration values for agricultural fields with their characteristically rapid conversion of the organic matter depend on the volume of roots of the last crop left in the soil and on the application of organic fertilizer (manure). It has been possible to prove by agricultural experiments (among others, Lemmermann, 1940) that agricultural crops do not benefit from increased respiration of the soil because the carbon dioxide is too quickly dispersed into the open air. This does not apply to a closed greenhouse where it is possible to increase the carbon dioxide content of the air by artificial supplies up to the optimum of 0·5 per cent, and, at the same time, to increase the temperature to the corresponding optimum value. If it is not possible under agricultural conditions to achieve a lasting and effective increase of the carbon dioxide content of the layers of air near the ground where, in this case, the assimilating leaf tissues find themselves, *the prospects for forests* are, as a rule, even *less favourable, because the assimilating tissues of the foliage are placed at a much greater distance from the ground.* If there were a complete absence of wind in a forest, the ascent of the carbon dioxide from the soil into the crown would depend on diffusion, which would take a very long time. The speedy conveyance of carbon dioxide into the crowns of forest trees requires some air movement.

The examinations made by Huber (1952), who measured the CO_2-concentration above assimilating potato crops at heights up to 200 m from a balloon with the help of IRGA, showed that the *changes in concentration resulting from assimilation extend up to heights of 100 m.* As, according to Huber's statements, the vegetation inside a layer of air of 6·5 m depth uses the entire carbon dioxide content of this air layer, one is bound to agree with his conclusion that *an adequate supply of carbon dioxide is possible only by means of the vertical exchange between deep layers of air.*

Several instances of annual increments of 30 m³ per hectare have been recorded for 30- to 40-year-old spruce stands attaining heights of 15—20 m on particularly favourable sites in the lower Alps. This volume production corresponds to an annual dry-substance production of approximately 12 tons per hectare. In addition there are approximately 10 tons of needles, branches and roots. *For the production of 1 g of dry vegetable substance approximately 0·5 g of carbon is required, which corresponds to approximately 1·83 g* CO_2. Basing our calculations on the net consumption, i.e. discounting the currently respired carbon dioxide, *the annual consumption amounts to $22 \times 1·83$ = approximately 40 tons CO_2 per hectare.* If it be assumed that this production is achieved in 150 vegetative days, then *the average daily consumption per square metre of stand area would amount to 27 g of CO_2 which corresponds to the total carbon dioxide content of a layer of air of 54 m in thickness.* This would be three times the height of the forest stand.[1]

Although the possible carbon dioxide production of the soil is remarkably large, it is, because of other adverse circumstances, not of decisive importance to the productive efficiency of forest stands. For the forest stand on loessic loam it corresponds, according to Walter and Haber, to 5·3 g per square metre a day which in our example would amount to only one-quarter of the daily requirements. Even the maximum value of 431 mg per square metre per hour for spruce stands which was discovered by Walter and Haber amounts at 10·3 g per day to scarcely half of the CO_2-consumption of the above stand in the course of one vegetative day.

---

[1] This indicates that Biolley's concept of a "fallow column of air", which is incapable of being utilized by young even-aged stands, is untenable. If a forest depended on the carbon dioxide content of the particular layer of air which it occupies, productivity equivalent to the one shown above would be impossible.

Rüsch (1955) in a number of experiments has examined the changes of the CO_2-content of lucerne fields in the lee of a shelter-belt (poplars with a height of 8 m and an under-storey of hornbeam) and also without wind protection. He found that, in the field with wind protection, the CO_2 from the soil increased over-night. But after assimilation had started in the early morning hours, the *CO_2-content was clearly and significantly lower there than in the lucerne field without wind protection.* The increased production of lucerne protected from wind is due to reduced evaporation and to the thereby improved regula-tion of the stomata and *not to the more extensive utilization of CO_2 from the soil.* The wind shelter, on the contrary, prevents fresh (side) supplies of air with a normal CO_2-content.

The large quantities of carbon dioxide which are continually consumed by assimilating forest stands can only be supplied by the carbon dioxide contained in layers of air which are many times thicker than the height of these stands. *Even though the carbon dioxide from the ground is indispensable to the current replenishment of the barely sufficient supply from the atmosphere it seems unlikely that the available quantities can have an important influence on the production of a growing stand.*

The new experimental results by Miller (1960, Diss. Munich, 1959) derived from young fir and spruce plantations at Bodenmais, and in particular, from a 52–60-year-old mixed larch–beech stand at Grafrath, do not call for any alteration of the above conclusion.

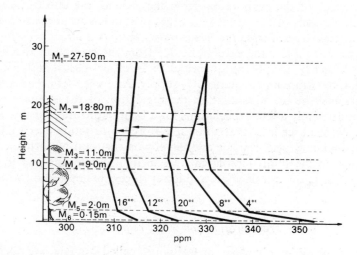

FIG. 5. CO_2 concentration profiles for different times of the day in a mixed larch–beech stand *(Miller)*.

The latter stand has a light upper storey of larch with an average height of 20 m and a lower and intermediate storey of beech of 2–18 m height. The CO_2-concentration measurements taken simultaneously above and within the stand at 6 points whose posi-tion is illustrated in Fig. 5 supplied a series of CO_2-concentration profiles under varying meteorological conditions. In a typical daily sequence, Fig. 5 shows the characteristic changes in the profile. The night profile (4.00 a.m.) with a high CO_2-concentration in the canopy layers (nocturnal respiration of the stand) and near the ground (soil respira-tion) is, in the course of a day, largely dispersed by the consumption during assimilation and by wind turbulence and begins to increase again by evening (20.00 hours). In a single-storeyed stand, the assimilatory profile change might have shown up even more markedly.

The daily CO_2-consumption of the stand which, according to Miller's estimate, amounts to at least 150 kg CO_2/ha is opposed by a carbon dioxide production of the soil in the daytime amounting to approximately 50 kg/ha. However, the CO_2-content of the whole 20-m high interior of the stand is reduced by only approximately 1·5 kg/ha (the reduction is estimated by the drop in the CO_2-concentration). Consequently, according to Miller, "the largest proportion by far" of the assimilatory CO_2-consumption must "during the day time come from the open air whose reduced content is subsequently more or less replenished by respiration during the night". On the basis of radio-carbon analyses which allow conclusions about the origin of the assimilated carbon in beech leaves, Miller concluded that the *proportion of carbon dioxide from the soil* which participated in the construction of beech leaves in 1958 (the year in which the measurements of gas-exchanges were made) amounted to approximately *15 per cent*. If one takes into consideration the fact that part of the beech leaves in this instance originated from positions near the ground, one is justified in assuming that the direct supply of CO_2 from the soil in stands with tall trees must be of minor importance. These latest results agree with Rubner's (1925) statement which at the time warned against "unrestricted optimism regarding the importance of CO_2".

By establishing dense covers of forests and plantations we prevent, in particular, an undesirable increase of the evaporation from the ground, the effect of which is clearly evident in the poor soils of the windswept edges of stands and in the reduced increment performance of edge trees. *Inside the forest stands there is a direct need for continual air circulation* in order to allow the carbon dioxide from the ground to rise into the crown space and, by a steady supply of quantities of fresh air with a still reducible carbon dioxide content, to ensure an adequate CO_2-supply. A severe vertical arrangement of the stand structure may be an advantage to the regulation of the stomata of forest trees but it does not decisively affect expectations for a better utilization of the carbon dioxide from the soil. We shall see later that a multiple-storeyed structure exerts a negative influence on the assimilatory performance and thereby on the total performance of a stocked area; this is due to the unfavourable changes in light conditions and in the radiation balance of the trees in the intermediate and lower storeys in connection with such a treatment of stands.

Transpiration and water requirements

Assimilation is possible only when the leaf pores, called stomata, are open as otherwise the carbon dioxide would be unable to enter into the leaves. The stomatic transpiration[1] is controlled by changes in the turgor pressure of the guard cells. In the peculiarly fast reaction of the stomata which occurs approximately 10–20 minutes after a brief exposure to light (Bünning, 1948) this latter factor plays a decisive part, the region of short-wave radiation being more effective than the long waves. *The stomata can remain open only if the plant has an adequate supply of water.* Without this the turgor of the guard cells slackens and accordingly causes the stomata to close and so interrupt the stomatic transpiration. The ascending transpiration stream however, carries a running supply of those

---

[1] Compared to the stomatic transpiration, cuticular transpiration is so small that we can neglect it in this connection. With full opening of the stomata, the latter amounts to only 6 – 8 per cent of the stomatic transpiration.

nutrients from the soil which are indispensable to the assimilating parts of the plant. Thus assimilation necessitates at the same time transpiration and therewith the consumption of water.

According to a summary by Stocker the production of 1 g of organic dry-substance requires the transpiration of 200–1000 g of water, depending on the particular local conditions and the plant species.

Eidmann (1943) estimated the transpiration rates of 2–3-year-old forest tree plants in pots (cf. Table 3, p. 26); these values are astonishingly high. According to Polster (1950), this is due to abundant water supplies whereby the plants were allowed a "luxury" consumption. However, if individual tree species are compared, the relative quantities harmonize quite well with the corresponding figures by Huber, Schubert, Pisek and Cartellieri.[1]

Conditions are similar for the values which Polster (1950), a pupil of Huber's, found when he made an examination of the assimilation of cut branches. These figures are again fairly high and supply unrealistic values when applied to a hectare of forest. Polster has been able in his experiments to deduce some day-assimilation curves showing satisfactory significance; he did this by joining together a sequence of carbon dioxide consumption measurements which had been repeated at short intervals. All these curves agree in showing a *peculiar depression* (see Fig. 6).

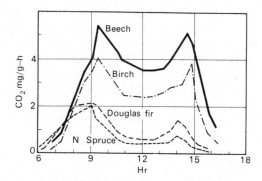

FIG. 6. Assimilation rates by different tree species in the course of a day *(Polster)*.

The assimilation rate reaches a peak during the forenoon which is followed by another, but lower, peak in the afternoon. Polster considers this typical drop in performance to be mainly due to a *physiological fatigue* of the chloroplasts. Dissenting from this view, Walter (1951) maintains that the reason for this depressed assimilation must be sought primarily in the *partial closure of the stomata as a result of strained water supplies*. Another

---

[1] Further transpiration measurements taken by Eidmann and Schwenke over a period of several years and shortly to be published (Supplement to *Forstwiss. Centralblatt*) have supplied values which are lower than those published in 1943. During these continued experiments the plants, which were kept in pots inside a well-aired greenhouse with an almost open-air climate, received irrigation which was no more than adequate for full transpiration and, at the same time, 51 per cent of open-air light. With a reduction of the supply of light to 15 per cent, the dry substance production dropped on an average to 45 per cent, whilst transpiration increased by 25 per cent. Similarly, unfavourable changes in the efficiency of transpiration, according to Neuwirth (1962, 1963), were caused by a pioneer crop of birch sheltering young coniferous woods, the nurse crop causing considerable increase in water consumption for a given rate of assimilation.

reason in his opinion might be a possible steep *increase* of the temperature-controlled *respiration*. Lately (1955) Polster himself has adopted the view that the main responsibility lies in the *hydroactive closure movements which are the result of inadequate water supplies*. It is probably this behaviour of the stomata which, apart from the increase in respiration, is responsible for the occurrence of a depression at midday.[1] While up to now cuvettes have been used which did not permit the interior temperature to be adjusted to the temperature outside, the observed reduction of the net assimilation around midday was probably caused mainly by *overheating* inside the cuvettes (Bosian, 1960). In the larger, more modern gas-exchange chambers which were developed by Koch in co-operation with the firm of Siemens, it is possible automatically to adjust not only the temperature but also the humidity to equal those of the air outside. It was found that an increase of humidity of the air inside the gas exchange chamber exerts a strong positive influence on the assimilation performance (Koch, 1966). According to advice from Koch, "genuine" midday depressions are possible only on bright hot days.

Koch (1957), who is another of Huber's pupils, succeeded recently in simultaneously recording the data for both the assimilation and transpiration of barley fields.[2] From these it appeared that assimilation, being dependent on light, becomes active much more quickly in the daily sequence than transpiration, which does not start until the atmosphere has "warmed up" and a saturation deficit has been created. Therefore, according to Huber (1957), the ratio of plant substance manufacture to consumption of water is 10 times greater in the early morning hours than the average for the whole vegetative period. Whereas in the morning 20–30 g of water were sufficient to produce 1 g of dry vegetable matter, the consumption of water by transpiration for the average of the vegetative period was 10 times as much. This appears to be due to particularly satisfactory conditions for the factors of assimilation in the early hours of the morning when, with relatively low temperatures, the effects of smaller respiration losses and lower water consumption work together. Huber attaches the hope that the outcome of these new results will have a favourable bearing on production. This is certainly to be expected in horticulture and in forest nurseries, but is scarcely likely in forest stands.

The influence of nutrient supplies

Mitscherlich's efficacy law

The assimilatory activities of given leaf areas or leaf quantities are decisively influenced by the supply of nutrients which in turn depends on the soil quality. As early as 1896 Robert Hartig discovered and postulated that "soil with a plentiful supply of nutrients is capable of producing, from the same quantity of foliage, twice the amount of timber that can be produced by soil with a poor supply".

The chloroplasts are constructed mainly of protein combinations. Of the protein-building elements N, P and S, those which are probably most often limiting are N and P. It has been known for some time that the needles of Scots pine and Norway spruce trees show a lower nitrogen content on poor soils than on good soils. By means of fertil-

---

[1] On the evidence of more recent examinations with air-conditioned "cuvettes" it seems probable that "midday depressions" are mainly caused by the excessive temperatures in the cuvettes and the resulting increased respiration.

[2] From the total observed data for daily sequences (the drop in the CO_2-concentration and water vapour) Koch has calculated an average water consumption of 90 g per 1 g of assimilated CO_2, which corresponds to a water consumption of approximately 330 g per 1 g of organic dry-substance.

izer experiments, Tamm (1956) succeeded recently in demonstrating beyond doubt that the *width of the annual rings* and thereby the increment of a pine stand increases *as the nitrogen content of the needles increases.* Figure 7 shows that in accordance with expectation on the basis of Mitscherlich's law, growth-rate improves along with the increase of N-concentration in the pine needles, at first quickly but then more gradually until it reaches its maximum value at a nitrogen content of a little above 2 per cent.

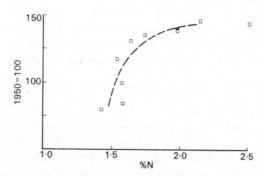

FIG. 7. Increasing width of annual rings related to the increase of the nitrogen content of pine needles in a fertilizer experiment *(Tamm)*.

More recent experiments made by Wehrmann (1959) in Bavarian *pine stands* suggest that there is a fairly *close correlation between the nitrogen concentration* of the previous year's needles (in the highest side shoots) *and the height quality class.* Whereas the N-concentration in fast-growing stands reaches values up to 2·2 per cent, concentrations do not exceed 1·0 to 1·5 per cent in stands of low vigour. Analogous conditions were discovered by Strebel (1960) in numerous Bavarian *spruce stands* which he examined. From these investigations, it can be concluded that good growth depends on N-concentrations of 1·3 to 1·7 per cent in spruce needles. Conclusive proof of the direct relationship between the N-content of leaves and their assimilation rate was supplied by the experiments of Keller and Koch (1962) on poplar branches which had been kept in solutions made up of different concentrations of the various nutrient elements. With a light incidence of 40,000 lux, for example, those leaves which had a 3·4 per cent N-content showed a net assimilation rate which exceeded that of leaves with a 1·8 per cent N-content by as much as 75 per cent.

The assimilation rate of the leaves, and the consequent growth of the plant, results from the combined effects of numerous growth factors. For a long time Liebig's (1855) "law of the minimum", according to which any growth factor which is limiting restricts the yield, was considered applicable to the total effect achieved by all the factors. This was opposed by the view stressed by Liebscher as early as 1895: "A plant can utilize a productive factor which is limiting so as to achieve an increased production if the other productive factors are brought closer to their optimum."

E. A. Mitscherlich (1910) has shown that by augmenting the particular growth factor which is limiting, for example, the addition of nitrogen by fertilizer applications, the yield *does not increase in simple proportion with the increased factor.* Instead, if the level of all other growth factors is kept constant, the yield increase is *proportional to the difference between the present and the maximum yields.* This law was postulated by Mitscherlich and is known as the "law of physiological dependence" ("Gesetz der physiologischen Beziehungen"). Subsequently it has been analysed mathematically by Baule (1917, 1924) and, in its extended form, is known as the "efficacy law" ("Wirkungsgesetz").

If the size of a particular plant yield $= y$ for a given quantity of the growth factor $= x$, and if the maximum possible yield $= A$, the following equation applies:

$$\frac{dy}{dx} = c(A - y), \tag{1}$$

i.e. the change in yield, dy, which corresponds to a given change in the growth factor, dx, is proportional to the difference between the maximum achievable and present yields, $A - y$. Mitscherlich calls the coefficient c the "response coefficient".

By integration, we get

$$y = A(1 - e^{-cx}) \tag{2}$$

or, expressed in logarithms,

$$\log (A - y) = \log A - c \times x. \tag{3}$$

Following a suggestion by Baule, Mitscherlich (1948) applies the term "effective quantity" to the nutrient supply x at which exactly one-half of the maximum possible yield is achieved.

If we use the values $A = 100$ per cent, $y = 50$ per cent, $x = 1$, the following calculation results:

$$\log (100 - 50) = \log 100 - c,$$

and from this $c = 2 \cdot 00000 - 1 \cdot 69897 = 0 \cdot 30103.$

From equation (3) we obtain further:

for x	y	Difference from the maximum yield $(A - y)$
1	50 %	50 %
2	75 %	25 %
3	87·5 %	12·5 %
4	93·75 %	6·25 %
5	96·875%	3·125%
6	98·437%	1·563%

If the nutrient supply x is doubled, the yield y is increased by only one-half of the disparity from the maximum yield. Figure 8(a) shows the trend of the corresponding curve. This particular behaviour of the plant, which to begin with—i.e. when near the minimum—responds to the augmenting of a growth factor by a large increase in growth but subsequently gives an ever-diminishing return, has been exhibited earlier in Fig. 2–4. We shall repeatedly encounter this kind of logarithmic progression.

The three curves in Fig. 8(b) demonstrate the way in which the yield responds to the effect of a second growth factor z, for which an equally big response coefficient c is assumed, and its development with a two-fold and finally an infinite increase of this factor z.

According to Mitscherlich the response coefficient c (in our example $= 0 \cdot 301$) should remain constant for a given growth factor independently of the other simultaneously operative growth factors. As against this Rippel (1926) and Meyer (1929) were able to show experimentally that, for example, the response coefficient for potassium changes when the nitrogen supply is increased. Whereas with a low (constant) supply of nitrogen, the maximum possible yield is achieved by a small increase of the potassium supply, the absolute and much higher possible maximum yield demands a much larger potassium supply together with an increased (constant) supply of nitrogen.

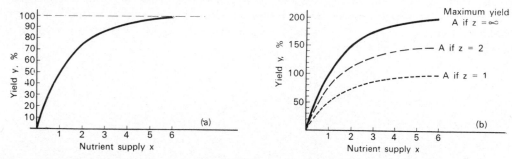

FIG. 8. (a) Yield increase in accordance with *Mitscherlich*'s efficacy law as a result of the increase of a growth factor x. (b) Yield if two growth factors x and z are increased.

Mitscherlich tested his efficacy law mainly by plant pot experiments in which the supply of certain nutrient elements was varied whilst retaining the other factors at an almost constant level, which of course is impossible in nature. Mitscherlich himself pointed out that, for example, the response coefficient of the water in the soil increases by the quantity of nutrients which are dissolved in this water and from which the plant benefits by way of the ascending transpiration stream. As mentioned by Laatsch (1957), Mitscherlich made a comparison between the yields obtained from two identical and neighbouring cereal fields with equal water consumption and showed that the yield from the field which had received full fertilizer treatment was twice as high as that from the field without fertilizer. *If, therefore, the nutrient content of the water in the soil is high, its response coefficient is considerably higher than when the nutrient content is low.*

Returning to the results of the fertilizer experiment by Tamm, we find that, clearly, *the assimilation rate of leaves and needles, with otherwise equal assimilatory conditions, depends decisively on the soil nutrients which are available, i.e. the particular site quality.* We shall have to stress on several more occasions the importance of this all too easily overlooked circumstance which influences the productivity of forests.

(b) THE CHARACTERISTIC BEHAVIOUR OF DIFFERENT FOREST TREES
IN THE ASSIMILATORY PROCESS

In the years 1938 and 1939 Polster succeeded, by a series of measurements at short intervals, in deducing *the daily sequence of assimilation and respiration in our most important forest trees.* For his experiment, he used small branches which had been cut from 7–8-year-old trees in the experimental nurseries at Tharandt. He determined the *apparent assimilation* of these branches by measuring the CO_2-consumption during short exposures to light, the *respiration* by measuring the discharged CO_2 when kept in darkness and the *transpiration* by calculating the loss of weight due to water expenditure. The curves for the daily sequence of assimilation, respiration, and transpiration which Polster managed to construct for different combinations of climatic factors show *special reactions of the different tree species to defined weather conditions* (radiation, warmth, air humidity). These observations agree with the practical experience of foresters and the concepts which have been developed as a result of this experience.

A feature which all assimilation curves for uniform weather conditions have in common is that they are *bimodal*, having a higher local maximum in the morning and a lower local maximum in the afternoon. Between these two local maxima lies a distinct *noon local minimum* (see Figs. 9 and 10). On days with alternating cloudy weather, several local maxima and minima may occur.

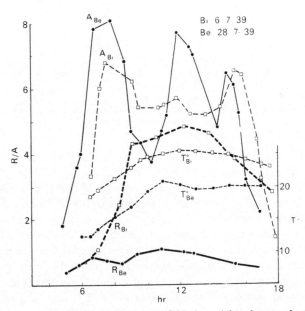

Fig. 9. Assimilation (*A*) and respiration (*R*) curves of birch and beech on a hot day and a cool day respectively together with the corresponding temperature curves (*T*) *(Polster).*

Figure 9 shows assimilation and respiration curves for *birch* and *beech*, those for birch corresponding to a hot day and those for beech to a cool day, as may be seen by the temperature curves which are also included. We find that the assimilation curve for birch has a relatively shallow noon depression despite the steep ascent of the respiration curve. Birch here displays its characteristically heavy and extravagant respirational demands.[1] Compared with birch, the assimilation curve for beech (which, owing to fluctuations in the degree of cloud cover, shows an abnormal daily sequence with three local maxima) is characterized by considerably greater fluctuations. The main feature, however, is the very flat trend of its respiration curve which proves the beech to be respirationally more economical in achieving a high rate of assimilation, especially on cool days with a high degree of air humidity and moderate radiation.

Figure 10 shows assimilation and respiration curves for Scots pine and European larch. The considerably higher intensity of respiration of pine as compared to larch is unmistak-

---

[1] Between the hours of 10–12 a.m. on a hot day in August, Polster observed a negative assimilation balance of birch, i.e. the quantity of CO_2 discharged by respiration was higher than the CO_2-consumption for assimilation.

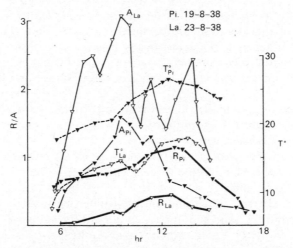

FIG. 10. Assimilation and respiration curves of Scots pine and larch *(Polster)*.

able. Larch is characterized by much more economical respiration and thus—as a conifer which loses its needles during the winter—represents a striking parallel to beech which is similarly economical.

The respiration economy of our native tree species

From the numerous individual values which Polster collected, he calculated *approximate annual averages of the assimilation and respiration rates*. Although these are problematic in many ways they do allow an interesting insight into the varying degree of economy used by the native forest tree species for the process of assimilation. Table 2 shows Polster's means for net assimilation (A) and respiration (R) as well as those for the gross assimilation $(A+R)$.

TABLE 2

MEAN ASSIMILATION RATES OF THE LEAVES OR NEEDLES OF DIFFERENT FOREST TREES GIVEN IN
MILLIGRAMS CO_2/HOUR ACCORDING TO EXPERIMENTS BY POLSTER

	Birch	Beech	Oak	Larch	Dougl. fir	Spruce	Pine
Net assimilation (A)							
per 1 dm² leaf area	3·46	2·41	2·09	2·33	1·54	1·58	1·65
per 1 gram fresh leaf weight	*3·88*	*3·74*	*2·51*	*1·83*	*1·00*	*0·87*	*0·91*
Respiration or breathing (R) Respiration of darkened leaves per 1 gram fresh leaf weight	*2·01*	*1·00*	*1·64*	*0·73*	*0·64*	*0·46*	*0·78*
Gross assimilation $(A+R)$	*5·89*	*4·74*	*4·15*	*2·56*	*1·64*	*1·33*	*1·69*
Quotient for economical respiration $\left(\dfrac{A+R}{R}\right)$	*2·93*	*4·74*	*2·53*	*3·51*	*2·56*	*2·99*	*2·17*
Order of rank	4	1	6	2	5	3	7

A striking feature of *assimilation* is the *superiority of broad-leaved trees* over coniferous trees in their performance per 1 square decimetre leaf area and even more so per 1 g fresh weight. Larch assumes a characteristically intermediate position.

Birch shows the highest *value for respiration*; the value for oak is also high whilst that of beech is more economical. Among the coniferous trees spruce and Douglas fir are also sparing.

The value obtained by adding the values for A and R characterizes the gross assimilation. The result of then setting $A + R$ proportional to R is an unnamed ratio which, according to a suggestion by Polster, can be used as a statistic for respiration economy. The larger this ratio, the smaller is the proportion of the gross assimilation which a particular tree species uses for respiration. A tree species with a high value of this ratio, therefore, can be regarded as "economical".

Among broad-leaved trees, beech and among coniferous trees, larch and spruce are economical in respiration. Oak and birch among the broad-leaves and pine among conifers are all uneconomical. Larch, which resembles the leaf-trees in many ways, holds a particularly favourable position, following immediately after the "best" broad-leaved tree, beech.

Respiration of the root system

The results of Eidmann's (1943) examinations of root respiration and transpiration of our principal timber species provide a very good insight into the special characteristics

TABLE 3

ROOT RESPIRATION AND TRANSPIRATION OF DIFFERENT TREE SPECIES ACCORDING TO EIDMANN (1943)

Tree species	Root weight as percentage of the total weight	Root respiration		Transpiration in g of water per 24 hours per 1 g dry weight increase
		in mg CO_2 per 24 hours per 1 g dry weight of the whole plant	in mg CO_2 per 1 g dry weight of root	
1	2	3	4	5
E. larch	33·8	14·8	63·4	4·61
S. pine (East)	26·2	14·2	62·3	5·17
S. pine (Rhineland)	24·5	12·1	48·4	3·83
Douglas fir	34·4	10·9	39·9	4·41
N. spruce	31·6	7·9	29·0	2·97
S. fir	37·1	6·1	17·8	2·64
Birch	46·9	32·0	108·4	6·59
Alder	42·0	25·1	74·5	3·59
Aspen	46·2	24·1	83·8	5·79
Lime	48·2	19·3	53·7	2·99
Hornbeam	40·1	15·7	43·6	2·57
Maple	53·7	12·8	30·8	3·76
Pedunculate oak	57·8	12·6	26·6	2·38
Sessile oak	58·8	10·1	20·9	3·75
Beech	45·1	11·6	30·3	3·11

The figures in column 2 are related to the final weight.
The figures in column 3 are mean values for the months May–September.

and the respiration economy of these species. When, however, these results are applied to older forest trees, or to whole stands, it must be remembered that Eidmann made his examinations on 2–3-year-old plants in pots, whereof root weight expressed as a percentage of the total weight of the plant is *considerably* higher than in the case of older trees. This is demonstrated by the data in column 2 of Table 3. According to this table, larch and pine have a high rate of root respiration among the conifers, whilst spruce and Silver fir are economical; among the deciduous trees, birch appears as a species with a high rate of root respiration whilst beech and both of the oaks stand out as decidedly economical.

The economy of transpiration

The economy achieved by our tree species in the process of assimilation must be examined also with regard to their water consumption. Even if, as mentioned earlier, the values given by Polster are in absolute figures fairly high, and their extrapolation to tree stands and vegetative periods of 120 days would—for example in the cases of beech and spruce—suggest rainfall values of 400 to 500 mm/ha, their comparative proportions would seem to be characteristic. Among the *mean day values* in Table 4 the *high figures for birch and oak* among broad-leaved trees and those for pine among conifers are outstanding. In its transpiration values *larch*, as a summer-green species, again exhibits a special position between the broad-leaved and the coniferous trees. Compared with the conifer spruce with an average value of 1·39 per 1 g fresh leaf weight, this value of 3·24 g for larch is conspicuously high. According to Schubert (1939) *larch* is characterized by its *extremely high rate of transpiration*. His measurements, which are particularly interesting because of the method he employed (measurement of the speed of the transpiration stream) produced the following noon values for a day in July:

Spruce	2·87 mg per 1 g fresh needle weight in 1 minute
Weymouth pine	2·80 mg per 1 g fresh needle weight in 1 minute
Larch	*8·56* mg per 1 g fresh needle weight in 1 minute

i.e. larch transpired approximately 50 per cent of its needle weight per 1 hour. The average of these figures by Schubert produces a daily transpiration rate for larch which is 4 times that for spruce.[1]

On the basis of his numerous measurements, Polster also calculated mean values for the transpiration per gram of dry matter produced. Thus these values state the approximate mean water consumption of the various species for the production of 1 g dry matter. As a result an "economic transpiration series" is obtained.

---

[1] The author had no knowledge of the work by the Russian forest scientist Sonn, published in German in 1960 (Jena), until his own book was published. This work by Sonn contains amazingly high values for the transpiration of larch stands, which, according to the author, generally use 1·5 to 2·5 times as much humidity as spruce stands. For example, in approximately 25-year-old stands on "leached chernozem" (the black earth of the steppes) Sonn found the following annual values for transpiration in millimetres (water column) per hectare:

Larch	437 mm
Pine	345 mm
Spruce	233 mm

Sonn gives the following explanations: The root system of larch is very strong and extends deeply into the soil; transpiration is intense and the growth period lasts longer.

TABLE 4

DAILY MEAN RATE OF TRANSPIRATION IN GRAMS PER DAY

	Birch	Beech	Oak	Larch	Dougl. fir	Spruce	Pine
Per dm² leaf area	8·48	3·12	5·02	3·60	2·20	2·53	3·42
Per gram fresh leaf weight	*9·50*	*4·83*	*6·02*	*3·24*	*1·33*	*1·39*	*1·88*
Economic transpiration figures (*T*:*A*)							
Mean water consumption in grams for the produc-tion of 1 g dry matter	317	169	344	257	173	231	300
Rank order	6	1	7	4	2	3	5

The following species reveal themselves as being "uneconomical": oak, birch and pine, i.e. the pronounced "light-demanding" species. "Economical" species, by comparison, are spruce, Douglas fir and especially beech, i.e. the semi-shade bearing and shade bearing species. Larch is intermediate between these groups.

However, on the basis of what has been said earlier, the *values for larch* must be assumed to be *too low* and larch must be regarded as a definitely *uneconomical consumer of water*. A few transpiration data for agricultural food plants are added here for the purpose of comparison:

Millet	293	Rye	685
Maize	368	Flax	905
Beets	397		

Compared to these values, those for our native forest trees can justifiably be considered as moderate.

(c) ASSIMILATION RATES AND LEAF QUANTITIES OF TREES AND STANDS

Polster made attempts to *extrapolate* his *results from individual leaves to trees and whole stands*. This "double integration", about which Huber has decided misgivings, can lead to considerable errors.

The quantity of light which, at a given radiation intensity, falls on the leaves depends on the angle of incidence of the light. If the intensity of light (*I*) falling perpendicularly to the leaf surface, i.e. at an angle of incidence of 90°, amounts to 1·0 then it diminishes along with a declining angle of incidence φ in the proportion $I \times \sin \varphi$; at $\varphi = 50°$ it is consequently reduced to 0·766, and at $\varphi = 30°$ to only 0·500. If, accordingly, under a clear daylight radiation of 30,000 lux, beech leaves receive that light even at an angle of incidence (φ) of 30°, they will still get 15,000 lux, which is sufficient to afford a full rate of assimilation.

Leaf area and stocked ground area

By *disposing their leaves, not perpendicularly but at changing angles to the main direction of the light*, individual plants and indeed whole plant societies succeed in *securing an adequate quantity of light upon leaf areas* which together *exceed the stocked ground area by many times*. Thus, Fig. 11 demonstrates that the assimilation rate of individual Sinapis leaves (a) has reached its highest value at 12,000 lux. Compared to this the assimilation rate of a crop of Sinapis plants with different angles of the leaves to the incidence of the light (b) continues its linear increase per square decimetre leaf area along with an in-creasing light power beyond 15,000 lux. Finally, by relating the assimilation rate *to the stocked area* (c) it becomes obvious to what degree organic production can be increased by changing angles of the individual leaves to the light so that, at the same time, the equivalent exposed leaf area is increased, in this case to 3·4 times the stocked area. At 15,000

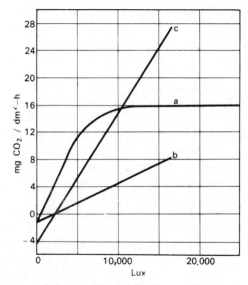

FIG. 11. Light assimilation curves of *Sinapis alba:* (a) for leaves which are perpendicularly exposed to the rays of light, (b) for a stand with variedly oriented leaf exposure, per dm², of leaf surface, and (c) related to the stocked ground cover of the stand *(Boysen-Jensen).*

lux the assimilation rate per square decimetre of stocked ground area is approximately three times that of the rate per square decimetre of leaf area. At the same time it becomes obvious that a light power of—let us say—10,000 lux, which is fully adequate for the optimal performance of an individual leaf (which is orientated so as to be at right angles to the direction of the light), is not enough for a *stand* of plants. The optimal performance for this very probably requires at least 20–30,000 lux.

The leaves of our forest trees are arranged in leaf patterns so as to afford the most favourable exposure possible to the light. Boysen-Jensen (1932) pointed out that, among native forest trees, the Common beech has a particularly well-developed "assimilation system". The buds are disposed on the sides of the twigs in two rows so that, as the leaves unfold they form a fan-like pattern. These leaf schemes are arranged in layers, the topmost leaves slanting obliquely upwards, the middle leaves having a nearly horizontal position and the lowermost leaves pointing obliquely downwards. By this arrangement the sunlight can be fully utilized on the stocked area.

Relative performances of sun-leaves and shade-leaves

The efficiency of individual leaves differs markedly. As a general rule, the leaves which are fully exposed to light in the crown periphery will achieve the highest gross and net assimilation rates whilst the performances of the shaded leaves in the lower and the interior parts of the crown are comparatively trifling. The contribution of the latter to the total assimilatory activity of the crown, both in absolute terms and relatively to their proportion of the total leaf weight is small. The highly informative investigations undertaken by Pisek and Tranquillini (1954) in a forest stand near Innsbruck (820 m above sea level, steep slope with a southern aspect and a gradient of 22–24°, morainic rubble) showed among other things that *insolated leaves at the apex* of a 20 metres high beech tree in a fairly open stand are *less productive* than the *leaves in sunlight at the base of the crown.* The stomatic regulation in the last-mentioned leaves was better than in the leaves of the powerfully lit upper crown which showed a more sluggish reaction to fluctuations in light intensity. On the same site, the stomata of a *spruce* tree 13 m high, possessing a deep crown and standing in an almost isolated position, proved to have more sensitive guard cells upon the shaded branches than on the branches in sunlight. It must be borne in mind that although the findings of the above two authors in some cases show favourable results for leaves and needles in shade, the data were obtained from a site experiencing an extremely high radiation intensity. We should certainly be cautious in applying these experimental results to conditions in average *closed forest stands* where the trees provide heavy mutual shading and where there are pronounced canopy differences.

The fact that the *integrated net result* of the production *of sun-leaves* over periods of several days and weeks is more favourable and *much more important than that of shade-leaves* is confirmed—apart from other factors—by the day values collected by Pisek and Tranquillini (1954) from a 10-m high *beech in Grafrath Forstgarten* (north-west of Munich). As shown in Table 5 the *night respiration of the shade-leaves* in this instance amounts to *nearly 40 per cent of the net assimilation of the previous day.* At the same time, the absolute values for the daily net assimilation of the sun-leaves are 4–5 times as high as those of the shade-leaves.

This agrees also with Burger's extensive investigations. He found that *Common beech and Norway spruce in the lower and middle storeys with leaves* or needles *in shade show considerably lower productive efficiency than trees in the upper storey, well exposed to light,* some of *which for a given leaf weight are nearly twice as efficient as the suppressed trees.* Ladefoged (1946) found that the increment of 21-year spruce stems possessing nine to eleven tiers of living branches would not be adversely affected if the two to three whorls at the base with their needles in shade were cut off. One-half of the increment is achieved by the upper four to five tiers of branches with their needles in sunlight, whilst the lowest third, bearing shade-needles achieves only approximately 15 per cent of the total performance.

The decisive factor for the assimilation efficiency of native forest trees therefore is—other things being equal—*light.* Even if one-quarter to one-third of the maximum daylight amounting to, say, 40–50,000 lux, or in other words, if only 10–15,000 lux would suffice

TABLE 5

DAY-VALUES FOR ASSIMILATION AND RESPIRATION OF THE LEAVES OF A 10 M HIGH BEECH IN GRAFRATH FORSTGARTEN ACCORDING TO PISEK AND TRANQUILLINI (1954)

Date	Weather		Part of crown	Daily totals in mg/g dry matter				Night respiration in % of the daily net assimilation
	Night	Day		Net assimilation	Respiration	Gross assimilation	Night respiration	
18.9.	clear warm 8–10°	bright to dull max. temp. 14·0°	Deepest shade, base of crown ≧ 400 lux	4·8	3·8	8·6	1·9	39·6
19.9.	overcast, warm 5–10°	dark cloudy with rain cool, max. temp. < 14°	≦ 2000 lux, lightly shaded base of crown	23·2	—	—	4·2	18·1
			Sun-leaves at tree top, ≦ 10·000 lux	24·9	—	—	6·4	25·7

for perfect assimilation by *individual* leaves, it seems that, owing to *mutual shading effects*, a large number of leaves have to put up with light which is by no means sufficient for their maximum performance. Moreover, it is to be assumed that the already mentioned *selective filtering of light itself leads to a considerably reduced performance of the leaves in shade*. Strange though this may sound, it is possible for light to represent a limiting factor in the productive output of a forest.

For this reason, it appears even more urgent to observe the exchange of gases in leaves of trees belonging to different strata and different parts of the canopy *in closed stands*. Such examinations by gas analysis in closed forest stands would have to be combined with careful observations of volume increments of individual trees and the annual increment of stands. This combination of gas-analysis methods and exact increment measurements in yield studies should, at last, provide the clarification of important basic questions of forest production.

Leaf quantities and increment

Some *data on leaf areas and leaf quantities per hectare* of whole stands are given in Table 6.

From the data in that table, we learn that the surface areas and dry weight quantities of the needles in conifers are larger than those of the foliage of broad-leaved trees. This is the reason why, despite lower assimilation rates per gram needle-weight, coniferous trees on a given site as a rule produce greater quantities of dry matter per unit of stocked area than leaf-trees. We must in this connection remember the fact that our native evergreen conifers have needles of several ages; thus, for example, spruce has needles of ages 5–9 years. Moreover, the conifers are able to assimilate all the year round, with the exception of frost periods, whilst the broad-leaved trees and larch depend on those 5–6 months during which they carry leaves or needles.

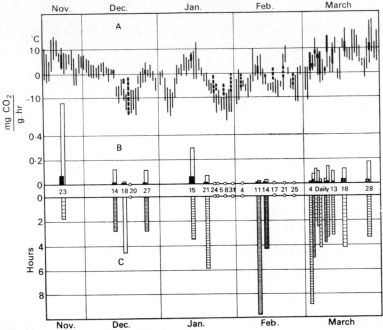

FIG. 12. Assimilation and respiration of spruce branches during the cold winter of 1946/7 *(Zeller* from *Walter)*.

Among the experiments which confirmed this were those by Zeller (according to Walter, 1951) who during the cold winter of 1946/7 observed the exchange of gases in a number of species, including *Norway spruce.* Figure 12 shows some noteworthy assimi-lation rates (white columns) achieved by Norway spruce during the winter months, frost periods apart; in some cases these rates were considerably higher than the simultaneously recorded respiration losses (black columns). The downward-directed columns represent the hours which were required for different degrees of light (shown in hatching) in order to achieve a daily balance between assimilation and transpiration.

TABLE 6

LEAF QUANTITIES FOR DIFFERENT TREE SPECIES AND THEIR CORRESPONDING INCREMENTS

| Tree species | Age | Leaf | | Achieved increment in | | Author |
| | | Dry weight | Surface | Volume | Dry matter | |
		(t)	(ha)	(m³)	(t)	
Ash	15	2·5	4·5*	6·9	3·5	Boysen-Jensen
Oak	40	1·7	3·1*	11·0	6·3	Mar:Møller
Beech	117	2·6	5·6*	10·0	6·0	Mar:Møller
Beech	98	2·8	6·1*	9·4	5·3	Burger
Spruce	65	10·3	13·1	16·4	6·4	Burger
Spruce	37	10·3	12·0	23·5	9·2	Mar:Møller
Douglas fir	41	16·9	27·1	34·0	16·3	Burger

* One-sided leaf areas.

Below, a list of leaf areas of some agricultural species:

Clover grass	5·4 square metres per square metre ground surface
Lucerne	5·3 square metres per square metre ground surface
Barley	3·7 square metres per square metre ground surface
Sugar-beet	3·3 square metres per square metre ground surface

The figures cluster about values which are similar to those for the native deciduous trees.

3. The Organic Production of Forest Stands and Its Components

Understandably many foresters, when contemplating the organic production of forest stands, are usually particularly concerned with yields in the form of harvestable or harvested timber. In so doing it is easy to overlook the fact that *the timber yield represents only a part of the total output of our forests*. For one thing, this output is composed not only of the woody produce of the trees but also that of the *ground flora*, i.e. the herbaceous and scrub layers. Under a pure stand of light-demanding trees, and particularly in the sparsely-stocked forest areas of alpine and polar regions, the *proportion represented by the ground flora is considerable*. According to data by Burger, which are reproduced in Table 7, the *proportion of wood and needles* of the total organic dry weight production for a sparsely stocked Norway spruce stand on a high mountain site amounts to 62 per cent, in contrast to 93 per cent for a spruce stand in mountains at a moderate altitude. In the former the *proportion of the ground flora is 38 per cent*, in the latter case it is only 7 per cent.

TABLE 7

SEPARATION OF THE ANNUAL PRODUCTION OF ORGANIC DRY MATTER OF NORWAY SPRUCE STANDS INTO WOODY GROWTH AND GROUND FLORA

| | The *annual production per hectare* amounted to | | | | | |
| | in a lightly stocked spruce stand on a high mountain site | | | in a 100-year-old spruce stand on a good site at moderate altitude (St. Gallen) | | |
	Dry weight (kg)	Wood (m³ (solid))	Per cent	Dry weight (kg)	Wood (m³ (solid))	Per cent
of woody growth	600	1·5	29	5800	13·9	71
leaf litter	700	1·7	33	1800	4·3	22
ground flora	800	2·0	*38*	600	1·4	7
Total production	2100	5·2	100	8200	19·6	100

But the proportion of wood in the total organic production must be even further subdivided. In order to transform the normal forest volume measurements (festmetres, cubic metres) into kilograms of dry substance produced, we use *volume density data (W)* which state the *dry weight in kilograms per cubic metre of fresh produce*. Further details are given on page 78.

The production equation of Boysen-Jensen

We are indebted to the Danish plant physiologist Boysen-Jensen for the first classification of the organic production of tree stands and approximate quantitative calculation. Boysen-Jensen distinguishes between the following components:

N_a = the net assimilation gain in leaves, known as apparent assimilation;
R = respiration losses from stems, branches and roots;
L_l = the loss of leaves by leaf shedding;
L_b = the loss of branch-wood by the shedding of branches;
L_r = the loss of roots (which can only represent a cautious estimate);
I_w = the increment of wood above and below ground;
S = the potential production of seeds.

The *production equation of* Boysen-Jensen is as follows:

$$N_a - R - L_l - L_b - L_r = I_w + S.$$

In this formula, the net assimilation by the leaves appears as the *gross production of the stand*; the *net production* is that quantity which remains after deducting the several *loss components* and appears in the shape of woody increment plus seeds.

All items are expressed as weights of organic dry substance.

Table 8 gives a classification of the organic produce of two young ash stands.

TABLE 8

CLASSIFICATION OF THE ORGANIC PRODUCE OF TWO ASH STANDS, 12–18 YEARS OLD, ACCORDING TO
BOYSEN-JENSEN AND MAR:MØLLER (VALUES PER HECTARE)

		No thinning	Heavy thinning
Timber volume above ground			
in the middle of the increment period 12–18 years	m³	75	51
Equivalent amount of dry substance	tons*	*36*	*25*
Leaf area per hectare	ha	4·9	4·0
Average annual *loss in dry substance* due to			
leaf shedding	tons*	2·6 = 26%	2·5 = 26%
respiration	tons*	3·4 = 34%	2·8 = 29%
branch losses (estimated)	tons*	0·5 = 5%	0·4 = 4%
Increment in dry substance	tons*	3·5 = 35%	3·9 = 41%
(volume)	m³	(6·9)	(7·5)
Gross production	tons*	*10·0 = 100%*	*9·6 = 100%*

* *Note:* metric tons.

Inspection of the data for the unthinned stand reveals that the *increment*, which is the main interest of forestry, makes *up only 35 per cent of the gross production*, i.e. approximately one-third. The most important and most striking item of loss is *that by respiration*, representing 34 per cent of the gross production.

In the heavily thinned stand, with a lower standing timber volume and reduced leaf area, the amount of the annual *gross production* is nearly the same, but the *net production*, or increment, is *slightly larger*. The net production, approximately 10 per cent higher, is apparently *due to the noticeably reduced percentage loss by respiration in the thinned stand*.

This reduction of the loss due to respiration in a heavily thinned stand is caused by the fact that the *stems which are removed* in the course of thinning consist *mainly of suppressed trees*. These trees have, as Boysen-Jensen discovered, a relatively low net production, owing to particularly high respiration losses. This "uneconomical" behaviour of the suppressed trees (Vanselow, 1943) is confirmed in Table 9.

TABLE 9

PERCENTAGE PROPORTIONS OF INDIVIDUAL TREE CLASSES REPRESENTED IN THE GROSS PRODUCTION AND INCREMENT OF AN UNTHINNED ASH STAND

Tree classes	of the growing tree volume	of the leaf area	of the gross production	of the increment
I. Dominant trees	47	52	61	66
II. Co-dominant trees	32	32	32	32
III. Suppressed trees	21	16	7	2

	Proportion of the respiration in the gross production	Proportion of the increment in the gross production
Tree class I	26%	42%
II	29%	41%
III	*50%(!)*	*8%(!)*

Boysen-Jensen discovered similar conditions in his examination of two young beech stands.

These results should not, by the way, lead us to conclude that moderately thinned, or indeed heavily-thinned stands, give unmistakably superior volume or dry-substance production. We shall see later that young stands react to early heavy thinnings by putting *on a spurt of rapid growth* which, however, gives them *only a temporary superiority* of attainment over unthinned or lightly thinned stands.

Foliage and increment

An exact determination of actual leaf quantities and the annual loss of leaves and branches poses difficult problems. Ebermayer's figures, on which we have for long relied, are founded on very extensive observations, but the methods employed have not been entirely free from criticism. More reliable information has been provided by Burger's investigations upon the timber, leaf quantity and increment of the different tree species. Valuable and accurate data have also been supplied by the investigations of Mar:Møller (1945) upon the leaf-shedding of actual stands of beech, oak, and Norway spruce. Some of these values are reproduced in Table 4. Mar:Møller's precise and methodical procedures in Danish beech stands (quality classes I to III) resulted in the striking disclosure that *dry leaf weights* were almost the same, regardless of the quality class of the site. Nevertheless, the total yield of the examined sites at the age of 100 years fluctuated between 550 and 1100 solid m³ of tree volume. *According to these investigations, the assimilation of equal quantities of leaves is considerably lower on poor-quality sites than on high-quality sites.* The explanation for this is obvious and has already been given[1] (p. 20). The efficiency of the leaves depends on the nutrient supply, especially of nitrogen and phosphoric acid. These nutrients are more abundantly present on the better quality sites. This runs counter to a still widely accepted view in forestry circles that the increment of our stands is a function of the actual leaf volume, a hypothesis which obviously cannot be maintained.

On very impoverished sites the leaf or needle weight per unit area is understandably low. This is the case especially for ragged, loosely stocked crops near the tree limit. Thus Mork (1942) ascertained in two Norwegian spruce stands at 80 (260 ft) and 180 m (590 ft) elevation that increments of 19 m³ and 9 m³ respectively with corresponding annual litter quantities of 3300 and 1883 kg dry weight were obtained per hectare.

Production spectra of Mar:Møller

On the basis of his revealing investigations Mar:Møller has drawn up production spectra for Common beech and Norway spruce which show the changing proportions of the components of organic production at different ages.

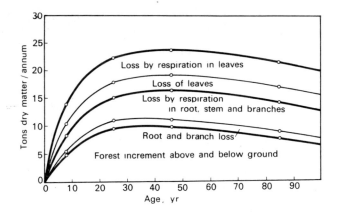

Fig. 13. Production spectrum of a beech stand *(Mar: Møller, 1954)*.

The production spectrum for *Common beech*, published in 1945, was based on apparent assimilation as the salient feature of total production. Following more recent researches by D. Müller and J. Nielsen (1954) upon the rate of leaf respiration in Common beech, Mar:Møller (1954) later revised his production spectrum (Fig. 13) using instead the gross assimilation as his essential quantity. The values in Table 10 placed below have been taken from the latter.

According to this table, gross production reaches a maximum between the ages 30–60 years, after which it declines markedly with increasing age. Leaf respiration losses appear to be relatively low. Whereas in the initial production spectrum for beech the respiration losses of the whole tree (including roots) show a tendency to increase steeply with age

---

[1] The reader is here again referred to the similar discovery stated by Robert Hartig in 1896.

TABLE 10

COMPONENTS OF THE ORGANIC PRODUCTION OF A DANISH STAND OF COMMON BEECH Q. CL. II (M.A.I.
AT 100 YRS. = 8·0 M³ TIMBER > 7 CM DIA. PER HA)
ACCORDING TO INVESTIGATIONS BY MAR:MØLLER, MÜLLER AND NIELSEN (1954)

| | Annual production in tons (t) dry matter per ha at the ages | | | | | | | |
| | 10 | | 30 | | 60 | | 90 | |
	(t)	(%)	(t)	(%)	(t)	(%)	(t)	(%)
Total gross assimilation	*15·9*	100	*23·2*	100	*23·2*	100	*20·9*	100
Losses by:								
Respiration of leaves	4·0	25	4·7	20	4·7	20	4·7	23
Leaf shedding	2·2	14	2·7	12	2·7	12	2·7	13
Respiration of roots stem and branches	3·6	23	4·8	21	5·6	24	5·1	24
Shedding of branches and roots	0·5	3	1·2	5	1·2	5	1·2	6
Total:	*10·3*	*65*	*13·4*	*58*	*14·2*	*61*	*13·7*	*65*
Net increment of trees (inclusive of roots)	*5·6*	*35*	*9·8*	*42*	*9·1*	*39*	*7·2*	*34*

Note: 1 ton = 1 metric ton of 1000 kg, or about 2205 lb avoirdupois.

and at 100 years attain approximately 60 per cent of the apparent assimilation, estimates in the more recent spectrum are considerably lower. It has been shown that the *respiration losses* of branches and stems *decrease rapidly as the diameters* increase. As indicated in Fig. 14, for example, branches of 1–2 cm in diameter have annual respiration losses of

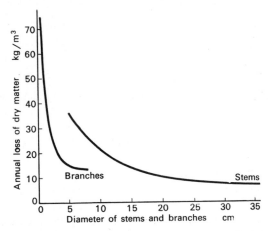

FIG. 14. Annual respiration loss (kg dry matter per m³) from the stem and branches of Common beech as a function of the diameter (cm) *(Mar: Møller, Müller* and *Nielsen).*

60–70 kg/m³, but branches of 5–8 cm in diameter have similar l sses of only 12–15 kg/m³. With an increase of stem diameter from 5 to 30 cm, the annual respiration loss falls off from about 35 to barely 10 kg/m³. Thus, the combined respiration losses from stems, branches and roots after the age of 60 years remain almost constant at 24 per cent of the gross assimilation. At the age of 30 years the *net increment* (which interests us more closely), when expressed as a proportion of the gross assimilation, reaches a maximum of approximately 42 per cent after which it reduces slowly. At the age of 90 years, the proportion has shrunk to only 34 per cent.[1] *The decrease in net increment after the peak growth-rate is past, would, according to this representation, be due, not so much to an increase of the respiration losses, but rather to the simultaneous reduction in the rate of gross production.*

In view of this fundamental change in the proportions following recent investigations, the components of the production spectrum of 1945 for Norway spruce will not be discussed. That spectrum was constructed on the basis of a similarly rapid increase of the respiration losses (from roughly 26 per cent at age 20 years to 46 per cent at age 70 years) as in the older spectrum for beech. Further investigations may also provide changes in these data for spruce.

TABLE 11

FRESH NEEDLE WEIGHT AND INCREMENT IN PURE FULLY STOCKED NORWAY SPRUCE STANDS ON DIFFERENT QUALITY SITES AND AT DIFFERENT AGES *(figures per hectare)*

Age	Quality Class I			Quality Class III			Quality Class V		
	Needle weight	Current ann. inc. in tree volume		Needle weight	Current ann. inc. in tree volume		Needle weight	Current ann. inc. in tree volume	
			per 1000 kg needle weight			per 1000 kg needle weight			per 1000 kg needle weight
	(tons)	(m³)	(m³)	(tons)	(m³)	(m³)	(tons)	(m³)	(m³)
40	*40*	*23*	0·59	*35*	*17*	0·48	26	9	0·34
60	35	22	*0·62*	32	16	*0·50*	29	*11*	*0·38*
90	31	16	0·53	30	12	0·40	27	8	0·29
120	29	11	0·38	28	7	0·25	26	4	0·15

The maximum values in each case are shown in italics.

According to Burger we must, in the case of Norway spruce, expect the fresh needle weight per hectare to decrease with increasing age. Table 11 shows that, on a given site, the fresh needle weights per hectare are correlated with the increments in each case. The culmination of the increment evidently coincides with the maximum fresh needle weights. On the other hand, the efficiency optima for increments with a given needle volume move to slightly older ages.

The figures in this table again stress *the narrow differences in fresh needle weight per hectare between quality classes I and III as also the reduced solid volume yields per 1000 kg of fresh needle weight which go along with a reduction of site quality.*

The reasons for the decrease in area efficiency of native tree stands corresponding to increasing age will be discussed later in the book in relation to optimal crown dimensions.

---

[1] If, in this instance, we relate net increment to net assimilation (= gross production minus leaf respiration), i.e. to the basic quantity of Boysen-Jensen's production equation then the corresponding proportions amount to 53 and 44 per cent respectively.

TREE GROWTH AND FORM

IN ORDER to obtain an insight into the growth of stands and trees, we must first analyse the pattern of growth and the resulting shape of individual trees. Our native forest trees make their annual growth by extension of their shoots and by the thickening of the stems and roots (cambial growth). It has become normal practice to characterize these two increment processes by two partial parameters: height and diameter increment.

1. Annual Shoot Growth and Height Increase

Every year, the buds which were formed during the preceding vegetative periop develop visibly into annual shoots. Depending on the bud arrangement, these shoots proceed as from the terminal bud in conifers or in the broad-leaved species Ash and Maple as also generally Oak and Common beech. In the majority of native broad leaved trees (Elm, Lime, Birch, Aspen, Hazel, Willow) the tip of the leading shoot perishes for some inexplicable reason and a lateral bud then develops into the annual shoot. The length of a fully grown annual shoot which has lignified remains unchanged, so that we are subsequently able to determine the length of each particular annual shoot.

From the changing pattern of long and short shoots the crown of the tree assumes its characteristic shape. Although growth by extension leads to a varying degree of elongation in *all* shoots, the assessment is, for the sake of simplification, often limited to *height growth*, i.e. the elongation of the main axis, or leading shoot.

In *coniferous trees*, which, as a rule, have one single leading shoot and a number of clearly distinguishable annual whorls of branches, it is not difficult to distinguish the height growth for a large number of past years. In some deciduous trees, as for example poplar, ash and maple, the last five to ten annual shoots can also be unmistakably distinguished at sight. However, when the spacing between the whorls is no longer clearly distinguishable, a count of the annual rings on a cross section of the shoot helps to provide the answer.

In older broad-leaved trees with wide dome-shaped crowns, or in older Scots pines with a convex crown it is difficult to determine the height and height increment beyond doubt. With such crown forms, it is impossible to distinguish one individual leading shoot at the top. Here, the mental construct of an even crown surface in the shape of a globular vessel or paraboloidal area can be of assistance. In that case, the top of the crown, necessary for the determination of height, may be defined as the point of contact of the crown surface and a tangent drawn horizontal to the ground surface.

(a) SEASONAL CHANGES OF THE ANNUAL HEIGHT INCREMENT

From phenological observations, in particular from the detailed investigations of Burger (1926) on various sites in Switzerland, we have learned that the start of annual shoot growth differs with species, the climate at the site and in the year of observation and with provenances (seed origins). Table 12 shows approximate data applicable to Central European sites at moderate altitudes.

TABLE 12

Species	Beginning and end of annual shoot growth			Length of growing period
Pine	Beginning of April to end of June			app. 80 days
Norway spruce	End of May to middle of July			app. 50 days
Larch (Europ.)	Middle of May to middle of August			app. 80 days
	Early growth:	*Rest period:*	*Secondary growth:*	
Common beech	Early May–early June = app. 30 days	App. 20 days	End June–mid. July = app. 20 days	
Oak	Mid-May–end of May = app. 20 days	App. 40 days	Early July–early August = app. 20 days	

Secondary or lammas shoots occasionally occur also on coniferous trees, e.g. in Norway spruce and Douglas fir where they are undesirable owing to the danger from frost to such shoots before they have completely matured during the autumn. By a hereditarily fixed tendency to early or late flushing the beginning of the annual growth can, under the same climatic conditions, easily change by a fortnight, a fact which is of great importance for regions with frequent incidences of late frost. Figure 15, according to Burger, gives a good illustration of the characteristic seasonal progress of the height growth in forest trees in the experimental nursery at Adlisberg.

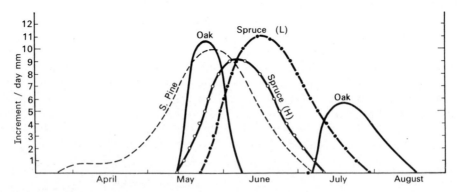

FIG. 15. Average seasonal development of height growth for different tree species in the experimental nursery at Adlisberg (670 m). *H*=high altitude spruce, *L*=low altitude spruce *(Burger)*.

The rate of the annual height increment fluctuates, and depends on weather conditions. Maximum daily increments of 4 cm for Norway spruce and 6 cm for Common beech have been observed.

The *rhythm* of the annual height growth is characterized by the occurrence of the maximum increment, which v. Sachs calls the "grand period". After a slow start, the rate of growth increases to a maximum, after which it again falls off. The seasonal pattern of growth thus closely parallels the pattern of growth as a function of age, a finding which will be discussed in more detail in connection with diameter growth.

The length of the annual height growth depends not only on the weather conditions of the year in which growth takes place, i.e. the *period of shoot elongation*, but also very largely on the weather of the previous year, especially between the months of July to September, when buds are formed. Those months of the previous year are vital for the development of reserve substances with which the elongation of the shoots in the following year is achieved.

(b) Height Growth Related to Age

Curves of total growth and increment

The development of height growth in trees (as of other growth phenomena in living things) follows a regular course in conformity with natural laws. This is exhibited by the successive height attainments of trees and their corresponding annual increases of height in relation to age. Figure 16 shows the heights which, according to an analysis by v. Guttenberg (1915), have been attained by a spruce at high elevation from Hinterberg in the Salzkammergut, plotted over the corresponding ages. This *growth* curve has a characteristic S-shape with an initially moderate, then steep ascent *convex* to the *X*-axis up to a point of inflexion beyond which the curve continues *concave* to the *X*-axis, flattening out increasingly with advancing age. This then represents a *cumulative curve* of growth which shows the total height attained by a tree at any particular age. It may be referred to as the *integral curve*.

If, instead, the annual *height increments*, i.e. the annual differences between the successive heights of the tree, are plotted against each year of the corresponding ages, a height *increment* curve is obtained. This can be regarded as the *differential curve*, or the first derivative of the growth curve.

In the *height increment curve, there are two points of inflexion* and one point of culmination. The culmination—or peak—of the increment curve occurs at the same age as the point of inflexion of the growth curve. The two points of inflexion of the increment curve mark the divisions between three characteristic phases of increment curves. The first phase which continues up to the first point of inflexion convexly in relation to the *X*-axis is the *juvenile phase*. Between the first and second points of inflexion, the curve is concave to the *X*-axis, and this phase, which includes the culmination point, is identical with the "grand period" of v. Sachs; it is the *phase of full vigour*. From the second point of inflexion onwards the curve is again convex to the *X*-axis; the increment decreases slowly; and this is the *phase of senescence or decline*.

These *natural increment phases: juvenile, full vigour* (culmination) and *senescence* (decline) are of extreme importance to the science of forest yields.

The Backman growth law

The continuity of the growth curve displayed in Fig. 16 demands a straightforward mathematical interpretation. In earlier attempts to provide this by R. Weber (1891) **and** Tischendorf (1925) the curve is satisfactorily described only from the point of time when increment reaches its maximum. The Backman *growth law* (1943) which is claimed to be valid for the height growth of trees represents a new attempt and has been specially recommended by Weck (1953) for the purposes of forest increment research.

Logarithmically, the law may be expressed as follows:

$$\log Z = K \times \log^2 T$$

In this formula, Z represents the increment of the tree, K represents a constant which is always negative, T represents the age of the tree, or time expressed as "organic time". This corresponds to the logarithm of "physical time".

The logarithmic time abscissa with its initially large, then steadily decreasing intervals for equal units of physical time does justice to the fact that equal periods of time appear longer to a young organism, for example a child, than to an old one, for instance an old man. The maximum increment which has been reached at the point $T = 1$ represents the increment unit. As the logarithm between 0 and 1 has a negative sign ($\log 1 = 0$) the increment for $T = 1$ must represent a maximum. From this point, $\log Z$ decreases with increasing values of T in proportion to $\log^2$.

Backman distinguishes between three growth cycles of which the first two, however, occur so early in youth that the final values reached by them can be neglected in comparison to the values of the third cycle.

Weck (1953) pointed out that the integration of Backman's function can be transformed into the well-known integral of Gauss. *On probability paper*, the cumulative values of the growth rates plotted as corresponding relative values of the Gauss integral over the logarithm of time form a straight line. The attainable end-value can be calculated from the cumulative value which has been reached at the time of the culmination of the increment. According to Backman's law, the different phases should be attained at the following percentages of the final value:

Culmination of the current increment	at	15·9 per cent
Maturity	at	50·0 per cent
Beginning of senility	at	92·1 per cent
Death from old age	at	95·3 per cent

If Backman's law is correct, the attainable end-value of the cumulative increment S can be calculated with the help of the cumulative value S_c, reached in the year of culmination, by the following relationship:

$$S = \frac{S_c}{16} \times 100.$$

The value of S_c for the spruce in Fig. 16 is $S_c = 11 \cdot 0$ m. Accordingly, this would produce an *attainable maximum height of*

$$\frac{11 \cdot 0}{16} \times 100 = \text{approximately 69 m.}$$

In Fig. 17 the cumulative percentages of the attained heights, related to the final value of 69 m, have been plotted over the logarithm of age on probability paper. It is evident that *representation by one single straight line* is *impossible*; the "break in development" between the ages 50–70 years requires a separate line from the age of 70 years. This example reveals an important limitation. Backman's *law applies* with admirable precision *for unchecked or uniformly controlled growth* processes, whenever the end value has been correctly estimated, which, in many cases, might be difficult. Every change of the environ-

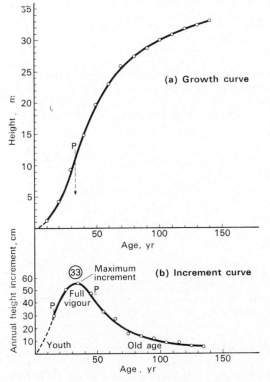

FIG. 16. Height growth and height increment curve of a spruce tree, from a stem analysis by *v. Guttenberg*.

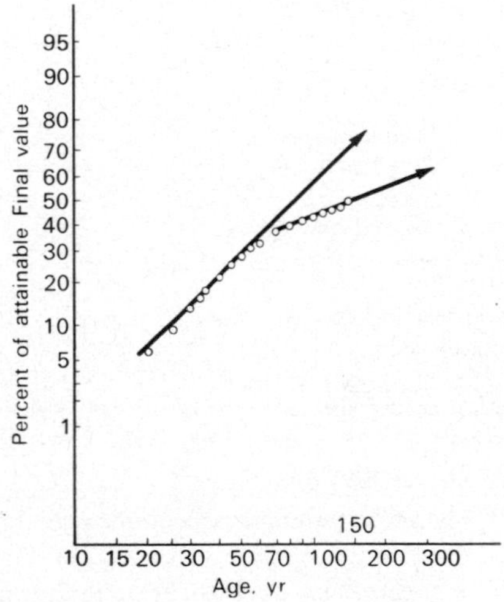

FIG. 17. Test of *Backman*'s growth law by reference to the height growth of a spruce (sample stem I) in a probability chart.

ment causes a change in the further progress of the growth curve. Spruce No. I from Hinterberg, after a brief period of suppression by shade during its youth, made even progress in development between the ages of 20 and 50 years without overhead or side competition. After this it became subjected to heavy side shade from dominant neighbours. From the age of 70 years it had become adapted to its new surroundings. Backman's function is evidently too rigid to give a complete description of such a history. The attainable end value, and thereby the progress of the total growth curve, is determined by the height and age at the point of time where the increment culminates. The spruce which we have been discussing had a relatively high value for S_c owing to slightly retarded development in early years, and the particular progress of the increment curve. In the case of v. Guttenberg's Norway spruce sample stem No. VII from Hinterberg, which maintained a fully dominant position throughout since it developed rapidly in the early years, the value of S_c, reached at the age of 22 years, is only 8 m with a subsequent potential end-value of 50 m, which corresponds much better with the true local conditions. The values for this sample stem on probability paper allow a comparatively satisfactory fit by *one* straight line.

The restricted utility of Backman's law and Schletter's (1954) sound criticism of it are consequently obvious.

(c) FACTORS INFLUENCING HEIGHT GROWTH

Height growth curves and their corresponding increment curves are influenced by a number of factors.

TABLE 13

CHARACTERISTIC VALUES FOR HEIGHT GROWTH IN DIFFERENT TREE SPECIES ON THE SAME SITE
(v. Guttenberg)

Tree species	Culmination of height incr.		Height at age
	at age (yrs.)	having maximum value of (m)	100 years (m)
Light-demanding species *Scots pine* (planted)	7 (5–15)*	0·54	app. 23
Semi-shade tolerant species *Norway spruce*	20 (8–32)*	0·58	app. 28
Shade-bearing species *Common beech*	23 (8–45)*	0·41	app. 26·5
Shade-bearing species *Silver fir*	33 (10–50)*	0·40	24·3

* Figures in parentheses denote period of most energetic growth ("full vigour").

The *special characteristics of* each particular *tree species* play an important part. In light-demanding species such as *larch, pine* and *oak* the point of inflexion of the growth curve, and therefore the *culmination of the increment curve*, occurs *early in life*. The *light-demanding species* generally reach their maximum of current height increment *earlier* than shade-bearing species, the curve both climbs and falls more steeply. On the other hand, in *shade-bearing species*, for example *fir* and *beech*, and in semi-shade-tolerant trees, for example *spruce*, the maximum is reached *later*, the rise of the curve is not so steep and its fall more moderate. This is effectually illustrated by Fig. 18 in which are given growth and increment curves for different tree species on comparable sites[1] according to v. Guttenberg (1885). Table 13 gives the characteristic values of the curves.

The effect of *site* is such that on *better sites, culmination* occurs *earlier* than on a *poor site*. This is demonstrated in Figs. 19a and b, which show the growth of two Norway spruce stems on sites of different quality. The growth and increment curves of different site qualities lie one above the other. The distances between the increment curves are

[1] For Scots pine, only the data of v. Guttenberg for planted trees with a rapid early development have been used.

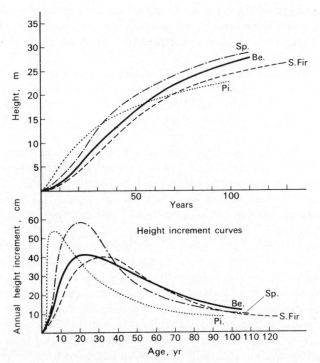

FIG. 18. Height growth and increment curves of different tree species on comparable sites
(v. Guttenberg).

greatest at the time of peak growth activity, but the values of the height increments
approach each other steadily with increasing age. The superior overall height growth
of trees on better sites is mainly the result of faster and bigger increments during the first
two growth phases.

The *intrinsic constitution* of individual trees and their *changing position in the social
structure of the stand* cause large deviations in the growing process and in the attained

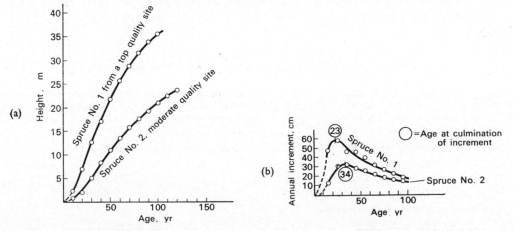

FIG. 19. (a) Height growth curves and (b) increment curves of two spruces on dissimilar sites.

total height. For example, in 100-year-old beech stands on a good site where, as a result of skilful crown thinning, some trees in the lower storey have survived, these latter trees did not exceed heights of 14 to 16 m compared to heights of 28 to 30 m amongst the dominants.

The height increments of conifers and broad-leaved trees are differently affected by *the amount of growing space afforded within even-aged stands*. With spruce, for example, a slight opening up has a favourable effect; as a rule, moderate thinning gives us the best height growth. A more severe opening of the canopy increases the diameter increment without increasing the rate of height growth. With the leaf-tree species beech and oak, the growth of shoots along the whole crown periphery is stimulated by widening of the growing space. Beech is furthermore capable of increasing rapidly the angle of its branches. As a result, the crown fans out and becomes much broader whilst the vertical increment decreases. This results in trees with wide crowns having heights for given breast height diameters which are considerably below those that could be expected as a result of light thinning.

Competition during the early years, which is a normal condition in natural and selection forests, suppresses height increment and *postpones the age of maximum growth-rate* sometimes by 50–100 years. Figure 20(a) shows height increment curves for Norway spruce and Silver fir from natural mixed stands on mountain sites which were examined by Magin (1959). In the special climatic conditions of a montane forest with high amounts of rainfall, low temperatures and short vegetative periods, not only Silver fir but also Norway spruce can endure crown competition over several decades without it inhibiting their later growing capacities. Figure 20(b) shows height growth curves of four Silver fir trees which had suffered suppression for periods of different duration; we find that by shifting the abscissae as Magin does, so as to bring together the ages at which unrestricted height growth begins, the growth curves exhibit very similar trends.

Weck maintains, on the basis of Backman's growth law, that trees which have grown under crown cover in their early life later persevere longer with their growth and ultimately reach taller dimensions than trees which, without crown cover, have developed rapidly in the early years. This contention may apply to trees growing to very great ages and to the final heights which can then be achieved, but has very little bearing upon trees grown with normal economic rotations. Table 14 shows that spruce No. I from an even-aged plantation at Denklingen forest in Oberschwaben at the age of 143 years reached the same impressive dimensions which similar trees, grown in a selection-like forest, achieve at 200–300 years.

TABLE 14

HEIGHT GROWTH OF NORWAY SPRUCE AT DENKLINGEN FOREST

No.	Age	d.b.h. $(d_{1 \cdot 3})$ (cm)	h (m)	Approximate number of years of inhibited height growth	Culmination of annual height increment at age (yrs.)	(cm)
(a) From the all-age ("Selection-like") forest in the "reservation" at Mittelaschtalrain VI. 7d						
1	204	107	49·6	20	30–40	110
2	311	130	43·0	60	90–100	25
3	192	120	40·0	20	70–80	70
(b) From a plantation at the same site						
I	143	125	47·1	8	20–30	115

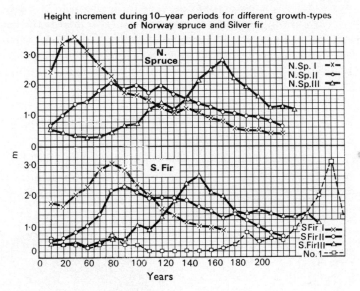

FIG. 20a. Height increment curves of Norway spruce and Silver fir from natural mixed stands in mountain regions *(Magin)*.

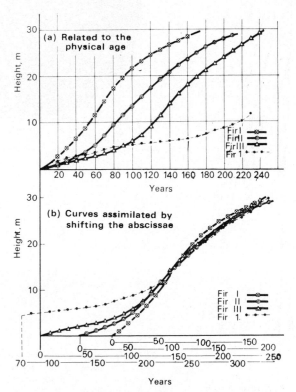

FIG. 20b. Height–growth curves of S. fir: (a) plotted over true age and (b) by shifting the abscissa, partially fitted to overlap *(Magin)*.

Over-dense stocking in single-storeyed crops, as for example in Norway spruce stands originating from dense sowing or natural regeneration, also retards the height increment whereas planting with wide espacement promotes height growth. A striking *acceleration of natural growth* can be induced by *heavy thinning before the culmination of the increment*. We shall examine this effect further in the discussion of the effects of thinning.

2. Width of Annual Rings and Diameter Increment

The diagrammatic longitudinal section of the leading shoot of a tree in Fig. 21 illustrates how new sheaths of tissue are laid on annually. Continuing from the pith (P) to the right we meet five well-defined growth layers of woody tissue; the outermost of these (I), developed during the previous year, is succeeded by the cambial layer (C). Every year

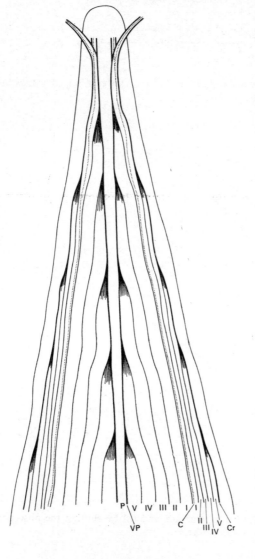

FIG. 21 *(left)*. Shortened longitudinal Section of a tree showing the sheaths of woody growth and bark.

FIG. 22 *(above)*. Cross-section of a spruce stem. Section taken at 23 m height.

this layer partitions off to form two new layers: one woody layer inside the dividing tissue and one bark layer outside it. The age sequence of the narrower bark layers (the oldest layer always outside) is in reverse order to that in the woody layers.

A cross-section of a tree stem, in this case a Norway spruce, taken at 23 m up the tree, shows the successive annual increments in the shape of the familiar annual rings. The fact that these are visible is due to the different formation of early wood with wide lumens and an abundance of vessels and of late wood with narrow lumens. Moreover, the cells which are formed at the end of every vegetative period are severely flattened in cross-section. Thus, the contrast between the dense and usually narrower late wood belt and the directly following vegetative year's belt of early wood with wide lumens enables us to define the annual rings. The divisions are particularly striking in the broad-leaved species of oak, ash, robinia and in the coniferous species of Scots pine, larch, Norway spruce and Silver fir; much more difficult to distinguish are the rings of Common beech and hornbeam. Damage by insects, for example damage in oak by the oak leaf-roller followed by a fresh development of leaves, can lead to the formation of *double rings*. The same effect may be produced by summer droughts which are followed by a wet period and favourable autumn weather. In a dry summer and on a poor site, considerable parts of the stem, particularly of dominated trees and trees in the under-storey, may not develop an annual ring at all.

(a) SEASONAL START, DURATION AND RATE OF FORMATION OF THE ANNUAL RING

In our native climatic conditions, the annual ring development in the stems of broad leaved trees starts, in all cases, at the beginning of May, and finishes approximately at the end of August. In coniferous trees it starts about the middle of May, and lasts till approximately the middle of September. By comparison, diameter growth in the *root* begins approximately *one month* later and lasts until well into November.[1]

TABLE 15

THE PROGRESS OF RADIAL GROWTH IN THE COURSE OF ONE VEGETATIVE PERIOD (ACCORDING TO TOPCUOGLU)

Month	Relative increment in per cent of the annual increment							
	Pine open grown		*Pine* crop tree		*Beech* crop tree		*Oak* crop tree	
	Stem	Root	Stem	Root	Stem	Root	Stem	Root
May	8	—	10	—	3	—	33	—
June	58	21	32	10	23	5	33	29
July	18	16	42	34	43	26	26	27
August	13	42	14	32	31	32	8	25
September	3	19	2	19	—	24	—	16
October	—	2	—	5	—	11	—	2
November	—	—	—	—	—	2	—	1

[1] Ladefoged (1946) found that, in the Danish oceanic climate, longitudinal extension of beech roots continues throughout the whole year, whereas in coniferous trees there is a resting period during the winter.

The observations made by Topcuoglu (1940) show a typical example of the annual progress of radial growth for different species. The strikingly early start in *oak*, a phenomenon which it has in common with other ring-porous leaf-trees, e.g. with ash and elm, is due to the essential annual development of water conducting tissues (vessels) because the tissues of the old annual ring no longer function properly. In ring-porous trees, radial growth activity of the cambium therefore begins even *before the unfolding of the leaves*. Table 15—according to Topcuoglu—shows a distribution of the annual growth activities in the stem and root regions of Scots pine, Common beech and oak for separate months. This illustrates time differences in the root growth for all species and the more rapid development of stem increment in open grown pine.

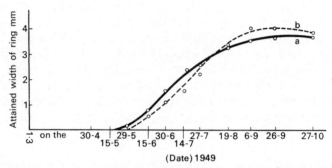

FIG. 23. Growth of the annual ring for 1949 in two Common beech trees from (a) 300 m and (b) 500 m above sea level *(Schober)*.

In the course of the vegetative year 1949, Schober examined the seasonal course of diameter growth at different altitudes (300 and 500 m above sea level) on the basis of repeatedly collected cores which were taken with a special borer. The short intervals between measurements enabled the construction of *growth curves* of the annual rings to be made. As we can see in Fig. 23, these curves have the same S-shape as the growth curves expressed as a function of age. *Seasonal growth therefore has the same general rhythm as growth expressed as function of the age.* This general rhythm is, as we know, built up from daily fluctuations, which Friedrich was able to record with the help of highly sensitive dendrometers. Characteristic for all the growth curves of annual rings found by Schober is the distinct *decline at the end of the vegetative period* which is caused by a shrinkage phenomenon in linear measure amounting to 1–9 per cent, and in larch even to as much as 15–20 per cent. This agrees with earlier observations by Friedrich (1897) and Chalk (1926).

The increment curves for the annual ring which are derived from these growth curves show a distinct culmination of the diameter increment during certain months, depending on the tree species. Notably early culminations are found in Larch, Scots pine and Douglas fir, where they occur approximately in June; medium early culmination, approximately at the end of June or beginning of July, occurs in *Norway spruce and Common beech*; markedly *late* culmination is shown in the curves for *oak and Red oak*. The early start of diameter growth in oak at both altitudes is characteristic.

A good illustration of these peculiarities is given in Table 16. Oak excepted, the percentage data for the different altitudes provide a clear demonstration of the *later beginning and longer duration of the increment activity at a higher altitude*. The *late wood development*, which had begun immediately at, or a few weeks after, the culmination of the diameter increment, also started 2–4 weeks later at the higher altitude.

TABLE 16

MONTHLY DIAMETER INCREMENT AS PERCENT OF THE TOTAL ANNUAL RING WIDTH, ACCORDING TO INVESTIGATIONS BY SCHOBER
EXPERIMENTAL GROUP "KATTENBÜHL" AT 300 M ABOVE SEA LEVEL
EXPERIMENTAL GROUP "STEINBERG" AT 500 M ABOVE SEA LEVEL

Timber species	Experimental group	Apr.	May	June	July	Aug.	Sept.	Oct.
Oak	Kattenbühl	4	17	22	33	24	—	—
	Steinberg	4	18	18	34	26	—	—
Common beech	Kattenbühl	—	8	32	33	21	6	—
	Steinberg	—	10	18	32	38	2	—
Scots pine	Kattenbühl	—	27	42	29	2	—	—
	Steinberg	—	15	23	29	27	6	—
Norway spruce	Kattenbühl	—	10	36	35	15	4	—
	Steinberg	—	3	24	33	28	12	—
Europ. larch	Kattenbühl	—	8	46	31	13	2	—
	Steinberg	—	8	25	30	22	15	—
Jap. larch	Kattenbühl	—	12	34	32	18	4	—
Douglas fir	Kattenbühl	—	10	32	29	21	8	—
Red oak	Kattenbühl	6	19	24	31	17	3	—

(b) THE GROWTH RHYTHM OF DIAMETER AND BASAL AREA IN RELATION TO AGE

On a growing tree, the diameter increment is conventionally measured *at a height of 1·30 m above the ground*. Diameter growth consequently cannot be measured until the tree has reached that conventional height of measurement. In contrast to height and its changes, the diameter at breast height does *not* represent a *"genuine" quantitative characteristic but a "false" one*. We have in this instance chosen a place of measurement which is *not homologous*; it is an arbitrarily fixed height of measurement which stands in no constant relationship to the continually changing dimensions of the tree body. Such a relationship would be found in a measurement height of approximately one-tenth of the total height of the tree, which changes along with its age.

The breast-height diameter plotted as a function of age gives a diameter growth curve analogous to the height growth curve. The corresponding curve of the differences, i.e. the diameter increment curve is analogous to the height increment curve. Figure 24 illustrates both of these curves for v. Guttenberg's sample stem No. I from Hinterberg. In consequence of the rapid early development of this tree, the culmination of increment is reached at 25 years. From this curve it is possible to estimate that the measurement height of 1·30 m had not been reached until the tree was approximately 10 years old.

If we compare the diameter growth curves and the diameter increment curves for different tree species on the same site, we find that their behaviour is similar to that of the height growth, i.e. the culmination of the light-demanding species occurs early in comparison with the shade-bearing species and, on the other hand, the performances of the light-demanding trees drop rapidly and sharply during later years.

The one-dimensional *diameter increment* of a supposedly circular cross-section of a tree *is equivalent to twice the radial increment*, or twice the annual ring width:

$$i_d = d_2 - d_1 = 2i_r;$$
$$d_2 = d_1 + 2i_r = d_1 + i_d \quad \text{(cf. Fig. 25)}.$$

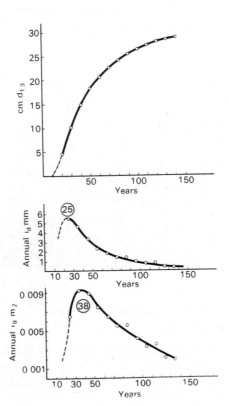

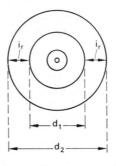

FIG. 24 *(left)*. Diameter growth curve (top), diameter increment curve (centre), and basal area increment curve (below) of a spruce, analysed by *v. Guttenberg*.

FIG. 25 *(above)*. Radial increment and diameter increment (schematic).

From this, the corresponding circular or basal area increment is obtained as follows:

$$i_g = \frac{\pi}{4}(d_1 + i_d)^2 - \frac{\pi}{4}d_1^2 = \frac{\pi}{4}(2d_1 \times i_d + i_d^2).$$

If the measured diameter increment is small in comparison to the initial diameter, the term i_d^2 can be neglected, and the approximate formula,

$$i_g = \frac{\pi}{4} \times 2d_1 \times i_d,^{[1]}$$

is obtained.

This means that *the area increment of the cross-section of a tree does not depend on the annual ring width alone* (or the diameter increment alone) *but also very largely on the diameter of the cross-section of the stem on which it accrues.* The larger the initial diameter,

[1] The approximate formula $i_g = \pi \times d \times i_r$, which is identical to the above formula, is given by the cross-sectional area increment as product of the stem girth and annual ring width.

the larger the sectional area increment for a given annual ring width, or for a given diameter increment. As a result the *basal area increment* at breast height (or the sectional area increment at a chosen stem height) always *reaches its culmination considerably later than the corresponding diameter increment.* Thus, as shown in Fig. 24, i_g in spruce No. I from Hinterberg does not culminate until the age of 38 years, i.e. 13 years later than i_d. Even after i_d has started to decrease, i_g may continue to increase for a while, because the narrowing annual ring is added to an increasing cross area.

The *available growing space* has an important influence on the diameter and basal area increment of individual trees. With increasing growing space–perhaps due to progressive opening up of the crop canopy—the basal area increment of individual trees also increases until the maximum utilizable growing space is reached. When this limit has been reached, a yet more liberal provision of light cannot produce further increment ("Lichtung", or open crop increment) by the individual trees.

(c) Annual Ring Width, Diameter and Sectional Area Increments at Different Stem Heights

Characteristic increment distribution on the tree stem

The problem of how diameter and sectional area increments vary along the stem at different heights was also discussed by v. Guttenberg (1915). According to him, the annual ring width in all spruce stems growing in stands decreases from the base of the stem upwards until it reaches a *minimum at a stem height of between 1 to 12 m,* and from there it increases again to the base of the crown and on within the crown. Therefore, as shown

TABLE 17

Diameter and Sectional Area Increments of a Norway Spruce at Different Stem Heights and for Different Age Periods, Related to the Increment at 1·3 m Height in Each Case
(Sample stem No. V of v. Guttenberg)

Cross-section height (m)	Diameter increment at the age							Sectional area increment at the age						
	30–40	40–50	50–60	60–70	70–80	80–90	90–100	30–40	40–50	50–60	60–70	70–80	80–90	90–100
0·4	103	125	127	148	126	129	115	**112**	**135**	**143**	**173**	**149**	**153**	**137**
1·3	*100*	*100*	100	100	100	100	100	*100*	*100*	100	100	100	100	100
4·3	127	109	*98*	*100*	90	86	87	108	101	*93*	95	86	82	82
8·3	**174**	142	108	103	*86*	86	81	*94*	110	93	92	77	77	72
12·3		**187**	134	113	91	*80*	77		101	98	91	*75*	67	64
16·3			142	141	112	95	81			72	89	79	69	*61*
20·3			**147**	173	155	127	96			*27*	67	82	78	63
23·3				**200**	186	151	113				*30*	65	73	62
25·3					**195**	**171**	132					*40*	60	60
27·3						170	130						*40*	44
29·3							**143**							*27*

$d_{1·3}$ cm

11·5	16·1	19·8	23·8	27·1	30·4	33·3	35·8

i_d cm 4·6   3·7   4·0   3·3   3·3   2·9   2·5

The maxima are shown in heavy print, the minima in italics.

in Fig. 26, we have a maximum annual ring width (and so a maximum diameter increment) at the base and also at the top of the tree, with a minimum somewhere in between.

It is otherwise, however, with sectional area increase, which is not solely dependent on
the annual ring width, but also very largely on the diameter of the cross section. The
spruce in Fig. 26 for the age period 90–100 exhibits a maximum increment at the base of

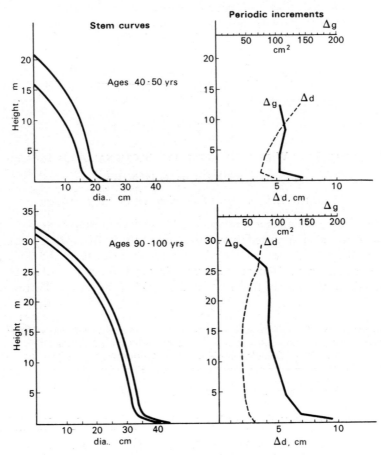

FIG. 26. Stem curves and diameter and sectional area increments of a spruce; measurements have been
taken at different stem heights and for two age-periods. Analysed by *v. Guttenberg*.

the stem; upwards from there the sectional area increment first decreases rapidly, in
the middle part of the stem more slowly, and in the upper part of the crown again sharply.
This applies for older trees in which the increment has already slowed down. In young
and middle-aged trees in which height and volume increments are lively and vigorous,
large quantities of woody substance are added in the upper part of the crown (elongation
and thickening of the shoots) and in the lower part of the crown as well as directly below
the crown. *In this process, the annual rings in the upper part can become so wide that the
sectional area increment also may once more noticeably increase from a minimum in the
middle part of the stem upwards to a maximum in the top part.* Table 17 and the corresponding Fig. 26 exhibit this well for the age period 40–50. According to v. Guttenberg this

behaviour is *normal for the medium aged classes in dominant Norway spruce* trees on a good site. In contrast to this, he found that the sectional area increment on a poor site always decreases upwards from the familiar maximum at the base of the stem.

This observation of v. Guttenberg's is confirmed by preliminary investigations conducted by the author upon stem analyses of sixty dominant Norway spruce trees taken from stands which had been subjected to normal thinning practices (locality: Iller–Lech Platte).

The analysed stems were 16 to 34 m high and up to 91 years old. Only in 62 out of 170 observed 5-year periods did the sectional area increment decrease right through from a maximum at the base of the stem upwards. The remaining 108 cases, however, showed *a minimum* at stem heights between 1 to 17 m *and an upper maximum* between 3 and 23 m. The trees with a pronounced upper maximum of the area increment, which in most cases lies in the vicinity of the base of the crown, often have a high breast height form factor (cf. p. 64). It would appear that the regular and usual decrease of the breast-height form factor with increasing height is delayed in these trees; some cases even show a noticeable increase of the form factor. Once tree heights of 26–30 m have been reached, a steadily increasing proportion of the timber increment is apparently added at the lower part of the stem, especially at the base, so that a continuous upward diminution of the sectional area increment results.

Changes of the increment distribution on the stem

Heavy thinning by which *older* trees are given ample free-growing space causes characteristic changes of the increment distribution on the tree stem. The data in Table 18 according to v. Guttenberg show that the distribution of the diameter increment on the

TABLE 18

DIAMETER INCREMENTS OF AN OLD NORWAY SPRUCE FROM RAURIS AT DIFFERENT STEM HEIGHTS BEFORE AND AFTER HEAVY THINNING ("LICHTUNG")

Height at which the cross-section is taken (m):		1·3	4·3	8·3	12·3	16·3	19·3	23·3	27·3	29·3
During the decade *before heavy thinning*	cm	1·06	0·97	0·91	0·98	1·05	1·07	1·18	1·36	2·02
During the 1st decade *after heavy thinning*	cm	1·09	1·00	0·81	0·84	0·95	0·83	0·80	0·69	0·74
During the 2nd decade *after heavy thinning*	cm	1·49	1·28	1·15	1·09	1·05	0·95	0·86	0·70	0·64
Percentage data related to the diameter at 1·3 m before heavy thinning										
During the decade *before heavy thinning*		100	92	86	93	99	101	111	129	190
During the 1st decade *after heavy thinning*		103	95	76	79	89	78	75	65	70
During the 2nd decade *after heavy thinning*		141	121	108	103	98	90	81	66	60

stem of an older spruce from Rauris became fundamentally altered after heavy thinning; *the increment is inevitably shifted to the lower part of the stem*. Whilst in this case the diameter increments are much increased, especially in the second decade after heavy thinning, they decrease in the upper part of the stem so as to result in *a continuous upward diminution of the diameter increments*. This is clearly shown in Fig. 27. The decrease of

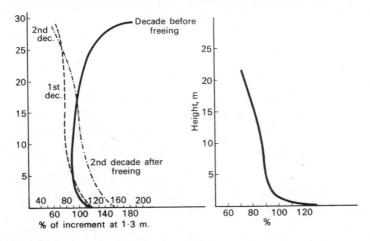

FIG. 27. *Left:* Diameter increments of a spruce tree, before and after release by a severe thinning. Increments at different stem heights as percentages of the increment at breast height (1·3 m) before severe thinning. *Right:* Diameter increment of an open-grown 220-year-old spruce during the age period 190–220, i_d at 1·3 m = 100 per cent. Analysed by *v. Guttenberg*.

the sectional area increments, for which there are unfortunately no data, would appear even more pronounced.

This tendency to more rapid radial growth in the lower parts of the stem continues throughout the entire life of trees that are afforded free growing space. The trunk of a Norway spruce with low branches and an almost conical stem structure, which was analysed by v. Guttenberg, showed very large diameters with a continuous decrease up the stem. A comparison of Fig. 27 with Fig. 26 and Table 17 shows how marked the decrease of the sectional area increment must be in spruce trees growing in such open conditions.

V. Guttenberg's observations on other coniferous species, such as Silver fir, Scots pine and larch (1915) presented basically similar characteristics. In beech and oak, the shift of growth to the part near the ground is not so pronounced, probably due to the fact that the timber in these species possesses different characteristic properties of density and strength.

Observations made by Topcuoglu (1940) on twenty-seven Norway spruce sample stems from poor sites (height quality classes III/IV to IV/V) with heights of 13–30 m, confirm the results of v. Guttenberg. The height of the *minimum diameter increment* in these individuals varied with tree class and weather; on average it occurred at 21 per cent of the stem height, or in absolute terms between 1·30 and 6·70 m height. Whilst weather had hardly any influence on the increment distribution of the stems of dominant trees, the co-dominant and suppressed trees showed a pronounced tendency towards a *downward* shift of the increment in dry years.

Topcuoglu's further discovery that the concentration of sap in the sieve tubes of the examined trees decreases towards the base of the stem by approximately 2 per cent per metre of stem gives occasion to stress *the importance of the descending nutrient flow of assimilation products to the distribution of new growth along the stem.* Whereas the ascending transpiration current takes place in the woody tissues, the descending flow of assimilation products moves, as we know, through the sieve tubes—or phloem—of the inner bark, which Theodor Hartig called "Safthaut" (sap skin).[1] The fact that the concentration of sap in the sieve tubes reduces in its descent from top to bottom of the stem emphatically testifies to the highly *favourable conditions for nutrition and growth which are enjoyed by the parts of the stem near the crown.* Robert Hartig (1896) was able to show this with the help of stem analyses of Norway spruce from Forstenrieder Park near Munich, whose crowns showed a varying degree of needle loss caused through defoliation by the Nun moth caterpillar. The development of the annual ring in these spruce stems completely failed sometimes even in the year of the attack, but more usually in the following year, the failure extending *downwards* by 6 to 7 m, in one case even from 17 m stem height. The same classic experiment of R. Hartig supplied early information about the influences of pruning, heavy thinning, and edge effects on the increment distribution of the stem. Hartig declared the growth-rate to be the resultant effect of interaction between the assimilatory capacity of the tree (crown size, needle quantity) and the nutritive supply potentials within the soil (soil condition, root growth). According to him, stimulation of the cambial cells from pressures caused mainly by the *effect of wind* has a decisive influence on the increment distribution of the stem. Hartig demonstrated the powerful effects of mechanical stresses when acting in opposition to the favourable effect of the assimilatory supply in his example of a spruce tree on the edge of a stand which, despite the fact that it had branches only on the SW. side (weather side), developed broader annual rings with compression wood on the NE. side (lee side) on which there were no branches. The great importance of wind effect on the form of trees will be discussed in more detail below.

3. The Shape of the Tree Stem

The growth processes which we have considered in the above paragraphs result in a characteristic tree shape. As compared with the many diverse and, in some cases, bizarre outlines of broad-leaved trees, conifers present regular forms as displayed, for example, by a Norway spruce tree in the geometrical severity of its whole structure, but especially the stem.

(a) THE STEM PROFILE

The outstanding feature in the longitudinal section of a Norway spruce stem (Fig. 28) is the characteristic shape of its outline, the so-called stem profile. Beginning at the roots, it runs convexly to the centre line of the stem, or pith, until at approximately one-tenth of the tree height, it reaches a turning point. From there on it proceeds concavely to the centre line, with a sharper parabolic curve up to the base of the crown, then taking a less sharp curve from the base of the crown to the top of the tree.

Thus the stem curve of a tree stem is divided into three sections:

1. The *base of the stem,* from where it joins the roots to the turning point of the stem

---

[1] A brilliant and easily comprehensible presentation of related plant physiological problems is given by Huber in his work *Die Saftströme der Pflanzen* (1956).

curve. This section is convex to the axis of the stem. The corresponding geometric solid is a neiloid.

2. The *middle section of the stem*, from the turning point to the base of the crown. This section is concave to the axis of the stem. The formal geometric solid is a cubic paraboloid with intermediate transitions to a quadratic paraboloid.

3. The *upper section of the stem*, from the base of the crown to the top of the tree. This section is slightly concave to the axis of the stem. The solid geometric form is a quadratic paraboloid with transitions to a straight-sided cone.

A mathematical interpretation and description of this characteristic shape by means of a stem profile equation naturally suggests itself. The known *stem form theories* are based on certain functions which may be assumed by the tree stem:

1. The so-called *physiological stem form theories* are founded on the function of water and sap conduction processes as formative agent.

2. The so-called *mechanical* stem form theories postulate the function of mechanical resistance against bending and compression as the main contributory cause of the developed shape.

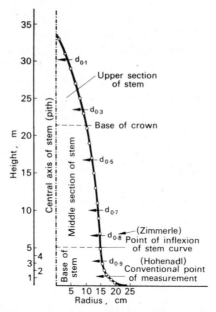

FIG. 28. Smoothed stem profile for a 73-year-old spruce.

Pressler in 1865, in his "law of stem formation", set up the following hypothesis: "The area increment on any part of the stem is proportional to the foliage capacity in the upper part of the tree and therefore is nearly equal in all parts of the stem which are free from branches." By "foliage capacity" Pressler meant the sum of the leaves multiplied by their assimilatory capacity. This theory is not correct, because—as shown above— only exceptionally and for limited distances does the sectional area increment in those parts of the stem free of branches remain nearly equal.

Jaccard (1913) regarded the tree stem as "a column of steady water-conducting capacity". In his view, the tree stem must have a nearly constant water conducting area from the base upwards, which it achieves by developing sectional area increment equally at all heights. We have already seen that this is not the case. Huber (1928) proved that in many cases there can be no talk of a "constant conduction area"; he considered that Jaccard's assumption would work to the disadvantage of those parts of the tree far removed from the roots. Jaccard's attempt to explain the deviations from his theory by ascribing them to obstructions in the water conducting channels by dry branches or by solidifying tissues which would thus reduce the conductibility of the cross section, is not convincing.

According to Metzger (1893) the tree stem must be considered as "a cantilever beam of uniform resistance against the bending force of the wind". Such a member, having unit length, one end of which is firmly anchored while a force P is applied to the other end, must have equal resistance to failure at all cross-sections. If l is the distance of a given cross-section from the point of application by this force (i.e. the leverage) and d is the diameter of the beam at this point, then by the rules of mechanics, if the bending stress is σ in kg/cm²,

$$\sigma = \frac{P \times l}{d^3} \times \frac{32}{\pi}.$$

The force P we envisage as consisting of the components w = wind pressure per area unit and F = crown area, i.e. $P = w \times F$.

If we transfer d^3 to the left-hand side the equation becomes

$$d^3 = \frac{32 \times w \times F}{\pi \times \sigma} \times l.$$

As w, F, σ can be considered constant for a given tree, the fraction can be replaced by the value c and as a result

$$d^3 = c \times l,$$

i.e. *the diameters raised to the third power increase proportionally* with the lengthening of the lever, or *with increasing distance from the central point of application of the wind-force*, which we can assume to be at the "centre of gravity" of the crown. The tree stem consequently must have the shape of a cubic paraboloid; or otherwise stated, the cubes of the stem diameters when plotted over the corresponding distances from the "centre of gravity" of the crown must approximate to a straight line.

Figure 29 shows a Norway spruce examined by Münch in the Tharandt nursery. The shape of the stem curve is typical. The diameters raised to the third power can be represented by a straight line drawn through the points in the region of the middle section of the stem. The straight line when extended joins the centre of gravity of the crown. As expected, the forms of the stem-base and of the upper section of the stem (within the crown) deviate from theoretical requirements. Metzger's *theory affords a close approximation for the middle stem section of our native coniferous species, especially spruce.* Metzger considers that the over-large dimensions of the stem-base can be ascribed to its function as a "pedestal" by which the imposed forces are conducted into the roots and the surrounding soil.

Hohenadl (1924) formulated the theory that the tree stem is constructed to serve as a *column of uniform resistance against the gravitational weight* of the stem and crown (+ load) themselves. If that were so, the cross sectional areas downwards from the top would have to increase in such a way that their bearing capacity in relation to the *pressure* load would be equally large. Fritzsche (1929) proved that this theory cannot be sustained as, in that case, the spruce and pine stems examined by him would need to be constructed with a more than 100-fold safety margin. A test of Hohenadl's stem curve equation (an exponential function) upon spruce stems stands up to reality only in respect of *relative* diameter values.

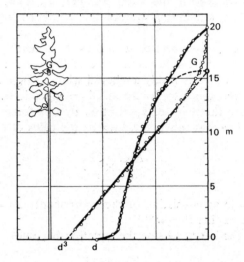

FIG. 29. Stem profile of a 76-year-old spruce from Tharandt nursery. The diameters of the middle part of the stem, raised to the power of 3, form a straight line which when extended meets the centre of gravity *(G)* of the crown *(Münch from Büsgen–Münch)*.

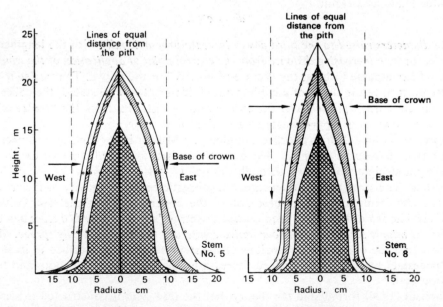

FIG. 30. Stem analyses of two spruce trees. *Left:* open position towards SSW. for 20 years. *Right:* sheltered position within a stand. Double hatching: longitudinal section 1927; single hatching: increment during the first decade after opening of the stand in 1937.

On the other hand, Fritzsche (1929, 1933) found that the structure of the middle section of many spruce and pine stems does conform satisfactorily with Metzger's theory. Other positive expressions in this sense were made outstandingly by Lars Tirén (1928) and Tor Jonson (1927) whose familiar "Form-point" method is founded directly on Metzger's theory. Henrik Petterson (1927) made a critical study of Jonson's method which runs into difficulties when applied to extreme forms. Lars Tirén (1928) has provided

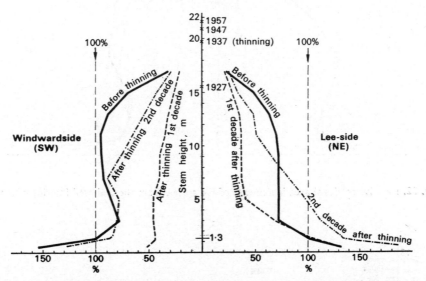

Fig. 31. Relative sectional area increments of the released spruce on opposite half-sections, before and after heavy thinning, compared with the increment of the half section at breast height before thinning.

us with an excellent discussion of the mechanical and physiological problems of stem structure. Windirsch (1936) also investigated the theories of Metzger and Hohenadl and formulated a mathematical expression of the way in which wind pressure and crown weight combined must affect the development of tree form.

Clearly none of the stem-form theories discussed above can provide a satisfactory explanation for the hypothetical shape of the stem curve. Each theory is based upon only one of the stem functions, whereas actual tree stems must fulfil *all* functions, "physiological" as well as "mechanical", under changing external conditions. Moreover, the structure of the tree body is *by no means homogeneous*; on the contrary, the properties of density and strength, although regionally located, are discontinuous in their occurrence within the stem. Thus we discover from the investigations of Trendelenburg, v. Pechmann, Volkert, Hildebrandt and others that heavy, close-textured wood in older trees is located particularly in the outer zones of the lower stem. Be that as it may, reactions to mechanical stresses *appear to be of such overwhelming importance that they have a decisive influence on the development of stem form.*

This was recently confirmed by investigations of the author and his fellow workers Siostrzonek and Zahn on trees at the edges of thinned stands. The left-hand illustration in Fig. 30 shows one of two spruces, now 64 years old, in longitudinal section. This tree was completely exposed to the SW. in 1937 during a felling operation for an autobahn. The spruce on the right, however, growing in a sheltered position within the stand, was not exposed to extreme pressure from the wind. Ten years before the felling operation,

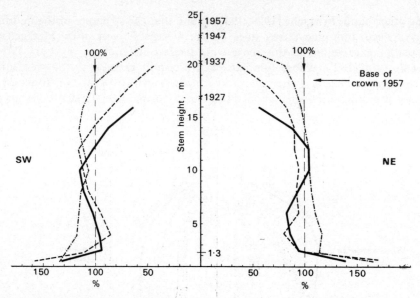

FIG. 32. Relative sectional area increments of the spruce from the sheltered interior of a stand.

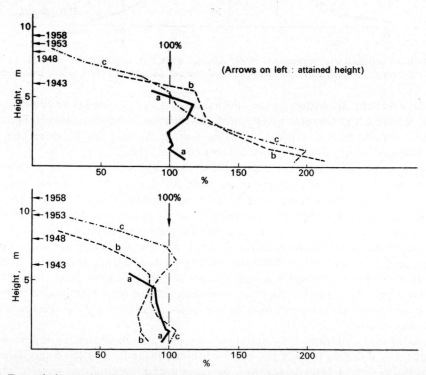

FIG. 33. *Top:* relative sectional area increments of a 42-year-old Scots pine exposed towards NW., related to the increment at breast height before thinning, (a) during the 5 years before thinning; (b) during the first 5 years after thinning; (c) during the second 5 years after thinning (1953–8). *Below:* the same for a Scots pine growing within the sheltered interior of a stand.

both stems were nearly identical in size and form, and their increments were also identical during the decade 1927 to 1937. As a result of the felling operation, further height growth of the spruce on the left became decisively checked. The sectional area increment on the lee-side had considerably increased in the course of the two subsequent decades and was deposited mainly at the base of the stem. The extreme change in the increment distribution within the stem is even more evident in Figs. 31 and 32. Whereas the sectional area increments of the spruce left inside the stand have a nearly bilateral symmetry on both the weather and lee-sides of the stem, clearly displaying sectional area growth maxima in the upper part of the stem, most of the wood substance produced in the spruce occupying an edge position is added on one side, the lee-side, at the base of the stem.[1] A very similar reaction is shown in Fig. 33, in which the increment distribution in young pine trees occurring at both edge and internal positions in stands are represented.

(b) The Form of Stem Cross-sections

The cross-sections of tree stems deviate more or less markedly from circularity which, in most cases, is the assumed basis for volume calculations. Apart from small irregularities in the circumference, the shapes are usually a combination of a circle and an ellipse, i.e. an oval (Tirén, 1929). However, examples also occur of the combination of a circle and a parabola (Müller, 1958) and occasionally of a so-called orbiform shape, i.e. a shape which differs from a circle yet has the same *diameter* in all directions (Matérn, 1956). The pith may have an eccentric position, even if the shape of the cross-section is almost circular (Siostrzonek, 1958).

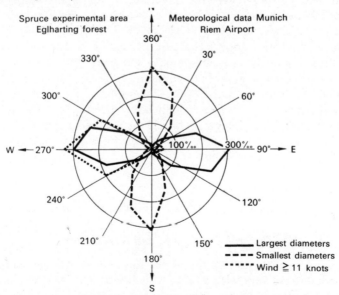

FIG. 34. Relative frequencies of the directions of the largest and smallest diameters at 1·3 m height and of wind speeds above 11 knots. All trees belong to the spruce research plots Eglharting 72 and 73. Frequencies per thousand *(G. Müller)*.

---

[1] This enables us to form an opinion about the misleading conclusions which could be arrived at if estimates of increment were based upon measurements of increment cores taken at breast height from one side only of the tree.

Conifers react to bending stresses by making faster growth on that side of the tree which, as a result of bending, assumes a concave shape and becomes shortened by compression of the fibres. The effect of wind action is to cause the development of "compression wood" or "Rotholz" on the lee side. Conversely, in broad-leaved trees growth is stimulated on the convex side, i.e. the side whereon the fibres are extended so that "tension wood" is developed in order to "pull" the bent stem or branch straight again. As at the same time in both instances growth develops normally on the "neutral flanks" where the fibre length remains unchanged, an oval or elliptical shape of cross-sections results. It has for long been known, as Fritzsche (1929) demonstrated, that spruce edge-trees display particularly marked eccentricity in their cross-sections, the largest diameter being orientated in the direction of the prevailing wind, with the largest radius developing on the lee-side. For conclusive evidences upon the differential development of radii in stem sections of *Norway spruce* consequent upon wind direction we are indebted to Zimmerle (1937, 1938, 1939, 1942), who at the same time substantiated a remarkable deviation from such behaviour by *Silver fir*. From the work of Flemes (1937) we learn that the reaction of *Scots pine* is similar to that of spruce.

More recent investigations by the Ertragskundliches Institut at Munich (G. Müller, 1958) yielded close relationships between the direction of the wind, the gradient of the slope, and the direction of the largest diameter. As shown in Fig. 34 for the spruce stand at Eglharting (approximately 90-year-old spruce on the gravel plain east of Munich), the percentage frequencies of the directions of the largest diameter at breast-height are highly correlated with those of the percentages of the wind frequencies (winds $\geqq 11$ knots). It appears that in mixed montane forests with several storeys situated in the Wettersteinwald near Partenkirchen, the direction of the largest diameter in the wind-exposed trees of the *upper storey* is determined mainly *by the wind*, whilst the decisive factor for the trees in the *lower storey* is *the direction of the slope*. In stands of Sessile oak in the Pfälzer Wald, the slope inclination proved to be the predominant influence on the average direction of the largest diameter. The oaks there developed tension wood on the uphill side of the trees in order to counteract the bending pressure caused by the lopsided weight of the crown on the down-slope side.

In calculating sectional areas, and especially sectional area increments by radial increment measurements, as with an increment borer, the particular shape of the cross-sections must be taken into consideration. This was proved by Siostrzonek (1958), who, at the same time, made practical suggestions.

(c) FORM FACTOR, VOLUME AND ASSORTMENT TABLES

The problem of form and form factor

Despite the many hypotheses relating to the theoretical average stem, the shape and volume of individual trees vary within fairly wide limits. The large dimensions of trees—with heights between 30 and 40 m—provide severe technical difficulties in the collection of measurements. For this reason methods and tables which enable estimates of tree volumes to be made from such dimensions as are most conveniently measured are of the greatest importance in forest yield studies. The customary conventional basic measurements are the diameter at breast height ($d_{1.3}$) and total height (h). The product of the corresponding basal area $g_{1.3} = \pi/4 \times d_{1.3}^2$ and total height is a cylinder $g_{1.3} \times h$ which is also known as the "basic cylinder". The ratio between tree volume (v) and this basic cylinder is known as

$$breast\ height\ form\ factor = f_{1\cdot3} = \frac{v}{g_{1\cdot3} \times h}$$

and

$$v = g_{1\cdot3} \times h \times f_{1\cdot3}.$$

We obtain the tree volume by multiplying the basic cylinder by this reducing factor $f_{1\cdot3}$, known as "the form factor". As the chosen basic sectional area is fixed at the conventional height of measurement of $1\cdot3$ m, the form factor $f_{1\cdot3}$ changes with increasing tree height, even when the stereometric or essential form of the tree remains unchanged, for which reason it is justly known as the "artificial form factor".

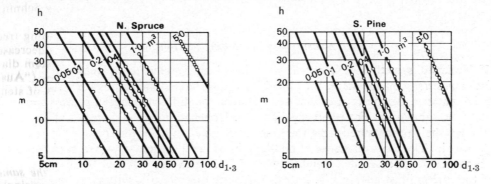

FIG. 35. Volumes of spruce and pine, according to the Bavarian volume tables, shown as lines of equal volume, on double logarithmic co-ordinates, i.e. as functions of log d and log h.
Log $h = \log c + b \log v - a \log d$ (*Müller* and *Zahn*).

If a basic sectional area were chosen at one-tenth or one-fifth of the tree height, we would obtain "natural" form factors, which are largely independent of the total height of the tree. Such a form factor is that proposed by Hohenadl, $\lambda_{0\cdot9}$, which shows smaller fluctuations than the commonly used artificial form factor and undergoes small systematic changes as the tree dimensions increase. However, its estimation on growing trees requires measurement to be taken of the diameter at one-tenth of the tree height and the calculation of—at least—the "Hohenadl quotient" $d_{1\cdot3}/d_{0\cdot9}$ or of the form quotient $d_{0\cdot5}/d_{0\cdot9}$ (cf. Fig. 28).

For this reason, "volume tables" and form factor tables which express tree volumes or form factors as functions of $d_{1\cdot3}$ and h, still have great practical importance today. It is noteworthy that the tables used in Germany (for example the one by Grundner–Schwappach which was re-edited by Schober in 1952) are based on total height (cf. p. 75) and, as a result of subjective graphical fitting methods, sometimes show systematic errors. This, amongst other considerations, was brought to light by Henriksen (1953) who constructed a new volume table for beech in Denmark. For volume tables constructed on the basis of modern statistical methods (regression analysis), as well as some general power functions for estimating volume (by $d_{1\cdot3}$, h and "crown per cent") we are indebted to Näslund and Hagberg (1950).

The construction of new tables is facilitated if we make use of the fact that the relationships between $d_{1\cdot3}$, h and v can be expressed as a power function, the so-called "allometric equation" which, when expressed in logarithms, is linear in form. Thus, when values of log h as ordinate are plotted over log $d_{1.3}$ as abscissa on double logarithmic graph paper, lines of constant volume are nearly parallel, as shown in Fig. 35. This fact enables an improved graphical construction (Müller and Zahn, 1958) as well as an easier numerical calculation of the parameters to be made, as shown recently by Schmitt and Schneider (1959).

In order to be able to predict what grades or assortments of timber a standing tree or crop will be capable of producing it is necessary to know how the diameters decrease with increasing height of stem or what percentage relation exists between the stem diameter at different heights and the basal diameter. Standard profile data series ("Ausbauchungsreihen") state these diameter percentages for even (or whole) metres of stem height in relation to the basal diameter at breast height.

Stem measurement according to Hohenadl

If Hohenadl's method is adopted, wherein all measurements are taken *at the same relative positions* on the stem, the resulting values are found to possess a surprisingly regular pattern, demonstrating that spruce stems of different lengths possess approximately the same form. For reference diameter, Hohenadl uses the diameter at one-tenth of the tree height, measured from the base, or at nine-tenths of the tree height measured from the tip. The mean diameters at mid-lengths of the five equally long stem pieces taken at each of the measurement heights 0·7, 0·5, 0·3, etc., are referred to that diameter. For the spruce illustrated in Fig. 28, this reference diameter lies within the region of the stem foot. The profile series of Zimmerle (1949), shown in Table 19, are reckoned on the diameter at 0·2 of the tree height measured from ground level. The calculated diameter percentages are practically equal for spruce with absolute tree heights of 18–36 m.

TABLE 19

PROFILE SERIES FOR SPRUCE ACCORDING TO ZIMMERLE, AS PERCENTAGES OF THE DIAMETER AT ONE-FIFTH OF THE TREE HEIGHT

Height class	m	18	24	30	36
Mean diameter at 1·3 m height	cm	15·1	21·8	30·7	42·6
Mean diameter at 20% of the height	cm	13·8	19·5	26·3	35·3
Relative diameter at 1·3 m height		110	112	117	121
10% of the height		107	107	106	106
20%		100	100	100	100
30%		94	94	95	94
40%		88	88	88	88
50%		80	81	81	80
60%		70	72	72	71
70%		59	60	61	61
80%		–	45	46	47

A comparison of form in both Table 20 and the corresponding Fig. 36, made by this improved method of Hohenadl for objectively selected sample stems, is informative in several respects. Above all it shows that *real changes in the form of spruce stems as age and height increase are due* mainly to the *enlargement of the base of the stems*. The reference diameter $d_{0.9}$ in the trees of sample stem group No. III with heights above 30 m has shifted completely into the butt portion of the stem, as a result of which the η^2-values of the corresponding diameters $d_{0.825}$, $d_{0.7}$, and $d_{0.5}$ are correspondingly *reduced*. With an assumed probability level of 10 per cent, however, only five of the examined differences are statistically significant. But the trend is obvious.

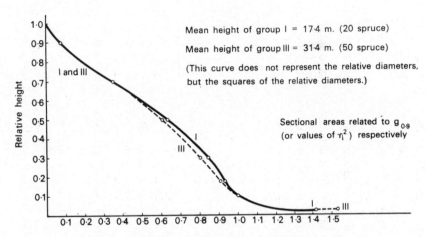

FIG. 36. Mean form curves of two groups of sample stems with 20 and 50 spruce trees respectively. *(Note: $g_{0.9}$ refers to sectional area at 0·9 of total height of tree measured from *tip*, i.e. at 0·1 of height above ground.)*

The static pressure on the stem cross-sections near the ground, which grows as the tree height increases, results in a continuous *thickening of the base of the stem,* whereby the point of inflexion of the stem curve can move upwards to as far as 8 m height. These form changes of the stem near the ground are not assessed by the original measurements of Hohenadl. In a modification of this method, which has been developed by the author, this is achieved by two additional measurements taken at the stem heights 0·875 and 0·975 from the top or at 12·5 per cent and 2·5 per cent respectively from the bottom. Thus, by the measurement of seven diameters in the same relative positions, a high degree of accuracy in the prediction of stem form is achieved. At the same time, the form quotients calculated for the lower section of the stem permit an assessment of the characteristic swelling at the base of the stem which has an important bearing upon the volume and form of tree stems.[1]

Even better information about the *changes* in form could be obtained if a sectional area *above* the point of inflexion of the stem curve (and thus above *the base of the stem*), approximately at 0·2 or 0·3, measured *from the base*, could be chosen as a reference point because the zone of the steadiest increment lies at approximately one-third of the stem height, measured from the foot. The choice of such a sectional area for reference is offset, however, by the difficulties encountered in measuring these diameters on tall crop trees.

[1] A similar solution was found by Altherr (1960) in a work published while the original German edition of this book was in the process of printing.

TABLE 20

FORM COMPARISON OF THREE GROUPS OF DOMINANT SPRUCE SAMPLE STEMS AT DIFFERENT HEIGHTS AND DIFFERENT AGES

Group	Number of sample stems	Means		Arithmetic means and their standard error for (Corr.)															Means	
		$d_{1.3}$ (cm)	h (m)	$\eta^2_{0.975}$	$m\pm$	$\eta^2_{0.825}$	$m\pm$	$\eta^2_{0.9}$	$m\pm$	$\eta^2_{0.7}$	$m\pm$	$\eta^2_{0.5}$	$m\pm$	$\eta^2_{0.3}$	$m\pm$	$\eta^2_{0.1}$	$m\pm$	$\lambda^*_{0.9}$	q^2_H	$\lambda_{1.3}$
I	20	16·7	17·45	1·418	0·043	0·933	0·010	1·088	0·010	0·843	0·016	0·630	0·018	0·348	0·019	0·072	0·009	0·596	1·064	0·560
II	50	25·7	24·26	1·445	0·042	0·931	0·007	1·094	0·007	0·837	0·009	0·617	0·011	0·335	0·013	0·064	0·005	0·589	1·132	0·521
III	50	38·4	31·42	1·534	0·042	0·910	0·009	1·111	0·009	0·806	0·011	0·606	0·011	0·347	0·010	0·070	0·005	0·588	1·247	0·472

$$* \; \lambda_{0.9} = 0\cdot2(\eta^2_{0.9} + \eta^2_{0.7} + \eta^2_{0.5} + \eta^2_{0.3} + \eta^2_{0.1})$$

Difference of the group means	$\dfrac{D}{m_D}$	$D:m_D$	$\dfrac{D}{m_D}$	$D:m_D$	$\dfrac{D}{m_D}$	$D:m_D$	$\dfrac{D}{m_D}$	$D:m_D$	$\dfrac{D}{m_D}$	$D:m_D$	$\dfrac{D}{m_D}$	$D:m_D$
II—I	0·027 / 0·060	0·45	0·002 / 0·012	0·17	0·006 / 0·017	0·35	0·013 / 0·016	0·81	0·013 / 0·023	0·57	0·008 / 0·010	0·90
III—II	0·089 / 0·060	*1·48*	0·021 / 0·012	*1·75*	0·031 / 0·013	*2·39*	0·011 / 0·014	0·79	0·012 / 0·016	0·75	0·006 / 0·007	0·85
III—I	0·116 / 0·060	*1·93*	0·023 / 0·013	*1·77*	0·037 / 0·019	*1·95*	0·024 / 0·016	*1·50*	0·001 / 0·021	0·05	0·002 / 0·010	0·20

The quantities $D:m_D$, which with a probability level of 10 per cent are significant, are shown in italics.

In the given example, the values for the Hohenadl quotients q_H^2 increase as the tree height increases; at the same time the artificial breast height form factors $\lambda_{1 \cdot 3}$ suffer a sharp decline. By contrast, systematic reductions of the natural form factor $\lambda_{0 \cdot 9}$[1] are considerably smaller. A similar behaviour is displayed in the observed distributions about the means; these are considerably wider with q_H^2 and $\lambda_{1 \cdot 3}$ than with $\lambda_{0 \cdot 9}$. Nevertheless, even if based on natural form factors and form quotients, the actual variations which occur around the theoretical average, or "typical" form are still so large that *significant differences and changes of form can be established only by examining extensive populations.*

Owing to the wide variations of breast-height form factor and the Hohenadl quotient, which can be used as a means to arrive at the less variable true form factor,[2] it is useless in forest yield study experiments to try to determine the locally exact form factor for each individual assessment with the help of sample trees. This may just be feasible for younger stands in which a sufficient number of sample stems (60–100) would become available from early thinnings. Noteworthy opportunities for the assessment of "local" form conditions are given in the works by Krenn and Prodan (1947) and Dittmar (1958). *Impeccably derived form-factor and volume tables are therefore even more important because, with their use, any likely systematic changes of the form factor occurring along with changes of $d_{1 \cdot 3}$ and h are correctly taken into account.*

TABLE 21

ASSORTMENT TABLE FOR SPRUCE BY MITSCHERLICH (1939); PROPORTION OF TIMBER ("LANGHOLZ") AS PERCENTAGE OF THE TOTAL STEM VOLUME

Total height in m	14	16	18	20	22	24	26	28	30	32	34	36	38	40	42	44	46	48	50	52	54	56	58	60
(cm breast height diameter)									Cl. 4				Cl. 5				Cl. 6							
36									91	82	85	87	90	92	93	79	82	85	87	89	90	91		
34						80	86	88	91	82	85	88	90	92	93	79	82	86	87	90	91	91		
32				Cl. 3	70	80	85	88	91	82	85	88	90	92	93	93	83	86	87	89	90	92		
30				85	88	81	86	89	91	92	86	88	90	92	93	93	94	86	87	89	90	92		
28		Cl. 2	80	86	89	83	87	90	92	93	89	91	92	94	95	95	96	96	97	91	92			
26			83	80	87	90	93	88	90	92	94	95	96	97	93	94	95	96	96	97			Cl. 6	
24	Cl. 1	76	85	89	87	91	93	94	91	92	94	95	96	97	98	98	98		Cl. 5					
22		92	78	85	90	94	91	93	94	96	97	97	95	96	97				Cl. 4					
20	87	93	78	86	90	94	97	94	95	96	97	97	98	98										
18	87	93	94	87	91	93	95	96	96	97	97				Cl. 3									
16	87	93	97	98	91	94	97																	
			Cl. 1				Cl. 2																	

[1] When the tree is divided into five equal parts, the true ("echte") or natural form factor is found by multiplying the sum of the squared form-quotients $(\Sigma \eta^2)$ by $0 \cdot 2$. The result is larger when calculated by the modified method than by the original one. In Hohenadl's equation, the section at $0 \cdot 9$ of the tree height (from tip) is taken as having the value $1 \cdot 0$ but in the modified method it has the corrected value of

$$\eta^2_{0 \cdot 9 \text{ (corr)}} = \frac{\eta^2_{0 \cdot 975} + 2\eta^2_{0 \cdot 9} + \eta^2_{0 \cdot 825}}{4}.$$

[2] *Editor's note.* For those readers unacquainted with Hohenadl's method an explanatory note is provided in Appendix 1 (p. 491).

Assortment tables

With the help of the assortment tables of Mitscherlich, Lang, Vogel and others, which were constructed from profile series ("Ausbauchungsreihen") a fairly accurate grading of the growing crop can be estimated. In the assortment method developed by Altherr (1953), local form assessments initiated by Hohenadl and Krenn-Prodan are employed. *Assortment tables for whole stands*, statistically based, which give the assortment classes as percentages of the total volume of a stocked stand according to different ages and quality classes, are less precise. Results obtained from such tables depend on the structure and treatment of the crops.

Mitscherlich's (1939) assortment table for the classification of individual Spruce stems give a brief demonstration of the importance of the stem dimensions for the different timber classes. The so-called "Heilbronn classification" demands the following dimensions for the conifers Norway spruce, Silver fir, Douglas fir:

Heilbronn class	At a stem height of metres	Upper diameter, under bark cm
1	6	8
2	10	12
3	14	14
4	16	17
5	18	22
6	18	30

Mitscherlich's table (Table 21) shows the minimum dimensions of breast-height diameter and total height required for a spruce to qualify for a certain Heilbronn class as well as the percentage fraction of total stem volume over bark occupied by a particular category of log ("Langholz") and class. The calculations must be based accordingly on average stem forms. In exceptionally full-boled trees a lower d.b.h. for a given total height might be acceptable for allocation to a particular Heilbronn class.

(d) FORMATION AND DIMENSIONS OF THE ROOT SYSTEM

From the investigations of Fritzsche, Hilf, Köstler, Krauss and others, we are fairly well informed about the root formation of native trees, especially regarding their changing span, which is dependent on soil characteristics and the specific rooting capacity of the different species. However, we know next to nothing about exact volume and weight measurements of root systems. According to R. Weber (1881), quoted by Trendelenburg, the proportion of root and stump wood in Common beech is supposed to amount to 20–30 per cent, with Scots pine 20–25 per cent, and with Norway spruce 25–34 per cent of the above-ground timber volume. This therefore includes the above-ground stump wood which is left after felling.

Recent investigations by Holstener-Jørgensen (1959) on the Danish island of Zealand supplied exact figures about the form and size of the root systems of oak, Common beech and Norway spruce, growing together in morainic soil under identical conditions. The entire root system of one representative dominant sample tree of each species was washed clean by jets of water under pressure and then the volume and weight were exactly determined.

Figures 37(a), (b), (c) show projections of the crown and root systems with their surface roots for the three sample trees. It is striking that in oak the projection of the close and dense root system is considerably smaller than the crown projection, whilst in beech and spruce the root and crown projections are very similar. In all three species, some

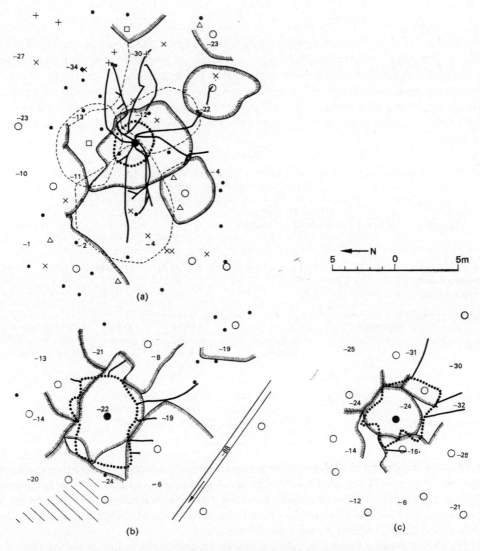

FIG. 37. Crown and root projection of (a) a 49-year-old oak *(Holstener-Jørgensen)*; (b) a 64-year-old beech; (c) a 45-year-old spruce. ○ = dominant neighbour trees; ● = felled oak; lines with shadowing = crown projection of the felled oak and of neighbours; dotted line = projection of the densely compact root system; thick black line = roots touching the surface.

TABLE 22

ROOT LENGTHS OF THE UPPER-STOREY TREES GIVEN IN KILOMETRES PER HECTARE ACCORDING TO
HOLSTENER-JØRGENSEN (1959)

Tree species	Diameter classes of roots in millimetres					Total in km	%
	0–1·5	1·5–5·5	5·5–10·5	10·5–40·5	40·5		
Oak	503	163·0	38·8	32·4	2·1	739	29
Common beech	1850	522	82·5	65·0	2·9	2520	100
Norway spruce	1030	228·8	36·7	28·4	5·7	1330	53

individual roots along the surface extend beyond the edge of the crown projection. Table 22 gives information about measured root *lengths* in all three species; the root lengths for the upper-storey trees have been recalculated for one hectare. The result shows the astonishing *total root length of 2520 kilometres per hectare* for *beech*. In comparison, spruce with 55 per cent and oak with 29 per cent of that value have modest root systems.

In Table 23 can be seen the root volume per hectare according to diameter classes and as a total:

TABLE 23

ROOT VOLUMES OF UPPER-STOREY TREES IN CUBIC METRES PER HECTARE ACCORDING TO
HOLSTENER-JØRGENSEN (1959)

Species	Diameter classes of roots in millimetres					Total in m³	%
	0–1·5	1·5–5·5	5·5–10·5	10·5–40·5	40·5		
Oak	0·39	1·13	1·85	10·02	3·99	17·4	33
Common beech	1·45	3·38	3·36	20·54	10·4	39·1	76
Norway spruce	0·81	1·39	1·73	10·29	37·0	51·3	100

Species	Volume of the stump-core (m³)	Total underground volume (m³)	%	Above ground volume (m³)	Total volume (m³)	Proportion of the root vol. in the total volume %
Oak	20·0	37·4	45	201	238	*15·7*
Common beech	37·8	76·9	92	316	393	*19·6*
Norway spruce	32·1	83·4	100	398	481	*17·4*

The share of the total overwood volume occupied by the root-system, including the stump-core ("Stubbenkern") amounts to 16 to 20 per cent, beech having the largest proportion, followed by spruce. The *root weight* including bark but excluding the stump-core for spruce amounts to approximately 32 tons per hectare, while for beech it is approximately 22 tons, and for oak about 11 tons per hectare.

If the above-ground volume is taken down to ground surface, i.e. including the stump wood which may be left after felling, then according to these investigations, *the subterranean woody volume* (= roots+subterranean stump volume) *amounts to approximately 15–20 per cent of the total tree volume* or 19–24 per cent of the above-ground tree volume.

(e) THE BARK FRACTION

The bark cover with which the tree body is invested differs in thickness depending on the species and the region of the stem where the bark is measured. In general, the rough-barked conifers Douglas fir, larch and Scots pine carry a thicker bark than the relatively smoother barked Norway spruce and Silver fir. Among the broad-leaved trees, the bark of oak is considerably thicker than that of Common beech. This is demonstrated in Table 24 with data for breast height. The information given for different stem heights in Table 25 and Fig. 38 shows that the bark thicknesses of larch and pine are less disparate at breast height than in the upper regions of the stem, where the bark of Pine is considerably thinner than that of Larch. Particularly thin is the familiar smooth unbroken bark in the upper region of pine stems. Significant bark thicknesses are found in the lower and middle sections of the (green) Douglas fir. According to Hengst (1958), the following bark measurements refer to Douglas fir:

At stem heights m	Mean bark per cent	
	By addition % (of vol. u.b.)	By subtraction % (of vol. o.b.)
10	9·4	8·6
16	10·8	9·8
22	10·7	9·6
28	13·2	11·7
34	18·5	15·6

The data stated are the true bark proportions of the stem volume.

TABLE 24

MEAN BARK THICKNESSES OF SOME TREE SPECIES AT BREAST HEIGHT FOR CERTAIN DIAMETER CLASSES ACCORDING TO DIFFERENT AUTHORS

Diameter class from to (cm)	Double bark thickness in cm					
	Oak	Common beech	Silver fir	Norway spruce	Scots pine	Europ. larch
10–20	—	0·5	1·1	0·9	2·2	2·1
20–30	2·7	0·8	1·4	1·3	3·0	3·2
30–40	3·3	1·0	1·8	1·6	3·7	4·5
40–50	3·9	1·3	2·2	2·0	4·5	6·0
50–60	4·7	1·5	2·6	2·3	5·3	7·6
60–70	5·9	—	2·9	2·7	6·1	

Furthermore, bark thicknesses albeit within the same species, vary according to site, age and racial characteristics of the trees. Thus, the bark of spruce at high altitudes can become particularly thick in old age.

Felled and converted logs are commonly measured under bark. To find their equivalent over-bark content the appropriate addition is made in each case of a "bark per cent" allowance taken from summary tables. The volumes so obtained may deviate from the actual values not only randomly but also systematically.

TABLE 25

MEAN BARK THICKNESS OF SOME TREE SPECIES AT DIFFERENT STEM HEIGHTS FOR CERTAIN BREAST-
HEIGHT DIAMETERS ACCORDING TO FLURY, MITSCHERLICH, SCHOBER AND ZIMMERLE

At stem height	Double bark thickness in cm								
	Common beech	Silver fir		Norway spruce		Scots pine		Europ. larch	
	> 40 cm	20–40	> 40	20–40	> 40	20–40	40–60	20–40	40–60
1	1·4	1·6	2·5	1·4	2·2	3·4	5·0	4·2	7·4
3	1·2	1·4	2·2	1·2	1·9	2·0	3·4	3·0	4·9
5	1·2	1·3	2·1	1·1	1·8	1·4	2·6	2·7	4·3
7	1·0	1·2	2·0	1·1	1·8	1·0	2·0	2·5	3·9
9	1·0	1·2	2·0	1·1	1·8	0·8	1·6	2·3	3·7
12	1·0	1·1	2·0	1·0	1·8	0·8	1·4	2·1	3·5
15	1·0	1·1	1·9	1·0	1·7	0·6	1·0	1·9	3·3
18	1·0	1·0	1·8	1·0	1·7	0·6	0·8	1·7	3·2
21	0·8	0·9	1·8	0·9	1·7	—	0·8	1·6	3·0
Mean bark per cent of stem volume over bark	6·3%	10·5%		9·8%		11·5%	10·4%	21·8%	20·7%

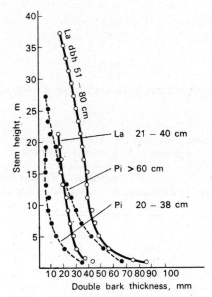

FIG. 38. Thickness of the bark layer (double bark-thickness) in larch *(Schober)* and Scots pine *(Zim-merle)*.

If volume increments of growing trees *including bark* are calculated on the basis of diameter and sectional area increments which have been obtained from borings or discs, it must be remembered that along with the growth of the timber, the bark has also increased in thickness.

The influence of the bark on the shape of the tree and the form of the stem is expressed in the differences between the breast-height form factor for stems with and without bark. The result of such a comparison of form for different tree species on the same site is given

TABLE 26
BREAST-HEIGHT FORM FACTORS WITH AND WITHOUT BARK FOR DIFFERENT TREE SPECIES FROM THE SAME
SITE (V. GUTTENBERG, 1915)

Tree species	Form factor	
	With bark	Without bark
Oak	0·475	0·453
Common beech	0·495	0·491
Larch	0·472	0·480
Silver fir	0·527	0·519
Norway spruce	0·486	0·475
Scots pine	0·457	0·486

in Table 26 according to surveys made by v. Guttenberg and relating to trees with but small variation in height.

We find that the well-known difference between the forms of Scots pine and spruce applies only to their over-bark dimensions. The under-bark form factor for pine in our example is even higher than for spruce. This is due to the particularly thick bark in the lower part of the pine stem. The stems of pine and spruce after removal of the bark are very similar in form.

(f) UNITS OF VOLUME AND WEIGHT EMPLOYED IN THE DETERMINATION OF GROWTH AND YIELD

Forest mensuration as commonly practised has hitherto been concerned *mainly with the assessment of the above-ground timber dimensions*. In this practice, the *timber volumes* are determined by measures of capacity; in Germany, the not very precise forest term "Holzmasse" is used for timber volume. The expression "mass" is subject to possible misinterpretation because of its accepted meaning in physics (= weight) and should therefore be avoided and replaced by the unambiguous and internationally used term *volume*.

Owing to the difficulties of measuring small branches accurately and their relatively small utility value, assessments are in many cases restricted to those parts of the tree which have a *diameter of 7 cm* and above ("Derbholz"). On the other hand, "Reisholz" is the wood of stem and branches with a diameter of *less than 7 cm.*

Wood of diameter 7 cm or more plus wood below 7 cm diameter together constitute the total above-ground *contents of the tree*. What is left of the tree *in situ* above and below ground after felling is known as *stump-wood*. In order to avoid any possible confusion arising in estimates of height, form factor, form quotient and volume on account of varying stump heights, volume should in principle comprise the *entire woody contents above ground*, without reference to the height of the stump. The most practical starting-point for all measurements is the *conventional point of measurement at breast height*, i.e. *1·30 m above the ground surface*, which on slopes is measured on the upper side of the stem. In order to obtain unambiguous measurements, the measuring of *total felled height* (= height from the butt of felled tree to the tip of the tree) should give way to the measuring of the *total tree height* (from the ground surface to the tip or from breast height to the tip + 1·30 m), and in the same way there ought also to be agreement on the definition of root and stump wood. A suitable method would appear to be by measuring that part of the stem nearest the ground in two 1-metre sections, the mean sectional area of the bottom section being determined at 0·80 m below breast-height and therefore 0·50 m above the ground surface. This would not include the buttressing at the junction with the roots, which would count as stump wood.

The term *stem-wood* refers to *the entire woody contents of the tree stem* irrespective of diameter all the way up to the terminal bud. This term is particularly suitable for conifers with a persisting stem which do not develop coarse branches of over 7 cm diameter whilst growing together in a closed stand, for example spruce, Silver fir, Douglas fir.

As a result of having this lower limit of 7 cm for measurement, *we must ignore substantial parts of the crop production*, especially in young stands. As these parts attain and surpass the limiting dimension, they later make their appearance as "recruitment". Thus, the true progress in growth of individual trees and young stands becomes undesirably distorted and obscured.

Figure 39 shows the percentage proportion of wood over 7 cm in diameter in the total above-ground volume of the tree wood of *Common beech* for trees of increasing height and breast-height diameter. This is based on average *h/d* relations such as are to be expected on quality II sites. Only after a tree has attained the height of 8 m, or a d.b.h. of 5 cm, does it begin to have any sizeable "timber" over 7 cm in diameter and the proportion increases from nil to 79 per cent when d.b.h. reaches 15 cm; only when the diameter reaches 40 cm does the "timber" content become a steady fraction of just under 90 per cent. It is obvious how much attention must be bestowed upon these relationships when comparing yields on the basis of "timber" production.

Figure 40 shows these conditions for *Norway spruce*. Here we find that from heights of 5 m and breast-height diameters of nearly 5 cm upwards, the proportions of "timber" wood rise to 76 per cent at a d.b.h. of 15 cm and reach a maximum value of approximately 88 per cent with a diameter of 40 cm, beyond which size they fall slightly. *The timber*

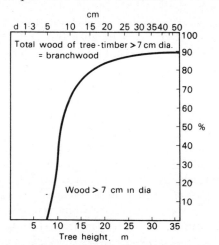
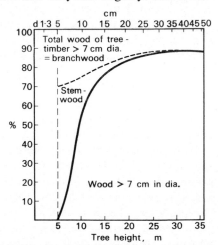

FIG. 39 *(left)*. Percentage proportions of timber over 7 cm in diameter ("Derbholz") and branchwood below 7 cm in diameter ("Reisholz") of the felled tree volume of Common beech.

FIG. 40 *(right)*. Percentage proportion of stem-wood ("Schaftholz"), wood over 7 cm in diameter ("Derbholz") and wood below 7 cm in diameter ("Reisholz") of the felled tree volume ("Baumholz") of Norway spruce.

fraction of the stem wood alone does not fluctuate nearly as strongly; the proportions vary between 70 and 88 per cent. From approximately 30 m height upwards, the differences between the percentages of stem wood and the "timber" content are trifling. The volumes of the stem tops have by then become relatively very small. A change-over to stem-wood assessment in conifers is then possible without any increase of work and would be in the interests of practical research; Norway spruce timber, for example, is measured and utilized down to 2 or 3 cm of top diameter so that converted yields are obtained which are not taken account of in yield tables.

Festmetres of standing and felled trees

In forest practice it is customary to distinguish between *the solid cubic metre in standing trees* (*"Vorratsfestmeter"*) and *the solid cubic metre of felled timber* (*"Erntefestmeter"*), the former (Vfm) referring to timber volumes measured or estimated upon *growing trees* in the usual manner, e.g. with the aid of yield or volume tables, whilst the latter (*Efm*) refers to the timber volumes measured on the ground *after felling and dressing of the trees* according to officially prescribed procedure ("Homa").[1] The difference between these values is known as *conversion loss.* In reality, as convincingly shown by Krenn (1943), this difference is not a genuine loss of yield at all. One such loss is caused by incomplete conversion of the felled trees, by leaving high or low stumps, by felling notches and saw-cuts, by consumption as firewood, etc. But the *conversion loss* is mainly a *measurement loss*, caused by systematic or random errors of measurement, especially by the prescribed *rounding* of timber measurement values, which itself is known to cause an average loss of 4·5 per cent. In high mountains, the so-called *extraction loss* also weighs heavily. To these must be added an important *loss of unused trees* which, owing to difficult extraction conditions, must be left to rot without being utilized. This loss of unused material can also play a part in more intensively utilized managed forests, if thinning is delayed or smaller trees which have suffered snow breakage are not converted. These terms require to be clarified and regularized in order to enable data upon performance obtained by yield studies to be translated into practical and potential yields. The following scheme appears to be a suitable definition:

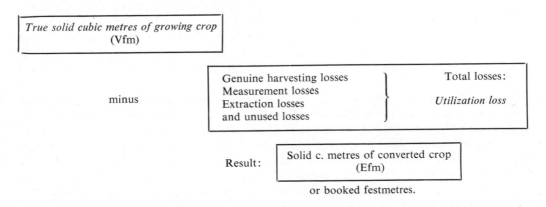

or booked festmetres.

---

[1] *Editor's note.* "Homa" stands for "Holzmessanweisung", a set of grading rules in standard use for round timber conversion in Germany.

The vexed question of summary bark addition or reduction has been touched upon above. The best solution would be the construction of yield tables for timber volumes without bark, so that it is possible to compare cubic metres of felled timber measured after debarking and cubic metres of growing crop measured inside bark.

It does not really seem necessary to mention that in yield study mensuration it is not possible to use different methods for growing and felled trees; sample stems of felled trees, for example, must be measured section-wise in such a way as if they had been felled at ground level, i.e. 1·30 metres below the breast-height line.

Timber production in terms of dry weight; volume/weight relationships

In the standard work *Das Holz als Rohstoff* by Trendelenburg and Mayer-Wegelin (1955), it is correctly stated that "in forest production it is out of date to think only in terms of volume units". If in order to estimate the total organic production of the forest it was found necessary to recalculate in terms of dry substance, then it becomes impossible to make a just comparison between the yields of tree species having different weights of timber by volume measure. We need only think of the conditions in woods of mixed species.

Whereas the *volume* of timber can be *accurately* determined for both moisture-saturated and kiln-dried timber, the determination of *weight* is possible *only in the kiln-dried condition*. This state is reached when, at temperatures of 100–105°C, the timber has been dried to a constant weight. The *dry weight related to the dry volume* and calculated in grams/cm³ then represents *the oven-dry weight* (r_0). In contrast to this the *dry weight related to fresh volume* and calculated in kilograms/cubic metre supplies *the specific weight* (R). This specific weight, which states the dry weight of freshly felled timber in the forest and thereby the weight of dry timber substance per volumetric unit of green forest timber, makes possible a translation from measures of capacity used in forest practice to uniform measures of weight.

Oven-dry weight and specific weight vary considerably within individual trees. Apart from the known differences between the heavier heartwood and the lighter sapwood there are characteristic fluctuations along and across the axis of the stem. Added to this, there are fluctuations between one tree and the next and between individual stands. The great number of separate existing results do not yet permit definite statements upon the range of variation[1] about the means and the variation coefficients for the several individual tree species to be made. An idea about these is given in Table 27 for which the values have been obtained from the above-mentioned standard work. It is gratifying to note that the variance of the sample mean is smaller than that of the individual sample. The distribution for two of the species is also very similar. According to Trendelenburg and Mayer-Wegelin, "the timber of Silver fir in one region is always lighter and has a narrower frequency distribution curve than the timber of Norway spruce from the same region". Accordingly we can expect *the mean values of the data for specific weight generally to give a reliable account at least of the relations between different tree species on a given site*, even if they deviate absolutely from the true values for a definite site. For exact comparisons of output performance a determination of the local specific weight is indispensable. Moreover, it must be taken into consideration that density decreases systematically with increasing elevation above sea level and with higher geographical latitudes.

---

[1] In the literature the term variance is frequently still used as an equivalent for the range of variation.

TABLE 27

OVEN-DRY WEIGHTS AND SPECIFIC WEIGHTS OF SOME TREE SPECIES

Tree species	Number of sample stems	Arithmetic means and largest percentage deviations from the mean						Estimated variation coefficient
		Oven-dry weight (g/cm³)			Specific weight (kg/m³)			
Norway spruce	56	0·448	−17	+17%	389	−16	+16%	±6%
Silver fir	12	0·406	−13	+10%	358	−12	+10%	±4%
Scots pine	115	0·486	−20	+25%	430	−18	+22%	±7%
Larch	425	0·544	−21	+27%	483	−21	+24%	±8%
	Individual samples							
Weymouth pine	22	0·360	−11	+ 6%	324	− 9	+ 7%	±3%
Common beech	32	0·672	−10	+10%	570	−10	+10%	±3%

For the rough transformations and comparisons in Table 28, which follows below, we use *average figures for specific weight* which have been calculated by Trendelenburg (1955).

TABLE 28

AVERAGE FIGURES OF SPECIFIC WEIGHTS FOR CONVERTING VOLUME (m³) OF FRESHLY FELLED FOREST TIMBER INTO WEIGHTS (kg) OF OVEN-DRY WOOD

Norway spruce	390	Beech	560
Silver fir	370	Oak	570
Scots pine	420	Ash	570
European larch	470	Maple	540
Douglas fir	420	Elm	460
Weymouth pine	320	Birch	510
		Alder	430

4. Volume Increment

It is in the accrual of tree volume, in the volume increment, that *the full measure of the vital activity of a tree* can be gauged. As we have already discovered, the phased development of its components, i.e. height and sectional area increments, do not coincide in time. The height increment culminates earlier, the basal area increment later. The sectional area increment is added to a continually lengthening and thickening tree body so that the culmination of the volume increment is reached even later than that of the basal area increment. As shown in Fig. 41, in v. Guttenberg's spruce No. I this point is not reached until the age of 62 years, i.e. 14 years after the culmination of the basal area increment and 29 years after the culmination of the height increment.

With the help of the volume increment curve, the three natural growth phases can also be defined; the actual ages for the points of inflexion, however, differ considerably from those of the height increment curve. Whilst Backman, in his growth law, uses tree height and *height increment* as basis, tree volume with *volume increment* suggest themselves as a more logical and natural basis. In the following passages, therefore, where no other factors are being determined, *the progress of the volume increment will be used to define the natural age phases.*

The speed of this progress is affected by the same internal and external factors which play a part in height and diameter increment. For example, we notice a generally rapid progress in the light-demanding species and a slow progress in the shade-bearing trees. An open position devoid of cover by mother trees speeds up the volume increment and, conversely, crown cover or dense side shade from neighbouring trees suppress it. Thus in multi-storey stands with wide age differences, growth not infrequently makes irregular[1] progress. An instance of this is shown in Fig. 42 in the shape of volume curves for v. Guttenberg's Spruce No. VII which originates from the same stand as Spruce No. I. We see that the first culmination of the volume increment was reached at the age of 80 years. Afterwards the curve falls away decisively to a trough value at the age of 115 years, but subsequently it resumes a fresh and vigorous ascent. This is probably due to a favourable change in the constellation of growth influences (see p. 85) following the natural elimination or felling of competing neighbours.

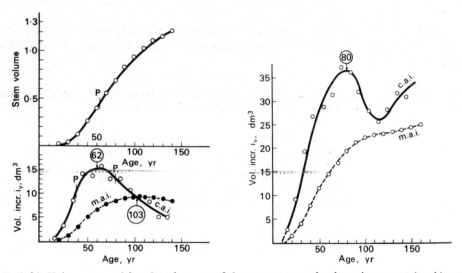

FIG. 41 (*left*). Volume curve (above) and curves of the current annual volume increment (c.a.i.) and the mean annual increment (m.a.i.) of a spruce tree (below). After stem analyses by *v. Guttenberg.*
FIG. 42 (*right*). Current and mean volume increment curves of a spruce (VII) analysed by *v. Guttenberg.*

Current and mean annual increment

Apart from the so-called "current" annual increment (c.a.i.) which we obtain by calculating the differences from the growth curve, we can also calculate the "mean" annual increment (m.a.i.) by dividing the attained growth or volumes by their corresponding ages. This m.a.i. reaches its peak at the point where it cuts the curve for current annual increment (c.a.i.); in other words, at the point where the m.a.i. culminates it becomes equal to the c.a.i. G. Heyer has given the following elementary mathematical proof for this:

[1] Irregularities which are due to the influence of changes in climate are smoothed out over a long period of time.

If the current annual increments are called i_1, i_2, etc., and the mean annual increments $\bar{i}_1$, $\bar{i}_2$ etc., then the current annual increment for the year $n+1$ is

$$i_{n+1} = (n+1)\bar{i}_{n+1} - n \times \bar{i}_n = n \times \bar{i}_{n+1} + \bar{i}_{n+1} - n \times \bar{i}_n.$$

$$i_{n+1} - \bar{i}_{n+1} = n(\bar{i}_{n+1} - \bar{i}_n).$$

Consequently for

$$\bar{i}_{n+1} \gtrless \bar{i}_n, \quad i_{n+1} \quad \text{must be} \quad \lessgtr \bar{i}_{n+1}.$$

When the mean annual increment reaches its highest value, it must become equal to the current annual increment. The m.a.i. and its starting time are important from a scientific point of view, particularly if we should decide to harvest an individual tree at the time when it has reached its highest mean volume. The volume culmination of the m.a.i. begins *very late in individual trees.* Guttenberg (1915) analysed and published the results of thirty Norway spruce sample stems, some of which are over 300 years old and, among this number, found only two (!) which had reached the volume culmination of the m.a.i., one of these being the Spruce No. I from Hinterberg. Figure 41 shows the culmination of the m.a.i. of this spruce at the age of 103 years, whereas the point of culmination for Spruce No. VII in Fig. 42 is evidently still a long way off. The reader's attention is drawn to the fact that the culmination of the m.a.i. of *stands,* i.e. a magnitude which is related to the stocked area, occurs *considerably earlier.* This is related to the *progressive reduction of the numbers of stems in stands,* whereby the *growing space is increased and the per-acre efficiencies of the trees are progressively reduced.* This is discussed in more detail on page 155.

THE CONSTITUTION AND DEVELOPMENT OF STANDS

I. THE SOCIAL STRUCTURE OF TREE CROPS

In this section we shall consider more closely the growth processes of tree crops. These cannot be looked upon simply as assemblages of trees that are all very much alike. They are much rather a social community of individuals whose widely varying outward appearance has been shaped by their innate characteristics and a manifold of external influences. The mutual interaction of these influences gives rise to a social ranking wherein the trees sort themselves into several classes according to their appropriate standing in the community.

1. Tree Classes

The typical social differences which are particularly prominent in regular closed stands that have grown up without any human interference are mainly the result of a merciless struggle for light and growing space. Defeat in this struggle means that a tree descends in the social scale, being driven firstly to an inferior status and finally to death as an outcast through lack of light beneath the crowns of the successful dominants. The outcome is a natural graduation and stratification of the crop which at the same time affords protection to the survivors within the stable structure of the community; here a meaningful parallel might be sought in the social communities of higher creatures and it holds philosophical aspects in relation to human society.

Even in cultivated stands which are subjected to human influences, we notice that predominant trees with strongly developed crowns stand out above their neighbours which themselves dominate other neighbouring trees of smaller heights and less developed crowns. In recognition of this, attempts to classify trees according to their social position have been made since early times in forestry, one of these, for example, by Ch. v. Seebach (1844), a great pupil of v. Cotta. An excellent and detailed representation of the problem of the division into tree classes was given by Lönnroth (1925) in *Untersuchungen über die innere Struktur... naturnormaler Kiefernbestände*.

Natural tree classes

Only a few basic questions which are of importance to yield studies are discussed here. We start with a classification which has become classic and can be taken as model of a *natural* or social *tree classification*, namely the tree class division of Kraft (1888). He distinguishes between the following classes:

1. *Predominant* trees[1] with exceptionally strongly developed crowns.

[1] The term "stems", used by Kraft, has been replaced by the (nowadays) more fitting word "trees".

2. *Dominant* trees, as a rule forming the main part of the stand and having comparatively well-developed crowns.

3. *Co-dominant* trees with fairly normal, but comparatively weakly developed and narrow crowns.

4. *Dominated* trees whose crowns are more or less stunted with one-sided (flag-shaped) development, or suffering severe pressure on one or more sides.

    (a) Trees with crowns in the middle storey, their heads mainly free but in most cases completely hemmed in.

    (b) Trees with crowns partly in the under storey.

5. *Completely suppressed trees*

    (a) With crowns capable of survival.

    (b) With crowns dying or already dead.

The several types are well illustrated in Fig. 43, after the original by Kraft.

Kraft has combined the notion of social position or dominance and the extent of crown development in order to allocate trees into classes so that all trees within any one class display the same quality of growth and vigour.

FIG. 43, Tree classes by *Kraft* (1888).

The social advantage which a tree enjoys in relation to its neighbours and the amount of light it accordingly receives depends primarily on its height.

The development of the crown frequently proceeds *pari passu* with the position the tree occupies in the canopy. The crown is, so to speak, an implement of aggression. If it is particularly strongly developed, it can serve the tree in a manner similar to that of the human elbow in a crowd. A *large crown* means *high increment performance* for the tree to which it belongs and at the same time *reduced light for its neighbours.*

Kraft's division into classes of equal vigour expresses the justified *expectation that those contestants which up to the present have* so obviously *held their own* in the hand-to-hand struggle with their neighbours *promise a corresponding proficiency for the future also.*

Now, it is for many reasons valuable to discover *whether qualification for the tree classes thus designated is determined mainly by chance circumstances up to the present*, that is to say, by a more or less random combination of growth influences upon individual trees, *or whether it is occasioned rather by genetically conditioned differences of vital energy*.

Borggreve, as we know, was still of the opinion that the larger dimensions attained by certain trees were due to small, coincidental advantages in the early years. This one-sided and mistaken hypothesis was founded on his selection-thinning experience. Today, the *decisive importance of genetically fixed characteristics* with regard to vigour and adaptation to local conditions has been recognized and acknowledged.

Stands of comparable growth which have been left for a long time without thinning to undergo a natural process of selection by elimination are likely to show *broad similarities in social position, crown development and growing capacity. With the large initial number of stems in such stands it is highly probable that those trees which have survived the eliminating competition are at the same time the most vigorous*. The number of trees per hectare in beech stands from natural regeneration on good sites reduces from over 500,000 at the age of 10 years to approximately 400 at the age of 100 years. This conveys an idea of how often the eliminating situations—one might say, the selective "trials"—must have repeated themselves for the finally remaining trees. On the other hand, we know many instances from thinning experiments of promising "trees of the future" which after early selection had repeatedly received favouring treatment and despite this did not by any means fulfil expectations.

And yet, we must not underestimate the importance of contingent advantages. Let us consider the sudden decease of a member of the community, the changing propensities of individuals when reacting to threatening influences or illness and other parallels with the human condition which here suggest themselves.

Figure 44 depicts in diagrammatic form the *complex of growth-controlling mechanisms* operating on each single tree: (i) the genotype, its more-or-less obscure heredity or

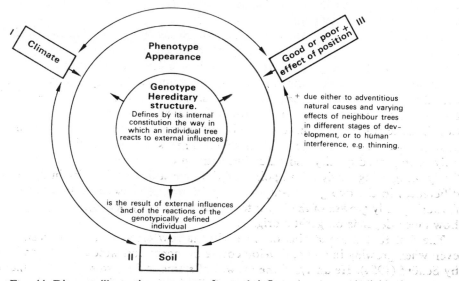

FIG. 44. Diagram illustrating structure of growth influences upon an individual tree in a stand.

provenance, (ii) the phenotype which distinguishes its outward shape, and (iii) the most important external agents acting in combination. Of the three complexes of external factors, the third one, "good or poor effect of position", is of special importance to us. In most cases, we must judge it by present appearances. We are prevented from looking into the past and can only overcome this handicap by observing what happens in experimental areas over long periods, and by using suitable methods of recording.

It is difficult to see such relationships *in uneven-aged stands*, especially if they have the structure of a selection forest where even-aged and uniformly grown sections of the stock occur only in the early years and on small areas, whilst the middle and upper storeys contain trees of a large variety of diameters and heights growing together in a motley mixture about which our knowledge concerning their ages and natural growth phases is restricted by the condition in which we find them. A tree in the middle storey with a crown showing relatively poor development may just as easily be a physiologically *young* tree with a large growing potential and future prospects as an *old* tree with decreasing growth potential. We meet here with the *problem of the rise and fall* in social ranking. This plays its part also in even-aged stands where there is little evidence of a multi-storey structure. Besides the preponderating number of cases of social decline, we find here instances of individual trees rising into higher classes. Passage from a lower to a higher class is observed mainly in trees belonging to the upper storey within the limits of Kraft's tree classes 1 and 2.

Thus, *in the definition of natural tree classes*, the contrasting pairs

dominant—dominated

large crown—small crown

are joined by another pair, namely

rising—falling.

Unfortunately the uses of the last-named pair *are limited*, as in many cases its application would require visionary abilities.

Prompted by the work and suggestions of Nesterow (1952), Erteld (1955, 1957) has recently attempted to include a further dynamic element in tree classification, namely by introducing the *hereditary differences in growth habit*. Some trees in pine stands, for example, which were backward in starting on account of having more vigorous, coarsely branched neighbours, later begin to overhaul them with a sustained renewal of growth; their slender branches and narrow crowns then unmistakeably single them out for retention in selective thinning practice. It is not improbable that the early removal of the coarser-grown trees with promotion of the finer specimens will result in a crop not only of improved quality and value but with an enhanced volume increment. Although freely recognizing newly raised points of view, we still find difficulty in deciding how far differences in the two growth-rhythms can be properly ascribed to chance conditions favouring early growth of the "sprinters"—as possibly by occupying a gap position—and how much depends on genetic origins.

The fact that those strains of pine with narrow crowns and fine branches do not, even when growing in a gap, develop coarse branches and wide crowns has been proved by Schöpf (1954). He analysed the growth of stems and crowns of Scots pine belonging to the celebrated high-level strain from Selb simultaneously along with an artificially introduced Scots pine of alien provenance. Figure 45 shows the crown analyses of a young native pine from Selb (left) and an introduced pine (right), both of which had occupied a gap position with one-sided exposure over a long period of time. Whereas the pine from Selb had continued to grow while retaining a narrow crown and fine branches, the pine of extraneous origin had developed widely projecting coarse branches on the side of the gap. In Fig. 46 we see side-by-side the stem and crown analyses of a 64-year-old pine from Selb with fine branches and a narrow crown (left), showing a moderately wide black knot zone, and a 40-year-old introduced pine with wide crown and coarse branches showing a broad black knot zone.

The great importance of locally adapted biotypes has recently (see Rohmeder, 1955) become more and more evident. Obviously, the latest genetic discoveries must also be taken into consideration in the definition of tree classes, especially when the combination of genetically conditioned characteristics and outwardly observed data enable a safe determination of the various types to be made. Thus we arrive at a further contrasting pair

locally adapted—locally foreign

or   genetically valuable—genetically doubtful.

Finally, there is one further contrasting pair to be considered:

healthy—sickly.

Technical and economic aspects of classification

Apart from these natural or biological considerations, technical and economic aspects have in the meantime gained importance in the definition of tree classes. Thus, Heck in 1897 defined *"stem form classes"* according to the degree of straightness, i.e. according to aspects of the technical usability of the tree stems, and in this endeavour arrived at the following division:

α — an elegant-looking, vertical, utilizable stem of more than 10 m in length which is straight in two mutually perpendicular directions.

β — a moderate or good, though short, utilizable stem, up to 10 m in length.

γ — bent, coarse, leaning stem with many branches (one or several of these characteristics).

δ — forked (at any height in that part of the stem which is free from branches).

ε — strongly forked or branched (in "wolf trees" of classes 1 and 2).

ζ — trees forked near the base of the stem.

η — dead or dying.

In this kind of *"technical classification"* it is possible to include further characteristics, especially the stronger or lesser degree of branch development. The determining opposite pairs in this case are:

straight stem—crooked stem (straightness)

coarse branches—fine branches (branch thickness)

numerous branches—no branches (branch frequency)

wide annual rings—narrow annual rings (annual ring width)

These can be added to by including the amount of heartwood, colour, stem rot, possible red heartwood development (in beech), as well as other characteristics which determine the technical value of tree stems.

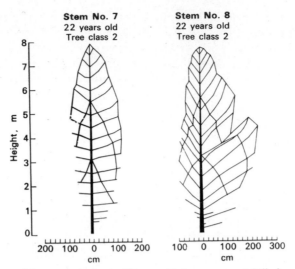

FIG. 45. Crown analyses of two young pines with one-sided exposure at Selb forest. *Left*, a native race; *right*, a foreign provenance *(Schöpf)*.

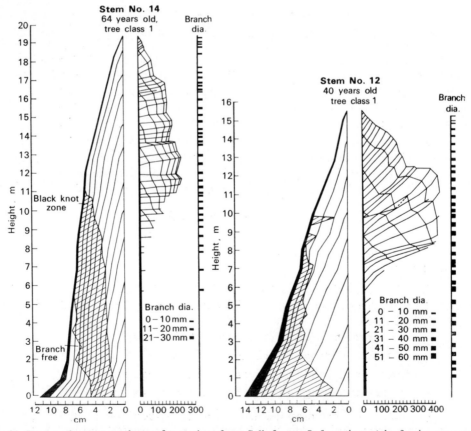

FIG. 46. Stem and crown analyses of two pines from Selb forest. *Left*, native; *right*, foreign provenance *(Schöpf)*.

With regard to silvicultural and maintenance aspects, *the trees* have also a *functional value*. Apart from their saleability, which depends on their dimensions (length and diameter) along with their stem and timber qualities, they also have an undeniable *functional value* with respect to the *soil cover* (in discouraging the growth of thatch, etc.) while contributing at the same time beneficial, as well as detrimental consequences upon each other. Their *favourable effects* consist in the deterrence of strong branch development or, in the case of members of the lower storey, in preventing the development of epicormic shoots by shading the stems of their taller neighbours. *Detrimental effects* are the whipping of crowns, abrasion of stems and the narrow confinement of crowns resulting from excessive competition. Instances also occur where neither favourable nor unfavourable influences preponderate or where they counterbalance each other.

A good example of a *functional tree classification* is given in the *Danish tree classification*, reproduced below, in which distinction is made between the following classes:

Class 1: Primary trees: Stems of the future and final crop owing to their straightness and good crown development.
Class 2: Harmful secondary trees, which hinder the growth of that part of the crop requiring to be maintained and furthered in its development (these stems must be felled in the course of thinning).
Class 3: Useful accessory trees, which assist in the prevention of branch development on other stems to the desired purpose in view.
Class 4: Indeterminate trees, which at the time of observation show no indication whether they are likely in future to develop into primary or secondary stems. (Indeterminate trees are retained until a decision can be reached.)

So long as we are dealing with more or less *even-aged stands whose crown canopy has not yet been permanently and lastingly interrupted, we can*, in the process of assessing the structure of crops and the future prospects of typical tree classes, *successfully employ* Kraft's *tree classification*. This may be combined with a division into stem quality classes. An example of such a relatively simple tree classification, derived from Schädelin—Hausrath, is given in Table 29. The decimal classification which has been used offers the advantage of brevity in writing and easy interpretation by punched-card systems.

Likewise with even-aged stands, especially if they have been fairly heavily thinned, it is also advisable to make a *separate* assessment by

social position, according to the relative height and

crown formation, according to assimilatory efficiency and shape of the crown,

and to characterize the crown formation with the help of special class figures. It is further desirable to make a separate assessment of

the extent of open space available to the crown.

In mixed uneven-aged stands with several storeys, a *division into height layers* of relative depth, like those suggested by Leibundgut (1953) and Olberg (1953, 1955) in their new classification systems, is to be recommended. A suggestion by Assmann (1954a) to classify the height strata into layers of uneven depth so as to make them correspond roughly with the diminishing utility-levels of light penetration was profitably adopted by Magin (1959) in his studies upon mixed natural montane forest.

TABLE 29

TREE CLASSIFICATION FOR COMMON BEECH (DERIVED FROM SCHÄDELIN–HAUSRATH, BY ASSMANN)

First number: Social position and crown formation of the tree:

The primary consideration is the position occupied by the tree, as determined by its relative height and crown projection and in relation to the average type existing in similar localities. If a tree fails to fulfil a stipulation with regard to position or crown formation, it is assigned to the next lower class. The classes are meant to reflect outwardly recognizable vigour and correspond to Kraft's classes.

10	*predominant* Crown exceptionally strongly developed.	
20	*dominant* Crown has average good development.	= Upper storey
30	*co-dominant* Crown shows comparatively poor development with evidence of some moderate deformation.	
40	*dominated* With weakly developed crowns suffering from the effects of competition; unsymmetrical or irregular in shape.	= Middle storey
50	*suppressed* Crown formation unimportant for classification.	= Lower storey

Second number: stem quality

01 Evidently straight, smooth utilizable stem, at least one-third of the tree length being free from branches (at least 20 per cent of the tree length belonging to quality class A).

02 A bole which, owing to minor faults, does not entirely fulfil the stipulations made for 01, being not entirely straight or slightly inferior in quality owing to a maximum of three thin branches or one thicker branch within the lower one-third of the tree length or some other defect slightly spoiling the quality of the stem (at least 10 per cent of the tree length belonging to quality class A).

03 A curved but utilizable bole of medium quality (less than 10 per cent of the tree length belonging to quality class A, more than 30 per cent of the tree length belonging to quality class B).

04 A bole which is bent or coarse or has too many branches and with fairly serious technical faults (less than 30 per cent of the tree length belonging to quality class B).

These requirements made with regard to the respective proportions of the separate Homa quality-grades apply to old trees with heights of upwards of approximately 28 metres.

Example: 21 = a dominant tree with a normal crown and perfectly straight stem, completely free from branches for up to one-third of the height of the tree.

TABLE 30

TREE CLASSIFICATION SYSTEM OF ASSMANN (1951 AND 1954)

(a) *For more or less even-aged stands*

1st numeral: *Social height stage*
1 = predominant.
2 = dominant.
3 = co-dominant.
4 = dominated.
5 = suppressed.

(*continued*)

TABLE 30 *(cont.)*

2nd numeral: *Crown quality*

The criterion is the *outwardly recognizable fitness of the crown* for its rôle of assimilation according to *size, all-round development, density* and even distribution of the *needles.*

1 = abnormally large, uniform all-round development, densely covered with needles.
2 = normal size, almost uniform development, fairly densely covered with needles.
3 = medium size, development not uniform or less densely covered with needles.
4 = small, a fair degree of deformation, sparsely covered with needles.
5 = very small, stunted, needles very sparse.

3rd numeral: *Degree of isolation of the crown*

1 = open position on all sides, no contact with neighbouring crowns at all.
2 = crown contact on one side.
3 = contact on two sides.
4 = contact on three sides.
5 = closely confined on all sides.

4th numeral: *Straightness of the stem*

1 = straight.
2 = sweep or bend along one axis.
3 = crooked.

5th numeral: *Branches*

1 = fine branches.
2 = medium branches.
3 = coarse branches.

6th numeral: *Freedom from branches*

On that part of the stem recognizable as being free from branches the dead knots have become completely *occluded.* The measured or carefully estimated length of the branch-free part is then recorded *in metres.*

An oblique stroke after the third numeral separates the purely biological characteristics from the more technical ones. Example: 112/336. Special characterizations can be chosen as desired: for example,

D   = Spiral grain (r, 1 = right or left).
Z   = Stem forks.
R   = Epicormic shoots.
S   = Bark abrasion damage.
Wx = Broken top at an estimated height x.
Kx = Canker at an estimated height x.

(b) *For uneven-aged multi-storeyed stands*

In this instance the *social stratification* (1st numeral) has been replaced by *relative height layers,* in which the average values for *light utilization* can be assumed to be approximately the same. The mean height of the highest trees of a stand (provided these have a minimum total of 1000 square metres canopy area and can be regarded as forming a layer) can in this case form a basis of comparison.

The division is therefore as follows:

Upper storey: trees having a height of over 80 per cent of the "top height".
Middle storey: trees having a height of 50–80 per cent of the "top height".
Lower storey: trees having a height of 0–50 per cent of the "top height".

The *degree of isolation of the crown* (3rd numeral) *is replaced by classes* showing the degree of advantage enjoyed; the class figure for these is calculated by a points system. In this points system, consideration is given to the *degree of side competition* (from trees of the same storey) as well as to the *degree of vertical crown coverage* (from trees of superior storeys).

An example of a very intensive tree classification of the type used for permanent sample plots is given in Table 30. This classification can, in the adapted form shown under (b), also be used for uneven-aged stands which consist of several storeys. In permanent sample plots where the individual trees have been numbered, all noteworthy observations should, as far as possible, be recorded; one cannot foretell the value such observations will have in the future. The use put to such a "warrant of identification" must be left to the future and to the progress of scientific and technical development.

The familiar tree classification of the Verein für Forstliche Versuchsanstalten (Union of Forest Research Institutes) of 1902 is a *"mixed" classification* in which all the above-considered aspects have been commingled in a sometimes not altogether fortunate manner. In Section D, this will be discussed in more detail in a different context.

2. Typical Structure of Stands according to Tree Classes and Storeys

Numerical tree classes

In crop mensuration, the breast-height diameters of the individual trees are usually calipered in 1 to 5 cm diameter classes. By thus arranging the population according to the observed value $d_{1.3}$, we obtain a tally by successive classes of increasing diameter along with their corresponding *numerical frequencies*. One might even speak of *numerical tree classes* which, depending on the chosen observed value ($d_{1.3}$, h, v) and the class range, will present a different and more or less comprehensive subdivision of the population of the stand. Whatever the designation, let us say, by diameter classes, chosen in any given instance, a complete correspondence between the numerical and the social or biological tree classes is unattainable. *The limits of the social tree classes overlap within a more or less*

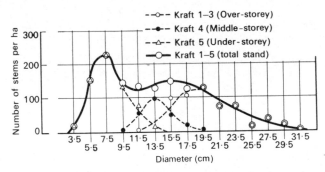

FIG. 47. Diameter distribution of three storeys of a crown thinned beech stand and of the total stand.

extensive diameter range. This shows itself particularly clearly in shade-bearing species. The example shown in Fig. 47, of the distribution of the social tree classes 1–3 (upper storey), 4 (middle storey) and 5 (lower storey) into diameter classes of 2-cm width in the beech stand at Wieda forest which had undergone a heavy crown thinning, clearly displays this overlap of the social tree classes and storeys upon a fairly wide diameter range. This might be regarded as a consequence of errors of estimation or subjective decisions in the classification which are unavoidable when ocular estimates are made.[1] They might

---

[1] In order to cancel out subjective errors, Wicht (1934) suggested a classification into height classes of an *absolute width* (3 m), marginal cases to be decided by measurements.

occur fairly frequently in decisions about marginal cases. The true cause is as follows: the decisive factor in estimation by social tree classes is mainly *the height of trees*. The connection between this factor and the simultaneously observed diameter, however, is not functional but merely involves an element of probability. In other words, trees with a certain diameter may have different heights, just as trees with certain heights may show considerable differences in diameter. The two-way distribution given in Table 31 shows the degree of correlation existing between these two variables in the case of a Norway spruce stand in which all heights were exactly measured after clear felling. We find that the range of variation of the diameters for trees of equal height is considerably greater than the range of variation of the heights for given diameter values.[1] If this population, commencing from the tallest or dominant trees, is divided into four height storeys each of 3 m depth then the *diameter distributions of adjacent storeys* (Table 31(b)) show *widely overlapping ranges*. Diameter classes 20–32 cm overlap height classes I and II, while diameter classes 16–20 cm overlap II and III.

TABLE 31

(a) *Classification of a 60-year-old Norway spruce stand into numerical diameter and height classes*
(Correlation table)

Height classes in metres	Diameter classes in cm												Frequencies
	12	14	16	18	20	22	24	26	28	30	32	34	
26										1			1
25						2	2	4	4	5	7	1	25
24					1	7	13	15	9	1	1	1	48
23				2	11	22	16	6	6		1		64
22				7	10	14	2	1					34
21			7	9	9	5	2						32
20			6	9	3								18
19		1	5	6									12
18	1	1	7	1									10
17		1											1
16			1										1
15	1												1
Frequencies of *d*	2	3	26	34	34	50	35	26	19	7	9	2	247

(b) *Diameter distribution of the same stand, separated into four height layers*

Height layers	Diameter classes in cm											
	12	14	16	18	20	22	24	26	28	30	32	34
I. 23·5–26·5 m					1	9	15	19	13	7	8	2
II. 20·5–23·5 m			7	18	30	41	20	7	6	—	1	
III. 17·5–20·5 m	1	3	18	16	3							
IV. 14·5–17·5 m	1		1								*(continued)*	

[1] This is expressed in the different magnitude of the correlation ratio η which is used as measure of the closeness of non-linear correlation and depends on the size of the "conditional" variance. For the relation h/d (height regarded as a dependent statistical variable, diameter as an independent variable) it amounts to 0·874, for the relation d/h (diameter as dependent variable) to only 0·849.

TABLE 31 *(cont.)*

(c) *Height distribution of the same stand within five classes of approximately equal basal area*

Diameter range of the classes	Height classes in cm											
	15	16	17	18	19	20	21	22	23	24	25	26
27·5–34·5 cm									2	9	17	1
24·5–27·5 cm								1	12	19	5	
22·5–24·5 cm							3	8	20	11	3	
19·5–22·5 cm						1	9	20	27	7	1	
11·5–19·5 cm	1	1	1	10	14	16	20	6	4			

(d) *Social height layers for ± even-aged stands according to Assmann (1964)*

The reference value used for the height layers of unequal relative depth is the mean height of the 100 highest trees per hectare, i.e. of the 25 highest trees in a sample plot of 0·25 hectare.

The following distribution arises:

Class figure	Social height layers Height range as percent of the top height		Definition
100	At least 95%	= predominant	*Upper storey (> 90%)*
200	90–95%	= dominant	
300	80–90%	= co-dominant	*Middle storey (70–90%)*
400	70–80%	= dominated	
500	Less than 70%	= suppressed	*Lower storey (< 70%)*

The diameter distribution curves of these height layers, as well as the distribution curves of the three social storeys (under, middle and overstorey) shown in Fig. 47, are closely approximated by the *normal distribution curve of* Gauss.[1] The addition of the three component curves of this beech stand, which had undergone crown thinning, produces a bimodal or two-peaked distribution curve. This is the result of the different development of the numerous trees belonging to the under storey which, despite unfavourable light conditions beneath the crowns of the dominant over storey, have survived and have been spared during the crown thinning operation.

In even-aged stands which have undergone more or less heavy low thinning, we obtain total distribution curves which are single-peaked and very closely resemble the normal curve. All diameter distribution curves of even-aged stands have a more or less decided *left-handed asymmetry*. If, following a suggestion by Pearson, we express the asymmetry or skewness of the distribution curves in terms of the *difference between the computed value of the arithmetic mean and the most frequent value* (mode), then with homogeneous even-aged crops, we must usually expect *positive skewness* or *left-handed asymmetry* of the *diameter* distribution. *Accordingly, when the weakest trees of a crop are for the most part removed,* either by natural elimination or by the customary *low* thinning (which means progressively "from below" upwards with increasing severity of the thinning into the trees of the upper storey), then the left-hand "tail" of the distribution curve is cut off or abbreviated. The computed value of the arithmetic mean, i.e. the abscissa of the frequency

[1] In the normal distribution of Gauss (cf. Fig. 48), the arithmetic mean, the median and the mode or most frequent value coincide: the distribution curve on both sides of the arithmetic mean is *symmetrical*. The arithmetic mean and the standard deviation are sufficient for the exact determination of the distribution curve and hence of the frequencies of the diameter classes within a population.

distribution curve corresponding to its centre of area, increases and moves to the right
in the diameter distribution whilst the peak of the curve, which marks the most frequent
value, now lies to the *left* of the arithmetic mean (see Fig. 48). The difference between the
computed values of the arithmetic mean and the most frequent value is positive. In order
to have a measure which is independent of absolute dimensions Pearson suggested that
this difference should be divided by the standard deviation.[1]

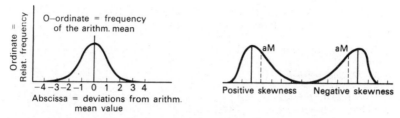

FIG. 48. "Normal" *(left)* and skew *(right)* frequency distributions.

Lönnroth (1925) discovered that the *height* distribution curves of homogeneous populations of stands of Scots pine have a *right*-sided asymmetry. This, as incidentally shown
in the correlation table in Table 31(a) by a displacement of the largest frequency of the
heights to the top third of the twelve height classes, applies *generally for even-aged stands.*
It is related to the fact that the trees which are retarded in their growth concentrate their
energies into the attainment of height at the expense of their diameter increase in order
to ensure at least sufficient light for the top of their crowns. This is also expressed in the
particularly large height differences and in the steep progress of the height curve within
the diameter range of the dominated trees (cf. Table 31(a), diameter classes 12–22).
The effects of this growth behaviour are shown further in example 3 of Table 32(A). Whilst
the mean *diameter* of the middle storey amounts to only 54 per cent of the predominant
trees, its mean *height* amounts to 84 per cent of the predominant trees.

On the whole, therefore, there is a more or less pronounced *similarity between numerical
and social tree classes.* Only in a stratification by numerical *diameter classes* are the divisions made arbitrarily, the height layers as well as the social tree classes being partly split
apart in the process. Nevertheless, in dividing the population of a stand into numerical
classes, for example by the method of Robert Hartig, who made a division into five
classes with equal basal areas, a certain degree of staging into social layers, whereby the
most efficient dominating layers receive due consideration, is effected. This can be seen
in Table 31(c). An off-hand opinion declaring such numerical divisions to be "unbiolog-
ical" is not justified. This shows itself especially clearly when stands are stratified according to Assmann's (1964) suggestion into height layers of uneven relative depth, staged
approximately in proportion with the decrease of light utilization—see Table 31(d). For
the reference value it is possible to choose either the arithmetic mean height of the 100
tallest trees per hectare or the height of the mean basal area stem from the 100 trees with
the *largest diameter* per hectare. As shown later (p. 100, Table 32(B)), the increment of
the stand is concentrated strikingly on the trees of the two top height layers.

---

[1] The deviations of actual distributions from the distribution of Gauss are generally expressed by
the coefficients of asymmetry and excess. In this connection, the reader is referred to the textbooks of
mathematical statistics. Pearson's definition has the advantage of being intuitively evident.

Examples of crop classification

Depending on site, species, age and silvicultural treatment, the structure and division of stands into tree classes changes. Even within completely even-aged stands we observe distinct layering.

TABLE 32(A)

RATIOS OF SOCIAL TREE CLASSES IN THE NUMBER OF STEMS AND THE BASAL AREA OF EVEN-AGED STANDS. STRATIFICATION OF THE STANDS

1. 74-year-old *Norway spruce stand* on a site of the best quality, height quality class I, in the region of the Lower Alps.
   Trial series *No. 2, Sachsenried*

| | | *Lightly thinned* | | | | | | | *Heavily thinned* | | | | |
Kraft tree class	Number of stems (N)	Basal area abs. (m²)	rel. %	d_m (cm)	Mean height abs. (m)	rel. %	N	Basal area abs. (m²)	rel. %	d_m (cm)	Height (m)	%
1	176	21·0	33	38·9	*31·0*=*100*		220	28·4	58	40·5	*31·6* =	*100*
2	492	35·1	54	30·1	29·6	95	232	18·9	38	32·2	29·9	95
3	160	6·2	10	22·3	26·9	87	40	2·1	4	26·1	27·3	86
4	60	2·0	3	20·8	26·1	84	—	—	—	—		
5	—	—	—	—	—	—		—	—	—	—	
Total	888	64·3	100	30·4	29·7 =	96%	492	49·4	100	35·8	30·8 =	97%

2. 102-year-old *Common beech stand* on a good quality site, height quality class II.
   Trial series *No. 116 Dalheim* (near Paderborn).

		Light low thinning							*Medium crown thinning*				
1	10	1·2	2	39·6	*30·3*=*100*	100	15·7	51	44·7	*28·3* =	*100*	
2	320	25·7	50	32·0	29·0	96	100	10·6	34	36·8	27·7	98
3	220	12·4	24	26·7	27·6	91	24	1·7	6	30·7	26·6	94
4	310	11·5	22	21·8	25·6	84	24	0·9	3	21·5	24·6	87
5	40	0·8	2	15·8	19·0	63	124	2·0	6	14·2	15·6	55
Total	900	51·6	100	27·0	27·8	92%	372	30·9	100	32·5	27·1 =	96%

3. Classification of a heavily crown-thinned *Common beech stand* aged 60 years, on a first-quality site (Diabas) in the Harz Mountains, Wieda forest.

Tree layer	Number of stems abs.	%	Basal area abs. (m²)	%	Mean diam. abs. (cm)	%	Meam height abs. (m)	%
Predominant trees (Kraft 1)	83	6	4·4	17	*26·1* =	*100*	*23·1* =	*100*
Upper storey (Kraft 1–3)	567	40	18·8	74	20·6	79	21·9	95
Middle storey (Kraft 4)	226	16	3·4	13	14·0	54	19·9	84
Lower storey (Kraft 5)	634	44	3·4	13	8·2	31	13·1	60
Total stand (Kraft 1–5)	1427	100	25·6	100	15·1 =	58%	20·4 =	88%

The means of the total heights are weighted by the basal areas.

In the *lightly* thinned, 74-year-old *Norway spruce stand* of Table 32(A), example 1, Kraft classes 1 and 2 occupy 33 and 54 per cent respectively of the total stand basal area. Class 3 is represented by only 10 per cent and class 3 by only 3 per cent. The *heavily* thinned stand no longer contains trees belonging to class 4, and only 4 per cent of the basal area belongs to class 3. On the other hand, we find an increased proportion of 58 per cent belonging to class 1 but a smaller fraction amounting to 38 per cent in class 2 (see Fig. 49). The mean diameters of the individual classes are noticeably increased by heavy thinning as a result of giving more growing space, whereas the mean heights have increased only slightly, and that only incidentally in consequence of the diameter increase.

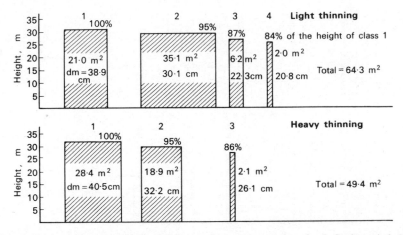

FIG. 49. Stratification of spruce stands by *Kraft* tree classes. Research series 2, Sachsenried, 74 years old. The heights of the rectangles correspond to the mean heights, the areas correspond to the basal areas of the tree classes.

The average height of trees with a given diameter is lower on the heavily thinned plot than on the lightly thinned sample plot. The relative mean heights of the four tree classes with light thinning seem to indicate only a trifling separation of the canopy layers in this stand which possesses a vaulted appearance. However, in view of the fact that the range of heights is from 23 to 33 m and that the total crown storey lies between 18 and 33 m, it is clear that even in an even-aged stand the part of the canopy contributing to the *processes of assimilation extends to a considerable depth.*

The comparisons in example 2, which refers to a 102-year-old *beech stand*, are even stronger (see Fig. 50). Under a light low thinning régime (removal of dead and dying trees) classes 1 and 2 together occupy 52 per cent of the basal area of the stand; this compares with classes 3 and 4 which occupy 24 and 22 per cent respectively and class 5 with only 2 per cent. Against this, under a moderately heavy crown thinning classes 1 and 2 make up 85 per cent of the basal area of the stand, compared to 6 and 3 per cent respectively by classes 3 and 4. Class 5, which had been intentionally spared (unfortunately decimated by thefts), made up 6 per cent. The mean diameters for the different classes increased markedly after crown thinning whilst, on account of the sideways-projecting crowns of beech, the mean heights were considerably reduced by thinning in the dominants, a feature particularly noticeable in classes 1 and 2. Layering of the crowns is more pronounced in a shade-tolerant species such as beech inasmuch as class 5 can be kept alive.

Example 3 shows the characteristic structure of a young heavily crown-thinned stand of Common beech. Here class 5 attains to 13 per cent of the basal area. Comparative differences in the mean height and the mean diameter graduations of the different tree classes have been mentioned earlier. This example illustrates the *inadequacy of having only one mean value* each of *d* and *h for the characterization of* such a *heavily layered stand of a shade-tolerant species.* The same applies for the increment, which varies markedly according to the tree classes. For example, the mean annual diameter growth in class 1 over the last 7 years amounted to approximately 6 mm whereas it was only 1·4 mm in class 4!

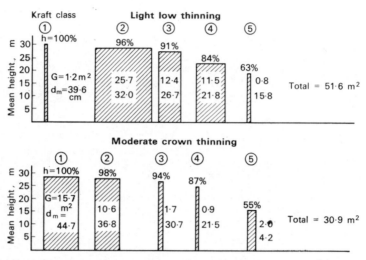

Fig. 50. Stratification of beech stands by *Kraft* tree classes. Research series 116, Dalheim, 102 years old.

Growth comparisons among the tree classes

The superior growth in diameter shown by the predominant trees should lead us to expect a corresponding superiority in their basal area and volume performances. And such is indeed the case. We are indebted to Kraft (1884), Japing (1911), Vanselow (1951) and Magin (1952) for the provision of valuable information in this respect. The last-named, in his work evaluating the long-term assessments made in the Bavarian thinning research series, devoted some attention to the *problem of interchange within the tree classes.* As might be expected, he found that transitions to a lower social level were the more numerous, especially under light or moderate thinning régimes where the treatment permits natural elimination to have powerful effect. The same conclusions arise also from a study by Zimmerle (1940). With heavy thinning, on the other hand, there is a greater number of trees rising in the social scale. Along with the general improvement in growing conditions for the crop remaining, a larger number of trees have a chance to improve their positions in the canopy. Thus the number of trees occupying a particular social class alters during the course of a prolonged period of observation; furthermore, a certain number of trees will have to be removed at each successive thinning. If then we wish to compare the relative increments put on by the different tree classes alongside their respective basal area or volume proportions, different results will be obtained according to whether we compute these proportions at the beginning or the end of the increment period.

In both the above instances, Magin showed that *tree class 1 achieved a higher increment in relation to basal area than the rest of the stand.* Conversely, the share of increment contributed by tree classes 3 and 4 was relatively smaller in comparison with their basal area. In class 2 these two proportions were approximately equal. Very similar relationships appear when using as a basis the proportions of volume increment and volume. *Thus the dominating classes (Kraft 1 and 2) not only produce the major proportion (85 to 95 per cent) of the increment of our more or less even-aged, moderately to heavily thinned stands but equally they reach a higher level of productivity, in terms of their comparative share of the growing crop volume, than that of the dominated trees.*

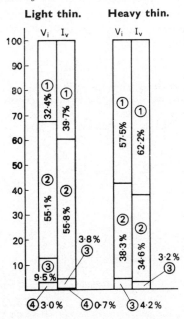

FIG. 51. Proportions of *Kraft* tree classes of the initial volume (V_i) and of the increment (I_v) for light and heavy thinning. Spruce. Trial series 2, Sachsenried.

As the supposedly almost untouched "A" plots in many of the Bavarian thinning research series had been subjected in recent decades to irregular incursions, Magin restricted his investigations to the B-grade ("moderate thinning") and C-grade ("heavy thinning") areas.[1] Figure 51 presents figures of typical responses in a comparative statement of the initial proportions and their corresponding share of the increments in the research series No. 2 at Sachsenried which had previously suffered no such disturbances. It is evident that *the difference in growth-capacities between the two pairs of classes under very light thinning is greater than that under heavy thinning:*

Tree classes	with *very light* thinning		with *heavy* thinning	
		Per cent of the		
	initial volume	increment	initial volume	increment
1+2	87·5	95·5	95·8	96·8
3+4	12·5	4·5	4·2	3·2

[1] The German "B" grade ("moderate thinning") and "C" grade ("heavy thinning") correspond closely with "light" and "moderate" low thinnings respectively in British practice. – Ed.

Thus heavy thinning increases the efficiency of production of the lower social classes bringing it on a level of equality with that of the dominating classes; the trees from lower social classes which have remained are, so to speak, given undeservedly favourable growing conditions. In Magin's studies these relationships appear to have largely levelled out because they do not take account of very lightly thinned areas.

How strongly the increment concentrates on the upper social strata of the stand is shown in Table 32(B) according to researches by Kennel (1965). The two relative height layers 90–95 and over 95 per cent of top height in the spruce stand produce together 62 per cent of the crop increment, and in the beech stand as much as 73 per cent.

TABLE 32(B)

PROPORTIONS OF THE THREE TOPMOST HEIGHT LAYERS OF PURE STANDS OF NORWAY SPRUCE AND COMMON BEECH IN THE NUMBER OF STEMS, THE CROWN CANOPY AREA AND THE INCREMENT (KENNEL, 1965)

	Number of stems %	Crown canopy area %	Volume increment %
Spruce			
Over 95% of the top height	15·1	23·8	31·4
90–95% of the top height	21·2	26·9	30·4
80–90% of the top height	38·0	35·6	31·6
Over 80% of the top height	74·3	86·3	93·4
Beech			
Over 95% of the top height	18·8	32·2	45·2
90–95% of the top height	18·1	24·2	27·8
80–90% of the top height	20·2	23·8	21·3
Over 80% of the top height	57·1	80·2	94·3

Top height = mean height of the 100 highest trees per hectare.

The particularly high production capacities of class 1 might suggest that thinning with the object of increasing the proportion of trees with such large crowns should improve the crop yield. However, *the annual volume* increment per hectare in the above example *for light* thinning amounts to *19·4 solid m^3* and for *heavy* thinning to *18·5 m^3*. Consequently *the area-related efficiency in the case of heavy thinning is 5 per cent lower* than in the case of light thinning.[1] *The loose degree of closure in the heavily thinned area apparently offers the predominant trees and the openly placed trees of classes 2 and 3 more free growing space than they can make up for by improved yield* as compared with the performance of trees in the densely stocked experimental area. In order to be able to answer *the question*

[1] These increment efficiencies, just as the rest of the comparison, are related *only to the trees which still existed at the end of a 10-year observation period*. During this period 240 trees were removed by light thinning and twelve (!) trees by heavy thinning. Taking into consideration the increment which had accrued on these, the annual increment under light thinning amounts to 19·8 and under heavy thinning to 18·7, thus the *lower yield by heavy thinning, 1·1 solid m^3 = 5·6 per cent.*

about the most favourable utilization of growing space, we must make a careful study of the structure, size and form of tree crowns as well as the relationships between crown dimensions, required growing space, and increment efficiencies. This is the more necessary as it is the only way by which we are able to obtain an insight into the complicated relationships between tree class and increment in stands consisting of more than one storey and mixed ages.

II. GROWING SPACE AND INCREMENT

1. Growing Space and Ground Coverage of Individual Trees in the Stand

Basal area and crown canopy

Each individual tree in a stand has a definite amount of growing space. Disregarding the imperfectly examined spacial relationships of the root systems, the extent of growing space is nevertheless limited by the available ground surface. As long as a tree is not overshadowed by the canopy of taller neighbours, the upward growing space is unlimited. However, lateral growth can be very sharply restricted by direct neighbours. In unthinned stands crown peripheries are very often in close contact with each other. But even with such close contact between the crowns, there may yet be many small gaps in the canopy, as is visually apparent. If that part of the space in a stand which is not filled by tree crowns is thought of as being apportioned out among the immediately surrounding trees, we can estimate the available *growing space* for each particular tree. The horizontal projection of this growing space is the *area potentially or nominally available*. To express this more simply: *The area potentially available to a tree is defined by its horizontal crown projection* (= crown canopy area) *plus its appropriate share of the uncovered area of the stand.*

The *average* area nominally available to trees in a stand is easily calculated by dividing the stand area by the number of trees. The following expression applies for a stand of 1 hectare in area:

$$\text{mean area per tree} = f_m = \frac{10,000}{N} \text{ square metres.}$$

The greater the number of trees per hectare the smaller is the average ground space nominally available. For example, with 10,000 trees per hectare it amounts to only 1 square metre, as compared to 100 square metres for 100 trees per hectare. The average area nominally available is inversely proportional to the number of trees. Simple as it is to calculate the average available area for a number of trees, it is more difficult to determine the exact nominal area actually at the disposition of an individual tree when the ground is more or less already under cover.

Let us, to begin with, consider two hypothetical borderline cases which will allow useful conclusions. We may think of the area of a stand as being stocked with trees of equal size whose crowns are uniformly developed on all sides and circular in shape about the axis which is the stem. The projected *crown canopy areas* are thus visualized *as circles* which are described inside the potential areas. Two theoretical cases are possible for the geometrical form of the potential areas, namely a *square* and a *hexagon*. In the former case, we have *square spacing*, in the latter case *triangular spacing*. The relative conditions are illustrated in Figs. 52 and 53.

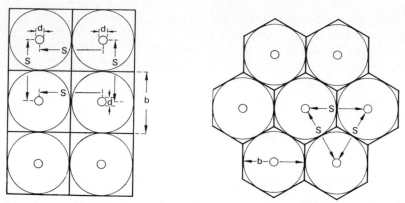

FIG. 52 *(left)*. Crown canopy areas and ground occupied with square spacing.
FIG. 53 *(right)*. Crown canopy areas and ground occupied with triangular spacing.

Square or quadrat spacing

The crown diameter is defined as b (crown width), the area of ground covered as c and the area of nominally available ground space as f. With square nominal areas, the length of a side is obviously b; this, at the same time, corresponds to the tree distance s, which is measured parallel to the sides of the squares.[1] Thus we obtain the following value for the *ground-cover area*[2] (i.e. ground actually covered by crown canopy):

$$c = b^2 \frac{\pi}{4} = b^2 \times 0.785$$

and for the *potential or nominal area* the value

$$f_q = b^2.$$

Triangular spacing

The potential areas are hexagons with the crowns as inscribed circles. The diameter of the inscribed circle is b, which at the same time is equal to the tree distance in all directions. The *ground cover area* is again

$$c = b^2 \times 0.785,$$

the *nominal area* is

$$f_s = b^2 \times \tfrac{1}{2} \sqrt{3} = b^2 \times 0.866.$$

Assuming ideal closure in such a hypothetical stand, i.e. if all crown circles are touching, we would find the following relations for the ratio ground cover area/nominal area, or c/f:

---

[1] The distance in directions not parallel to the sides of the nominal area is larger than s, namely $= s\sqrt{2}$.

[2] This expression is used to distinguish it from "crown surface area" used later. — Ed.

With square nominal areas:

$$c/f_q = 0 \cdot 785/1 \cdot 000 = 0 \cdot 785.$$

With hexagonal nominal areas:

$$c/f_s = 0 \cdot 785/0 \cdot 866 = 0 \cdot 906.$$

The two ratios represent the *theoretical degrees of ground coverage* for square and triangular spacing. The difference between the two figures and the value 1·000 is the *proportion of the stand vacant of ground cover*, i.e.

0·215 with square espacement and

0·094 with triangular espacement.

The figures, along with Fig. 53, demonstrate the more complete utilization of growing space by triangular spacing.[1] Of course, in naturally grown stands there is no uniform spacing. On planted sites, with strictly maintained initial spacing, the random elimination of individual trees also gradually produces *irregular* spacing. There is, however, some justification in assuming that the true spacing lies somewhere between the two theoretical cases. With *mixed spacing* accordingly *c/f* lies within the limits

0·785/0·866 to 1·000.

Using the arithemetic mean of the last two values as an approximation, we obtain

$$c/f_m = 0 \cdot 785/0 \cdot 933 = 0 \cdot 841.$$

This value would correspond to the *theoretical maximum degree of ground coverage,* if the tree distribution for the area of the stand lies between square and triangular spacing.

The practical importance of this value is proved incidentally by the crown maps which Wiedemann (1931) produced for more or less single-storeyed beech crops with low thinning. Figure 54 shows two such crown maps. The mean canopy coverage fraction (from the sum of the ratios: ground cover area/stand area) for seven light to moderately low-thinned beech plots lies between 0·76 and 0·86, in fact in three cases at 0·84, in one case at 0·86 and *averaging 0·81* overall. In the case of *Norway spruce* with moderate thinning Wohlfarth (1935) found an approximate value of 0·80. In a typical Scots pine research series in the East German diluvium where light, moderate and heavy thinnings had been applied, Toma (1940) found values between 0·71 and 0·73.

It should not be overlooked that these values were derived by a vertical projection of the crown peripheries and so are fraught with some uncertainty. This is explained in

---

[1] This shows itself also in a calculation of the number of trees per hectare from the mean crown diameter. We then obtain

1. With square spacing $\qquad N = \dfrac{10,000}{b^2}$

2. With triangular spacing $\qquad N = \dfrac{10,000}{b^2 \times 0 \cdot 866} = \dfrac{10,000}{b^2} \times 1 \cdot 155$, i.e. 15 per cent more

3. With mixed spacing $\qquad N = \dfrac{10,000}{b^2 \times 0 \cdot 933} = \dfrac{10,000}{b^2} \times 1 \cdot 072$, i.e. 7 per cent more!

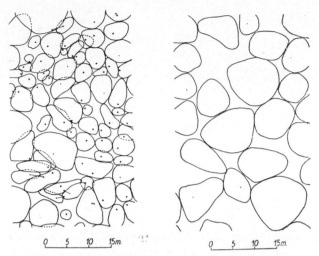

FIG. 54. Crown maps of beech experimental series 195 at Freienwalde. *Left:* light thinning, crown density per cent = 85, mean c = 15 m². *Right:* heavy thinning, canopy = 70 per cent, mean c = 46 m² (*Wiedemann*).

FIG. 55. Photographic crown projection of a 38-year-old spruce trial area with heavy thinning. ("Natural Stocking Gr." = 0·61) (phot. by *Kennel*).

Figs. 55 and 56. The first-named shows a photographic crown map from a 38-year-old heavily thinned spruce research plot whose natural degree of stocking amounts to 0·61. Forstassessor R. Kennel obtained this by systematic vertical shots taken at very short distances apart at ground level. It shows the irregularities of the outer peripheries and uneven crown density. The crown map in Fig. 56 was obtained by cand. forest. Klocke in the normal way; the crown edges were marked by perpendicular lines on a horizontal

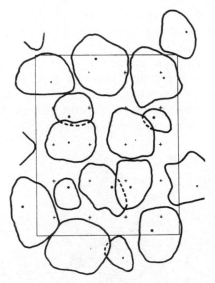

Fig. 56. Crown map of the same section as in Fig. 55; crown edges have been cut by perpendicular lines. Crown cover=0·66.

close-meshed string net. According to whether the photographic map was planimetered so as to include all projecting small branches in a wide circuit, or whether these were excluded, Kennel obtained ground cover values of 0·74 or 0·59 respectively. A procedure whereby the projections and indentations are approximately equalized gave the same degree of ground coverage as that shown in the crown map of Klocke. Any portion twice covered is counted once only. Besides expecting fairly large random errors, which lead to a special lack of reliability for small crowns (the mean error for a ground cover area of 4–5 square metres is approximately ±5 per cent), we must also strongly suspect biased subjective errors. The *average* density of the crown cover is more suitably calculated by means of systematic samples. Yield study measurements are concerned rather with the dimensions of individual crowns which are then related to the increment efficiencies. Reliable results therefore can be obtained only when it is possible to deduce sufficiently *significant mean values* by the use of numerous individual measurements.

Deciduous trees, as a rule, should be in a leafless state when a vertical projection of the crown peripheries is made; if in leaf, however, the degree of ground coverage must be estimated at a higher figure. R. Mayer (1957) discovered the following degrees of ground coverage in *oak* stands:

Without leaves between 0·43 and 0·74
With leaves between 0·47 and 0·81.

Badoux (1939) in his exemplary work about the Swiss *Common beech* thinning series found ground cover fractions of between 0·84 and 0·96, the means amounting to

0·94 with crown thinning
0·94 with light low thinning
0·89 with moderate low thinning
0·86 with heavy low thinning.

The *differences in the extent of ground coverage which result from different grades of thinning again are noticeably small*; they continue to diminish with the time that has elapsed since the last thinning operation. This, by the way, generally applies to all tree species, provided that the thinning treatment applied is not of the very severe type which may, with light-demanding species especially, result in a *permanently* interrupted canopy. The crown map of the crown-thinned sample plot at Tisch, which we owe to the careful measurements carried out by Badoux, admirably displays the fairly complicated ground cover conditions in a stand with vertical closure (Fig. 57).

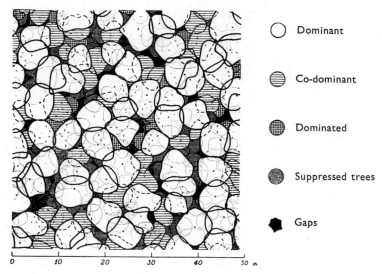

FIG. 57. Crown map of the 88-year-old sample area at Tisch which had undergone crown thinning. Only 4 per cent of the total area of the stand is without a crown canopy *(Badoux)*.

Severe breaking of canopy, extent of ground coverage and degree of disengagement

How decidedly a severe opening of canopy (e.g. an increment felling) can reduce the extent of ground coverage, even if the distances between the crown edges are only slightly increased, is shown in the following theoretical consideration of Kraft (1884). Assuming square-shaped nominal areas, the tree distances are, as seen above, equal to the crown diameters b. If the tree distances and thus the distances between the crown edges are increased by the amount β while the crown diameters b remain unchanged, then the following relation applies for the enlarged potential area:

$$s^2 = (b+\beta)^2;$$

as the crown distance β increases, the degree of ground coverage is reduced by the following ratio:

$$\frac{b^2}{(b+\beta)^2} \cdot$$

If, in the case of $b = s$, we set the theoretical degree of ground coverage equal to 1·0 and measure β in units of b, then we obtain the ratios shown in Table 33. Accordingly, the original theoretical degree of ground coverage is halved as soon as the distance of the crown edges amounts to 0·4 of the mean crown diameter. From *85 per cent as the original*

TABLE 33

Crown edge distance β measured as proportion of b	$b+\beta$	Theoretical degree of ground coverage	True extent of ground coverage	Mean ratio: nominal area to ground cover area
0·0	1·0	1·00	0·85	1·18
0·1	1·1	0·83	0·71	1·41
0·2	1·2	0·69	0·59	1·70
0·3	1·3	0·59	0·50	2·00
0·4	1·4	0·51	0·43	2·33
0·5	1·5	0·44	0·37	2·70

proportion of ground-cover afforded by full stocking (double cover counted only once) *the actual ground-cover afforded by a stand after such a thinning amounts to only a little more than 40 per cent* and the mean ratio of nominal area to area covered is about 2·4. The nominal areas in this case would be 2·4 times as large as those covered by tree canopy!

Planimetering of crown maps can furnish the mean ground-cover percentage of a *stand* with satisfactory accuracy. At the same time it supplies the *mean ratio of nominal to canopied area*. This relation, however, is very difficult to determine *for individual trees*. When a crown map of the stand is available this may be achieved by *drawing lines of equal distance to the crown edges* and assigning any gaps in the crown canopy to adjoining trees in proportion to their nominal areas. In this manner Freist (1960) calculated the ratio of nominal area/canopied area for each individual tree of a beech stand at Fabrik-schleichach which threw 71 per cent of cover after it had been severely thinned for increment 15 years previously. We shall henceforward refer to this ratio for a single tree as the "measure (or degree) of disengagement" ("Umlichtungsgrad"). Freist discovered that the degree of disengagement for *trees with small crowns* was about 1·5, which turns out to be *greater than for trees with large crowns* where it amounts to 1·2, as may be seen in Fig. 58(a). From the values given in Table 33, the average measure of disengagement for all trees corresponding in this case to a ground cover of 71 per cent amounts to 1·4. It is easy to see that the enlargement of the crown spaces by margins of equal width so as to afford equally broad areas of light access must increase the degree of disengagement of trees with a small crown diameter more than for trees with a large crown diameter. The provision of definite crown distances for trees in the same social layer is inducive to *an improvement upon their original growing prospects which is the more effective the smaller their crown diameters*. It is also understandable that when favouring certain trees, for example those with particularly good stems, by applying a disengagement cutting, the required absolute area thus exposed will be the smaller the earlier the thinning is started.[1] Further, as may be seen in Fig. 58(b), the superiority in efficiency of performance of trees with small crowns over that of large-crowned trees when related to their corresponding nominal growing-space ("Standflächenleistung") is much smaller than when their efficiencies are calculated relative to the ground areas actually covered by leaf-canopy ("Schirmflächenleistung").

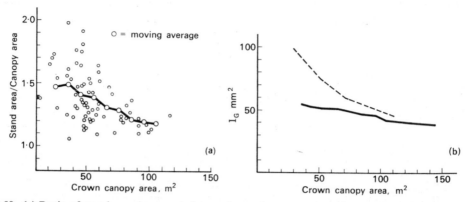

FIG. 58. (a) Ratio of stand area (= occupied ground space) to crown canopy area plotted upon the crown canopy area. Open stand of beech at Fabrikschleichach *(Freist)*. (b) Annual basal area increment per 1 m² crown canopy area (top curve, interrupted line) and per 1 m² of ground area (lower curve, continuous line) plotted over the crown canopy area for the same stand.

The degree of disengagement must be correctly estimated if the incremental efficiencies of individual trees as also of stands, are to be calculated in terms of their nominally available growing space. We shall return to this subject later in the book.

The "growing-space index" of v. Seebach

The area of shaded ground immediately beneath the crown ("Kronenschirmfläche") of an individual tree in a closed stand can be regarded as *approximately proportional to the growing space ("Standraum") or the nominal area* ("Standfläche") possessed by this tree. If we begin with the area of covered ground which we are always able to measure with sufficient accuracy, we are led to ask ourselves whether any definite relationships exist between the covered area and the other values which at any given time have been observed for a particular tree. Chr. v. Seebach, in his time, based his work on such reflections in order to determine the number of stems by which it was possible to reduce crops under his severe thinning régime. He defined the ratio crown diameter/tree diameter at breast-height, i.e. the ratio b/d, as the *"growing space index"*. We can determine the crown diameter b as the diameter of a circle whose area is equal to that of the shaded ground beneath the crown:

$$c = b^2 \frac{\pi}{4} \; ; \text{ arising from the fact that } b = \sqrt{\frac{c \times 4}{\pi}}.$$

[1] In order to provide free access of light to a beech crown in the pole stage when it stands at a height of some 20−25 m with a clean bole of 8−10 m and a crown diameter of, say, 5·6 m (= 25 m² in area), the additional space which must be sacrificed will be 0·40 m wide amounting to only 3·7 m² of exposed ground as compared with 5·5 m² for an old beech tree with a crown diameter of 8·6 m.

With reference to this v. Seebach (1845) stated: "According to the general concept and statement of the same, the stem and crown diameter of even-grown beech trees are so related that the thicker stem, compared with the thinner stem, has a comparatively smaller crown diameter and consequently requires less growing space." This inference of v. Seebach, which was based on extensive measurements, is not generally confirmed by

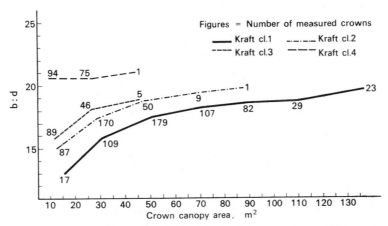

FIG. 59. Mean crown diameter/stem diameter ratio for the *Kraft* tree classes 1–4 in beech stands plotted over the crown canopy area *(Freist)*.

the more recent investigations of Eule (1959) and particularly Freist (1960). As shown in Fig. 59, which is based on 1173 measurements of the crowns of 70 to 170-year-old beech stands, *the projection ratio*, by which we shall call b/d, *at first increases rapidly but subsequently more slowly with increasing size of the ground cover area* (i.e. with increasing crown diameter). For example, with a ground-cover area of 20 m² ($b = 5$ m), trees belonging to Kraft class 1 have a projection ratio of 14; with a ground-cover area of 120 m² ($b = 12.5$), however, the ratio is only 19. At the same time, the projection ratio for equal ground-cover areas becomes *noticeably larger as social position declines*. Thus the projection ratios for trees with a *cover area of 20 m²* are as follows:

Kraft class	Average projection ratio
1	14
2	16
3	17
4[1]	21[1]

Furthermore, as proved by Freist, there is a marked *dependence on age*. For example, the projection ratio for a ground-cover area of 40 m² ($b = 7.1$ m) in Fig. 60 amounts to approximately

23·5 in the 74-year-old open stand (compartment 50),

17·5 in the 116-year-old open stand (compartment 61).

Thus, for trees casting equal cover it decreases systematically with increasing age.

[1] In the underwood (Kraft 5) where the crowns are well below those of the dominant trees and so can develop freely in plagiotropic forms which give broad shade, extreme values of up to 40 are found
? or b/d!

The large fluctuations and systematic changes in the projection ratio b/d will be explained if we remember the following fact: even in a completely closed stand, when further lateral growth of the crowns is impossible, the stem diameters continue to increase, so that b/d becomes smaller. On the other hand, after a drastic opening up of a beech stand, for example, the size of the crowns increases at a faster rate than the stem diameters so that b/d then becomes larger.

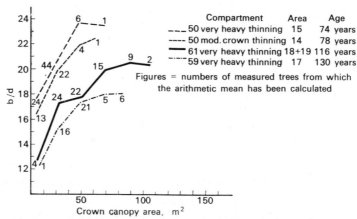

Compartment	Area	Age
50 very heavy thinning	15	74 years
50 mod. crown thinning	14	78 years
61 very heavy thinning 18+19	116 years	
59 very heavy thinning	17	130 years

Figures = numbers of measured trees from which the arithmetic mean has been calculated

FIG. 60. Mean crown diameter/stem diameter ratios of beech tree classes 1+2 plotted over the crown canopy area for two young stands (upper curves) and two older stands (lower curves) *(Freist)*.

Owing to this inconsistency between lateral growth of the crown and the stem cross-sectional increment, *the degree of ground coverage and the degree of stocking are not identical*. The *degree of stocking* is customarily determined from the basal area of the stand, i.e. the total breast-height cross-sectional areas *per hectare*, by comparing the measured basal area of the stand to the postulated basal area given in a yield table. *Even with large differences in the intensity of thinning, the degree of ground coverage remains nearly the same*, as we have seen earlier. Thus Toma (1940) discovered that in the case of pine, even with differences in the number of stems of up to 50 per cent no definite differences in the degree of ground coverage could be measured.

If the extreme values of b/d for a species are known, the possible limiting value of the basal area of the stand per hectare can be calculated for an assumed maximum degree of canopy coverage.[1] If, for single-storeyed stands of Common beech, this is assumed to be 0·85, corresponding to 8500 m² of ground-cover per hectare, and if the values used for b/d are those observed by Assmann (1954) for pole-wood and timber trees, namely 13·6 and 21·6 respectively, then the following results arise out of the proportions

$$\frac{\sum b^2}{\sum d^2} = \frac{8500}{x}; \quad \frac{x}{8500} = \frac{d^2}{b^2}; \quad x = 8500 \times \frac{1}{185 \text{ to } 462}.$$

From this are calculated

45·9 square metres basal area per hectare as *maximum value*

and   *18·4 square metres* basal area per hectare as *minimum value*,

[1] b/d with full crown contact and if b is set equal to the stem distance becomes identical with König's familiar distance factor $a = s/d$. If this is squared, then $a^2 = s^2/d^2 = b^2/d^2$, and thus equal to the "crown cover area quotient" on p. 112.

for beech stands with full crown closure. These are values which correspond satisfactorily to practical observations.[1] They demonstrate *the wide range within which the density of stocking with full ground coverage may fluctuate.*

According to the results of Freist which we have just reviewed, the projection ratio on average increases systematically with increasing size of the ground cover area. *Large-crowned trees possess relatively small dimensions of stem for their size.* Does this allow the conclusion that the trees with large crowns in a certain social layer do not utilize their growing space as well as those with small crowns? In order to answer this question, obviously we must take into consideration the fact that the production of a stand on a given area and within a certain period of time consists not only of the trees which have remained, but includes also those which have been harvested. The available space which is now occupied by trees with large crowns was previously taken up by neighbouring trees which have in the interval been extracted, but whose production must be taken into consideration. If we want to find out *which trees use the growing space* or the corresponding available area in the stand *most economically*, then we must *determine the increment which, with a certain crown dimension, is at present being achieved by them.* Investigations carried out up to the present concerning the relationships between tree crown and increment have supplied noteworthy contributions to the solution of this problem and we shall discuss them in more detail in the following chapter.

2. Tree Crown and Increment Efficiency

(a) STRUCTURE AND FORM OF THE CROWN

With the help of the model of the *crown of a Norway spruce* in Fig. 61, which we owe to the pioneering investigations of Burger, we can easily inform ourselves about its typical structure. The spruce crown is nearly a rotated paraboloid (not a cone) in shape. From the top downward, the crown radii increase up to a *maximum value* which is reached approximately at two-thirds *of the crown length from the top*. The part of the crown lying *above* the largest diameter of the crown is defined by Burger as "Sonnenkrone" or "Lichtkrone", i.e. the *part of the crown exposed to sunlight*, and the part lying *below* this as "Schattenkrone", i.e. the *shaded part of the crown*. In addition to this, Burger distinguishes between the *needled crown mantle* and the *core* which is *bare of needles*.

Descriptive crown measures

Not only the tree height h but also the mean *height of the base of the crown* and thereby the *crown length* l can be measured from the ground (cf. Fig. 62). The latter is divided into the *length of that part of the crown which is exposed to sunlight* l_0 *and the length of the shaded part of the crown* l_u. The crown projection or *ground cover area* is determined by measuring four to eight radii. The mean maximum crown diameter, which we define as $b = crown\ width$, is found either by doubling the mean radius or—after planimetering the crown area which must be drawn true to scale—by computing the diameter of a circle with the same area as the ground cover area.

[1] The minimum value is characteristic for the upper storey of an old crown-thinned pole-wood stand; the maximum value is for an old lightly thinned stand with extremely dense stocking.

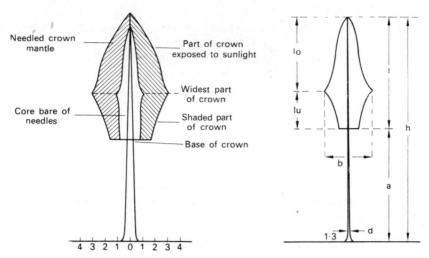

FIG. 61 *(left)*. Model of a spruce crown *(Burger)*.
FIG. 62 *(right)*. Descriptive crown measurements.

From these basic measurements arise the following important *descriptive crown measurements*:

l/h is the *crown* per cent,
l_0/l supplies the *proportion of the part of the crown exposed to sunlight*,
l_u/l the *proportion of the shaded part of the crown*,
b/h, i.e. the ratio of the width of the crown to total height of tree is known as *degree of spread* ("Spreitungsgrad").
b/l, i.e. ratio of the crown width to the crown length, is known as the *crown fullness ratio* ("Plumpheitsgrad"); the larger this ratio the more rounded is the crown. The reciprocal value l/b has also been used as the crown index (R. Mayer, 1957).
b/d, i.e. the ratio which states by how many times the crown diameter is larger than the stem diameter, is called the *crown projection ratio*[1] ("Ausladungsverhältnis"). It is identical to Seebach's growing-space factor.
b^2/d^2, i.e. the square of the projection ratio, will be called the *quotient of ground cover area* ("Schirmflächenquotient"). Its value states by how many times the ground cover area is larger than the cross-sectional area of the stem at breast height.

Crown morphology

Burger and Badoux have carried out systematic measurements of a large number of crowns of the species Norway spruce, Scots pine and Common beech and deduced *average crown forms* for trees belonging to the most important social classes. Figures 63, 64 and 65 each show a crown model of the mentioned species for *dominant trees from moderately thinned, closely stocked stands*. The idealized longitudinal sections, when rotated about the axis of the stem by 180°, create *rotated paraboloids* of different kinds.

---

[1] This term has been suggested in an earlier work of Assmann (1954) for the relation b/h. From Eule (1959) this term is now used for the ratio b/d, whilst the ratio b/h is known as *degree of spread*.

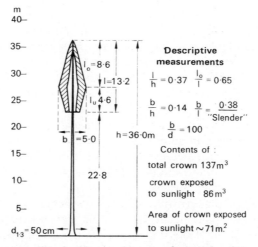

FIG. 63. Crown model of a 98-year-old spruce from a closed stand *(Burger)*.

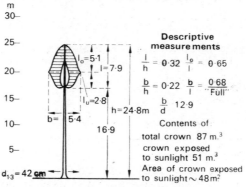

FIG. 64. Crown model of an 88-year-old Scots pine *(Badoux)*.

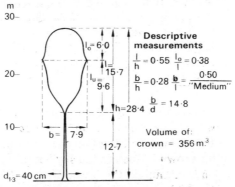

FIG. 65. Crown model of a dominant 88-year-old beech *(Badoux)*.

The *coniferous trees Norway spruce* and *Scots pine* have average crown forms of which the largest diameter lies approximately two-thirds from the top. *That proportion of the part of the crown which is exposed to sunlight* l_0/l on average amounts to 0·65 or approximately two-thirds, the proportion of the shaded part of the crown therefore approximately one-third. The *form of the part of the crown which is exposed to sunlight* lies somewhere *between a cone and a quadratic paraboloid,* corresponding to mean crown form factors of 0·35 to 0·45 as found by Burger and Badoux. The *shaded part of the crown* is obtusely paraboloid, with crown form factors from 0·50 to 0·60.

Norway spruce, the crown fullness ratios of which mostly lie below 0·5, as a rule has a *more slender crown than Scots pine* whose b/l values are mostly larger than 0·5. Table 34, which gives crown measurements of Scots pine, Norway spruce and Silver fir in mixed stands side by side on the same site, shows that *pine and Silver fir* have *fuller crowns than spruce.* The differences between these two species and spruce are satisfactorily significant. At the same time, however, the degrees of spread in all three species show very little variation; the greater crown fullness in pine and Silver fir is due to their having a *shorter crown.*

The crown shape ratios in pine crowns increase with increasing age. They reach particularly high values in some old pines in the Rhine-Main plain where they have broad, arched crowns, shaped like the crown of the stone pine. On the other hand, there are local races of pine and spruce with particularly narrow crowns, especially in mountainous areas, for which the above general rule does not necessarily apply.

TABLE 34

RESULTS OF CROWN MEASUREMENTS OF DOMINANT TREES IN MIXED STANDS AT LINDAU (LAKE CONSTANCE) FOREST, ACCORDING TO ASSESSMENTS BY MANG

Species	Number of measurements	Mean values					Crown fullness ratios b/l arith. mean	standard error of the arithm. mean $\pm$
		$d_{1.3}$ (cm)	h (m)	l (m)	b (m)	b/h		
Scots pine	17	31·5	26·4	8·1	4·4	0·17	0·55	0·031
Norway spruce	13	28·2	24·6	10·7	4·0	0·16	*0·39*	0·026
Silver fir	14	29·8	26·8	8·4	4·3	0·16	*0·54*	0·042

Species compared	Differences D	Standard error of the diff. S_D	$\dfrac{D}{S_D} = t$	Diff. significant with $P = \%$
Scots pine—Norway spruce	+0·16	±0·04	4·0	0·27
Silver fir—Norway spruce	+0·15	±0·05	2·9	1·0

In the broad-leaved species beech (cf. Fig. 65) and *oak* (R. Mayer, 1957), *the biggest diameter of crown lies considerably higher up than in the coniferous species,* namely at between one-third and one-half the crown height measured from the top. So l_0/l is always *smaller than* 0·5. The more the crown is open to the sky because of social dominance or in consequence of a disengagement thinning, the lower down is the position of its greatest width and the more pronounced becomes the relative length of that part of the crown which is exposed to sunlight.

In beech, the shape of the upper, exposed part of the crown approaches that of a cubic paraboloid or hemisphere; its crown form factor is larger than 0·50. In contrast to the conifers, the shaded part of the crowns of broad-leaved trees is more tapered, approaching a conical shape, with form-factors below 0·40.

Calculation of the volume and surface of tree crowns

The exact calculation of volume and surface area of tree crowns is impossible. We must make do with approximate values which can be calculated without too much effort by using the basic measures b and l.

The *volume* of the pointed crown of a coniferous tree has hitherto usually been calculated by assuming it to be roughly that of the volume of a *cone with sides of even length*:

$$V = \frac{1}{3} \times \frac{\pi}{4} \times b^2 \times l = \frac{\pi}{12} \times b^2 \times l.$$

The volume of a quadratic paraboloid with a value of $\frac{1}{2} \times \pi/4 \times b^2 \times l$ is larger. Corresponding to Burger's crown form factors a good approximation appears to be given by the equation:

$$V = 0.4 \times \frac{\pi}{4} \times b^2 \times l.$$

The crown *surface area* of coniferous trees ought to be calculated as the surface of a paraboloid which is possible with exactness only by the use of unwieldy formulae. For this reason the approximate equation used for the surface areas of *cones with sides of even length* is:

$$S = \frac{\pi}{4} \times b \sqrt{4\,l^2 + b^2}.$$

The surface of the paraboloids which occur in practice is probably 1·2 to 1·4 times larger. As the surfaces thus calculated would be nearly proportional to the conical surface areas, the use of the cone surface formula seems adequate for comparative calculations.

Badoux used the formula for the surface area of a truncated cone as an approximation: R = radius of the area of the larger end, r = radius of the area of the smaller end,

$$S = \pi \sqrt{(R-r)^2 + h^2}.$$

For the surface of that *part of the crown which is exposed to sunlight in* broad-leaved trees, we can use the formula for the *surface of a hemisphere* (without lower limiting area):

$$S = \pi \times b^2.$$

Mean needle and leaf quantities for individual trees

The data in Table 35, which Burger gave as average values of his extensive surveys, present an account of the *fresh weights of needles and leaves* as well as of the fine branches for the different species and for different diameters.

Among conifers, *spruce and Silver fir*, which, as is well known, keep their needles for 5 to 6 years, have particularly *large leaf weights*. In comparison to this, *pine has lower needle weights per tree*.[1] For example, in trees with a diameter of 40 cm we find for spruce

[1] In more recent works by Wehrmann (1958) and Zöttl (1960) it has been proved that pine needles, on the average, show a higher nitrogen content than spruce needles. The efficiency of pine needles, on average, is higher.

TABLE 35

AVERAGE WEIGHT OF THE FRESH NEEDLES OR LEAVES AND OF THE TOTAL FAGGOTWOOD (IN BRACKETS) PER TREE FOR DIFFERENT SPECIES ACCORDING TO BURGER

| | Weight with the diameter | | | | |
	10 cm	20 cm	30 cm (in kg)	40 cm	50 cm
Norway spruce, even-aged high forest	—	—	—	—	—
	(19)	(47)	(98)	(173)	(302)
Norway spruce, shelterwood forest	7	22	43	70	108
	(20)	(54)	(114)	(212)	(371)
Norway spruce, selection forest	6	22	48	85	132
	(19)	(64)	(150)	(285)	(473)
Silver fir, even-aged high forest	7	24	53	88	129
	(20)	(57)	(146)	(275)	(430)
Silver fir, selection forest	7	31	66	112	163
	(21)	(78)	(178)	(329)	(542)
Scots pine	4	12	21	35	52
	(20)	(40)	(78)	(150)	(272)
Larch	2	5	10	17	28
	(17)	(30)	(65)	(125)	(216)
Common beech	3	9	19	34	54
	(26)	(70)	(156)	(312)	(541)
Oak	3	8	18	33	52
	(21)	(65)	(136)	(236)	(373)

(shelterwood forest) 70 kg, Silver fir (high forest) 88 kg compared to the weight for Scots pine which is only 35 kg. Lower still is the needle weight for *larch* with only 17 kg per tree. The leaf-trees *beech and oak* have nearly equal foliage weights for trees of given diameters.

(b) LEAF QUANTITIES, CROWN DIMENSIONS AND INCREMENT EFFICIENCIES

(i) *Factors which influence the efficiencies of given leaf quantities*

The influence of site, climate, age and seed origin

How strongly the efficiencies of given leaf quantities may fluctuate has been shown before in Section A. *The less favourable the site and climate, the larger the leaf quantities which are required to produce equal quantities of wood.*

Thus, according to Burger, for 1 festmetre increment of stemwood, *larch* demands

600–800 kg needles   in the Swiss hill country
2000 kg and over   in high elevations of the Engadin.

Similar reductions in efficiency with increasing altitude are also recorded by Burger (1953) for *spruce* of identical age and occupying a similar position in the stand, in which case the production of 1 festmetre increments of stemwood demands

2900 kg of needles near Mett-Biel   520 m above sea level
6900 kg of needles near St. Moritz   1800 m above sea level.

The reduced efficiency with increasing altitude is due to less warmth, shorter vegetative periods, extreme radiation and evaporation conditions in the climate of the central Alps, the specific soil conditions and unfavourable changes in the soil life.

The *influence of the soil under equivalent climatic conditions* is evident in the already mentioned example (C. Mar: Møller, 1945) of *Danish stands of Common beech* which, *with nearly equal leaf quantities and under favourable soil conditions produce double the timber quantity that is produced under unfavourable conditions.* The explanation lies in the different nitrogen and phosphoric acid content of the leaves which is higher on sites of better quality.

The *physiological age* of the trees also has a considerable influence. The highest efficiencies with a given leaf weight, are achieved according to Burger's figures by trees of an even-aged high forest with diameters of 20–25 cm and heights of 12–20 m. These have reached *the phase of full vigour*, which, if the trees do not grow under a crown cover, is attained at an early age, often as early as 40–60 years.

Of further importance, according to Burger, is *the degree of adaptability* of the trees *to certain sites.* Provenances which are not adapted to local conditions often have lower efficiencies than the native ecotypes. The differences in the individual efficiencies of spruce trees are proved by the investigations of H. Schmidt (1952).

Social position and productive capacity

As Burger showed, *beech and fir under shade in the lower storey* require *nearly twice as much leaf weight as dominant trees in the upper storey with a good supply of light* in order to produce 1 festmetre of timber. The same applies to the separate parts of the crowns of trees in the upper storey. *The contribution to the net assimilation made by that part of the crown which is fully exposed to sunlight is,* in terms of the quantity of leaf material, *much higher than that of the shaded part of the crown* which, on account of its manifestly high respiration losses, has a low assimilation surplus. The proof for this was provided by Burger and Ladefoged (1946) who were able to remove shaded whorls of needle-bearing branches of Douglas fir and Norway spruce without causing any reduction in the increment efficiency of the particular trees.

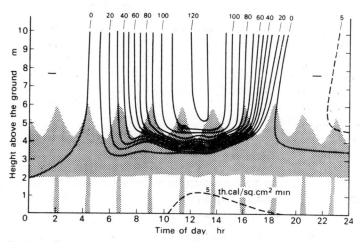

FIG. 66. Distribution of radiation levels on a summer day in a young spruce stand *(Baumgartner)*.

One possible contributory cause of the unsatisfactory economy of the shaded part of the crown and of dominated trees has already been discussed. It is not only the general lessening in the light intensity by its passage through the upper and outer crown foliage, but the selective filtering out of the energy content of those regions of the spectrum which are most effective for photosynthesis. This can still be important even if, as is assumed today, the proportion of the photosynthetically effective radiation amounts to only 1 per cent of the total available radiation.

The investigations of Baumgartner (1956, 1957), who made continuous daily recordings of the *energy of total radiation* at different levels within and above a crop of Norway spruce 6 m tall, provide results which are of decisive importance to the problem posed. The differences between the measured values, or radiation levels, enabled him to discover the regions within the space of a stand in which the energy consumption is highest. The lines of equal radiation in Fig. 66 show a distinct *maximum of energy consumption in the region of the tree-tops above the point of actual crown contact.*

Vertical distribution of the radiation consumption on 7.7.1952

RADIATION TOTALS AT DIFFERENT HEIGHTS OF A NORWAY SPRUCE STAND AND THEIR PERCENTAGE DISTRIBUTION

Height (m)	Region within the stand	cal/cm²/day	%
10	Above the tree tops	565	100
5	In the tree tops (part of the crown exposed to sun)	555	98
4·1	At the point of crown contact	223	39
3·3	Within the shaded part of the crown	36	6
0·2	In the stem region near the ground	35	6

As nicely displayed by Baumgartner's figures above, *approximately 60 per cent of the total flow of energy has already been arrested when the level of crown contact is reached* Baumgartner wrote: *"The active surface in the life of the forest therefore is not the crown space but the space of the tree tops!"* And: "In the space between the upper region of the shaded part of the crown and the tree tops, *every decimetre of height by which the crown of a tree exceeds its neighbours means a large increase in energy.* Since the nutrient supply of the assimilatory organs *has a direct relationship with the transpiration* and the amount of transpiration depends on the energy which is available for the evaporation of water, the increased energy utilization is apparent also in a larger increment of the woody substance. [Italics by the author.]

It is obvious that plants with such large dimensions as our forest trees must use large amounts of energy to maintain their transpiration. One need only think of the obstacles which have to be overcome in traversing the long distances that must be covered within the conductory vessels. Those new discoveries of forest climate made by Geiger at the Munich Institute supply adequate explanations also for the relative growth behaviour of our forest trees in stands consisting of several storeys, expecially in selection forests.

(ii) *Crown size and area-related efficiency with different structures of stands and different silvicultural treatment*

The economical use of growing space by our forest trees is dependent on the efficiency they can employ in putting on increment with given crown dimensions.

A suitable measure of increment is the growth in volume over a period of moderate duration, that is approximately 5–10 years. This period must not be too long as otherwise considerable deviations from the pattern of growth influences upon individual trees might possibly intervene before the end of the assessed increment period. The basal area increment at breast height which is frequently used as a substitute for volume increment is of doubtful value because volume increments also depend on changes of tree height and stem form, and thus differ widely.

In order to ascertain the shape and size of crown most conducive to a high rate of growth the best plan is to relate the capacities of individual trees to their respective *areas of crown surface*, taking either the whole crown or, better still, the unshaded part of the crown; this then serves as a useful index to the volume of foliage enjoying favourable light conditions. The *crown volume* can be used in order to discover the most favourable ratio of superficial crown area to volume in each particular case. *As crowns grow larger, those of ordinary common shape always increase in volume relatively faster than the superficial areas they present.*

As we have shown, it is possible to calculate *the nominal areas appropriate to individual trees in the stand, or within a certain social layer*—or even the actual growing space— only by taking many measurements. The best *approximation* to the required nominal areas is the *canopy area*, i.e. the horizontal projection of the largest lateral spread of the crown. The *ground cover area efficiency*, i.e. *the volume increment capacity per square metre of canopy-covered area*, most suitably measured in cubic decimetres per square metre (litres of woody increment per square metre), is a *useful measure for testing the economy of growing space.* Here, however, it is necessary to take into consideration the *ratio nominal area/canopy-covered area* which we have earlier defined as the *degree of disengagement* as, when this increases, the conditions for the assimilatory process of individual trees become more favourable. The productiveness of the forest is not decided by the isolated performances of individual trees but by *the yield performance* per unit of nominal area which is *always smaller* than the canopied area efficiency. If perhaps, to obtain corresponding productivities per hectare, we wish to convert the canopied or ground cover area efficiency into nominal area efficiency, we must either *divide the ground cover area efficiency by the disengagement factor* or reduce it through multiplying by the corresponding coverage fraction. This is easily done for the average of all trees of a social layer,[1] provided the ground-cover per cent is known. If, for example, the average ground cover area efficiency for a given social layer amounts to 2·0 cubic decimetres per square metre and the cover per cent is 55, then the result of the calculation shows a mean *capacity per hectare* of $2·0 \times 10,000 \times 0·55 = 11,000$ dm^3 = 11 m^3.

In any case, when comparing the ground cover area capacities of individual trees, it is always necessary to take into consideration the individual degree of disengagement.

---

[1] If the total increment capacity and the size of the stocked area are known, the efficiency per hectare obviously is more easily and more quickly calculated in the ordinary way.

Crown size and capacity in even-aged stands

According to Toma.(1940), the increment capacity per square metre of crown surface area in Scots pine stands at first increases with the increase in crown size and then remains approximately constant. This seems to be an indication of an optimum size of crown. Badoux (1945) discovered very close relationships between superficial crown surface area and increment efficiency. In Table 36 the increments of timber over 7 cm in diameter in three social classes of Scots pine are given according to increasing diameter classes (and accordingly also by crown sizes), their respective ground-cover areas, the crown surface areas and crown volumes. Generally speaking, the relative efficiencies drop with a decline in social position and the corresponding diminution of light conditions, which is, of course, to be expected. It is nevertheless remarkable that among the dominant trees, efficiencies per square metre both of the ground-cover area and of crown surface area remain approximately constant, which is in contrast to the distinct reduction of productive capacity in terms of crown volume shown by trees of larger stem diameters. The *efficiency maxima for the lowest diameters* (and crown sizes) *in each case of co-dominant and dominated trees are striking.*

TABLE 36

CROWN SIZES AND INCREMENT RATINGS IN THE SCOTS PINE RESEARCH PLOT B 17 AT LETZHOLZ, CANTON CHUR, AFTER BADOUX (ENUM. 1935; AGE = 88 YEARS)

Annual increment of wood over 7 cm in dia. calculated *in dm³* (litres) for the last increment period:

(a) per square metre area of *ground cover* at the end of the increment period,
(b) per square metre *crown surface area* at the end of the increment period,
(c) per cubic metre of *crown volume*.

$d_{1.3}$	Dominant trees			Co-dominant trees			Dominated trees		
	a	b	c	a	b	c	a	b	c
18							1·20	0·35	1·29
20				1·60	0·46	1·20	0·79	0·23	0·65
22				1·27	0·34	0·79	0·60	0·16	0·40
24				1·07	0·27	0·59	0·48	0·13	0·28
26	0·92	0·28	0·47	0·94	0·24	0·47	0·41	0·10	0·21
28	0·94	0·26	0·44	0·84	0·21	0·40	0·35	0·09	0·17
30	0·96	0·25	0·41	0·79	0·20	0·35	0·31	0·08	0·15
34	0·93	0·24	0·36	0·73	0·19	0·29	0·25	0·08	0·12
38	0·92	0·24	0·33	0·73	0·19	0·27			
42	0·97	0·28	0·34						

In his far-reaching researches, Burger also arranged the crown dimensions and their production in order of increasing diameters for which he then gave smoothed average values. If these are calculated for the ground cover area efficiencies, we find that, with only one exception (oak at Winterthur), the *optimum* lies with *the largest dominants.* The question is: Do these trees really show the best growing-space economy?

R. Mayer (Dissertation, Munich, 1957) has examined this question, among other cases, in two oak stands of the same quality class in the Steigerwald (Fabrikschleichach forest), one of which was 50 years old ("Reisigrangen") and the other one 105 years old ("Rennerkreuz"). In Fig. 67 the absolute volume increments are plotted, by Kraft tree classes, over the ground-cover areas as a measure of the crown sizes. The absolute increment capacities of the socially favoured trees with better light conditions are—with given crown dimensions—in all cases larger. The increase in productivity with increasing crown size is, however, strikingly low for tree class I, especially in the older stand.

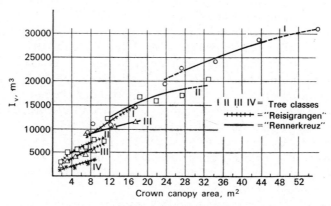

FIG. 67. Volume increment, by *Kraft* tree classes, plotted over the crown canopy areas for two stands of Sessile oak *(R. Mayer)*.

The above picture becomes remarkably changed in Fig. 68, where the ordinates represent *the increments per square metre of ground cover area* instead of the absolute increments. We find, similarly with Badoux's results in Table 36, *a considerable superiority in efficiency*

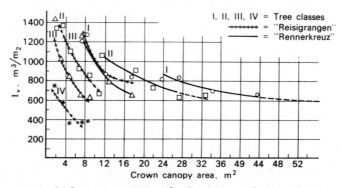

FIG. 68. Increment per 1 m² crown canopy area for the same tree classes and stands as in Fig. 67.

of the trees with small crowns of every social layer over the trees with large crowns. As R. Mayer discovered, these trees with small crowns have at the same time *more slender crowns* (i.e. a smaller crown fullness ratio) and thereby, for a given ground cover area and correspondingly smaller growing space, *a relatively larger crown* surface area, and this is important. Thus, among the four old Scots pine trees of approximately equal height which were carefully analysed by Dengler (1937), the one with the smallest ground cover has —despite a scarce supply of needles—the highest ground cover area efficiency.

It is evident that, with increasing crown width and fullness ratio, the relation of surface area to cubic content must *change in a manner which adversely affects the efficiency of assimilation. For along with this increase in size there is a simultaneous increase in the proportion of the total crown claimed by strongly respiring shoots bearing needles or leaves; these form the subsidiary framework of the crown structure as compared with that constituting the actively assimilating outer mantle which has ample light.*

The Sessile oak trees examined by R. Mayer show an optimum efficiency of ground cover in trees with small crowns of tree class No. 2. In contrast to this, Freist (1960) found an optimum for *Common beech* trees with small crowns of tree class No. 1, where the ground cover area efficiency for equal areas is in all cases larger than in the trees of class No. 2. He discovered, furthermore, that after apportioning the open uncanopied spaces into strips of equal width as earlier described, the degree of disengagement of trees with small crowns is higher than for trees with large crowns. Following a conversion into nominal area efficiencies, the picture must accordingly now change to one which puts small-crowned trees in a relatively unfavourable light (cf. Fig. 58(b)) and we can assume that *the optimum of the area-related efficiency within any given social stratum lies as a rule in the region of the medium crown sizes.*

In broad-leaved trees, as for example beech, the surfaces of the parts of the crown which are exposed to sunlight resemble semi-ellipsoids with transitions to hemispheres. The surfaces of hemispheres, however, are proportional to the areas of their lower limiting circles. Assuming that the crowns have closed canopy, the sum total of the fully exposed surfaces of all such as are of like shape remains very nearly constant, however much the average crown width may increase. After heavy thinning in the upper storey of *beech* stands, the relative length of the part of the crown which is exposed to sunlight increases from one-third (in a closed stand) to one-half of the total length of the crown and, therefore, even after heavy thinning, the original total superficial area of the parts of the crown which are exposed to full light can soon be restored.

Conditions are less favourable for conifers which have pointed and slender crowns, as for example Norway spruce. Here the total exposed surface area of densely packed crowns possessing correspondingly low crown fullness indices may possibly be larger than is the case with more open stocking and broader crowns. Moreover, the length of that part of the crown which is exposed to sunlight, can only increase after heavy thinning by a vertical extension of the crown, i.e. by further growth in height, which in older stands takes a long time.

Next to the relative measurements, the *absolute* crown measurements are also important. *In young dominant conifers the insolated part of the crown* (with Norway spruce perhaps up to heights of 18 m and crown widths of a maximum of 4 m) *has not yet developed a bare inner core being still fully covered with living needles* (in this connection, cf. the figure supplied by Burger on p. 8, vol. XXI of *Mitt. d. Schweiz. Versuchsanstalt*). This circumstance—which incidentally was pointed out long ago by Metzger (1893)—is in all probability decisively significant for the time when the increment per acre of even-aged coniferous stands reaches its peak rate.

The effects of thinning on crown dimensions and increment efficiency

Thinning enlarges the growing space of individual trees in a stand and after a period during which this increased space becomes effective, thereby also the crown dimensions. Indeed, the crown widths as well as the absolute and relative crown lengths are quite considerably increased, as demonstrated, *inter alia*, by Wohlfarth (1935) for Norway spruce, and Toma (1940) for Scots pine. After heavy thinning over a period of several decades, the mean crown volumes of individual trees, as well as *the total crown volumes of stands, increase considerably, whilst* under a light thinning régime *the total crown surface areas* of stands *hardly change* by comparison.

TABLE 37

CROWN DIMENSIONS AND INCREMENT IN THE NORWAY SPRUCE THINNING SERIES AT OLTEN, SWITZERLAND, AFTER BURGER

Commenced in 1888 at the age of 22 years in even-aged plantations after a clear felling; B–C–D grade treatments uniformly carried out for 47 years up to the 1935 assessment at the age of 69 years.

(a) *Data for the stand* (state in 1935, figures per hectare)

Thinning grade	No. of stems	Basal area G (m²)	Volume V (m³)	d (cm)	h (m)	Crown length (m)	Crown width (m)
						Mean basal area stem	
B	1016	61·7	813	27·8	29·3	9·4	3·4
C	692	51·2	713	30·7	29·7	11·3	4·1
D	556	47·5	651	33·0	30·1	12·2	4·6

Thinning grade	Ground cover (m²)	Total of crown Superficial area (m²)	Contents (m³)	Annual incr. of wood over 7 cm diam. in the last 5 years (m³)
B	9058	50,290	30,530	20·6
C	9173	50,520	35,550	20·0
D	9448	50,870	39,420	21·2

(b) *Influence of the different grades of thinning on the crown dimensions of trees of the same stem diameter*

Diameter Thinning grade		d.b.h. = 22 cm B	d.b.h. = 22 cm D	d.b.h. = 40 cm B	d.b.h. = 40 cm D
Tree height	m	26·7	25·5	32·3	31·7
Crown length	m	7·2	9·0	13·8	14·1
diameter	m	2·6	3·4	5·0	5·6
ground cover	m²	5·5	9·1	19·4	24·3
superficial area	m²	29·2 = 100%	49·4 = 170%	110·0 = 100%	125·6 = 115%
volume	m³	13·2 = 100%	27·3 = 207%	89·0 = 100%	114·0 = 128%
Projection ratio (b/d)		11·8	15·5	12·5	14·0

TABLE 38

DESCRIPTIVE MEASUREMENTS OF MEAN STEMS AND CROP VALUES FOR TWO NORWAY SPRUCE STANDS AFTER BURGER (1939)

(a) 98-year-old stand at Tablat, *densely stocked.*
(b) 132 year-old stand at Kerns *severely thinned long ago.*

Definition			(a)	(b)	(b) as % of (a)
Mean stem values					
Mean diam.		cm	37	52	140
Mean height		m	34	34	100
Crown length					
total	l	m	11·3	18·2	161
insolated part	l_0	m	7·5	12·0	160
shaded part	l_u	m	3·8	6·2	163
Crown width	b	m	4·1	7·6	185
Ground cover area	c	m²	13·2	45·4	337
Crown volume					
total	v	m³	76	433	570
insolated part	v_0	m³	48	278	**580**
shaded part	v_u	m³	28	155	553
Crown surface area					
insolated part	s_0	m²	49·2	149·5	**304**
Relative measures					
l/h			0·33	0·54	
l_0/l			0·66	0·66	
b/h			0·121	0·222	
b/l			**0·364**	**0·417**	
s_0/v_0			**1·02**	**0·54**	
s_0/c			**3·7**	**3·3**	
Mean weight of fine branches		kg	132	502	380
Mean needle weight		kg	42	131	312
Increment in vol.		litres	20	75	350
per m² cover area		litres	1·52	1·65	109
per m² surface area		litres	0·41	0·50	**122**
per m³ vol. of crown					
exp. to light		litres	0·42	0·22	**52**
per 1000 kg needle weight		litres	476	572	**120**
Crop values per hectare					
Number of stems			712	112	16
Basal area		m²	76	24	32
Timber volume		m³	1229	348	28
Crown canopy areas		m²	9156	5082	56
Total cr. volume		m³	54000	48000	89
Vol. of insolated crowns		m³	34200	31100	**91**
Superficial area of					
insolated crowns		m²	34350	16800	**49**
s_0/v_0			**1·00**	**0·54**	
s_0/c			**3·75**	**3·31**	
Needle weight		kg	30000	14700	**49**
Increment in volume		m³	**13·9**	**8·4**	**60**

These effects are clearly brought out in the example of the Norway spruce thinning series at Olten, Switzerland, which was carefully analysed by Burger. The data for the stand given in Table 37 show the numbers of stems, basal areas and volumes for the standing trees after 47 years of different types of treatment. The crown measurements of the average stems show the increase of crown length and width. As against this, the *totals* (for the stand) *of the ground cover and surface areas of the crowns have hardly changed*; they are practically the same today! At the same time, however, the *crown volume of the heavily thinned stand at* approximately 39,000 m³ today *exceeds by a third that of the lightly thinned stand.* The average increment of the last 5 years was nearly equal on all three plots.

The results of thinning are most clearly apparent in the crown measurements of trees which today have the same breast-height diameter.[1] The percentage values for surface area and volume show that *the increase of the surface areas is noticeably smaller than that of the volumes.* This is one of the reasons why heavy thinning, *notwithstanding that it causes a notable general enlargement of the crown, cannot impart a lasting impetus to the volume growth of the crop.*

The effects of strongly varying treatment for crown size and efficiency are admirably displayed in two Norway spruce stands, analysed by Burger (1939), one of which was 98 years old and densely stocked; the other was 132 years old and had been severely opened up some considerable time previously.[2] The younger stand falls into a better height-quality class than the older stand. From the mean stem data we find the following characteristic differences in Table 38. The mean tree of the severely thinned stand has, with equal total height, a greater proportion of crown (0·54 as compared to 0·33) but at the same time also a larger crown spread and crown fullness index. The surface area of the insolated parts of the crown does not show the same extent of increase as the crown volume, as illustrated by the relative value s_0/v_0 of 0·54 compared to 1·02; also, s_0/c amounts to only 3·3 compared to 3·7. *The parts of the crowns which are exposed to sunlight in the severely thinned stand, while possessing an equal ground cover area or making equal demands in nominal growing space, have therefore a smaller surface area.*

The mean stem of the severely thinned stand has a larger quantity of needles (131 kg as compared to 42), with which it produces, not only in absolute terms (75 litres compared to 20), but also in relative terms per 1000 kg needle weight, a larger increment (572 litres compared to 476). This is quite understandable, just as is the higher efficiency per square metre of ground cover area and crown surface area, when considered as the consequence of much better light conditions for the crowns in the severely thinned stand, which shows a total ground cover area of only 5082 m² (mean degree of disengagement = 1·97) compared to 9156 m² (degree of disengagement = 1·09) in the densely stocked stand and with 24 compared to 76 m² of basal area per hectare. Despite this, the volume increment capacity per hectare at 8·4 compared to 13·9 m³ is yet considerable; in fact, with this low degree of stocking, it is unexpectedly high. However, because of the differences in age and site, it is not possible to draw final conclusions from these comparisons.

We are also indebted to Badoux (1939) for giving us some highly informative data about the comparative effects of thinnings on the crown dimensions and performance

---

[1] For trees of equal diameter, the lower heights which are recorded under heavy thinning are by no means an indication of a lower "quality class" for this area, but a *regular result of heavier thinning*, which promotes diameter growth — especially at breast height — more strongly than height growth.

[2] Figure 61 shows the relative dimensions of a predominant spruce tree in a severely thinned stand, Fig. 63 those for the same type of tree from a densely stocked stand.

of Common beech. The more powerful effects of crown thinning (Table 39) have considerably enlarged the crown ratio, crown spread and crown fullness index as well as the canopy projection ratio of trees having comparable stem diameters. *The heights are however considerably lower than with moderate low thinning*, owing to the concentration of shoot elongation mainly into the increased lateral space surrounding the exposed parts of the crowns. Very similar tendencies become apparent from the corroborative measurements, taken by Assmann (1950b) upon dominant beech trees in the experimental series at Dalheim.

TABLE 39

CHANGES IN CROWN DIMENSIONS IN STANDS OF COMMON BEECH AS A RESULT OF DIFFERENT THINNING
METHODS

(a) After Badoux (1939), in the experimental thinning series at *Tisch* near Zurich;
  B = light to moderate low thinning,
  H = moderate to heavy crown thinning.

(b) After Assmann (1950), in the experimental series at *Dalheim* near Paderborn.
  A = light low thinning.
  H = heavy crown thinning.

Definition	$d_{1.3}$ (cm)	h (m)	l (m)	b (m)	c (m²)	$\dfrac{l}{h}$	$\dfrac{b}{h}$	$\dfrac{b}{l}$	$\dfrac{b}{d}$	Remarks
(a)										
Tisch B	20	25·1	10·1	4·0	12·8	0·41	0·16	0·40	20·0	
H	20	21·6	11·0	4·9	18·6	0·51	0·23	0·45	24·5	
B	30	27·3	14·2	6·0	28·3	0·52	0·22	0·42	20·0	
H	30	24·7	14·2	6·6	34·0	0·58	0·26	0·46	22·0	
B	40	28·4	15·7	7·9	49·6	0·55	0·28	0·50	19·8	
H	40	26·1	15·9	8·4	55·3	0·61	0·32	0·53	21·0	
(b)										
Dalheim A	32·6	29·2	12·7	4·7	17·4	0·43	0·161	**0·371**[1]	14·2	Mean of 12 trees in the top storey
H	42·8	28·0	15·1	8·5	15·1	0·54	0·304	**0·562**[2]	19·9	Mean of 22 trees in the top storey

The measurements at Dalheim were made on trees in the leafless stage.
[1] Standard error of the arithm. mean = ±0·010.
[2] Standard error of the arithm. mean = ±0·016.
$D = 0·191$; $\mu_D = ±0·019$; $t = 10·0$.

We have seen that the efficiency of production in terms of the ground cover area occupied by individual trees in densely stocked stands *rises* markedly throughout from the lower to the higher tree classes, but *that, within any given social stratum the trees with small to medium crowns, show larger ground cover area efficiencies and therefore a more favourable economy of growing-space than the trees with large crowns. Heavier thinning treatment improves the light conditions and thereby the ground cover area efficiencies of all trees in a stand,* including the smaller and weaker trees, if they have not been removed by thinning. *In order to achieve this average increase in efficiency of individual trees the number of actively growing trees, some of which may be taking up too much growing space, must be reduced to the extent that the total yield crop per unit area cannot be raised, at least for a long time.*

Crown size and efficiency in stands of several storeys and mixed ages

One question which suggests itself is whether or not it would be possible to increase the productive capacity per unit area by creating *several stages or layers of crowns* similar to those found in multiple-storeyed crops of mixed ages.

Weck (1944) examined the relationship between the "crown area" $l \times b$ (Busse, 1930) and the increment of diameter or basal area at breast height during the last 20 years, especially in *Scots pine* of 40–180 years of age belonging to site quality classes I to IV on drift formation soils in East Germany. In this investigation, the *productivities of Scots pine trees, 140 years or more in age, were compared: in the one case they grew as standards, and in the other they grew within closed even-aged stands.* The measures of dependence, namely the coefficient of rank correlation ϱ and the correlation ratio η produce *high values* for the examined relationship which is *closest for pine standards.* We must expect this, because the combination of influences on growth varies rather widely for individual trees in a closed stand while standards in all cases enjoy complete freedom for their crowns.

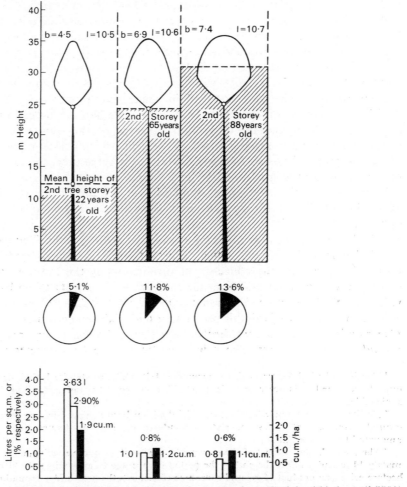

FIG. 69. Crown dimensions and yields of pine standards *(Lindau)*. Explained in the text.

Weck found *optimum production* per square metre of crown area *in pine standards with crown areas of 50–70 m²* $(b \times l = 5 \times 10$ or $6 \times 12)$ but, *in pine trees within closed stands the optimum was given with crown areas of only 10 square metres.* This is explained with the help of the data provided by Badoux in Table 36. According to that table, *the optima for production per unit area in a closed pine stand, within a social class, lie in the trees with the smallest diameter* and the smallest crowns. Yet *the efficiencies of the pine standards* with crown areas of 50–70 m² are approximately *twice as high as those of pines* of equal dimensions *in a closed stand* which is not surprising, as the crowns of the standards enjoy incomparably better light conditions.

For ten standards with a total ground cover area of 227 m², Weck calculated an annual volume production of 0·264 m³, which amounts to a ground cover area productivity of 1·16 litres/m². By assuming a nominally available area of 310 m², i.e. *a canopy cover ratio* of $227/310 = 0·73,$ he further calculated a *potential growth per hectare for the standards* amounting to $0·264/0·0310 = 8·5$ solid m³. This would have to be achieved by $10,000/31·0 = 323$ standards with an average crown width of 5·4 metres distant 5·6 m apart in square espacement, which means that if these same trees were growing *in a closed crop,* their crown peripheries would be separated a mere 20 cm apart.[1]

By comparison the crown and increment measurements of pine standards taken by Mang (Diss. Munich, 1955) on optimum sites at Lake Constance show the average crown dimensions and productivities (one circular sample plot, or mean of two and three sample circles each), represented in Fig. 69. The crowns of these trees during their first decades as standards are relatively slender $(b/l = 0·43)$; subsequently, however, they become progressively more rounded in shape (in the end $b/l = 0·69$). In their final position, the crowns of the standards have become half-submerged in the rising second-storey crop. The percentage of ground coverage of the standards (related to the area of the stand) increases from 5·1 to 13·6 per cent, which corresponds to mean degrees of disengagement of 19·6 and 7·4 respectively; at the same time, the production in terms of ground cover area drops from 3·6[2] to 0·8 litres/m² and the increment rate from 2·9 to 0·8 per cent. As the number of standards per hectare of the stand amounts to only approximately 30, their *productivity per hectare*[3] *at the beginning amounts to only 1·9 and at the end to only 1·1 m³.*

Whether a "change-over to forms of irregular crop structure" actually does—as Weck concluded from his results—offer "prospects of a sustained improvement in volume growth" depends on the efficiency of production by the lower storeys. We can form some impression about this from the further measurements taken by Mang. The figure values in Table 40 *show that even on optimal sites at Lake Constance* (recent morainic soils with 1300 mm of rainfall per annum and high temperatures) *the cover cast by the pine standards causes a considerable reduction of ground cover area performance in the second storey of the crop.* The values for trees of 15 cm diameter apply to those with

[1] The hypothetical degree of disengagement is 1·36 whilst as standards their degree of disengagement must be assumed to increase to at least 6·0. The efficiency per unit area hoped for by Weck is not achievable.

[2] 3·6 litres is an extremely high value, which had not been achieved by any other standard. The mean ground cover area efficiency for sixteen standards of different diameter (43 – 82 cm), for example, amounted to 1·32 dm³/m².

[3] The mean distances apart of the crown edges, assuming square spacing, at first amounts to approximately 14 m and towards the end of the period on average to approximately 11 m! The efficiencies per hectare arise as a product of ground cover area efficiency × the area under ground cover in square metres (1000 litres = 1 festmetre).

TABLE 40

GROUND COVER AREA PRODUCTIVITIES IN A SYSTEM OF HIGH FOREST WITH PINE STANDARDS ACCORDING TO MEASUREMENTS BY MANG (1955)

(a) Of *trees not growing under cover* (mean values for 58 Silver fir, 88 Norway spruce, 68 Scots pine).
(b) Of *trees within the ground-cover region of standards* (mean values for 70 S. fir, 82 N. spruce, 58 Sc. pine)

The mean annual sectional area increment at breast height for the previous 10 years (I_g in square centimetres) has been used as a basis.

Category	$d_{1\cdot3}$ (cm)	S. fir			N. spruce			S. pine		
		c (m²)	I_g (cm²)	$\dfrac{I_g}{c}$ (cm²/m²)	c (m²)	I_g (cm²)	$\dfrac{I_g}{c}$ (cm²/m²)	c (m²)	I_g (cm²)	$\dfrac{I_g}{c}$ (cm²/m²)
a)	15	9·1	26	2·9	6·7	26	3·9	5·7	26	4·6
b)		7·4	32	4·3 (148%)	8·6	32	3·7 (95%)	5·4	32	5·9 (128%)
a)	20	12·0	52	4·3	9·4	52	5·7	8·1	50	6·2
b)		10·7	49	4·6 (107%)	11·0	48	4·4 (77%)	10·0	47	4·7 (76%)
a)	30	17·8	136	7·6	15·0	130	8·6	13·3	112	8·4
b)		17·2	117	6·8 (89%)	15·8	99	6·3 (73%)	16·1	88	5·5 (65%)
a)	40	23·7	282	11·9	20·4	251	12·3	18·8	198	10·5
b)		23·7	262	11·0 (92%)	20·8	193	9·3 (76%)	22·3	178	8·0 (76%)

crowns which lie yet well below the crowns of the standards, so that the loss of light is relatively small. The shade-tolerant Silver fir, with mean diameters of 20 cm and less, significantly shows an even slightly higher ground-cover area efficiency under shade. On the other hand, the other two species undergo very considerable reductions of about 25 per cent with trees of 20 cm diameter and above. A typical tendency of trees growing under shade (Silver fir excepted) is to have spreading crowns due to the development of plagiotropic, shade-tolerant forms. In another instance (see Figs. 139–40), six circular sample plots under partial shade from standards were compared at the beginning and end of a period of observation with six similar and adjacent plots which were without overhead shade. At the commencement of the period, the shaded plots under standards had the advantage by about 10 per cent in volume growth but at the end, the growth was 14 per cent less than that of the single-storeyed plots. More detail will be found in the discussion on the system of pine standards (p. 395).

If the total production proves to be so unexpectedly disappointing for types of crop consisting of several storeys, where a light-demanding species with relatively thin crowns forms a widely spaced top storey, then expectations of an *increased* efficiency under multiple-storeyed shade-tolerant crops of mixed ages, as for instance in a mixed selection forest of fir, spruce and beech, must be even less justified.

Crown size and performance in selection forests

In order to be able to judge correctly the crown measurements and yields of selection forests comprising trees of many ages, we must first understand one basic difference. In more or less even-aged stands of a "Schlagwald",[1] the dominant and co-dominant trees of the upper canopy layer *are all in the same natural age phase*, be it the phase of increasing growth-rate, full vigour or declining increment. *In a selection forest with a marked admixture of ages, on the other hand, only the trees in the topmost storey have reached the phase of full vigour* or they may already have passed into the stage of declining increment. The trees in the middle crown storey are still in the phase of accelerating growth or in a transitory stage to full vigour *which they do not achieve*, as we shall see presently, *until they have reached in effect considerably more advanced ages and also much higher dimensions, than the trees under the "Schlagwald" system.*

At a given point in time the average stem and crown dimensions in the several height strata of a selection forest, therefore, represent different phases of development, such as are found in the mean stems of even-aged stands for different ages of the stand.[2]

TABLE 41

GROUND COVER, CROWN SPACE, LEAF WEIGHTS, GROWING STOCK AND PRODUCTION DATA OF SWISS SELECTION FOREST RESEARCH AREAS AFTER BADOUX (1949) (VALUES PER HECTARE)

Research area	Tree species	Crown cover area	volume	Stand values for N	G	V_D	Long-term M.A.I. per m² of cover area		Fresh leaf wt.	Incr. per 1000 kg
		(m²)	(m³)		(m²)	(m³)	(m³)	(dm³/m²)	(kg)	(m³/1000 kg)
Dürsrüti										
1947	Fir	10,500	93,100	365	48·9	742	12·6	1·20	37,200	0·339
900 m elev.	Sp.	1,500	10,300	104	5·9	76	1·3	0·87	3,700	0·351
	total	12,000	103,400	469	54·8	818	13·9	1·16	40.900	0·340
Schallenberg-										
Rauchgrat	Fir	8,100	55,600	492	25·8	343	10·1	1·25	23,600	0·428
1946	Sp.	700	4,700	44	3·0	39	0·9	1·29	2,100	0·429
1060 m elev.	Be.	3,200	20,000	84	6·6	94	2·2	0·69	1,500	1.467
	total	12,000	80,300	620	35·4	476	13·2		27,200	
Hasliwald										
1947	Fir	10,000	63,800	432	26·5	356	9·5	0·95	28,500	0·333
570 m elev.	Sp.	1,700	12,200	67	6·9	88	2·6*	1·53*	5,200	0·500*
	total	11,700	76,000	499	33·4	444	12·1		33,700	
Biglenwald										
1945	Fir	7,900	37,500	466	13·1	148	4·6	0·58	14,700	0·313
930 m elev.	Sp.	4,100	34,900	124	20·0	267	5·1	1·24	15,600	0·327
	total	12,000	72,400	590	33·1	415	9·7	0·81	30,300	0·320

* Non-significant values.

[1] A "Schlagwald" is produced by planned regeneration measures; this enables new generations of forest trees to grow within limited periods of time on specified forest areas, so that it is possible to achieve a planned spacial layout along with appropriate time-intervals for realization. This is not to be confused with a *clear felling* system.

[2] An analogy with a selection forest, as in general to stands with a heavy mixture of the ages, is the working section of a "Schlagwald" (cf. p. 435). This represents a combination of stands of different ages for the purpose of planned management.

TABLE 42

CROWN MEASUREMENTS AND GROUND COVER AREA EFFICIENCIES FOR SWISS SELECTION FOREST RESEARCH AREAS, ACCORDING TO DATA OF BADOUX (1949)

Selection forest res. plot V, Dürsrüti

	S. fir — Crown measurements								N. spruce — Crown measurements							
$d_{1.3}$ (cm)	h (m) (h/d)	l (m) (l/h)	b (m) (b/l)	c (m²)	s (m²)	v (m³)	s/v	Ground cover area efficiency (dm³/m²)	h (m) (h/d)	l (m) (l/h)	b (m) (b/l)	c (m²)	s (m²)	v (m³)	s/v	Ground cover area efficiency (dm³/m²)
10	9·5 (95)	5 (0·53)	3·9 (0·78)	12	34	29	1·17	0·05	9·8 (98)	5 (0·51)	3·0 (0·60)	7	25	16	1·56	0·09
30	25·6 (85)	15 (0·59)	5·6 (0·37)	25	134	167	0·80	0·70	27·2 (91)	16 (0·59)	4·7 (0·29)	17	119	119	1·00	1·04
50	34·6 (69)	20 (0·58)	7·0 (0·35)	39	223	365	0·61	1·57	36·2 (72)	21 (0·58)	6·3 (0·30)	31	208	302	0·69	1·93
70	40·4 (58)	24 (0·59)	8·2 (0·34)	53	312	619	0·50	2·16	42·2 (60)	25 (0·59)	8·0 (0·32)	50	319	611	0·52	1·97
90	44·5 (49)	26 (0·59)	9·2 (0·35)	67	380	912	0·42	2·28	45·3 (50)	29 (0·64)	9·9 (0·34)	77	459	1103	0·42	1·54
100	46·2 (46)	28 (0·61)	9·6 (0·34)	73	426	1072	0·40	2·18	45·9 (46)	30 (0·65)	11·0 (0·37)	95	525	1440	0·37	1·24
120	49·1 (41)	31 (0·63)	10·5 (0·35)	87	518	1413	0·37	1·55								
140	51·0 (36)	34 (0·67)	11·3 (0·33)	101	613	1767	0·35	0·49								

Selection forest res. plot V, Biglenwald

	S. fir — Crown measurements								N. spruce — Crown measurements							
$d_{1.3}$ (cm)	h (m) (h/d)	l (m) (l/h)	b (m) (b/l)	c (m²)	s (m²)	v (m³)	s/v	Ground cover area efficiency (dm³/m²)	h (m) (h/d)	l (m) (l/h)	b (m) (b/l)	c (m²)	s (m²)	v (m³)	s/v	Ground cover area efficiency (dm³/m²)
10	9·0 (90)	6 (0·67)	3·6 (0·60)	10	35	26	1·35	0·19	9·8 (98)	6 (0·61)	3·2 (0·53)	8	31	22	1·41	0·24
30	23·8 (79)	14 (0·59)	6·0 (0·43)	28	134	170	0·79	1·05	26·0 (87)	13 (0·50)	4·8 (0·37)	18	100	107	0·94	1·06
50	30·3 (61)	16 (0·53)	7·4 (0·46)	43	191	337	0·57	1·30	32·3 (65)	17 (0·53)	6·7 (0·39)	35	184	276	0·67	1·35
60	31·8 (53)	18 (0·57)	8·4 (0·47)	55	244	483	0·51	1·16	34·4 (57)	20 (0·58)	7·8 (0·39)	48	249	451	0·55	1·27
70	33·0 (47)	21 (0·64)	9·4 (0·45)	70	318	711	0·45	0·99	36·0 (51)	23 (0·64)	9·0 (0·39)	64	333	732	0·45	1·11
80	34·0 (43)	24 (0·70)	10·6 (0·44)	89	408	1073	0·38	0·81	37·0 (46)	28 (0·76)	10·4 (0·37)	85	467	1187	0·39	0·92

The totals of some typical Swiss experimental selection forest areas in Table 41 show high values for total canopy area and strikingly high figures for total crown volume. This, with 70,000–100,000 m³ is nearly twice as high as in middle-aged and mature stands of a "Schlagwald" or even-aged high forest.[1]

Not quite as large, but still considerable, is the superiority in fresh leaf weight per hectare. This, for a working section consisting of pure spruce stands of Quality Class I (for mountain stands according to the yield table of Flury) and for a rotation of 120 years, would, according to data by Burger, amount to approximately 30,000 kg. By contrast, we have about 41,000 kg in the experimental selection-forest area at the Dürsrüti containing maximum stocking in a locality equivalent to Quality Class I. The increments per hectare so achieved are, however, less impressive than the large tree dimensions; they are lower than the productive performance per hectare of high forest felling series in comparable site conditions, at least for rotations of 100 to 120 years.

A fuller comprehension of the tree and crown dimensions, as well as their corresponding efficiencies of performance, is given in Table 42; they differ altogether from those of high forest trees. The mean values of Badoux shown there are arranged in order of increasing breast-height diameters ($d_{1.3}$). As indicated by the heights, *these correspond to strata enjoying increasingly favourable social position and light conditions.* A striking feature is the *low ratio of total height/d.b.h.* ($h/d_{1.3}$) among trees of 30 cm and more, and the *high crown per cent (l/h) which, in all cases, is greater than 0·5.* The crowns of the trees with the largest diameters make up two-thirds and more of the total heights of the trees! The crown fullness ratios are generally high. With S. fir, the stems are invariably stouter and the crowns fuller than those of Norway spruce. Notwithstanding

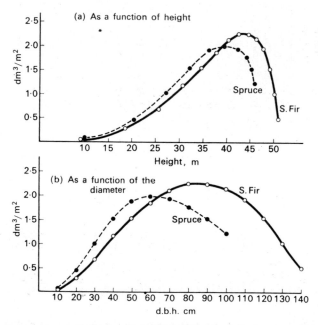

FIG. 70. Mean ground cover area efficiencies of selection forest trees in the experimental area at Dürsrüti. (According to data by *Badoux.*)

---

[1] Strictly speaking, this should be compared to the mean crown space of a working section of a "Schlagwald".

the increasing measurements of *c*, *s*, and *v*, *it is remarkable how rapidly values of the relation s/v decrease with increasing tree height.* The *relation between crown surface area and crown volume* (for breast-height diameters of 50 cm and more) *in selection forest trees of the upper storey is extraordinarily low.* If, despite this, their ground cover area efficiencies up to large tree diameters are considerable, they owe this to their superior social position and favourable light conditions.

Figures 70 and 71 are very informative. There we can recognize pronounced *optima for the ground-cover area efficiency* along with certain diameters; thus, for *Silver fir* at the Dürsrüti it is reached between 70 and 100 cm and in the Biglenwald between 35 and

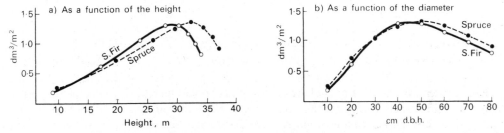

FIG. 71. Mean crown canopy efficiencies in the experimental area of the selection forest, Biglenwald (data by *Badoux*).

55 cm; for *Norway spruce* at the Dürsrüti between 50 and 75 cm and in the Biglenwald between 40 and 60 cm. The *efficiencies of the smaller diameter classes are*, by comparison, *very low.* Furthermore, we notice *a marked decline in productiveness beyond the optimum diameter values.* This becomes even more pronounced if we regard the ground cover area efficiency as a function of the tree height. As the height growth *becomes ever slower* with increasing height and age, so we find *a marked drop in the efficiency of the tallest trees which, of course, are generally also the oldest ones.*

If we now compare this picture with the ground cover area efficiencies of even-aged Norway spruce stands when shown as a function of the crop mean heights as in Fig. 72, we find there a completely different trend. The peak productivity values[1] of 2·57–

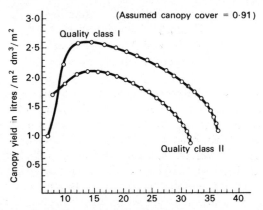

FIG. 72. Mean ground cover area efficiencies of even-aged spruce stands as a function of the mean height for the stand (yield table data by *Flury*).

[1] It should be noted that these are *mean values* which have been calculated by the inclusion of *trees from Kraft classes 1–4.*

$2 \cdot 60 \, dm^3/m^2$ are already reached in Quality Class I *with heights of 12–16 m* and in Quality Class II peak values of $2 \cdot 07 – 2 \cdot 10 \, dm^3/m^2$ *with heights between 13 and 17 m*. In the two selection forest areas we find, on the other hand, the following values:

	Peak values	Heights
	for spruce	
Dürsrüti	$1 \cdot 96 – 2 \cdot 02 \, dm^3/m^2$	$36 \cdot 5 – 42 \cdot 5 \, m$
Biglenwald	$1 \cdot 28 – 1 \cdot 35 \, dm^3/m^2$	$30 \cdot 5 – 34 \cdot 0 \, m$
	for fir	
Dürsrüti	$2 \cdot 26 – 2 \cdot 30 \, dm^3/m^2$	$42 – 45 \, m$
Biglenwald	$1 \cdot 28 – 1 \cdot 32 \, dm^3/m^2$	$27 \cdot 5 – 30 \cdot 5 \, m$

The spruces and firs in the Biglenwald which achieve these high efficiencies occupying as they do the upper storeys, at the same time provide the canopy for an area of approximately 4500 m². There are additionally some 500 m² of area under the tallest trees whose productivity is already beginning to fall off. *The crowns of these well-separated selection forest giants* (mean degree of disengagement = 2·0) *thus enjoy the full benefit of the light, whilst those trees in the lower storeys which are partly in the shade cast by those dense and overhanging crowns can achieve only very modest performances.*

This becomes evident when we regard Figs. 73 and 74—based on data by Burger—where the ground-cover area efficiencies of *individual* selection forest and high forest trees of various social classes are plotted over their respective tree heights. Admittedly, these selection forest trees belong to stands growing on only medium-quality sites. But even the highest ground-cover area efficiencies of selection forest areas to be found among the figures given by Badoux, namely 2·35 dm³/m² for fir and 2·14 for spruce do not reach the highest efficiencies of *dominant trees* from stands of the even-aged high forest. For, among 167 individual values of Burger, relating to spruce, we find

1 value of 5·0   dm³/m²
2 values of 4·0–5·0 dm³/m²
9 values of 3·0–4·0 dm³/m²
19 values of 2·0–3·0 dm³/m²

The explanation for these different efficiencies is obvious from the foregoing: with full light available to the crowns at an early stage, *high forest trees reach the phase of full vigour* not only at an earlier age, but also *at a relatively lower tree height. In contrast to this, selection forest trees do not enter into that phase until, after a period of much-impeded development, they attain a considerable age and correspondingly commanding height.* Only when the tops of their crowns can enjoy full sunlight by rising into the upper canopy, i.e. into the "active surface of the forest" according to Baumgartner, can their assimilatory powers unfold without hindrance. In the meantime, however, they have reached crown dimensions at which the ratio between the fully active crown surface and the bare internal core carrying only respiring shoots is no longer advantageous. Moreover, at tree heights of 30 m and over, they appear to require large amounts of energy in order to overcome the frictional resistance to the passage of fluids in the vessels. The result is a relatively

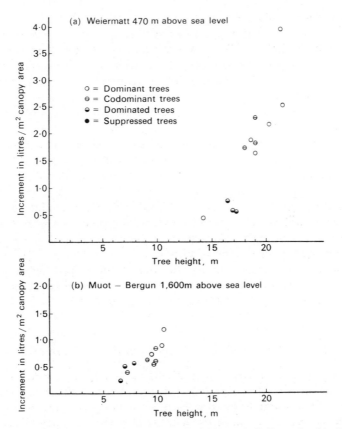

FIG. 73. Canopy efficiencies of spruce high forest *(Burger)*. (1 litre=1 cubic decimetre.)

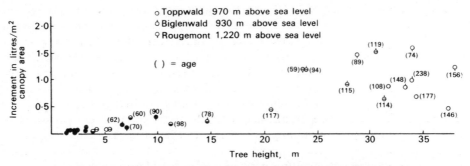

FIG. 74. Canopy efficiencies of selection forest spruce *(Burger)*.

low ground-cover area efficiency despite enjoyment of full sunlight. At the same time, the *trees in the lower social strata* show only *very small increments*, because growing under the total canopy pressure of trees with very large crowns in the upper storey and numerous trees of the middle storey, they not only receive far too little light but also an insufficient share of the total radiation. Arguing on the basis of Baumgartner's radiation measurements one would conclude that the "active region" (cf. p. 118), within the strongly swaying and irregular crown profile of a selection forest must be raised to such an extent that the trees of the lower social strata, even though they may stand in a narrow shaft of light and not directly under cover, *no longer receive sufficient energy for them to achieve their full quota of assimilative activity.* When planners of huge towns with swarming populations have to solve the problem of lack of space by building tall flats and constructing skyscrapers, the old existing houses of earlier periods may survive in dismal dark and cold corners. Whereas in that instance however, artificial lighting and additional heating can remedy those conditions, this is not possible for the trees of a selection forest which stand under dense cover.

The area-related volume productivity of trees which tolerate shade or semi-shade cannot be increased by way of deeper vertical staggering of the social strata, such as is achieved in a selection forest, and an opposite effect must on the contrary, be expected. The frequently held expectation of a superior volume efficiency with this form of stocking, in which the space of the stand is, in an ideal manner, "filled with an assimilating leaf volume", partly rests on hypotheses which are untenable from the point of view of natural science and partly on the mistaken practice of equating the efficiencies of single trees with the corresponding area-related production efficiencies.

The striking fall-off in efficiency among the oldest and largest selection forest trees is ascribable in part to disease, but also to age and hormonal disturbances, which cause a slackening of vitality—albeit less noticeably than in animals.

Crown size and productivity in natural mixed forests

Magin (1959) succeeded in discovering in the Bavarian Alps remnants of natural mixed forests (in positions where extraction is impossible) which had never been affected by human influences; he was able to analyse with the greatest care thirteen typical areas[1]; six of these lie in the Wettersteinwald in Partenkirchen forest at altitudes between 1200 and 1400 m. As a typical example of such an original natural fir–spruce–beech mixed forest we shall take a closer look at Partenkirchen area No. 1: Tables 43 and 44.

With a total crown volume of 79,500 m³, the stand approaches very closely the conditions in the Swiss selection forests. The outward impression of a general age-equality in the upper and middle storeys is deceptive. Magin in fact established the existence of three generations each differing in age by as much as 90 to 100 years. The stem-number distributions shown in Fig. 75 indicate certain peak frequencies. Remnants also exist of a largely extinct generation 350 years old. The figures of basal area and stocking per hectare give evidence of extremely dense stocking, similar to that of the selection forest at the Dürsrüti. Owing to the high altitude, increments are modest; the performance of spruce in terms of canopy-covered area is superior to that of fir. The curves of the mean canopied area efficiencies for both species in Fig. 75 resemble those of the Biglenwald in Fig. 70, except that the culminating points lie with considerably lower diameters.

With many parallels to the selection forest values in the Biglenwald, Table 44 shows *strikingly slender spruce crowns.* This indicates a spruce population containing a proportion of whips. Upon the higher levels of Partenkirchen, this proportion becomes so large that it must be taken into consideration when calculating the canopied-area efficiencies and when comparing these with crops on submountainous and foothill localities.

---

[1] Amongst other values in this area all heights were measured and all ground cover areas assessed by vertical projection of the crown peripheries. 54- to 300-year-old sample stems were felled and fully analysed.

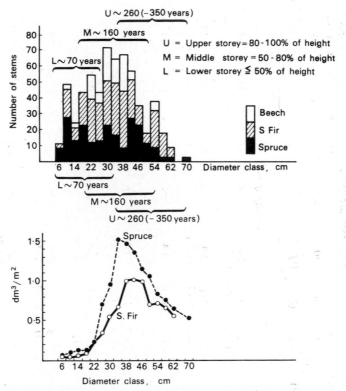

FIG. 75. Diameter distribution with age classification (top) and mean canopy area yields (bottom) for the mixed species sample plot 1 at Partenkirchen *(Magin)*.

Apart from the impediments to a good performance which are implied in the dimensions given for growing trees and crowns this example also distinctly displays *the influence of age on the area-related efficiency of trees in a natural forest.*

TABLE 43

THE MOST IMPORTANT CROWN DIMENSIONS AND CROP VALUES OF A NATURAL MIXED MONTANE STAND
AFTER DATA BY MAGIN (1959)

Area: Partenkirchen No.1. 1200 m above sea level. Slope 20° NW.
Dolomite, approximately 1900 mm annual rainfall.

Species	Crown		N	Crop values		P.M.A.I. of volume in the last 10 years	
	canopy area	volume		G	V	per ha	per m² can. area
	(m²)	(m³)		(m²)	(m³)	(m³)	(dm³/m²)
Fir	4,590	29,700	278	29·2	376	2·97	0·65
Spruce	2,510	22,100	227	21·1	255	2·31	0·92
Beech + Maple	3,290	27,700	98	8·7	127	0·84*	0·26
Total	10,390	79,500	603	59·0	758	6·12	0·59
In "conifer festmetres" =						6·51	0·63

* 1 "conifer festmetre" calculated as 1·23 m³.

TABLE 44

MEAN GROWTH MEASUREMENTS AND GROUND-COVER AREA EFFICIENCIES IN A NATURAL MONTANE MIXED STAND FROM DATA OF MAGIN

Wettersteinwald near Partenkirchen (area 1)

Silver fir

$d_{1.3}$ (cm)	h (m) (h/d)	Crown measurements l (m) (l/h)	b (m) (b/l)	c (m²)	s (m²)	v (m³)	s/v	Gr. cover area eff. (dm³/m²)
10	6·5 (65)	2·5 (0·38)	2·5 (1·00)	4·8	11	10	1·10	0·03
18	13·4 (74)	6·3 (0·47)	3·7 (0·59)	10·9	38	49	0·79	0·09
26	21·5 (83)	10·6 (0·49)	3·9 (0·37)	12·1	66	87	0·76	0·35
34	25·5 (75)	11·7 (0·46)	4·3 (0·37)	14·7	80	125	0·64	0·68
42	27·9 (66)	12·4 (0·45)	5·0 (0·40)	19·2	99	179	0·56	**1·02**
50	29·8 (60)	14·3 (0·48)	5·6 (0·39)	24·9	128	247	0·52	0·70
58	31·0 (53)	16·2 (0·52)	6·5 (0·40)	33·3	169	344	0·49	0·66

Norway spruce

$d_{1.3}$ (cm)	h (m) (h/d)	Crown measurements l (m) (l/h)	b (m) (b/l)	c (m²)	s (m²)	v (m³)	s/v	Gr. cover area eff. (dm³/m²)
10	9,2 (92)	4·0 (0·43)	2·1 (0·52)	3·4	14	10	1·40	0·09
18	15·9 (88)	7·4 (0·47)	2·9 (0·39)	6·6	34	35	0·97	0·13
26	22·0 (85)	12·0 (0·55)	3·4 (0·28)	9·2	65	67	0·97	0·71
34	26·7 (78)	13·8 (0·52)	3·5 (0·25)	9·6	77	85	0·91	**1·52**
42	29·8 (71)	15·1 (0·51)	4·3 (0·29)	14·4	103	143	0·72	1·36
50	31·6 (63)	17·1 (0·54)	5·0 (0·29)	19·0	136	200	0·68	1·06
58	32·4 (56)	19·0 (0·59)	5·5 (0·29)	23·6	166	255	0·65	0,76
66	32·8 (0·50)	21·6 (0·66)	6·2 (0·29)	30·7	197	336	0·59	0·66

III. THE PATTERN OF DEVELOPMENT AND GROWTH OF PURE STANDS IN DEPENDENCE ON AGE AND SITE QUALITY

1. Dependence on Age

As soon as we intend utilizing the timber which is produced in forests for commercial purposes, *the time factor* assumes special importance. Then the length of time taken to produce a certain quantity of timber in a given forest area is not a matter of indifference. The productive capacity of trees and stands, moreover, depends on their age. Only if the age is known does it become possible for us to form reliable assessments of performance in trees.

Having obtained in the last chapter a deeper understanding of the interplay between tree dimensions, social position, light conditions and growth performance we now come to discuss briefly the problem of age.

The age problem of our forest trees

In the growth of trees, as much indeed for the appropriate storage location of nutrient materials as for general volume increase, processes of hormonal control play a highly significant part; yet there are marked differences in this regard as compared with animals, more particularly highly developed mammals. With the latter, growth and certain vital processes are so closely linked with age that there seems little scope for the intrusion of other influences. But trees whose structural organization Mar:Møller has compared with that of coral stocks have in theory an almost unlimited potential span of life. Just as all life processes in plants are slower, less responsive, more passive than in the animal kingdom, so the control of their growth processes by hormones is probably also less intensive.

Rohmeder (1957) pointed out that the juvenile and mature forms of our forest trees are distinguishable by the habits of the leaves, and certain other well-marked characteristics. Thus, according to Shaffalitzky and Muckadell (1954, 1955) the youthful form of Common beech does not shed its leaves in the autumn and winter. In contrast to this, the mature form, which is accompanied by the full development of an annual ring, sheds its leaves in the autumn. Both the young and the mature forms may occur simultaneously on the same tree. Schaffalitzky has been able to prove with the help of scions obtained for grafting from an old beech (on the lower part of its stem it had epicormic shoots which kept their leaves throughout the winter) that the characterizing features of the two age phases are locally fixed within the tree. Rohmeder has, in an appropriate manner, transferred Passecker's doctrine of the age phases to our forest trees. In these we must, from the foot upwards, distinguish between a juvenile form, a transitional form and an *older though still fertile form*. This point has to be taken into careful consideration in the collection of scions for grafting (for breeding purposes) and cuttings (for vegetative purposes, clone propagation). The fact that, according to Passecker (1952), symptoms of degeneration and decline occur in vegetatively propagated clones as a result of shoots of a mature stage having been repeatedly used for propagation by grafting or cuttings, allows the conclusion that *genuine old age phenomena* occur even in trees.

We have already seen that the enlargement and elongation of the tree stem are accompanied by an increased energy consumption for transpiration and water conduction and that the enlargement of the crown is accompanied by an unfavourable change in its productive economy. This in itself surely points to a close and distinct connection between growth processes and increment rates on the one hand and age on the other. Again, there are dangers of disease, especially from fungi, which increase with the enlargement of the tree stem and the increasing proportion of dead cell complexes in the interior of the stem. This increasing danger from fungi[1] is probably responsible for the strikingly low maximum age-limit of Common beech, for example. Even oak, whose dead heart wood is protected against fungal attack by tannin impregnation, is subject to heart-rot between the ages of 300 and 400 years and with the first severe gale the ancient giant will break. This happens, even though its living cells evidently maintain full vitality.

As the growth process in trees depends so very much on their access to light and radiation—and accordingly upon the particular social position each occupies in stands of many and diverse structures—it is very important *to distinguish between the actual and the physiological age. The former may be estimated by a count of the annual rings, the latter may be recognized by the physiological age phase reached in each case.* As explained earlier, we *define* the physiological age phases, *juvenile* ("Aufschwung"); *prime* ("Vollkraft") and *decline* ("Abschwung") *with the help of the two points of inflection of the volume increment curve. This enables us to determine the level of performance appropriate to the age and later yield expectations—the productive trend—of trees, of even-aged stands and of separate tree storeys.* Unfortunately, a clear determination of the physiological or natural age phases is possible only by conducting a stem analysis upon trees which have reached a sufficiently mature age. Furthermore, it is necessary to take into consideration the fact that the volume increments of individual trees and the area-related performances of stands comprising these do not culminate at the same time; the culmination of the stand precedes that of the trees, as will presently (p. 157) be shown. But as a rule, it is possible to decide which of two stands is physiologically younger or older in the sense of our definition and also, to estimate fairly closely whether the culmination of the current volume increment has been reached, or has already been passed. The diagnosis can be made more trustworthy by careful inquiry into the relationship between the more easily observed height increment and the volume increment.

From the time when even-aged stands can grow up without being kept in check by shade cast from parent trees, frost effects, game browsing and similar retarding influences, we may expect their physiological and actual ages to take a parallel course. *Uninhibited growth processes as well as those subject to uniform disturbances follow the natural growth rhythm; they display a regular functional dependence on actual age.* In even-aged stands, therefore, the quantitative assessment of growth as well as the increment prognosis are simpler and easier to make.

With stands, working sections and forests which *are to be reconstituted, the actual age* becomes an *economically decisive* factor. *Time, and accordingly the actual age of trees and stands, determines with harsh severity not only the increment rates* and yields *for limited growth periods but also the average yield for the mean age of felling at any particular time.*

---

[1] Those species which reach an exceptionally advanced age are protected against attacks from fungi by specially effective fungicidal components; among these are, for example, *Sequoia sempervirens* and *Thuja plicata*.

Whilst the growth of crops and their productive performance over some unit of time thus depend on age, it is the site which determines the potential average level of performance. As *the growth process on a good site is quicker,* stands growing on poorer sites reach the same natural age phases at later actual ages. One might say that they follow in pursuit of the stands on better sites which have hurried ahead. Another advantage offered by *better sites,* especially if they have a satisfactory supply of water, is *an adequate nutrient potential* for a *larger number of trees* of given dimensions.

In the following passages we shall examine first the dependence on age and subsequently take a closer look at the dependence on site.

(a) The Development of Stem Numbers

The sequence in the numbers of stems reflects the continuous elimination process which takes place in the course of the life of a stand from young thicket to mature crop. All the time, trees which have been overcome in the struggle for light and living space and have arrived on the lowest stage of the social scale, are dying. Thus, the number of trees per hectare which in dense natural beech regeneration at the age of 3 months may amount to 7 million, is reduced by half within the first year of life. In this early process of elimination, harmful biotic as well as inanimate influences play the main part, whereas after the thicket stage has been reached it is mainly competition which causes the reduction of the number of trees. As shown in Table 45, on a good site, the number of trees is reduced from approximately 500,000 at the age of 10 years, to approximately 50,000 at the age of 20 years, and to approximately 1200 at the age of 60 years. At the age of 140 years, scarcely 200 old trees remain.

Similar conditions obtain for Norway spruce and Silver fir crops grown from dense natural regeneration. By contrast, planted crops have far smaller initial numbers of

TABLE 45

DEVELOPMENT OF STEM NUMBERS AND THE MEAN DIA-
METER OF COMMON BEECH STANDS ON A GOOD SITE
UNDER MODERATE THINNING

Age		Stem number	Mean diameter
Months	Years	per ha	(cm)
3	—	7,200,000	—
6	—	4,600,000	—
12	1	4,300,000	—
24	2	3,700,000	—
	5	1,750,000	—
	10	530,000	—
	15	160,000	—
	20	50,000	1·5
	30	4,600	7·4
	40	2,520	10·4
	60	1,205	17·8
	80	665	24·8
	100	405	32·0
	140	185	47·9

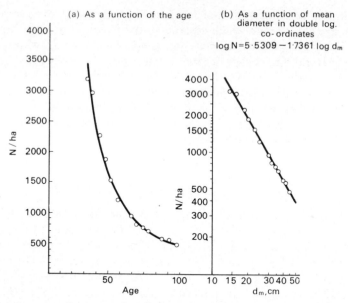

FIG. 76. Development of stem numbers in the spruce sample plot 2 (grade B) at Sachsenried.

stems; for example, with square spacing at 1·4 m, the number of stems per hectare amounts to 5100. Figure 76(a) shows the development of stem numbers (main crop after thinning in each case) of a planted stand of Norway spruce on a site of the best quality plotted over age. The curve at first drops very sharply and then gradually levels out. The evidently smooth outline of the curve suggests that it may be mathematically expressed, *in the manner demonstrated by* Reineke (1933) and G. Müller (1957a), by an approximate function of very versatile application: but instead of age as abscissa, we shall use the *diameter of the stem with the mean basal area* (d_m). The exponential function $x = bx^{-a}$ or $N = bd_m^{-a}$ when expressed in logarithmic form becomes:

$$\log N = k - a \log d_m.$$

As the relationship is now linear, the two parameters k and a can easily be calculated by the method of least squares. This is what happened in our example which is based on the original values of the experimental Norway spruce trial plot 2/II at Sachsenried. The curve, entered on double logarithmic graph paper, thus appears in Fig. 76(b) as a straight line with an obviously excellent fit to the series of points.[1]

As stem numbers are reduced more rapidly on better sites, stands of any given species, for example Norway spruce, have, age for age, higher numbers on the poorer sites. If, however, we look at the stem numbers *at equal mean heights* in each case, then the example of Table 46 shows that the *stands growing on poorer sites* (lower height quality class) *have lower stem numbers.*

In general, the light-demanding species, such as Scots pine and larch, have lower stem numbers than the shade-tolerant species for the same mean height of crop.

---

[1] Simultaneously determined with the relation $N = f(d_m)$ is the basal area per hectare (the product $N \times d_m^2 \pi/4$). This explains the reason for Reineke's initial use of the above function as "stand density index".

TABLE 46

STEM NUMBERS, BASAL AREAS AND MEAN DIAMETER OF NORWAY SPRUCE STANDS FROM WIEDEMANN'S
YIELD TABLES FOR MODERATE THINNING

(a) for the age of 60 years

Quality class	I	II	III
Age	60	60	60
Mean height h in metres	24·7	20·5	16·2
Stem number N	*1007*	*1276*	*1849*
Basal area G in square metres	41·9	38·9	34·6
Mean diameter d in centimetres	23·0	19·7	15·3

(b) for a given mean height of 25·0 m

Quality class	I	II	III
Age	61	77	100
Mean height h in metres	25·0	25·0	25·0
Stem number N	*982*	*842*	*729*
Basal area G in square metres	42·2	42·5	38·4
Mean diameter d in centimetres	23·4	25·4	25·9

(b) THE HEIGHT DEVELOPMENT

The manner in which height develops in tree crops can be studied, in the same way as diameter growth, only by using characteristic *mean values*. As the age of the stand increases, *these values must*, however, *represent not a constant number of trees but a steadily diminishing population on account of continuous casualties or removals.* Under a process of natural elimination, as equally by judicious low thinning treatment, it is mainly the *weakest individuals* that are weeded out in this way.

Only death from old age can remove by natural means the tall and stout ancient monarchs and for that reason it is usually preferable to remove trees of the larger diameters when carrying out a crown thinning.

We should also take note of the fact that, in addition to the normal and natural increases of height and diameter, a separate upward boost is imparted to the *mean values for the entire stand* every time there is a removal of smaller trees, so causing what may be termed a *"statistical shift"*. With skilled heavy low thinning, this upward shift secured by the mere process of reckoning can lead to a distinct increase of the mean height and to changes in the curve of mean height development upon age. The so-called *"top height"*, on the other hand, is hardly influenced at all by low thinning.

Mean height—top height

Figure 77 shows the respective development of mean and top height (in this case, of the 100 trees with the largest diameter per hectare) plotted over age for two experimental Norway spruce plots. Whereas the *development of top height*, in spite of different grades of thinning, follows almost the same trend, the *mean height* of the C-grade plot, *following heavy thinnings* at the ages of 52, 58 and 69 years, is raised in consequence of the calculation. Thus, whereas the difference between top height and mean height at the age of 69 years in the A-grade amounts to 2·10 m, in the C-grade plot it becomes reduced to only

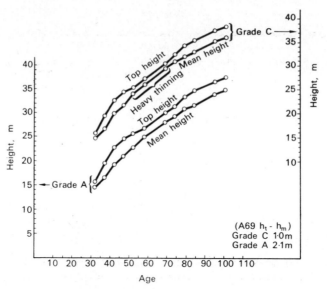

FIG. 77. Development of top height and mean height in spruce stands with light and heavy thinning. Experimental series, Sachsenried (2).

1·00 m! The distance between the two height values later increases again, because the C-area subsequently received only light thinning.

This lack of sensitivity to low thinning is an advantage of "top height". As such, the height of the mean basal area stem among the 100 trees with the largest diameter per hectare has been used in this instance, having been obtained from the height curve (see also Fig. 78 on p. 146). If the compass of such a *numerical top height* is extended so as to embrace the 200 largest diameter trees per hectare, then the frequency with which trees can interchange by moving into and out of this range must increase. Moreover, active thinning operations sometimes intrude upon this socially expanded sub-population. The feasibility of singling out a number of nearly identical trees occupying dominant positions and of observing their average growth behaviour over a long period is thus reduced. If, according to the suggestion of Weise (1880), the top height were defined as the average height of a 20 per cent fraction of the trees, counted from the largest end of the diameter distribution, the values thus obtained would be averages for a continuously decreasing sub-population. Finally, a "biological" top height might be envisaged as the average height of the predominant, or the predominant plus dominant, trees.

Such a biological top height was used by Zimmerle (1949), being expressed as the mean height of the predominant trees (h_t) and this is compared with the yield table mean height in the table below.

As the height and age of the stand increase, so the proportion of dominant and predominant trees in the total stem number of the stand also increases, especially with heavy thinning. Thus the smaller difference between top height and mean height is explained. Such small differences as the ones appearing in the above table are, however, only to be expected in stands which have undergone heavy thinning. More recent tables showing the relationship between top and mean heights, such as for example those recently published by Mitscherlich (1958), are based on extensive statistical data and similarly show relatively small differences. The use of such a table for the conversion of observed top

TABLE 47

MEAN HEIGHT AND TOP HEIGHT (MEAN HEIGHT OF THE PREDOMINANT TREES) IN NORWAY SPRUCE STANDS

| Mean height | Top height | Difference: top height − mean height | |
| | | absolute | as per cent of the |
(m)	(m)	(m)	mean height
8	10·6	+2·6	+33%
12	14·5	2·5	21%
16	18·3	2·3	15%
20	22·2	2·2	11%
24	26·1	2·1	9%
28	30·0	2·0	7%
32	33·9	1·9	6%
36	37·8	1·8	5%

heights to mean heights is, however, not free from misgivings, as the actual differences may vary in individual cases according to the severity of thinning and the method of establishing the crop and also deviate considerably from the calculated average values given. It would be an improvement if the top height in yield tables were stated in addition to the mean height.

The mean height of the stand can be defined and calculated in different ways. Arithmetical ("Reine") mean height values (Assmann, 1943) reckoned without consideration of the diameters of the measured trees are hardly likely to be used, as they necessitate a *knowledge of all height values* in the stand, or at least of a sample height distribution. "Qualified" *mean height values*, for which the diameters of the measured trees are stated or presumed, are in common employ. They are determined by reading off the (graphed) mean height corresponding to a stipulated diameter from the height curve. The mean heights in Fig. 78 have been found in this way. "Weighted" mean heights are also frequently used, for example, the so-called "Lorey" mean height formula (Lorey, 1878) which is weighted by the basal area of the corresponding diameter classes

$$h_L = \frac{g_1 h_1 + g_2 h_2 \dots}{g_1 + g_2 \dots}.$$

Many yield tables contain mean heights which have been calculated in this way.

Figure 78 gives an example of how we can locate and read off the "qualified" mean heights—in this case the mean and top heights of the crop corresponding to the calculated mean trees for the crop and the dominants respectively. It also shows at the same time the marked shift of position in the stand height curve (Assmann, 1936b, 1943) as the crop gets older. These height curves describe the relationship between height and diameter in even-aged stands. For comparison, Fig. 77 shows curves of height development upon age.

These last-named curves, which are intentionally shown without smoothing, owe their irregular increases—errors of measurement and calculation apart—mainly to climatic changes. Also playing a part are specific site characteristics which are effective in determining growth. For the *mean* height curves, these influences are largely masked by the effects of thinning (especially for C-grade thinnings). But the height/age curves of the yield tables, with which we must concern ourselves in detail in a later chapter (cf. p. 163, Fig. 88), are *smoothed and are thus free from disturbing climatic influences*. They reflect the average trend of the mean height of stands. Their characteristic S-shape resembles the *height curves* for individual trees.

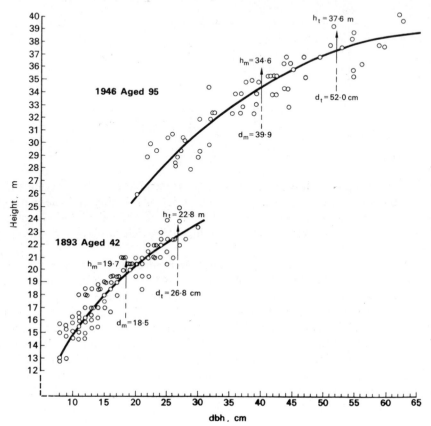

FIG. 78. Curves of height/diameter for the spruce experimental plot 2 (B-grade) Sachsenried at ages 42 and 95 years respectively.

The same applies to the *increment curves* which are deduced from the height curves. The height increment curves of stands, moreover, show us the familiar features which, one might say, characterize the properties of the different tree species, with early culmination and rapid decline for light demanding species, and late culmination and slower decline for shade-tolerant species.

Quality class, or to be more precise, height quality class as an expression of the quality of site, shows itself in the fact that, on better sites there is an earlier acceleration of growth, continuing to rise steeply with increasing annual height increments to a peak value before falling off. Curves of total height and of height increment for the different quality classes of a species furnish sheaves of similar curves (cf. Fig. 19(a), (b) on p. 45 and Fig. 88 on p. 163).

(c) PROGRESS OF DIAMETER GROWTH

Very similar conditions and trends are found in the development of the *mean diameter* of stands. The representative average chosen in all cases is *not the arithmetic mean of the diameters of the individual trees but the diameter of the mean basal area stem*,[1] i.e. the arithmetic mean of the breast height sectional areas, involving the mean of the squares of the diameters. This mean basal area stem is commonly preferred because in even-aged and uniform stands its diameter corresponds approximately to that of the stem with the mean volume (Gehrhardt, 1901).

The development of the mean diameter of a crop is, to a far greater extent than height development, dependent *on stem numbers and therefore on the greater or smaller growing space available to the trees.* Heavy thinning provides not only a general stimulus to the diameter increment, but at the same time occasions a considerable "statistical shift" in the mean diameter. This is demonstrated by the growth curve of the mean basal area stem in Fig. 79. The diameters of the mean stem are, in each case, plotted before and after thinning. The perpendicular distance between the two values shows the "jump" imparted to the mean diameter in consequence of the removal of many small trees in the

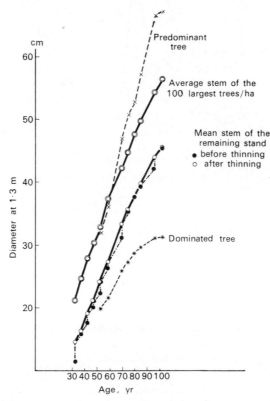

FIG. 79. Diameter growth curves of average stems and individual trees in trial plot 2 (grade C) at Sachsenried.

$$1\frac{G}{N} = g_m = d_m^2 \frac{\pi}{4}.$$

thinnings. The extent of this shift is especially large for the first thinning at the age of 32 years, and for the heavy thinning at the age of 69. No thinning took place at the age of 79; the number of stems remained constant and so there was no upward displacement. The values for diameter read off at the beginning and the end of the growing period 74–79 years show the increase in the mean value of the very same trees.

How widely *diameter growth differs between the different social strata* is demonstrated in Fig. 79 by the diameter curves of a predominant and a dominated tree as well as the mean diameter of the 100 largest trees per hectare.

The distinction between the genuine increment of the same trees and an apparent shift because of calculation becomes clear in Fig. 80. The points in curve (c) represent the differences between the mean diameters at the beginning and end of the growing period for the same number of stems, i.e. before the extraction of trees by thinning at the end of the period. Curve (b) links the mean diameters after each thinning. The difference between the two is the shift due to calculation. The increment values of the mean of the 100 trees with the largest diameter (curve (c)) are in several instances greater than the increments of the mean stem even when including the said shift.

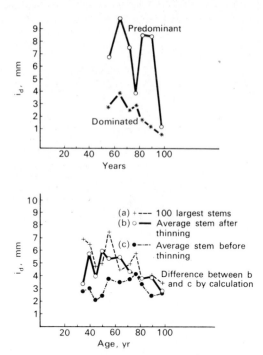

FIG. 80. Diameter increment curves for Fig. 79.

The relationship between mean diameter (d_m) and age (A) can, in stands which have undergone the same uniform thinning treatment, be described by a simple linear function, as shown in Fig. 81 for plot B of the trial series No. 2 at Sachsenried. We have already seen earlier, that in a similar case log N is a linear function of log d_m (p. 142). As shown by G. Müller (1957), log N is also nearly a linear function of the logarithm of the *volume of the mean stem* (v_m). Thus, on the basis of twelve remeasurements of the trial plot 2/II at Sachsenried, the following parameters for the corresponding fitted straight lines were

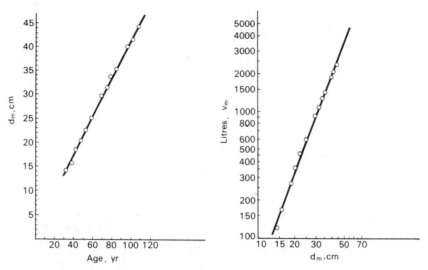

FIG. 81 *(left)*. Diameter of the tree of mean basal area as a function of age. Sachsenried 2 (grade B).

FIG. 82 *(right)*. Logarithm of the mean stem volume as a function of the logarithm of the mean diameter. Sachsenried 2 (grade B).

calculated by the method of least squares:

$$\log N = k - a \log d_m \quad \log N = 5{\cdot}53094 - 1{\cdot}7361 \log d_m \tag{1}$$

$$\log N = k - a \log v_m \quad \log N = 4{\cdot}95275 - 0{\cdot}6711 \log v_m. \tag{2}$$

The combination of the two equations provides the following result:

$$\log v_m = 2{\cdot}5869 \log d_m - 0{\cdot}86156 \quad (v_m \text{ in litres for } d_m \text{ in centimetres}). \tag{3}$$

In Fig. 82, this function is shown as a straight line on double logarithmic graph paper, and the observed values show a good fit. Together with the equation

$$d_m = 0{\cdot}402 \, A + 1{\cdot}50 \tag{4}$$

and equation (1), the development of the standing crop of this trial plot—in the way it would take place *with consistent thinning* and without climatic influences or other disturbances—is thereby clearly determined for any chosen age.[1] The value of such functions for the construction of yield tables is obvious.

(d) BASAL AREA AND VOLUME INCREMENT

The basal area of the stand is the sum of all the breast-height sectional areas of the individual trees. It can also be considered as product of the number of stems and the basal area of the mean stem. In symbols, $G = N \times g_m$, in which case $g_m = G/N$.

As soon as the trees of a stand have reached the conventional height of measurement of 1·30 m at which the basal area is determined by caliper measurements the basal area of the stand at first increases very rapidly, but afterwards more slowly. In the absence

[1] The attempt by G. Müller to calculate the current increment by integration of the stem number – volume function (equation (2)) is based on incorrect hypotheses and results in values which deviate markedly from reality.

of thinning, the basal area of the stand goes on increasing with age, as it does if stands are thinned *to a uniform degree*. In contrast to this, a number of yield tables, which foresters like to use as models for the average pattern of growth, portray *arbitrary distortions of natural development*.

For example, for a *lightly* thinned experimental plot of *Common beech* the basal area of the stand on a good site increases as follows:

Age	Basal area of stand (true)	According to the Y.T. by Wiedemann for *moderate* thinning	in per cent of the true basal area of the stand
	(m²)	(m²)	
60	32	28	88%
100	40	32	80%
140	45	33	78%

The yield table which has been used for comparison evidently presupposes that the severity of thinning increases with the age. Therefore, by the use of this yield table, the stocking at greater ages of the stands is systematically overestimated.

The following example concerns the experimental *Norway spruce* plot No. 2/I at Sachsenried which was also *lightly* thinned:

Age	Basal area of stand (true)	According to the Y.T. of Vanselow (1951) (*moderate* thinning)	in per cent of the true basal area of the stand
	(m²)	(m²)	
40	60	49	82%
70	72	59	82%
100	76	64	84%

This table corresponds more closely to the natural development and shows an almost uniform degree of thinning.

The *basal area increment curve* culminates so early in the life of the stand that yield tables usually show only the declining branch of the curve. Where, for example, a yield table begins at an age of 30 years, the point of culmination of the basal area increment curve will have already been passed.

For stands attaining a mean height of 28 m at an age of 100 years, we find in the yield tables of Wiedemann (moderate thinning) the following basal area increments:

Tree species	Age	Basal area increment (m²)	Age	Basal area increment (m²)
Norway spruce	30	1·4	120	0·4
Common beech	30	1·1	120	0·5
Scots pine	30	1·3	120	0·3
Larch	25	0·8	120	0·2
(*Schober*)				

The differences between the basal area increment of Common beech at the age of 100 years for the different height quality classes are strikingly small, namely:

Height quality class I	0·53 m²
Height quality class II	0·50 m²
Height quality class III	0·45 m²
Height quality class IV	0·44 m².

The greater differences between the corresponding volume increments result from differences in height or form height, which are larger for the better height quality classes.

Relationships between basal area and volume increment; the form-height

The volume increment results from the combined effects of basal area and height increments in addition to changes in the form factor. A formula which reflects the changes of all components and their relative contribution to the volume increment would be complex and difficult to interpret (Wiedemann, 1931). The product of height and form factor, the so-called form-height, may be conceived geometrically as the height of a cylinder whose volume is identical to the volume of the tree. If we define the basal area increment as i_G, the basal area of the tree or stand at the beginning of the increment period as G_a, the form-height at the end of the increment period as fh_e and the form-height increment as i_{fh}, then the volume increment i_V may be shown by the simple formula (Assmann, 1950)

$$i_V = i_G \times fh_e + i_{fh} \times G_a.$$

Decisive for the volume increment therefore, apart from the basal area increment, are the form-height at the end of the increment period, the form-height increment, and the basal area at the beginning of the increment period. Whilst the height increment decreases regularly with age for all tree species, the mean form factor for the stand (breast-height form-factor for wood over 7 cm in diameter) increases in the broad-leaved species beech and oak. In coniferous trees, on the other hand, it decreases noticeably from a maximum which is reached at mean heights of approximately 15–20 m. The form-height of the stand, i.e. the product of height and form factor, therefore, in beech and oak continues to increase with age, even if the height growth ceases. In spruce, on the other hand, the form-height may, at greater ages, remain constant, in fact, in extreme cases of tall trees with a strongly developed butt swell, the form-height may even drop (cf. p. 167 and Fig. 91). This would result in the second term of our formula becoming negative. The relationships between height, form-height and form-height increment are demonstrated in Table 48. The considerable drop of the form factor for spruce is due to the increased relative basal areas at the fixed measurement height of 1·30 m, which in spruce, because of its inclination to develop marked butt-swell with increasing height of the tree, reach considerable dimensions. Common beech however, shows this tendency, because of the different density of its timber, to a far lesser degree. And furthermore, it develops with increasing age considerable quantities of wood of "timber" dimensions in the shape of large branches in the crown, so that the numerator in the equation $f = v/(g \times h)$ increases more than the denominator.

TABLE 48

DEVELOPMENT OF THE FORM-HEIGHT OF TIMBER OVER 7 CM IN DIAMETER IN BEECH AND SPRUCE STANDS, ACCORDING TO THE YIELD TABLES OF WIEDEMANN (MODERATE THINNING), HEIGHT QUALITY CLASS II

| Age | Beech | | | | Spruce | | | |
	h (m)	wood > 7 cm dia.	fh (m)	i_{fh}	h (m)	wood > 7 cm dia.	fh (m)	i_{fh}
40	12·3	0·378	4·66		12·8	0·466	5·96	
				4·66				4·58
60	18·6	0·457	8·50		20·5	0·514	10·54	
				3·04				2·13
80	23·8	0·486	11·54		25·6	0·495	12·67	
				2·18				1·16
100	27·7	0·496	13·72		29·3	0·472	13·83	
				1·78				0·90
120	30·8	0·503	15·50		32·1	0·459	14·73	

The volume increment

Table 49 shows the observed results so far in the experimental Norway spruce plot 2/II at Sachsenried under moderate thinning. As may be seen, the total crop volume at a given age is calculated as the sum of the volumes of all thinnings to date, plus the standing volume. If we calculate the *difference between the total crop volumes* for two ages of the stand and divide it by the difference between the ages, the result is the mean annual increment for that period, the so-called *current annual increment* (c.a.i.).[1] If we again divide the total crop volume by the corresponding age, we obtain the *mean annual increment* (m.a.i.) for that age.

In Fig. 83 the total crop volumes and the standing volumes are plotted against age. Whereas the former show a smooth progress and therefore can easily be fitted by a curve, the latter fluctuate considerably owing to the varying severity of thinning incursions employed on different occasions. The difference between the two quantities in each case is the total volume of thinnings to date.

In Fig. 84 the current annual increment and the mean annual increment for the stand are plotted. *Considerable fluctuations* of the c.a.i. are found, which are not only due to climatic effects but also to unavoidable measurement and calculation errors. By comparison, the observed m.a.i.'s show considerably smaller fluctuations. Fitting of the *curve for current annual increment* with the help of the curve for total crop volume provides the familiar and typical curve which culminates approximately at the age of 43 years and has its period of greatest vigour between the ages of 35–50 years. The curve for mean annual increment, with its considerably more level course, cuts the curve for current annual increment at the age of 74 years, when the m.a.i. reaches its maximum value of 18·9 solid m³ of stemwood. The mathematical relationship between the c.a.i. and the m.a.i. have already been discussed on page 81.

---

[1] Strictly, a "perodic annual increment", but when computed over a short period is usually taken as synonymous with "current annual increment" for a specific year. (Br. Comm. Forest Terminology.)—Ed.

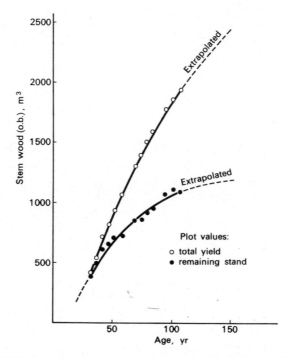

FIG. 83. Total volume yield and volume of the remaining stand plotted over age. Sachsenried 2 (grade B).

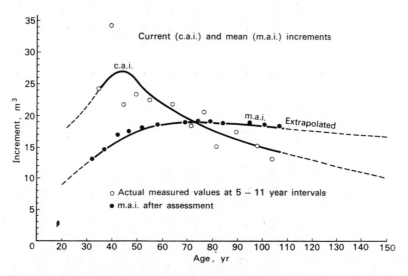

FIG. 84. Current and mean annual volume increment in experimental plot Sachsenried 2 (grade B).

TABLE 49

PRINCIPAL RESULTS SO FAR OBTAINED FROM THE EXPERIMENTAL NORWAY SPRUCE PLOT 2/II AT SACHSENRIED (MODERATE THINNING)

Assessment year	age (yrs)	Main crop d_m (cm)	h_m (m)	f O.	top height (m)	N	G (m²)	V (m³)	Thinnings d_m (cm)	h_m (m)	N	G (m²)	V (m³)	Total thinnings G (m²)	V (m³)	Inter med. yields per cent	Mean basal area for obs. period	Total production G (m²)	V (m³)	Current annual incr. G (m²)	V (m³)	Mean increment for age V (m³)
1883(S)	*32*	14·2	14·8	522	15·9	3196	50·65	391·5	6·3	8·0	2056	6·30	27·2	6·30	27·2	6		56·95	420·3			*13·1*
1888(S)	37	15·7	16·8	517	19·2	3972	57·53	499·7	10·4	13·9	224	1·89	13·9	8·19	41·1	8	55·0	65·72	540·8	1·754	24·1	14·6
1893(S)	42	18·5	19·7	508	22·8	2256	60·80	608·6	11·6	15·6	716	7·56	62·3	15·75	103·4	15	62·9	76·55	712·0	2·166	34·2	17·0
1898(S)	47	20·4	21·7	500	24·5	1868	60·91	660·9	13·9	18·3	388	5·88	56·2	21·63	159·6	20	63·8	82·54	820·5	1·198	21·7	17·4
1902(A)	*52*	22·5	23·5	493	25·9	1532	60·86	705·4	16·1	20·5	336	6·82	72·2	28·45	231·8	25	64·3	89·31	937·2	1·354	23·3	*18·0*
1908(A)	58	25·0	25·5	482	27·1	1212	59·79	734·9	19·0	23·2	320	9·00	105·7	37·45	337·5	31	64·8	97·24	1072·4	1·322	22·5	18·5
1919(A)	69	29·6	28·8	462	30·7	940	64·45	857·6	20·7	24·7	272	9·22	113·9	46·67	451·4	34	66·7	111·12	1309·0	1·262	21·5	19·0
1925(A)	74	31·5	30·1	453	32·5	816	63·51	866·0	25·2	28·3	124	6·13	83·6	52·80	535·0	38	69·0	116·31	1401·0	1·038	18·4	18·9
1929(A)	*79*	33·7	31·4	444	34·1	748	66·38	925·5	24·7	27·9	68	3·20	43·2	56·0	578·2	38	66·5	122·38	1503·7	1·214	20·5	*19·0*
1934(A)	84	35·3	32·3	439	35·6	696	68·22	967·4	26·4	29·0	52	3·05	42·2	59·05	620·4	39	68·6	127·27	1587·8	0·978	15·0	18·8
1946(S)	95	39·9	34·6	428	37·6	572	71·66	1061·3	26·7	29·3	124	6·94	96·6	65·99	717·0	40	73·4	137·65	1778·3	0·944	17·3	18·7
1951(A)	101	41·5	35·3	425	38·6	552	74·83	1122·5	35·9	33·6	20	2·02	29·7	68·01	746·7	40	74·2	142·84	1869·2	0·865	15·1	18·4
1957(A)	*107*	44·1	36·7	418	39·6	472	71·91	1100·2	32·8	33·1	80	6·75	101·0	74·76	847·7	43	76·7	146·67	1947·9	0·638	13·1	*18·2*

Increment values for long observation periods

	Mean basal area for obs. period	Current annual incr. G (m²)	V (m³)
Age 32—52	61·5	1·618	25·8
Age 52—79	66·3	1·225	21·0
Age 79—107	73·4	0·868	15·9
Age 32—107 *Total observation period*	67·7	1·196	20·4

(S) in col. 1 denotes Spring.
(A) in col. 1 denotes Autumn.

Culmination and decline of the mean annual increment of stands

The shape of the curve for mean annual increment exerts a controlling influence upon the approximate age at which a stand achieves its maximum average rate of volume production. No one would be foolish enough to harvest a stand at the time of the culmination of the c.a.i. If one's object were the highest possible average volume yield one would much rather wait for the culmination of the m.a.i. The slow decline of the m.a.i. beyond the point of culmination makes it appear unnecessary to be in too much of a hurry, especially as the mean value increment of a stand, as rule, culminates much later than the mean volume increment. Be that as it may, *this progressive falling off of the mean increment is of the greatest importance for considerations of management.*

From the yield tables of Wiedemann and Schober, we can take the following values for the age and amount of the maximum m.a.i. for different species (Table 50).

TABLE 50

CULMINATION OF THE MEAN ANNUAL INCREMENT IN DIFFERENT TREE SPECIES AND QUALITY CLASSES ACCORDING TO THE YIELD TABLES OF WIEDEMANN/SCHOBER

	Scots pine		Larch		Common beech		Norway spruce	
Quality class	I	III	I	III	I	III	I	III
Age at culmination	72	90	55	68	140	?	90	120
m.a.i.$_{max}$	8·1	4·7	9·5	5·1	8·9	?	12·2	7·6
m.a.i.$_{100}$	7·8	4·6	8·5	4·8	8·3	5·1	12·2	7·5
m.a.i.$_{140}$	7·0	4·4	7·2	4·5	8·9	5·6	—	—

As may be seen, the light-demanding species Scots pine and larch reached their culmination of the mean increment considerably earlier than the shade-tolerant beech and the semi-shade-tolerant Norway spruce. Also, the m.a.i. in light-demanding species drops faster after culmination than in the shade-tolerant species, so that their earlier large dimensions are reached at the expense of some considerable loss in long-term performance.

The total crop volume and corresponding mean annual increment up to the age of 150 years has been carefully extrapolated for the experimental area 2/II at Sachsenried (cf. Fig. 83). It is estimated that the m.a.i. which had dropped from 18·9 m³ at the age of 74 to 18·1 m³ at the age of 107 years (measured values) will, *by the age of 150 years, have dropped to 16·4 m³.* This clear trend, which may be found in all stands under observation over a sufficiently long period of time, is evident in all well-constructed yield tables.

The course of the mean annual increment for a crop anticipates the mean annual increments of individual trees

The decline of the mean annual increment of stands is particularly noteworthy because it *begins at a considerably earlier age than in the individual trees which constitute the stand.* It has already been pointed out, on p. 81, that only two of the thirty Norway spruce from high mountain sites which were analysed by v. Guttenberg reached the culmination of their mean annual increment, although they included some trees of up to 300 years old from natural stands. Nevertheless, we find in the yield tables which v. Guttenberg constructed from his measurements upon these sample stems and from numerous sample plot data, that the mean annual increments of stands culminated relatively early. Thus, in the general yield table for Norway spruce in high montane sites, quality class I culminates with 13·1 m³ at the age of 90 years and in the local yield table for Paneveggio, "best-quality site", with 8·9 m³ at the age of 120–130 years. In the first case, the m.a.i. at the age of 150 years drops to 11·2 m³ and, in the second case, at the age of 200 years to 8·0 m³.

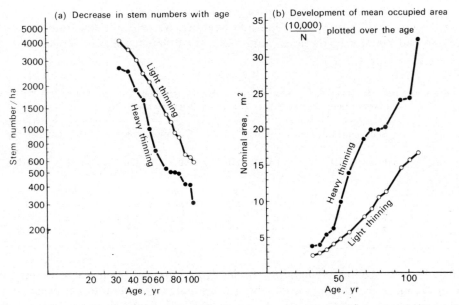

FIG. 85. Development of the stem numbers and mean area occupied, plotted over age, with light and heavy thinning. Experimental plot, series (2) at Sachsenried.

The explanation why the mean and current annual increments of a crop culminate earlier than they do for individual trees in that crop is to be sought in the decrease of stem numbers with age. As stem numbers (N) decrease, the average space available per tree (s) grows in the ratio of s = 10,000/N. Figure 85 shows this diminution of stem numbers along with age in a double logarithmic scale of coordinates; the graph alongside shows the simultaneous increase in the average available space per tree for the two research plots 2/I and 2/III of Sachsenried (light and heavy thinnings respectively). From this it may be seen that under a light thinning regime the average space per tree increases from 3 m² at age 40 years to 6 m² at 60 years, i.e. a two-fold increase; and under heavy thinning, the average space increases from 5 to 15 m², which is a three-fold increase. It would follow therefore, that if the current increments of individual trees in Plot I, for example, were to culminate no earlier than about 60 years of age, the *average volume production when considered in relation to available growing space* must culminate appreciably sooner, owing to the progressively marked increase with time of the space appropriated by each tree. As there is a functional relationship between the mean annual increment and the current annual increment, the culmination of the former for the entire crop must again forestall those for individual trees which are not referred to growing space.

The diagram further shows that this anticipatory interval alike for c.a.i. and m.a.i. must be further increased by heavy thinning. In fact, the current and mean increments of stands culminate earlier with heavy thinning than with light thinning.

A conclusive proof of the difference of the culmination of the area-related volume increment of individual trees is given in the following example. Five dominant or predominant sample stems of Norway spruce from each of four 80–90-year-old stands were analysed; the height of these trees was about the same. The mean annual volume incre-

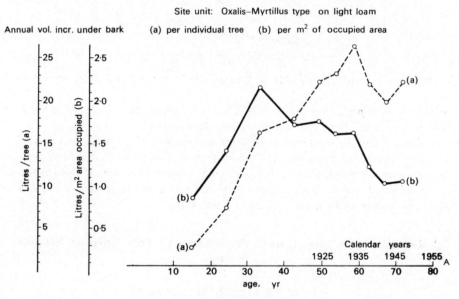

FIG. 86. Progress of single tree increment and the increment per unit area of occupied ground. Details in the text.

ments (without bark) for 5- or 10-year increment periods for one of these sample stem groups are plotted in Fig. 86 by means of curve (a) over the period means. We recognize a *distinct culmination of the current volume increment at the age of 60–65 years.*[1] In Fig. 87 the simultaneous development of the crown width and crown projection[2] is entered against the height development of these sample stems. As might have been expected, the crown projections ($\pi/4 \cdot b^2$) increase progressively with increasing tree heights and ages. For the calculation of the area-related growth-performance, square stand areas (length of side = crown width; $f_q = b^2$) were assumed. Curve (b) in Fig. 86 thus shows

---

[1] The rise of the curve during the last five years (1950–5) is due to favourable climatic conditions.

[2] The relation crown width/tree height, i.e. the degree of spread (p. 112), is based on averages, supported by Burger's data for high forest spruce (dominant trees). The average degree of spread, which was determined graphically, decreases from 0·33 in 5-metre-high spruce trees to 0·16 at a height of 22 m, after which it remains constant up to approximately 30 metres. A rising trend is recognizable for greater heights. In our example the value for b/h from the age of 50 years is assumed equal to 0·16.

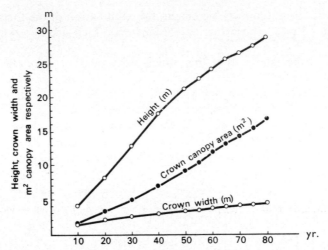

FIG. 87. Development of height, crown width and canopy area for five analysed spruce trees (mean values).

the volume increment per unit of area. This culminates approximately at the age of 35 years, i.e. 25–30 years earlier than the individual tree increments.[1]

The regular decrease of the mean increments and mean yields per hectare, which sets in from a certain age when the crop has reached certain average dimensions, applies not only for pure even-aged stands and their working sections, but *for all types of stand*[2] *and so, also for selection forests*. This follows from the trend of the ground cover efficiencies (p. 133) but is further supported in Section E (p. 461).

2. Dependence on Site: Growth Performance of Tree Crops in Relation to Site

(a) THE PROBLEM OF SITE QUALITY

The considerable uncertainties surrounding the recognition of productivity on the basis of soil characteristics and climate alone make it necessary to include the total plant yield for the assessment of site quality. In agriculture, which produces annual and easily measurable yields, this is not difficult. The agricultural site quality classification system can be based on yield statistics for a large number of years. Nevertheless, a whole series of separate criteria based on edaphic and economic considerations are also used in agriculture. In contrast, forest site qualities have been assessed up to the present solely on standing crop yields which can be readily sized up, while soil properties have been neglected, to say the least, if not even completely overlooked (Magin, 1958).

While the practice was to thin only lightly and to remove at the most only one-third of the total crop volume, partly as thinnings and partly by way of unserviceable, or

---

[1] Incidentally, the increments of this curve harmonize well with the current increments in the site table for spruce stands of the *Oxalis myrtillus* type on p. 185. Here, the c.a.i. culminates at the age of 35–40 years with 18·0 m³ and drops at the age of 75–80 years to 10·8 m³. If the increment values in litres per square metre of curve (b) are multiplied by 10, the result shows the amount in cubic metres per hectare. If curve (b) were fitted, one would obtain corresponding increments per hectare.

[2] Knowledge and consideration of these relationships would have saved German forestry the ridiculous proclamation of "Einzelbaumwirtschaft" (individual tree management) in the middle of the thirties.

decayed trees, the standing volume of stands provided an adequate gauge of site quality. However, with the introduction of heavier thinning, the standing timber per hectare could be so markedly reduced that a crop of a given age standing on a good productive site might show lower standing volume than one on a poorer site. In the search for a suitable and less susceptible measure of site quality the *mean height of the stand, achieved at a given age*, offered itself.

Whereas Carl Heyer (1845) had stressed the need for yield studies to be directed not exclusively towards the size of natural yields, but towards "the investigation and gauging of site quality factors", Franz v. Baur (1881) saw in the mean height of the stand the "most exact and only accurate guide not only to the evaluation of a reasonably stocked and normally-grown stand but also its quality class". This inadequate and partial view of v. Baur's against which Robert Hartig ventured a warning note (1892), was the foundation for the combined project drawn up by the forest research institutes between 1874 and 1880 for the construction of yield tables. It has since been maintained so successfully that, today, an almost subconscious *identification of height quality class with a definite total crop yield* predominates. This is demonstrated by the widespread but by no means justified synonymous use of the terms "height quality class" and "yield class" (Assmann, 1959a).

In accepting this thesis of v. Baur's we find it easy to construct yield tables which enable estimates of the present and future yields of forest stands to be made, if their age and mean height are known. To do this, we must measure the crop components of a sufficient number of stands of different ages and on sites of different productivities. If then the mean heights are plotted over the corresponding ages, a scatter diagram is obtained which narrows towards the origin of the co-ordinate system and with increasing age spreads out like a fan. The broad outline of the scatter is defined, according to v. Baur, between a lower and an upper limiting curve and the intervening space is then divided into *five bands* splaying out from the origin, these being separated by intermediate curves drawn so as to be equi-distant at the upper age of 100 or 120 years and so shaped that the widths of the bands are almost proportional with the age. The term "band method" thus becomes self-explanatory. *The mean curves of these five bands then define the mean heights for given ages whereby five height quality classes are determined.* All stands which at a given age are of a height indicated by such a mean curve, are considered as belonging to this height quality class. Figure 88 provides an illustration. Stands of this kind are expected to:

1. continue the development of their mean height corresponding to the particular quality class curve (height/age curve),
2. supply approximately equal yields in total crop volume at determined ages.

Stands whose chief components of growth show equal or at least similar development in relation to age can be considered as belonging to a single *growth series*. In the case of stands which have been measured up only once, it is clearly impossible to decide with any confidence whether or not they belong to a particular growth series having the corresponding development of mean height along with age. To be able to do this beyond doubt the growth pattern must have been observed over a long period, at least 50 years, in fact, strictly speaking, throughout the whole life-cycle.

Information about the growth development of stands which hitherto have been measured up only once may be obtained by an analysis of sample trees in order to discover whether the separate sections of the height development curve thus obtained can be joined up successfully. Such a method, in which *the development of the growth components of analysed mean stems is used as an indicator of the homogeneity of sample stands of different ages which have been surveyed once only*, is known as the *"indicator method"*. The problem attached to this method lies in the *difference between the development of statistical stand averages and of actual sample trees* which we have already noted. The omission to take this circumstance into account, as for example by Huber (1824), has brought it some measure of discredit, albeit with small justification. In 1868 Robert Hartig constructed by this means some yield tables for Norway spruce in the Harz mountains which were, on the whole, quite applicable. These were the outcome of Hartig's judicious selection of sample crops, according careful consideration to site conditions and methods of establishment. Hartig also analysed the mean stems of five separate ("numerical") diameter classes, giving them equal basal areas; the mean stem of the largest diameter class, representing a number of very closely similar trees, gave the development of the predominants.

The insertion of figures of *top height* alongside mean height in the construction of new yield tables, and equally for verifying existing tables, suggests itself as a useful improvement. For conifers which are commonly subjected to low thinnings, the "numerical top height" corresponding to the 100 largest diameter trees per hectare, as already recommended, p. 144, appears particularly suitable. In the course of making analyses of sample trees in the top-height category it is possible at any time to check whether the past height development of actual stands corresponds with that assumed by any particular yield table which contains data of top height for given ages.

The all-important question approaching us now is: can we expect stands reaching the same mean heights, or top heights, at a certain age always to have the same total crop yields?

The basic relations

The production of a tree crop on an area of one hectare at a definite age A, consists of:

the sum of the volumes of the trees still standing at a given age $= \Sigma v_s$
and of the trees which by that time have been removed, either by
natural means or by thinning $= \Sigma v_t$

Σv_s can in all stands be assessed by measurements. The exact value of Σv_t on the other hand is known only if all trees which have been extracted up to age A have been recorded and measured, which, as a rule, is the case only in permanent sample plots. Knowledge of these two magnitudes, however, is absolutely essential if we wish to state the total crop production between two definite epochs of time. If the simplified definition of the sum of the two magnitudes is $\Sigma v = \Sigma v_s + \Sigma v_t = V$ then this represents the familiar "total crop yield to date".

If, after observing this magnitude at suitable intervals, we succeed, by calculation of the curve parameters or by graphical curve fitting, in deducing the "final relation"

$$V = \Sigma v = f(A)$$

then, by taking the difference between two total crop yields, we can state the increment for any intervening period of years:

$$\text{p.m.a.i.} \quad (\text{or "c.a.i."}) = \frac{\Delta V}{\Delta A}.$$

Furthermore, we can calculate the corresponding average increment m.a.i. $= \dfrac{V}{A} = \Sigma v / A$ for any chosen age. This magnitude can be determined for all stands of a given age in which the eliminated trees have been measured. If that is not the case, or if we wish to save ourselves the work of measuring the standing crop Σv_s then we must form an estimate of the total crop yield.

Our common yield tables facilitate this problem by means of two relations which Assmann (1949b) called "basic relations I and II".

I. It is assumed that the stands which are to be estimated undergo a *definite mean height development as function of the age*. If the mean height is defined as h_m, then each of the already named five quality classes are based on the relation

$$\boxed{h_m = f(A)}$$

This basic relation might also be called a "classifying relation", because it uses the two magnitudes height and age for arranging into a scheme of quality classes.

II. It is assumed that *a given mean height* is accompanied by a *definite total crop yield Σv*:

$$\boxed{\Sigma v_{\text{.}} = f(h_m)}$$

This basic relation can also be called an "auxiliary relation". If this basic relation exists, without regard to the age at which the particular mean height is reached, then one such relation, or its corresponding representation as a curve, is sufficient. Otherwise, a separate "auxiliary relation" must be used as a basis for each "quality class". With the help of the two basic relations, it is then possible to deduce the "final relation" for which we have been searching:

$$\boxed{\Sigma v = f(A)}$$

We can then state the corresponding total crop yield for every stand of which the age and mean height are known. Thereby the current increments for any chosen age periods and the mean increments for all ages are determined, *provided that the particular stand follows the yield table relationship.*

The so-called Eichhorn's rule

Eichhorn (1904) found that in stands of Silver fir, "a given mean height of stand is matched by the same volume in all site classes". This law *was extended* by Gehrhardt (1909) to spruce and pine, implying *that the total crop yield was also without exception a function of the mean height*. Later, he corrected this statement in favour of a differentiation by yield classes. This would mean that his "extension of the Eichhorn law" is valid only for defined height quality classes, i.e. for mean heights which are achieved at a certain age. We shall see later that, even with this reservation, it is still possible for *site-dependent differences to occur in the total crop yields.*

However, in so far as the relationships already discussed may be assumed to be approximately valid for a range of different stands and sites, the *use of such a standard "basic*

TABLE 51

EXTRACT FROM THE NORWAY SPRUCE YIELD TABLE OF GEHRHARDT, 1921. MODERATE THINNING

Age	Stem number	Main crop Basal area	Mean height	diam.	Stem wood vol.	Thinnings vol.	accum. vol.	Total stem-wood	Increment c.a.i.	m.a.i.	Age
(yrs.)		(m²)	(m)	(cm)	(m³)	(m³)	(m³)	(m³)	(m³)	(m³)	(yr.)
Height quality class I											
10	–	8·2	2·4	–	12	–	–	12	–	1·2	10
						7			6·9		
20	–	18·2	6·5	6·7	74		7	81		4·0	20
						30			13·9		
30	2880	27·9	11·3	11·1	183		37	220		7·3	30
						58			18·3		
40	1820	35·9	16·1	15·8	308		95	403		10·1	40
						75			**20·2**		
50	1255	42·0	20·5	20·7	435		170	605		12·1	50
						84			20·1		
60	905	46·4	24·3	25·5	552		254	806		13·4	60
						84			18·5		
70	705	50·0	27·4	30·1	653		338	991		14·2	70
						75			16·2		
80	575	52·7	30·0	34·1	740		413	1153		**14·4**	80
						65			13·5		
90	490	54·8	32·0	37·6	810		478	1288		14·3	90
						55			11·1		
100	430	56·4	33·6	40·9	866		533	1399		14·0	100
						48			9·6		
110	380	57·6	34·9	43·9	914		581	1495		13·6	110
						41			8·3		
120	345	58·8	36·0	46·7	956		622	1578		13·2	120

Thinning yield per cent = 39·4

Age	Stem number	Main crop Basal area	Mean height	diam.	Stem wood vol.	Thinnings vol.	accum. vol.	Total stem-wood	Increment c.a.i.	m.a.i.	Age
Height quality class II											
10	—	6·8	1·85	—	4	—		4		0·4	10
						3			4·7		
20	—	15·0	5·15	4·8	48		3	51		2·6	20
						15			9·7		
30	4000	23·6	9·1	8·7	130		18	148		4·9	30
						37			13·8		
40	2400	31·2	13·2	12·9	231		55	286		7·2	40
						56			16·0		
50	1620	37·3	17·1	17·1	335		111	446		8·9	50
						63			**16·3**		
60	1185	42·0	20·55	21·4	435		174	609		10·2	60
						62			15·1		
70	890	45·5	23·45	25·5	524		236	760		10·9	70
						57			13·3		
80	730	48·2	25·9	29·0	600		293	893		11·2	80
						51			11·5		
90	620	50·3	27·8	32·1	664		344	1008		**11·2**	90
						45			9·7		
100	540	51·9	29·3	35·0	716		389	1105		11·1	100
						38			8·1		
110	480	53·2	30·55	37·6	759		427	1186		10·8	110
						34			6·9		
120	430	54·3	31·6	40·0	794		461	1255		10·5	120

Thinning yield per cent = 36·7

relation II", or "auxiliary relation", offers *big advantages as a basis* for the construction of yield tables. Gehrhardt and more recently Krenn (1946) availed themselves of these in the construction of a yield table for Norway spruce in South Germany.

Gehrhardt's Norway spruce yield table of 1921

This is the product of the compilation of an older yield table of Gehrhardt's (1901) and the tables of Grundner (1913), Schiffel (1904) and Schwappach (1902) in which extensive material from north-, middle- and south-German, as well as Austrian, temporary and permanent sample plots had been used. Because of its perfect fit and the harmonious agreement of all its data, this table can be considered as a model, and will therefore be scrutinized more closely as an example for the construction of a yield table.

The excerpt for the height quality classes I and II in Table 51 contains age value data at 10-year intervals with statements about the standing crop, the part which is removed during each 10-year period, the total crop yield and the increment. Columns 1 and 4, showing the mean heights for given ages, represent the "classifying relation". In Fig. 88 this is shown in the shape of five height/age curves or "site quality curves". In this graphic form, it permits of a rapid site quality assessment of stands of any given age and mean height without laborious numerical interpolation. For example, we find for a 65-year-old stand with a mean height of 24·5 m that the height demanded for Q. Cl. I is 25·9 m and for Q. Cl. II it is 23·0 m, so the stand roughly corresponds to Q. Cl. I.5, i.e. midway between Q. Cl. I and Q. Cl. II.

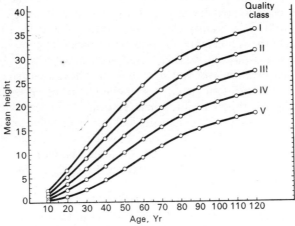

FIG. 88. Sheaf of quality class curves according to the yield table for Norway spruce by *Gehrhardt* (1921).

Column 9, which states the total crop yield, and column 4 (mean height) together provide the "auxiliary relation", i.e. the total crop yield as function of the mean height: the "extension of Eichhorn's law". Such an auxiliary relation is common *for all* quality classes. Column 1 (age) and col. 9 (total crop yield) together provide the "final relation".

Column 8 shows the sum of the thinnings per decade of col. 7. If the totals of the intermediate returns are added to the standing volume in col. 6, the result shown in col. 9 is the total crop volume. The total of all thinnings, expressed as a percentage of the total crop volume, supplies the "thinning volume per cent". This shows what percentage of the achieved total crop volume has been utilized as thinnings. If the differences between the total crop volumes by decades is divided by the number of years (10) of the growth period, the result shows the values for the "current" increment during these periods (c.a.i.) or more precisely, the mean annual increment accruing in each 10-year period (p.m.a.i.). Division of the total crop volumes by the corresponding ages provides the "mean annual increment" (m.a.i.) in col. 11. The peak values for the c.a.i. and m.a.i. are shown in heavy type. We see that the culminations tend to occur later in the lower quality classes.

Yield tables and reality

Whether or not a yield table constructed from height quality classes reflects accurately the present and future total crop yields of stands, as well as their current and future increments, depends on two main conditions:

1. The height growth of the stands must correspond to that of the yield table.
2. The total crop yields assumed for certain heights, or—more precisely—for certain quality classes, must actually have been achieved.

Whether condition 1 is fulfilled may be checked by height analyses of predominant trees, whose height growth must then be translated into terms of mean height development of the stands, a process which is, to be sure, not free from considerable uncertainties.

The method of establishment and the thinning treatment applied to a stand have decisive influence on the mean height as well as the differences between top and mean heights. By one single, heavy low thinning, the "height of a tree of average basal area" of a 65-year-old stand can be increased from 24·5 m to 25·9 m (our example on p. 163) which would be equal to a "rise in quality class" by a semi-stage to Q. Cl. I. For this reason it is necessary to state the top heights, in addition to mean heights, in yield tables.

How far condition 2 is met can be discovered accurately *only by keeping experimental areas under* careful *observation over very long periods*. These areas should have undergone only moderate thinning or—still better—be included in an experimental series which contains one very lightly thinned plot. Furthermore, the experimental areas should be free from unusual pathological or climatological damage. Such undisturbed and evenly treated experimental series of Norway spruce have been observed in the Lower Alps by the Bavarian Forestry Research Establishment, in some cases for over 70 years. The careful comparisons made by Assmann (1955a, 1959a) on the basis of these experimental series are therefore of special importance.

According to Assmann it is *the total crop yield achieved for a given mean height* (or top height) which should determine the *yield level of a site* in terms of crop height. The larger the total crop yield attained at a given height, the higher is the site quality. The age is not, at least initially, relevant. If the "extension of Eichhorn's law" applied generally, then the site quality would have to be constant. How strongly the yield level may vary, however, even within a geographically small growth range, is proved in Fig. 89 where the total crop yields of six Bavarian research series of Norway spruce (in each case the mean of three experimental areas with light, moderate and heavy thinning) are plotted over the respective top heights.

The series Ottobeuren 8 and Sachsenried 2 (planted), standing on high terrace sites with a good water supply, have a very high yield level, which even exceeds the one assumed in the yield table of Vanselow (1951). In contrast to this stand are the two experimental series

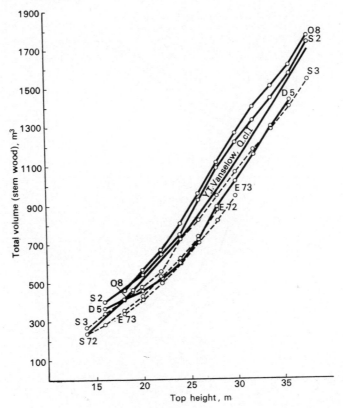

FIG. 89. Total volume production of six Bavarian spruce experimental plots against top height.

Eglharting 72 (close spacing) and 73 (wide spacing) on sites of the Munich Schotterebene (rubble plain) with a poor supply of water, where the yield level is markedly low. Strikingly low is the yield level of the experimental series Denklingen 5 which, only 8 km distant from the experimental series No. 2 at Sachsenried, lies in the same forest region on a site which outwardly is hardly distinguishable from the site at Denklingen. The explanation lies in the *different depth of the rooting*, which at Sachsenried 2 is over 1 m, but only 30 cm in Denklingen 5. In the series Sachsenried 3 which has grown from dense broadcast sowing and was not thinned until the age of 33 years the growing conditions are exceptional.

Height and total crop yield

These results strongly suggest that the site exercises a decisive influence on the level of yield which can be achieved, at least for Norway spruce stands. The relation $\Sigma v = f(h_m)$ assumes a relationship between the total (integrated) volume increments of the stand and the total increments in the *mean* height of the stands. This relation can also be expressed as follows:

$$\Sigma g \times \Sigma fh = f(h_m)$$

in which case the total volume increments are separated into their component basal area and form-height increments. The latter is reduced by heavy thinning whilst, on the other

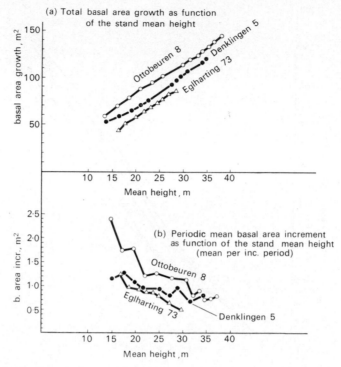

FIG. 90. Total growth of basal area, and basal area increment as functions of the mean height. Details in the text.

hand, the mean height of the standing crop (the magnitudes on the left side relate to the standing *and* the removed trees of the stand) is increased. As calculations of the Bavarian experimental Norway spruce series have proved, the *products Σfh for the same degree of thinning are, irrespective of site, approximately equal for given mean heights of the stands.* These products are easily calculated by dividing the total crop volumes by the corresponding total crop basal areas.

In contrast, *the total crop basal area as function of the mean height*, i.e. the relation $\Sigma g = f(h_m)$ shows *equally large differences from site to site as those we have already met for the relation $\Sigma v = f(h_m)$.* Figure 90 shows these for the lightly thinned A-areas (control plots) of the series Ottobeuren 8, Denklingen 5 and Eglharting 73. The rounded values for a *mean height of 28 m* amount to:

Trial plot	Total crop, m²	Basal area per cent
Eglharting 73	85	90
Denklingen 5	94	100
Ottobeuren 8	109	116

On p. 151 we met a simple formula which describes the combined effects of the components of the volume increment:

$$i_V = i_g \times fh + i_{fh} \times g_a$$

The form height fh has such a close correlation with h_m that, for Norway spruce stands without extreme treatment, we can assume $fh = f(h_m)$. Krenn (1946) expressed this relationship approximately by a parabola of the 2nd degree, which is shown in Fig. 91. As we can see, the form height does not increase in proportion to the height, the amount of the increase becoming progressively smaller with increasing height. At a height of 42–45 m, a *maximum* is reached *beyond which the form height decreases*. This is due to the strong decrease of the breast height form factor of tall spruce trees, due to the marked butt-swell. *In stands* at high elevations with generally *low form factors* the trend of the curve *is lower* and the maximum value of the form height is reached at 32–34 m as shown by the other curve in Fig. 91 illustrating investigations of high elevation mixed stands of the northern Kalkalpen made by Magin (1957). A similar trend is also to be expected from selection forest spruce. The suitability of Krenn's curve for stands in hilly country and submountainous situations, incidentally, was proved with the help of extensive material of the Forestry Research Establishment at Munich.

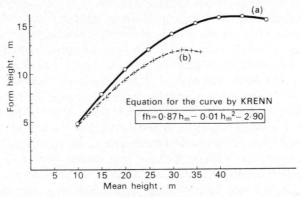

FIG. 91. Form height of spruce stands as a function of the mean height (a) according to *Krenn*, (b) according to *Magin*. See text.

If, therefore, the form-height and its variations can, with the above reservations, be considered as functions of the mean height of the stand, then, in the case of the Bavarian experimental Spruce series, *only* the *components i_g and g_a of the above formula remain as determining factors for the different yield levels attained*, i.e. *the basal area increment and the basal area of the stand at the beginning of the particular increment periods* or the mean basal area over the period of development of the stand. In actual fact, as shown by Fig. 90, *the basal area increment seen as a function of height differs to an unexpected degree* for the three trial plots.

Even in the geographically small region of the lower Alps south of the Danube, in which the Bavarian experimental Norway spruce series are situated therefore, *a uniform relationship $\Sigma v = f(h_m)$ cannot be assumed. The large differences in the yield level*, which exceed 20 per cent, *are determined not by differences in the form factors but by differences in the basal area increment and the local basal area potential during the period* (= maximum density of stocking) *of the stands for a given mean height.*

Height quality class and total crop yield

We have examined the total crop yield as a function of the height. What about the total crop yields which are achieved along with mean heights at a given age, that is to say according to *certain height quality classes?*

In the yield tables of Gehrhardt and Krenn, the c.a.i. and the m.a.i. of the five height quality classes are clearly determined by their appropriate relationship $h_m = f(A)$, with the help of the auxiliary relationship $\Sigma v = f(h_m)$. The assumption of a uniform relationship $fh = f(h_m)$ gives rise to a further specific consequence in the construction of tables. A certain degree of thinning, such as is given, for example, by stated percentages of intermediate yields (cf. p. 163), results not only in predicted volumes but *also in predicted basal areas* of the standing crop (cf. Krenn, 1946). Thus, not only volumes but *also basal areas* are determined for the individual height quality classes.

We have already mentioned, that the *mean height* can be *systematically increased* by intensifying the degree of low thinning which is practised. As will be demonstrated later in Section D, thinnings of more than moderate intensity (that is, removing more than 35 to 40 per cent of the total crop up to 100 years of age) must reduce the total crop yield. *Under a heavy thinning régime the trend of the curve of total crop performance on mean height is perceptibly lower than that for light or moderate thinning.* Gehrhardt, in his later yield table of 1928 for Norway spruce, made allowance for the increase in mean height with increasing degrees of thinning in such a way that, in his C-table for *rapid growth management*, the mean height for quality class I at the age of 100 years is larger by 3·2 m than in his A-table. As his calculations are based on the assumption of an unvarying auxiliary relation $\Sigma v = f(h_m)$, *the total crop volume with rapid growth treatment* (64 per cent intermediate yields) *thus increases by approximately 18 per cent* compared to moderate thinning (36 per cent intermediate yield). In reality, this degree of thinning, maintained up to the age of 100 years, must be expected to result in *a reduction of total crop volume of approximately 10 per cent.*

Krenn assumed in his table that for the same order of classification total crop volumes remained unaltered with intermediate yields ranging between 10 and 50 per cent of the total. As a result, the total crop volumes given for thinning yields of above 40 per cent are systematically overestimated.

Yield tables may be used to assess the total crop performance to date with any given height quality class. We can accordingly *estimate the yield actually attained by* a stand for some given mean height and age. We can also *deduce the future total crop performance at some* more or less *distant date.* The *probable yield* of a stand at some future time (the age of reference) is thus predictable on the basis of its performance up to a certain date (the age of assessment).

Let us take a look at the errors of estimate occurring in six Bavarian Norway spruce thinning series by using the yield table of Vanselow (1951) which was constructed from data for these plots and which contains, in addition to the mean height, estimates of top height. In Table 52 a comparison is made between the observed m.a.i.s and the expected values of the yield table. In cols. 7–9, we find statements about top height, the corresponding height quality classes and m.a.i.s, expected by the table for the age of 80 years, and beside these, in cols. 10 and 11, the actually achieved m.a.i.s, expressed in absolute terms and as percentages.

The errors of estimate arising from this *method of assessing productivity to date* are

TABLE 52

ACTUAL AND EXPECTED M.A.I.'S FROM THE YIELD TABLE OF VANSELOW FOR SIX EXPERIMENTAL NORWAY SPRUCE SERIES.
MEAN OF EACH OF THREE TRIAL PLOTS OF THE A, B AND C-GRADE IN EACH EXPERIMENTAL SERIES.
QUALITY CLASSIFICATION ACCORDING TO TOP HEIGHT

| Experimental series | At 50 years | | $M.a.i._{80}$ (>7 cm in diameter) | | | At 80 years | | $M.a.i._{80}$ (>7 cm in diameter) | | |
| | Top height (m) | Height quality class | expected in table (m³) | actual abs. (m³) | per cent of table | Top height (m) | Height quality class | expected in table (m³) | actual abs. (m³) | per cent of table |
1	2	3	4	5	6	7	8	9	10	11
Eglharting 72 Sp. 0·9×0·9	20·5	II·23	12·49	10·96	88%	28·3	II·55	11·46	10·96	96%
Eglharting 73 Sp. 1·2×2·0	21·6	I·92	13·56	11·02	81%	29·3	II·35	12·10	11·02	91%
Denklingen 5 Sp. 1·4×1·4	25·5	0·89	17·81	14·47	81%	32·3	I·58	14·97	14·47	97%
Sachsenried 2 Sp. 1·4×1·4	25·1	I·0	17·36	17·91	103%	34·1	I·0	17·36	17·91	103%
Sachsenried 3 Broadcast sowing	23·8	I·34	15·96	15·92	100%	34·0	I·03	17·24	15·92	92%
Ottobeuren 8 Sp. 1·4×1·4	25·3	0·95	17·57	19·64	112%	35·5	0·55	19·22	19·64	102%

Note. Col. 4 shows the $m.a.i._{80}$ which, according to the table, was to be expected in the basis of height quality class at the age of 50 years; col. 9 on the otherhand shows the $m.a.i._{80}$ estimated by the table for the height quality class attained at the age of 80 years.

comparatively small, but evidently *systematic* in that, with less favourable sites they are positive, and with optimal sites (except the sown series Sachsenried 3) negative. On the other hand, the *estimate of the expected productivity* at the reference age of 80 years involves *quite large errors of estimate* because of the need to gauge the future height quality class on the basis of the quality class at the age of 50 years, as in cols. 2 and 6.

Whilst the actual performances of the research series at Sachsenried agree well with the predicted yields, other research series which exhibit a lower level of performance are from 12 to 19 per cent below those given in the table and, in the case of Ottobeuren, which has the highest yield level, they are even 12 per cent in excess.

These deviations from the yield table are not caused by site-dependent differences in the yield level alone but also *by the particular age–height developments of the experimental series which deviate from the quality classification curves* (cf. p. 163) *of the yield table.* These cause a considerable *drop* of the height quality classes of the first three experimental series from the age of 50 to 80 years (by as much as 0·7 quality class stage) whilst on the other hand, the height quality class of the Ottobeuren series rises by 0·4 stage. The primary cause of error in the estimation of attained yield to date is the yield level of the table which is being used; for the errors in estimation of the *forecasted* yield, on the other hand, the decisive factor is mainly the shape of the quality classification curves. If the trends of the height–age curves of the yield table are steeper than the true curve for the stand in question, then the yield forecast is overestimated; in the reverse case, it is underestimated. If the yield level of the classified stands is lower than that of the yield table, then the yields to date, as well as the expected yields, are overestimated; in the reverse case, both are underestimated.

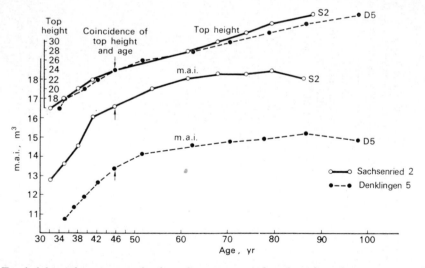

FIG. 92. Top height and mean annual volume increment as a function of age for two spruce trial series.

The dubiety of the common assumption which speaks of height quality class and yield performance as synonymous terms is demonstrated in Fig. 92 in which the top heights as well as the m.a.i.'s of the two experimental series Sachsenried 2 and Denklingen 5 are shown plotted over age. Although the top heights of the two experimental series coincide at age 46 years (i.e. at that age, there exists complete *equality of the height quality class*) the m.a.i.'s for the age of 46 years differ by 16·6 − 13·3 = 3·3 m³ (solid), i.e. approximately

20 per cent. *Therefore, in geographically restricted regions, such large differences in the total crop yields can occur within the same height quality classes, that in the construction as well as in the use of yield tables, they must unquestionably be taken into account.*

How large the disproportion between height quality class and total growth performance may be is suggested by the percentages of top height and m.a.i.$_{80}$ of the six Bavarian experimental Norway spruce series which are compared in Table 53. It is a sad irony that four of these series were established by Franz v. Baur who was so firmly convinced of the strict proportionality between height growth and volume production. If one wished to construct a yield table on the basis of these experimental series, one would, of necessity, have to construct at least two tables with yield levels differing by approximately 20 per cent, and, as a logical consequence, use at least two "auxiliary relations".

TABLE 53

Top Height and Total Crop Yield of Bavarian Spruce Research Series at the Age of 80 Years

Experimental series	Top height		Total crop volume stem wood (m³)	m.a.i.$_{80}$	
	(m)	Percentage		(m³)	Percentage
Eglharting 72	28·3	88%	914	11·43	76%
Eglharting 73	29·3	91%	917	11·46	77%
Denklingen 5	*32·3*	*100%*	*1196*	*14·95*	*100%*
Sachsenried 2	34·1	105%	1477	18·46	123%
Sachsenried 3	34·0	105%	1313	16·41	110%
Ottobeuren 8	35·5	110%	1613	20·16	135%

Weck in his *Forstliche Zuwachs- und Ertragskunde* (2nd edition, 1955, p. 105) declared the following: "Careful observation teaches us that a given mean height of stand is accompanied by a given total increment which is the higher the longer it takes the stand to reach this given mean height." This law *cannot apply to spruce stands in general* as is proved by the following values for three Bavarian experimental Norway spruce series. For each of the three areas (A-, B-, C-grade) a *mean height of 28 m* is reached

by the experimental series	at the average age of	with a mean total crop volume of fm
Eglharting 73	86 (!)	980 = 78%
Denklingen 5	72	1065 = 85%
Ottobeuren 8	59 (!)	1250 = 100%

Here, on the contrary, the stands which have reached the given mean height at a considerably later age show considerably lower total crop volumes.

As a rule, a general impoverishment of the nutritive element supply within the same range of climatic conditions, coincidently with a reduction in height growth will prompt us to look for a lower density of stocking (for given mean heights) and accordingly a smaller basal area held over a given period and a reduced basal area increment. If, together with the nutrient supply, the water supply also deteriorates—either by a change in the macro-climate or by a change in the soil type—then we shall have to bear in mind the example cited above, which contradicts Weck's proposition. If, however, a lessening supply of nutritive elements is accompanied by an *improved* water supply, resulting from greater rainfall or an improvement in soil-dependent circumstances (crumb size, moisture-retaining capacity), then, together with an increase of the potential basal area over a period, we can expect a *rise in the yield level along with a drop in the crop quality class.* In this case, we must—agreeably with Weck's assertion—expect the total crop volume for a given mean height to be larger if this mean height is reached at a later age, for the lower the height quality class, the later a given mean height is reached.

On our mountain escarpments which are exposed towards the north or west (SW. to NW.) the rainfall increases with increasing height above sea level, whilst at the same time, the temperatures decrease. This, in most instances, causes a noticeable rise in the yield level for given height quality classes. However, for stands at markedly high elevations, belonging to the high montane regions, we can expect only a moderate yield level because of their open spacing and the small breast-height form-factors (and form height, cf. p. 167) which are peculiar to them. It should be noted that as a rule, the high basal areas occurring on mountain sites are not, *by themselves*, an indication of correspondingly high levels of yield. The basal area *increment* may, despite the high basal area, be *low*. In these localities, suppressed trees survive for a very long time in the absence of thinnings thus promoting a high density of stocking and basal area. The mean age of such stands, which in fact often show a marked admixture of ages, is in most cases underestimated, especially when rough guesses at "economic" ages are made. As a result, the yield contribution of such stands is as a rule overestimated, especially if unsuitable yield tables are used.

A relatively low yield level is to be expected for Norway spruce stands if they are planted on sites having scanty moisture supplies and with relatively *warm* temperatures. There, more often than not (Mitscherlich, 1957; Weihe, 1955) we can observe an almost impetuously rapid height growth up to the pole-crop stage but this need not be matched by a correspondingly fast basal area or volume increment.

In order properly to assess the yield potential of a site it is necessary to make increment investigations as well as to examine the site itself. At the least it is advisable to find out the maximum possible basal area capacity of the locality and the basal area growth-rate for a period long enough to rule out any bias due to minor climatic irregularities.

The small differences in total crop volume for given mean heights which can be distinguished between the five quality classes[1] of the spruce yield tables in common use by us, *must* to a large extent *be considered as due to the statistical determination of averages derived from heterogeneous material whereby opposing fluctuations in the yield level cancel themselves out.* For this reason, all endeavours to inform or demonstrate *by yield tables* the manner in which our tree species grow must be viewed with suspicion. Although a good fit of the yield table values and a satisfactory agreement between them is clearly essential, as otherwise the tables would be useless for estimation and comparison, *one does detect in the tables evidences of the very same principles which were presupposed, justifiably or not, in their construction.*

Peculiarities of the customary yield tables for spruce

The auxiliary relation $\Sigma v = f(h_m)$ on which the yield tables for spruce in common use today are based show such small differences between the height quality classes I to IV of each particular table that Assmann (1955) was able to calculate *average values* for the

---

[1] i.e. for mean heights which are reached at different ages.

total crop performance as a function of the mean height for three German yield tables and a new table by Hummel and Christie (1953) for Great Britain. These are shown in Table 54 together with the corresponding values in Krenn's table for which a uniform auxiliary relation was used. The "mean yield level" so obtained is lowest in the table of Wiedemann and, among the German tables, highest in that of Vanselow. The latter table, which includes only three height quality classes, is applicable only within the limits of south Bavaria. But even there, such a high yield level is reached only on the best sites (Assmann, 1959), so that with an unrestricted use of the table we must in many cases, apprehend a considerable overestimate of the yield potential.

The yield table by Zimmerle (1949) presents a fairly high yield level and shows a particularly steep trend in the sheaf of quality class curves.[1] Such *high productivities* are postulated that, even when given a high local yield, *dangerous overestimates* of the mean and current annual increments are possible. This table, like the one by Vanselow, is based on data which are *not representative* for the intended region of application. It is, however, very well fitted and, by a lowering of the yield level and adjustment of the quality classification sheaf, could be made applicable to a wider region.

The table by Wiedemann (1936/42) is based on Schwappach's table (1902). From this Wiedemann took over, not only the quality classification curves but—unfortunately— also the *basal area framework*. Schwappach determined the basal areas of the standing crop fairly freely and therefore, for crop ages of approximately 60 years and upwards, *systematically underestimated them*. Wiedemann reduced the yield level of Schwappach's table by approximately 8 per cent by curtailing the thinning yields. The quality classification curves of the table assume a rapid height development during the first five or six decades, such as is common in planted stands on relatively warm sites. For this reason, and because of its cautious assessments, the table gives figures which are not too high and which can be used over a wide region.

For general application over the region of the Federal Republic of Germany, Gehrhardt's yield table of 1921 would also be suitable. With an average level of yield higher by approximately 11 per cent, this table supplies more fitting values for the basal areas and volumes of the standing crop. Furthermore it offers not only estimates for timber sizes over 7 cm in diameter, but also stemwood values which, with the extensive conversion of wood of smaller dimensions (poles, pit-wood and pulp-wood assortments) are much in demand.

Macro-climatic and local site influences on the total crop yield

It has been known for some time (among others through Wiedemann, 1939) that the average crop yields of spruce stands belonging to the same quality class in south German and Alpine regions in all cases exceed those of north and middle German growth regions. The extensive work by Mitscherlich (1949, 1950, 1953) shows a *climatically conditioned fall in the yields of similar height-quality classes* whose mean positive gradient is directed approximately from NE. to SW. It would probably be correct to consider this general SW. direction as the resultant of an approximate westerly trend in the maritime character of the middle European climate (atmospheric humidity and precipitation), and of the

---

[1] A large part of the experimental areas which are used as a basis for the tables is on old morainic soils showing slow height development in the early years and a prolonged height growth among the older stands.

TABLE 54

MEAN CURVE VALUES OF TOTAL CROP VOLUME FOR NORWAY SPRUCE GIVEN BY DIFFERENT YIELD TABLES: TIMBER VOLUMES ("DERBHOLZ") AS FUNCTION OF MEAN HEIGHT

The figures were obtained by graphical fitting of the original values for Q. Cl. I–IV, with the exception of those by Krenn who adopted a standard total volume curve

Mean height	Total timber crop volumes								
	Absolute values					Percentage values, related to the values of Wiedemann			
	WIEDEMANN		ZIMMERLE		HUMMEL*		ZIMMERLE		HUMMEL
		KRENN		VANSELOW		KRENN		VANSELOW	
(m)	(m³)	(m³)	(m³)	(m³)	(m³)	%	%	%	%
10	140	140	128	137	122				
11	172	173	166	180	160				
12	206	208	205	228	200				
13	241	245	246	277	243				
14	276	283	289	326	289				
15	312	323	333	376	338	104	107	121	108
16	348	365	378	426	390				
17	385	408	424	477	445				
18	423	454	471	528	503				
19	462	501	519	580	564				
20	502	550	568	633	627	110	113	126	125
21	544	600	618	686	691				
22	588	653	669	740	756				
23	634	707	721	795	823				
24	681	763	775	851	892				
25	729	820	831	909	962	112	114	125	132
26	778	880	890	969					
27	829	941	951	1030					
28	882	1004	1014	1093					
29	937	1068	1080	1157					
30	995	1135	1149	1222		114	115	123	
31	1056	1203	1221	1288					
32	1121	1273	1295	1356					
33	1190	1345	1370	1425					
34	1263	1418	1446	1496					
35	1340	1494	1523	1569		112	114	117	
36	1420	1571	1601	1643					
37	1500	1649	1680	1719					
38	1581	1730	1759	1798					
39	1662	1812	1839	1883					
40	1743	1895	1919	1976		109	110	113	

* Norway spruce yield table for Gt. Britain by F. C. Hummel and J. Christie. Cf. Schober, The Yield Performance of the Coniferous Trees of Gt. Britain and Germany, *Forstwissen. Centr.* 1955, pp. 36 ff. Hummel's table has been converted into German measures by G. D. Schmidt.

southerly direction of increase in mean temperatures. Naturally, this general inference is powerfully modified by the special climatic conditions on mountain slopes (Mitscherlich, 1953). Broadly stated, the following rule applies: the greater the rainfall and atmospheric humidity when accompanied at the same time by sufficient warmth the higher are the yields and the total crop volumes of spruce, as also in general of those coniferous species which demand plentiful supplies of water. The values of the new yield tables for Great Britain of Hummel and Christie in Table 54 suggest an exceptionally high level of yields. With the height increment impeded by the strong winds of a maritime climate, but with the vegetative period lengthened from 5 to 7½ months,[1] as shown by Magin (1957), considerably larger basal area increments are obtained for given heights and ages of stands than on the European continent. This is shown in Fig. 93, in which height

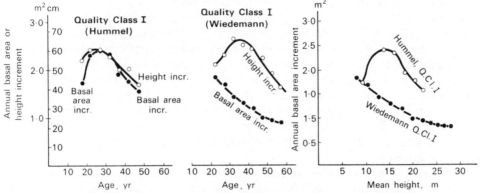

FIG. 93. Comparison between the basal area and height increments of the yield tables by Hummel and Christie and Wiedemann.

and basal area increments of the table by Hummel and Christie are compared to those of the table by Wiedemann. The basal area increment of the former for equivalent mean heights occasionally lies up to 80 per cent above that of Wiedemann's table. The research plots in Great Britain which underwent early and heavy thinning have low form factors so that their superiority in volume increment is not so great. As a result of the *accelerated growth effect* (cf. p. 233) their increment is, moreover, temporarily increased. When it becomes possible, after a further 20 years, to extend the tables for ages up to 80 years, it will probably be found that the superiority of the overall mean increment, by comparison with continental standards, has become smaller for these higher ages of reference.

Since 1955 extensive *investigations into the growth of Norway spruce* have been in progress on various sites in the Federal Republic. In the course of these investigations, the actual height growth during the last 30 years was, with the help of analysed sample stems of dominants, compared with the yield tables of Wiedemann and Zimmerle. Considerable deviations became apparent, and these are due to site characteristics (soil and climate) as well as to methods of establishment and treatment. Partly, however, the deviations are also due to the incorrect construction of the quality classification curves.[2] Moreover, the method of establishment (sowing, close- or widely spaced planting), possible growth

---

[1] Even if the cambial activity is extended only by a few weeks, large quantities of assimilates can be produced and stored with the mild winter temperatures. Besides, in the mild Atlantic climate, the *growth in length* of the roots (Holstener-Jørgensen, 1959) continues throughout the winter.

[2] Because of lack of data, these were extrapolated towards the zero point of the co-ordinate system for the first decades so that the lower parts of the curve are misplaced.

checks (late frost, browsing by game) and thinning treatment (e.g. early start of thinnings) have such a strong effect on the height growth during the first five or six decades that, without knowledge and consideration of all the factors, the *height quality class of young stands may be incorrectly estimated* by 1 or 2 classes, a danger which is enhanced by the small height differences between the quality classification curves at these ages. As a rule, such differences in the height development are evened out by the age of 60 to 70 years, so that later it is possible to make a more reliable height quality classification.

The fact that the volume increments are not evened out in the same way as the heights is proved by the example, amongst others, of the sown research plot Sachsenried 3 (cf. Table 52 on p. 169) which, although it reached the same height quality class at the age of 80 years as the neighbouring planted plot on the same site (S.2), is nonetheless still inferior to it by 11 per cent in total growth performance.

It is further to be noted that in the above-mentioned investigations the *volume increment of the last 10 years* was determined with the help of borings. This led to the discovery of *large fluctuations in increment due to climatic changes*, especially on sites with restricted water supplies. In order to be able to make comparisons with the yield table, it is necessary to eliminate the influence of the climate. Such a "correction for climate" is difficult because, on many sites, the normal "*trend*" of the increment curves for height, basal area and volume can only be correctly determined by continuous observation over many decades. For this reason, any endeavour to calculate the total crop yield by summating the current annual increments of stands of identical quality class but of diverse ages is questionable.

Mitscherlich (1958) who collected and evaluated by far the most extensive material, no less than 309 temporary sample plots in Baden, was compelled, on account of the lack of site maps to divide them up not into standard site units (in the sense of Krauss), but into broadly comprehensive groups (for example, recent moraine, early moraine). He then tried to deduce *average deviations* of the fifteen site groups thus determined from the height growth curve of Zimmerle's table. These deviations, calculated over a fairly long period, are defined as "quality class changes" and, in the event of their being positive, as "quality class promotions", or if negative, as "quality class recessions". Although the average deviations appear in many cases to be typical, a number of characteristically local deviations due to site are obscured by this method. The same applies to the mean values for total crop volumes, which Mitscherlich derived by taking the means of the c.a.i.'s of all age stages of the fifteen site groups. They characterize the yield level with regard to the height quality class and lie partly below, partly above the values of the table of Zimmerle. A low-ranking performance in the current annual increment is particularly prominent for the most important age-period from 50 to 100 years.

Investigations by Petri (1957), which were soundly based on a good knowledge of the site conditions applicable to Norway spruce stands in the northern part of the province Rhineland-Pfalz (Westerwald, Taunus, Eifel and Hunsrück) demonstrate how *closely* height growth, yield level and total crop yield are *dependent on site*. Amongst other facts, it is evident that the contingent density of attainable stocking is strongly dependent on the water supply. This maximum possible density of stocking can be measured to advantage by the "maximum basal area sustained over a period" according to Assmann (cf. p. 229), which shows how many trees of a given diameter are capable of growing and surviving on an area of one hectare. With the maximum attainable basal area for a certain mean height, the yield level is at once indicated, and a corresponding basal area increment can be assumed.

The work of Moosmayer (1955/57) upon spruce and beech forests of the East Swabian Alps, also shows differential growth behaviour with reference to site. A mean total crop yield curve[1] which he derived for Norway spruce stands of the East-Alb, is accompanied by gratifyingly small variances, but the simultaneously published total crop volume curves of experimental spruce areas under long-term observation permit of cause to suspect typical deviations due to site.

How strongly *the special characteristics of the micro-site* predominate by comparison with the influences of the macro-climate and the forest region is suggested by an informative example from investigations into the growth of Norway spruce carried out by the Munich Institut für Ertragskunde (Institute for Yield Studies). In the sample plot series No. V of a private forest in Franken-Jura, the data for the stand and increments of the sample plot V/1 are exceptional and fall well outside the frame of the average results. Moreover, they differ basically from those of the neighbouring area V/2[(2)] which is 20 years younger, although with regard to site, vegetation and height quality class, they appear to be highly comparable. Thorough soil investigations[3] on the basis of subsequently prepared soil profiles suggests an explanation. From Table 55 we find that the sample plot V/1 with a degree of stocking density of 1·56 (!) exceeds the current increment values set forth in Wiedemann's table during the last decade by 34 per cent and those of the probable m.a.i.$_{100}$ by about 30 per cent, whilst the immediately adjoining area V/2 with a degree of stocking of 1·19 reaches only 93 per cent of the c.a.i. expected in the table and 105 per cent of the figures given for the presumed m.a.i.$_{100}$. Decisive factors for the exceptionally high yield level are obviously the *good water supply* and the *intensive and deep rooting* which are due to the soil type and the favourable soil structure. The plot V/2 with a slightly higher-quality class has lower yields, only just corresponding to those of the yield table. Plot V/3 grows on a different site and, despite a noticeably higher-quality class, does not reach the c.a.i. of the yield table. The height analyses which were carried out show that plot 1 has, during the last "humid" five years from 1950 to 1955, completely recovered from the height increment depression of the "dry" five years from 1945 to 1950, which is not the case with the younger plots 2 and 3.

Once more we see how strongly at variance the volume yields for the same height quality class can turn out to be in consequence of local site differences. *The neglect of all individual local characteristics in the hitherto almost exclusively employed process of estimating yields by height quality class, must give way to a careful consideration of all site characteristics which are important to the determination of the yield.*

Height quality classes or m.a.i.-quality classes?

Wiedemann (1939) specified the commonly used yield table height quality classes, with the Roman figures I to V, as "relative" quality classes. In so doing, his main attention was directed to the differing height frames of the quality classification curves which, for a given tree species, lead to different quality classes, depending on the yield table which

---

[1] The trend of this curve is below that of the curve of Zimmerle (quality class I/II) but higher than that of the curve of Wiedemann (quality class I).

[2] The approximately 20-year age intervals between the sample plots were, together with the height analyses (for 30 years), intended to make possible the construction of a local "growth series".

[3] These were taken on by Prof. Dr. Laatsch and Dr. Strebel to whom I wish to express my thanks.

TABLE 55

SITE AND YIELD STUDY INFORMATION ABOUT THE NORWAY SPRUCE SAMPLE PLOTS SERIES No. V IN A PRIVATE FOREST OF FRANKEN–JURA, ALTITUDE APPROXIMATELY 600 M ABOVE SEA LEVEL

Climate values:		
Temperature	Annual average app. 7·5°	May–August app. 15°
Rainfall	barely 700 mm	300–350 mm

Sample plot No.	1	2	3
I. Site description			
Position	Upper slope, gently inclining towards N.	Upper slope, gently inclining towards N.	Almost level; faintly sloping towards NW.
Parent rock	Medium crumb, broken decaying Eisensandstein (sandstone rich in iron) with an app. 2 dm cover of pleistocene loam	Loose decaying, fine sandy Eisensandstein (sandstone rich in iron)	Opalinus clay, mixed into the upper 2 dm together with fine sandy remains of the Eisensandstein (sandstone rich in iron)
Soil species	Fine sandy loam over skeletal fine sandy loam	Silty fine sand	Fine sandy loam over clay loam
Humus form	Moder	Mull-like Moder	Moder
Soil type	Brown earth	Brown earth.	Pseudo gley/pelosol-Brown earth
Soil water supply	Moderately fresh	Moderately fresh to moderately dry	Alternating between moderately dry and moderately damp
Rooting	On the exposed stump to 4 dm depth very good and uniform roots, downwards to 8 dm gradually decreasing, at 8 dm bush-like branching of roots: main-root system.	On the stump to 8 dm depth well rooted, main-root system	Main rooting on the upper 2 dm of the stump, deeper down to 6 dm still individual, fine roots already dead
II. Yield study data			
Age	109	88	69
Mean height in metres	27·0	24·2	21·2
Height quality class according to Wiedemann	II·9	II·7	II·4
Basal area m²	59·2	47·7	52·1
Degree of stocking according to Wiedemann	1·56	1·19	1·31
Stem volume m³	769	575	571
Annual Iv of the last 10 years, m³	11·0	9·0	10·0
% of Wiedemann's Y. T.	134%	93%	84%
Probable m.a.i.$_{100}$, m³	10	8·5	8·5
% of the Y. T.	130%	105%	98%

is being used.[1] For his "absolute" quality classes, he gives as alternatives a quality classification based on the height of the stand at the age of felling or on the average total volume production at that age, i.e. on the m.a.i. Philipp (1931) had already used the m.a.i. at the age of 100 years as a scale for quality class. So—unfortunately—Wiedemann gave his preference to an *absolute quality classification based on the m.a.i.* A system of *absolute height quality classes* based on the height of the stand at the conventional reference age of 100 years for all tree species has, however, *decisive advantages:* e.g. clearness of the quality class specification, direct comparability with the avoidance of dubious conversions, information about the comparative behaviour of the tree species in competition on a given site, and others.

On the other hand it is only too easy to overlook the fact *that the existing m.a.i. tables have been drawn up and converted from tables covering large regions and therefore represent only transcriptions of the original height quality classes, for which the yield levels are thus already established.* This kind of transition from height classes to m.a.i.-quality classes reminds one uncomfortably of the adventure of Münchhausen, when he dragged himself out of the swamp by his own hair. Such tables, graduated by the m.a.i. $_{100}$, suggest a productivity which in individual cases, depending on the level of yield, may be over-, as well as under-estimated. They can thus lead to fatal deceptions, especially if they are used for the quality classification of young stands whose future development is affected by uncertainties regarding their height and volume production. Qualms must also be felt about the transformation of the height quality classes of one table to classes based on the m.a.i. at a fixed age base. It does, however, seem useful to construct *m.a.i.-quality classification tables for certain sites* in which the local yield level and the mean height growth trend of the stands (method of establishment, treatment in the early years, etc.) is adequately taken into consideration. An example of such a table is given in Table 56. This concerns planted stands which get away fast during the early years, unimpeded by serious obstacles to growth and with moderate thinning which was started at a relatively early stage.

It was proposed by Weck in 1948 that the mean height at age 100 years should be used for all tree species as the criterion of "absolute" height quality class.[2] An "absolute height quality class 24" in that case would mean that a mean height of 24 m would be expected for a particular stand of a given tree species at the age of 100 years. Assmann (1959) suggested defining the height quality class generally by stating the achieved, or expected top or mean height at some selected age of reference, in which case the uncertainty surrounding a still unattained future value could be expressed by showing it in brackets, for example $h_{dom.\ 100} = (36)$, i.e. the probable top height or top height quality class at the age of 100 years.

The total yield or m.a.i. of a stand which is fitted into such a system of height quality classes on top height can only be deduced from secondary considerations after the inclusion of additional descriptive magnitudes for the stand (G, N, d_m) and site characteristics (e.g. water supply). The respective top height quality classes must therefore be divided

[1] In order to exclude these disagreements from tables to be constructed for large regions, Schober (1942) suggested a uniform height frame for Norway spruce, Common beech, Scots pine and oak at the age of 100 years, in which the height intervals per quality class were to amount uniformly to 4·5 m for spruce and 4·0 m for the others.

[2] Weck (1955) would like to see the term "absolute quality class or yield class" reserved for those yield classes which are *graduated by the m.a.i. of dry substance*. This is problematic because the dry weight production of the different tree species on a given site also shows fairly big site-dependent differences. In this connection see p. 186.

TABLE 56

M.A.I. QUALITY CLASSIFICATION TABLES FOR NORWAY SPRUCE STANDS ON THE RUBBLE PLANE IN UPPER SCHWABEN (OBERSCHWÄBISCHE SCHOTTERFLUR), SOUTH-EAST OF ULM

Site unit: *Oxalis myrtillus* type on fine loam. The m.a.i. in solid m^3 of growing timber is uncurtailed, with no falling-off of production

Age	m.a.i.$_{80}$ =	13	12	11	10	9	8 m^3
				Top heights in metres for the m.a.i. in m^3			
20		9·7	9·3	8·9	8·3	7·7	7·1
25		13·1	12·5	11·8	11·3	10·9	9·8
30		16·1	15·4	14·6	13·9	13·2	12·4
35		18·7	17·9	17·0	16·2	15·4	14·6
40		20·8	19·9	19·0	18·2	17·4	16·5
45		22·6	21·7	20·8	20·0	19·0	18·2
50		24·2	23·3	22·3	21·4	20·4	19·5
55		25·7	24·7	23·7	22·7	21·6	20·6
60		27·1	26·0	24·9	23·8	22·7	21·6
65		28·4	27·2	26·0	24·9	23·8	22·5
70		29·5	28·3	27·1	26·0	24·7	23·4
75		30·6	29·4	28·1	26·9	25·6	24·2
80		31·6	30·3	29·0	27·7	26·4	25·0
85		32·5	31·1	29·8	28·5	27·1	25·7
90		33·3	31·9	30·6	29·2	27·8	26·3
95		34·0	32·6	31·2	29·8	28·4	26·9
100		34·6	33·2	31·8	30·4	29·0	27·5
	m.a.i.$_{100}$ =	12·2	11·4	10·5	9·7	9·0	8·0

into productivity grades as is the case with the new Norway spruce yield table for Bavaria (Assmann–Franz, 1963, 1965). This new table, similar to the new Norway spruce yield table for Gt. Britain of 1966 (Johnston and Bradley, 1963), is divided into three production classes. The directly measurable heights of the stand are, together with the age, the primary dividing characteristic for normal practical use, as well as for programmed quality classification with an electronic computer. Equal intervals of top height, as required for a primary characteristic, now correspond in decreasing order of height quality with increasing intervals in the m.a.i. See also Assmann (1966). There is, however, no objection against the use of the deduced m.a.i. at a fixed age of 100 years as descriptive scale of the local "production class".

"Static" or "dynamic" quality classification?

The problem as to whether quality classification ought to be made "statically", i.e. according to the determined height at a certain age, or "dynamically", i.e. by consideration of the probable further height development, has been discussed recently (among others by Mitscherlich, 1955; Magin, 1955; Assmann, 1955). From the arguments so far advanced, there is no doubt that quality classifications should be "dynamic", because in most cases the future height development of young and middle-aged stands can be estimated only on the basis of the mean or top height of older stands on the same site. The question remains, however, as to what final total crop yield is to be expected from an aberrant height development. The yield level of an certain locality might be found to correspond roughly with that of the table which is being used. The supposition is then made that the final crop yield at the age of 80 or 100 years will be in accordance with the indicated quality class at that age. But should that quality class have fallen short, the true total crop yield or the m.a.i. for the concerned age will be slightly *under*-estimated, whilst with too steep an upward trend, the crop will be *over*-estimated. Since a completely parallel behaviour of height and basal area increments is not to be expected, it is advisable in cases of doubt to count on a lower figure of crop yield. If the local yield level is lower or higher than that of the table, then a corresponding over- or under-estimate of the true total crop yield will result. The most serious over-estimates are to be feared when yield tables are employed which assume both a higher yield level as well as a steeper trend of height development with age than those existing locally.

Further development of yield tables

General tables and local tables

Notwithstanding the inevitably critical attitude held towards the tables in present-day use, there is no doubt that in the future we must still remain dependent on yield tables. Without such, forestry would be roughly in the same position as life insurance companies without life tables (Assmann, 1949b).

Yield tables are indispensable for the evaluation of current increments and future yields of stands, as well as the ascertainment of the required stocks and the sustained yields achievable by different working sections. *A big* and hitherto insufficiently regarded *advantage of the increments forecast on the basis of yield tables consists in the fact that,* the smoothed growth curves of *yield tables rule out short-term climatic effects.* How much such incalculable climatic influences can upset the indisputable advantages of local increment control by the so-called "control method" in selection forests will be further discussed in a later chapter of this book (p. 460). Even if the yield level of the table does not correspond to the true level, *short-term* increment forecasts (for example, estimates of the current increment of stands and working sections) should not be affected by serious errors because the mean total-crop yield curves of the tables run approximately parallel, and so have approximately equal gradients. Systematically faulty estimates, however, must be expected even in these circumstances, if the height curves of the table deviate markedly from the true height growth curves. The danger of systematic errors of estimate occurring is greatest with long-term increment forecasts, especially in estimating the m.a.i. for fairly advanced ages of reference, for example with working sections in afforestation. With the employment of the tables in present-day use, these errors can be avoided only if the average local yield level, as well as the mean height-growth trends of the stands are known and the tabulated values are accordingly corrected.

For the future, we shall require general tables for wide regions as well as special local tables for areas having similar growth relationships.

Essential corrections of commonly used yield tables

General yield tables can be obtained by correction and improvement of existing tables or by the derivation of new tables. In both cases, they must be constructed in such a way that they can be considered as approximately *representative of the region in which they are to be applied.* Fundamentally, general tables ought to be made applicable for light to *moderate thinning,* i.e. *for natural degrees of stocking* (Assmann, 1956, cf. further below, p. 231) *which guarantee full,* nearly optimal *volume production,* for example, for spruce 0·85, beech 0·80, pine 0·90, oak 0·85. For spruce, for example, this would mean that the thinning yield on good sites at the age of 100 years can amount to approximately 35 per cent or, at the most, to not more than 40 per cent. Tables which are based on heavy thinning or special types of thinning are not suitable as general tables, for which reason Assmann (1949) suggested the term "thinning tables" for them.

Arbitrary alterations to the natural development such as those which Schwappach, introduced *in his tables for moderate thinning,* in pursuance of his concepts regarding soil rental values (achievement of higher increment, yield and rentability percentages by progressively reducing the growing crop beyond the polewood stage), and which Wiedemann subsequently took over together with a basal area framework (Assmann, 1956a, 1959a), ought not to be tolerated in general tables.

Those systematic cyclic changes in the yield which are dependent on the macro-climate, as well as the fluctuations resulting from local environmental influences, are conspicuous for *spruce* which has "erratic yields". As a result, the geographical region of application for general tables for spruce is probably limited.[1] If they are to be used for different sites of a fairly large geographical region they must be arranged *by yield classes* as in the new Norway spruce yield tables for Bavaria of Assmann–Franz (1963), in which, for example, the following values are found:

Top height quality class 36	m.a.i.$_{100}$ in m^3 stem-wood	Quality class definitions
for the upper yield level	16·1	O 36
for the medium yield level	14·4	M 36
for the lower yield level	12·9	U 36

The maximum difference of the m.a.i.$_{100}$ for quality class 36 thus amounts to 3·2 m^3 of standing timber. The tables are accompanied by *increment reduction tables* which state the increment losses due to under-stepping of the degrees of stocking of the table down to a degree of 0·4.

Johnston and Bradley (1963, 1966) arrived at a similar solution for Norway spruce in Gt. Britain. In the new Management Tables the yield classes, which are divided into m.a.i.-classes of 20 cu. ft. per acre (=1·78 m^3/ha), are combined with three production classes each, corresponding approximately to the yield classes of the table of Assmann–Franz.

Similar relationships exist also for *Scots pine,* whose regularly higher basal area content in south-west Germany caused Schwappach (1886) at that time to construct a special Scots pine yield table for the granddukedom Hesse.

From the extensive sample plot data which he collected and published for this table

---

[1] In the meantime, Assmann and Franz (1963, 1965) have constructed a new Norway spruce yield table for Bavaria. This is staged with 2-m intervals by the top heights at the age of 100 years, and subdivided into three yield classes (lower, middle and upper yield level). The thinning programme on which this is based is directed towards optimal volume production. With different treatment, the increment changes can, with the help of the added increment reduction tables, be estimated down to a degree of stocking of 0·4. The tables have been computed with the help of an electronic computer, are fully programmed, and can at all times be transformed for special thinning programs.

and for the subsequently constructed Scots pine yield table for north Germany (1889), the basal areas per hectare for the quality classes better than II0 have been extracted. In this process, the north German material was limited to the administrative districts of Potsdam, Frankfurt, Bromberg and Posen which are climatically fairly similar. We shall call the two comparative growth regions "East-Elbe" and "Hessen". The basal areas, plotted over the corresponding mean heights of the stands, could be relatively significantly fitted, whereby the following characteristic differences become apparent:

| Growing region | Basal areas for the mean heights | |
	20 m (m²)	30 m (m²)
"East-Elbe"	39	45
"Hessen"	47	58
Per cent of "East-Elbe"	120%	130%

The following comparison shows further the unnatural reductions of the basal areas with increasing age in the later Scots pine yield tables of Schwappach (1908) and Wiedemann (1948).

TABLE 57

TRUE NATURAL BASAL AREA VALUES AND VALUES ACCORDING TO TABLE FOR SCOTS PINE OF QUALITY CLASS I

| Age | Mean height (m) | True mean basal areas acc. to the sample plots | | Basal areas acc. to the table of Wiedemann | |
		(m²)	of this 85%	(m²)	as % of col. 4
40	15·7	35·7	30·3	30·3	100%
60	21·6	40·3	34·3	33·0	96%
80	25·4	42·5	36·1	33·7	93%
100	28·0	43·8	37·2	33·8	91%
120	30·0	44·8	38·1	33·3	88%
140	31·5	45·5	38·7	32·4	84%(!)

From the above-mentioned data, the basal areas for certain ages and the corresponding mean heights have been determined for Wiedemann's Q. Cl. I. In order that these figures of basal area, which have been taken mostly from lightly thinned stands, shall correspond to the present-day concept of "moderate thinning", they have been reduced to 85 per cent (Table 57).

This unnatural and arbitrary reduction of the basal areas for higher age values is typical of the more recent yield tables of Schwappach, the basal area frame of which was subsequently taken over by Wiedemann.

The otherwise excellent Scots pine yield tables of Wiedemann (1948) are founded predominantly on East German plots. Accordingly, the mean basal area figures in the table for moderate thinning[1] are consistently *too low* by as much as 20 per cent for sites in the

[1] For height quality class I, between the ages 30–140 years and with a thinning removal percentage of 53, they amount to only 33·9 m². For the same final height at the age of 140 years (31·5 m) the table of Zimmerle, with a thinning removal of 51 per cent, gives a mean basal area content of 37·6 m², i.e. approximately 10 per cent more.

hill country of Hessen. The deviations to be expected for good sites in south and south-west Germany are larger still. The basal area content in the table of Zimmerle, lying approximately 10 per cent above the table of Wiedemann, is also likely in all cases to be too low for south German conditions.[1]

We must expect the growth of *Sessile oak* and *Pedunculate oak* to differ. At least half of the values of the oak yield table of Schwappach (1920) are based on stands of pedunculate oak the structure of which in some cases resembles that of a coppice with standards. Just like the oak yield table of Wiedemann (1946), which is identical to this apart from very minor differences, it indicates extremely low basal area values, which in some cases are only about 50 per cent of the local potential. It has been demonstrated that, if the degree of stocking in East German stands of Sessile oak were kept on a level basis with this table, we would in all cases have to expect volume reductions of 20 per cent (Assmann, 1956). In Sessile oak stands in the Spessart and the Pfälzer Wald, R. Mayer (1957) found such marked deviations in the growth trend and the increment conditions from those depicted in this oak yield table that it must be regarded as completely unsuitable, at least for the stands in question and for the method of establishment of these stands. The south German oak yield table of Zimmerle (1930) is also based on such very low basal area values as to resemble those following an *increment felling*. Mitscherlich (1953) calculated on the basis of sample plots in Baden that there, the maximum possible increment will not be achieved below a degree of stocking of 1·40 in relation to Zimmerle's table.

In the course of determining the frame for basal area and growing stock in these tables, certain concepts of soil rentability (Martin, 1894) became incorporated, which are supported by somewhat over-optimistic ideas regarding the effects of heavy thinning. They find characteristic expression in the "management grades" devised by Phillip which separately identify each of several grades of thinning intensity reckoned in terms of so many "tenths" of the total yield extracted by way of thinnings (for example, management grade III = 30 per cent, VI = 60 per cent removed in thinnings). There is an obvious intention to identify the degree of thinning carried out in each case with maximum profitability.[2]

The yields of beech are strikingly constant, although they seem to increase systematically from NE. to SW. Owing to a higher specific gravity in beech wood as compared with, for example, Norway spruce, the measurable changes in dimensions and volume increment are smaller, so that systematic changes in beech yields are more difficult to assess.

The question of possible *yield tables for mixed stands* will be discussed in a later chapter of the book (p. 348). Their presentation *in the hitherto usual form*, however, incidentally appears to make sense only for combinations of light-demanding species (e.g. pine, larch) in the upper storey and shade-tolerant species in the lower storey, with the light-demanding species only making any significant contribution to yield.

---

[1] The basal area content of a Scots pine yield table recently constructed by Kern (1958) for Bunter Sand sites in the Pfälzer Wald lies above the Y.T. of Zimmerle.

[2] This tendency is pertinently illustrated in Mitscherlich's publication *Das Wachstum der Kiefer in Baden*, Freiburg, 1956, also in *Allg. Forst. u. Jagdztg.* 1955, on p. 138, Fig. 11, and in Mitscherlich's expository comments on pp. 137–9. The intrusion of these concepts into the treatment of sample plots in Baden has had particularly unfortunate consequences for their subsequent interpretation as there are no control plots under light thinning, and exceptionally only a very few plots under moderate thinning. The value of such experiments for yield studies is very low!

Construction of local tables

The difficulties in the way of constructing a large number of tables for local use must not be over-estimated. The encouraging progress achieved in site reconnaissance and map-

TABLE 58

SITE TABLE FOR NORWAY SPRUCE STANDS OF THE *Oxalis myrtillus* TYPE ON THE RUBBLE PLANE OF UPPER SWABIA (OBERSCHWÄBISCHE SCHOTTERFLUR) SOUTH-EAST OF ULM

Age	Main crop				Thinning		Total crop volume (m³)	Increment	
	Top height (m)	Mean height (m)	Basal area (m²)	Stem wood (m³)	(m³)	total (m³)		current (m³)	mean (m³)
10	(3·0)	(2·2)							
15	(5·8)	(4·8)							
20	8·8	6·9	25·6	99			99		4·9
					8			10·6	
25	11·9	9·4	27·9	144		8	152		6·1
					12			14·6	
30	14·7	11·9	31·7	205		20	225		7·5
					18			17·2	
35	17·1	14·2	35·8	273		38	311		8·9
					22			18·0	
40	19·2	16·2	39·1	341		60	401		10·0
					25			17·2	
45	21·0	18·0	41·8	402		85	487		10·8
					25			15·4	
50	22·6	19·7	43·3	454		110	564		11·3
					30			14·0	
55	24·0	21·2	44·0	494		140	634		11·5
					30			13·0	
60	25·3	22·7	44·7	529		170	699		11·6
					30			12·4	
65	26·4	23·9	45·3	561		200	761		11·7
					35			11·8	
70	27·5	25·3	45·7	585		235	820		*11·7*
					35			11·4	
75	28·5	26·3	46·0	607		270	877		11·7
					35			10·8	
80	29·4	27·2	46·5	626		305	931		11·6
					30			10·6	
85	30·2	27·9	47·3	649		335	984		11·6
					30			10·2	
90	30·9	28·6	48·0	670		365 (329)*	1035 (999)*		11·5 (11·1)

The following values are found in the yield table of Wiedemann:

Age	Rel. height quality class	m.a.i.$_{90}$
30	0·9	12·5 m³ (solid) timber compared with an actual m.a.i.$_{90}$ of 11·1 m³
60	1·5	10·9
90	1·75	10·2

* Figures in parentheses = values of timber over 7 cm in diameter.

ping will in future simplify the task of bringing together into appropriate growth categories crops standing on similar sites. The question as to whether crops under examination which have received only one appraisal belong to the same or separate categories can be settled by conducting height analyses of dominant sample stems. Some such *combination of indicator and strip methods* would recommend itself because, even *within well-defined ecological limits* (in the sense used by Krauss), fairly large *differences in height quality class and in the individual development of crops* may occur. For a site table, one can as a rule assume a single "auxiliary relation" (total crop yield $=f(h_m)$), so that knowing the local top- and mean-height development and adopting suitable thinning yield percentages (augmented with increasing height of the stand) it is easy to calculate the most important values of the table. By deducting the total of thinning volumes achieved at each step, we can determine the volume of the remaining stand. If this is divided by the form-height corresponding to the mean height of the stand, we obtain the basal area per hectare. Data for stem numbers per hectare and diameter of the mean basal area stem are not absolutely essential, especially as N and d_m for equal values of crop basal area (G) are to a certain extent variable.[1] A model of a site table is given in Table 58. It represents the average of the enumerated sample plots and could, without much difficulty, be supplemented by two tables with a lower and a superior height quality class so that interpolations are possible. Tables of this kind have in the meantime been constructed by Franz for some sites occurring in a fairly large area in Middle and Upper Swabia according to Krauss–Schlenker. Having one standard yield level in every case, they show the development of top height and mean height upon age for a medium as well as an upper and lower height quality class. An advantage of these tables is the fact that they are based on the height growth trends typical of the habitat so that an established "dynamic" quality classification becomes possible after about the age of 40 years.

The greatest possible importance should in future be attached to bringing *into closer proximity the permanent sample plots* which in many countries and regions are decidedly too loosely knit. As an ancillary measure, a system of "double plots for yield control" suggests itself such as the one recently recommended by Assmann (1959b). In this, a sample plot under very light thinning (removal of dying trees only) is placed under permanent observation side by side with one in which the applied type of thinning is considered to be the local "optimum" (according to the degree and method). For mixed crops a system of control plots, developed and recommended by Speidel (1957) mainly as a basis of yield control in management is considered suitable.

(b) PRODUCTIVE EFFICIENCIES OF NATIVE AND EXOTIC TREE SPECIES ON DIFFERENT SITES

The automatic identification of height quality class with volume production, which although not fully justified, is still customary, must be considered responsible for many misleading ideas that are widely held today about the mutual relationships existing between tree production and factors of the habitat. About this, as well as the deviating growth pattern of the various tree species little is known as yet.

---

[1] Some data in our present-day yield tables appear, like artistic ornaments on a building, of doubtful substance.

Growth patterns and increment performances of tree species compared on a given site

Informative answers to this question, which is of equal importance in yield studies, silviculture, management and mensuration, were given in the Munich dissertation by Günther (1955) about the yield capacity of the principal tree species within the range of

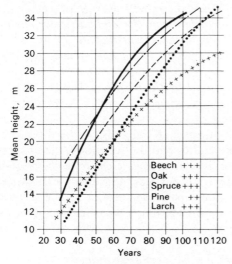

FIG. 94. A. Fresh beech–maple forest type on fine loam.

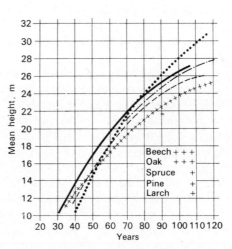

FIG. 95. D. Beech forest type on medium and deep layers of chalky loam.

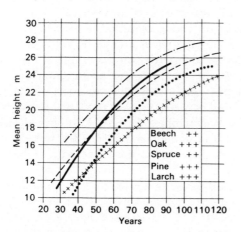

FIG. 96. E. Beech–oak forest type on acid soil consisting of sandy loam or loamy sand.

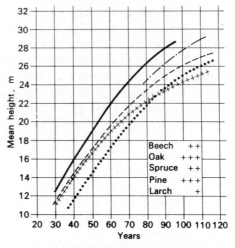

FIG. 97. F. Mixed beech-oak forest type on loami "kerf" and light Keuper marl.

FIGS. 94–97. Mean height/age curves for different tree species in pure stands upon various sites *(Günther)*.

(Mean height = height of mean basal area tree)

Beech · · · ·	+ + +	goodness of fit very significant
Oak + + + +	+ +	goodness of fit significant
Spruce ———	+	best estimate
Pine – – – – –		
Larch –·–·–·–		

the different local habitat units of the Neckar region in Württemberg. This concerns a region in which the macro-climate is characterized by great warmth (it is partly wine-growing country) with moderate to average precipitation (600–850 mm). Figures 94 to 97 show the specific mean height development of five tree species on four of the seven observed site units (according to Krauss and Schlenker). The difference between the height development of oak and beech in the site units D and F, as well as that of spruce and beech in A and D is striking. *Evidently, the innate height capacity and particular mode of height development of a species operate in its favour to the extent that the factors of the habitat correspond with its individual requirements or as it is capable of adapting itself to them.*

That this applies also for yield production is proved by the values in Table 59. There, the mean m.a.i.$_{100}$ is given for oak, beech and spruce respectively on six sites, together with the standard errors of the means.

On the *typical beech site* (A), *oak is inferior to beech* ($P=$slightly above 5 per cent) whilst, on the extreme site (F) with its rooting difficulties and podsolization, the converse is the case (not significant; $t=0.5$). The situation is similar *when comparing the relationships between spruce and beech.* Comparing the volume yields, this relation fluctuates between $2.3/1.0$ and $1.6/1.0$.[1] Characteristically, the superiority ratio of spruce is lowest with $1.6/1.0$ in the beech forest on chalky loam, i.e. on a site which is particularly agreeable to beech. *The superiority of spruce becomes more marked with increasing acidity of the site* and greater availability of water supplies.

That this *superiority of spruce remains, even when it has been transformed to dry matter,* is not surprising. Although Rudolf Weber (1891) taught that the *dry-weight production of the different tree species on a given site is approximately equal,* he at the same time pointed out that the quality classes given in the yield tables are not mutually comparable, and drew attention in particular to the results of Robert Hartig's investigations in 1888. The latter found that a 52-year-old spruce stand on young morainic soil near Grafrath produced 2.7 times the volume and *1.8 times the dry-matter* of a 62-year-old neighbouring stand of beech. Compared with the further productivity ratios in Table 60, the superiority of spruce in dry-weight production on the sites investigated by Günther was not particularly high, which perhaps is due to the special climatic conditions. The superiority in dry weight production there fluctuates between $1.1/1.0$ and $1.6/1.0$. As the investigations of Moosmayer upon sites of the Württemberg Eastern Alps have shown, the productivity ratio fluctuates between $2.1/1.0$ (volume) or $1.5/1.0$ (dry weight) on chalky loam and $3.0/1.0$ or $2.1/1.0$ on silty loam. Here again, the superiority of spruce is more marked on the more acid soils.

The outstanding superiority of out-turn here displayed by spruce in comparison with that of beech applies generally to coniferous trees as compared with broad-leaved trees. It is a consequence of their evolutionary development. As stressed by Huber (1956), coniferous woods are "tracheid woods". Owing to their slowly operating water-conductive system they require *larger cross-sections of wood* and thus a relatively larger bole than the broad-leaved woods with their highly specialized and wide-pored conductive system. The more primitive structure of coniferous timbers thus procures us advantages in technical production.

Striking differences in the yield ratios, depending on sites, are proved also by the

---

[1] The differences in the efficiencies of spruce and beech shown in Table 59 are all significant with probabilities of exceeding below 0.27 per cent.

TABLE 59

YIELD PERFORMANCES OF OAK, BEECH AND SPRUCE ON SITE UNITS OF THE NECKAR REGION IN WÜRTTEMBERG. AFTER GÜNTHER (1955)

Site unit	Oak			Beech			Spruce			Yield ratios		
	Number of sample plot	m.a.i.$_{100}$ (m³)	±μ	Number of sample plot	m.a.i.$_{100}$ (m³)	±μ	Number of sample plot	m.a.i.$_{100}$ (m³)	±μ	Spruce/Beech by vol.	Spruce/Beech by dry matter	Oak/Beech by vol.
A. Fresh Beech–Maple forest on fine loam	23	6·1 (3·48)	0·33	10	7·2 (4·03)	0·46	18	13·8 (5·38)	0·70	1·9 : 1·0	1·35 : 1·0	0·85 : 1·0
B. Beech–Oak forest on fine loam	27	5·2 (2·96)	0·31	31	5·7 (3·19)	0·24	23	12·0 (4·68)	0·55	2·1 : 1·0	1·5 : 1·0	0·9 : 1·0
C. Acidic Beech–Oak forest on fine loam	13	4·8 (2·74)	0·39	22	5·3 (2·97)	0·24	10	10·6 (4·13)	1·17	2·0 : 1·0	1·4 : 1·0	0·9 : 1·0
D. Beech forest on medium and deep layers of chalky loam	28	4·7 (2·68)	0·27	17	5·9 (3·30)	0·30	10	9·5 (3·71)	1·14	1·6 : 1·0	1·1 : 1·0	0·8 : 1·0
E. Acidic Beech–Oak forest on sandy loam or loamy sand	38	4·2 (2·39)	0·22	26	4·7 (2·63)	0·36	14	9·0 (3·51)	0·66	1·9 : 1·0	1·3 : 1·0	0·9 : 1·0
F. Beech–Oak forest on loamy "kerf" and Keuper-clay	19	5·1 (2·91)	0·21	25	4·9 (2·74)	0·37	31	11·3 (4·41)	0·50	2·3 : 1·0	1·6 : 1·0	1·05 : 1·0

* Values in parentheses = dry-weight yield in tons.

TABLE 60

COMPARATIVE PERFORMANCE OF BEECH AND SPRUCE GROWING SIDE BY SIDE ON THE SAME SITE

Source	Site	Species	Age	Av. ann. total production in		Ratio: Beech/Spruce acc. to	
				timber vol. (m³)	dry weight of wood (t)	volume	dry weight
R. Hartig (1888)	*Young morainic soil* near Grafrath	Beech	62	4·77	2·67	*1 : 2·7*	*1 : 1·8*
		Spruce	52	13·02	4·68		
Württ. Res. Inst.	*Swabian Alps*	Beech	70	4·49	2·51	*1 : 2·9*	*1 : 1·20*
Lfm. Hausser (1953)	near Mochental	Spruce	74	13·03	5·08		
Württ. Res. Inst. Moosmayer (1957)	Site and site unit *Eastern Alps*	C. Beech forest on medium and deep layers of chalky loam				*1/2·1*	*1/1·5*
		D. Beech forest on loamy schists with *Luzula* sp.				*1/2·5*	*1/1·7*
		F. Beech forest on silty loam with *Luzula* sp.				*1/3·0*	*1/2·1*

The last three values apply for a reference age of 100 years.

figures in Table 61.[1] This, however, concerns fairly young stands whose advance is still comparatively strongly prejudiced by transitory checks to growth, such as occasional late frost, as well as by the different growth rhythms. Local habitat influences apart, the superiority of exotics in comparison to the indigenous species is impressively apparent. This is particularly marked with *Red oak* as compared to the native oak species. This superiority, amongst other things, stands out also in Baur's monograph and in a contribution by Mitscherlich (1957a).

A *comparison of the performance of Douglas fir* (var. *viridis*) *with those of other species* can be drawn from the extensive sample plot data collected by Flöhr (1956) on East German drift soils and published as part of the yield-study investigations of the same author in a book by Göhre (1958). Flöhr arranged the sites in accordance with the system of site types developed by Scamoni (1951, 1954). Of the ninety-three comparisons of the yields of Scots pine and sixty-five of Norway spruce, only those without big age differences and without disturbance have been used for Table 62. Flöhr estimated the probable total crop volumes (of timber over 7 cm in diameter) and the m.a.i.s for Douglas fir at the age of 80 years in the compared species at different economic rotation ages in each case by the statistical height quality class at the age of assessment. For the comparison in Table 62, a *rotation of 80 years* instead of the 120 years chosen by Flöhr, was used for Scots pine also because, in this comparison, the natural productive capacity over the same reference periods was to be assessed.

The manifest superiority of the Douglas fir yield over that of Scots pine is demonstrated by the average productivity ratio of 1·66/1·00.

In contrast to this, the average *superiority in comparison to Norway spruce at 1·27/1·00*

---

[1] I should like here to express my thanks to Landforstmeister Hausser for putting the figures at my disposal.

TABLE 61

PERFORMANCE OF DIFFERENT TREE SPECIES OCCURRING SIDE BY SIDE ON THE SAME SITE

Source: Bad.-Württ. Forstl. Versuchsanstalt, field-station, Hechingen

Site	Tree species	Age	Mean height (m)	m.a.i. in V (m³)	m.a.i. in dry subst. (t)	Productivity ratio % vol.	Productivity ratio % dry subst.
Baindt Forest, Upper Schwaben, young morainic soil	Norway spruce	68	29·1	13·2	5·15	100	100
	Douglas fir (viridis)	68	37·4	20·5	8·61	155	167
	Jap. larch	62	29·1	12·3	5·78	93	112
Freudenstadt Forest (Steinwald), Black Forest, top: bunter-sand	Norway spruce	61	16·9	6·6	2·57	100	100
	Douglas fir (viridis)	60	26·0	14·7	6·17	223	240
Ochsenhausen Forest, Upper Schwaben, old morainic soil	Norway spruce	65	24·4	10·2	3·98	100	100
	Jap. larch	63	27·5	11·3	5·31	111	133
Ditto	Jap. larch	61	29·9	13·4	6·30		
	+N. spr. u-storey		16·2	1·0	0·39		
	Total			14·4	6·69	100	100
	Dougl. fir	59	27·3	15·6	6·55	108	98
Ravensburg Forest, Upper Schwaben, young morainic soil	Pedclte. oak	48	19·3	4·7	2·68	100	100*
	Red oak	47	24·2	9·1	5·19	194	194*
Einsiedel Forest, Schönbuch, "Knollenmergel"	Jap. larch	63	27·1	9·5	4·46	100	100
	Douglas fir	73	30·9	9·1	3·82	96	117
	Red oak	73	26·9	9·1	5·19	96	116
Ditto	Oak	54	16·2	3·8	2·17	100	100
	Red oak	63	26·4	9·2	5·24	242	242

* Incl. broad-leaved wood under storey.

for volume and 1·37/1·00 for dry weight is less marked. It is possible that a comparison of trial plots under long-term observation of both species would yield other efficiency ratios with clearer ecological differences.

The superiority of Douglas fir when compared to Japanese larch with corresponding ratios of 1·58/1·00 and 1·41/1·00 is unexpectedly high, at least measured against the figures for the sample plots in Württemburg in Table 61. It is possible that in this instance, the very early culmination of the m.a.i. of the Jap. larch works to its disadvantage.

We are indebted to G. Jahn (1954) for informative comparisons between the efficiencies of *green Douglas fir* and *Norway spruce* on north German mountain sites of medium altitude. As a measure of comparison G. Jahn used the mean height at the age of 60 years. Table 63 shows average efficiency ratios for twenty-four comparisons of neighbouring stands of pure species (comparisons which were considered untrustworthy were excluded) on the remaining site units; the comparison concerned the mean height as well as the probable total crop volume and dry weight. The calculated mean ratios of yield attainments for all sites at 1·23/1·00 (by volume) and 1·33/1·00 (by dry weight) agree well with the values obtained from the measurements of Flöhr. The superiority of Douglas fir on slopes with deep soils and a good water supply is most remarkable whilst, at the same time, the attainments of the two species on similar types of soils with an apparently shallow root horizon are more alike.

TABLE 62

COMPARISON OF THE PERFORMANCES OF DOUGLAS FIR (VIRIDIS) WITH OTHER SPECIES ON SITES OF THE
EAST GERMAN DILUVIUM

After Surveys of Flöhr (1956)

Basis of comparison: m.a.i.$_{80}$ according to height quality classification

Site	Compared species	Number of comparisons	Ratio by volume	by dry weight
Sites with loamy sub-soil (L$_2$, L$_3$)	Douglas fir/ Scots pine	15	1·63 : 1·00	1·63 : 1·00
Sandy sites (S$_b$, S$_{b-c}$, S$_c$)		13	1·57 : 1·00	1·57 : 1·00
Sites influenced by ground water (GS$_2$ and GS$_3$)		19	1·74 : 1·00	1·74 : 1·00
All sites		47	*1·66 : 1·00*	*1·66 : 1·00*
Sites with loamy sub-soil	Douglas fir/ Norway spruce	25	1·25* : 1·00	1·35 : 1·00
Sandy sites		10	1·29 : 1·00	1·39 : 1·00
Sites influenced by ground water		14	1·28 : 1·00	1·38 : 1·00
All sites		49	*1·27 : 1·00*	*1·37 : 1·00*
All sites	Douglas fir/ Jap. larch	11	1·58† : 1·00	1·41 : 1·00

* Standard error of arithmetic mean = ±0·04.
† Standard error of arithmetic mean = ±0·10.
The values used are those of Flöhr in the book by Göhre but with exclusion of comparative pairs
which showed too large differences in age and disturbances. In deviation from Flöhr, the values were
related to a rotation of 80 years instead of 120 years.

As displayed by provenance trials with Douglas fir (cf. among others Dittmar, 1954;
Flöhr and Dittmar, 1954; Rohmeder, 1956a; Schober 1954), significant differences are
to be found also between the three known varieties, so that the value of the above comparisons is merely of an instructive character. Knowledge of the correct productivity
ratios of exotic species in relation to the indigenous species is of such great importance to
economic and yield studies that in future silvicultural and yield experiments the inclusion
of a species indigenous to the locality on a sufficiently comparable scale should be
regarded as indispensable.

*Certainly, the productivity ratios for the different tree species are not constant among
themselves but fluctuate considerably according to site.* Consequently the construction of a
general table for comparing volumes and dry weight production of the several individual
species on the basis of given mean crop heights, as Weck has done (*Zuwachs- u.Ertragsk.*,
1st edition, 1948) seems to be of doubtful value.

In addition to studies of pure stands, an examination of the structure and productivity
relations of typical *mixed stands* suggests itself. However, in Europe we must usually
deal with mixed stands which have been subjected to a wide variety of silvicultural techniques. The possible effects of these must first be studied in pure stands, so that they can
be included in our analysis of the complicated relationships of mixed stands. We shall
therefore discuss this category of mixed stands as influenced by silvicultural techniques
in Section D. In order to be able to form an opinion of the structure and behaviour
of natural, uneven-aged, mixed stands we must first make ourselves acquainted with

TABLE 63

COMPARISON OF THE EFFICIENCIES OF GREEN DOUGLAS FIR AND NORWAY SPRUCE ON DIFFERENT SITES IN THE NORTH-WEST GERMAN MOUNTAINS OF MEDIUM ALTITUDE BY G. JAHN

THE MEAN HEIGHTS AT THE AGE OF 60 YEARS OF NEIGHBOURING STANDS OF PURE SPECIES WERE COMPARED

Site unit	IVb	IIIb	IIb	IIc	IIa+Ia	IId	Together
Relief	Lower slopes and slope trough	Slope positions leaning + steeper	Level–gently sloping positions	Level–gently sloping positions	Flat summits, level–gently sloping pos.	Level + gently sloping positions	
Soil type	Base-poor brown earth	as before	as before	Brown earth changing to gley-type in sub-soil	Base deficient brown earth	Gley-type soils	
Development stage	Fully developed	as before	Fully developed	—	Light to moderate	—	
Forest community	Touch-me-not, beech forest	Fern–beech for., wood sorrel–fern, variant of the wood–rush–beech fern forest	Wood–rush–beech forest, wood sorrel– fern variant	Wood sorrel– fern variant of the wood– rush–beech forest	Wood–rush– beech forest, *Deschampsia flexuosa*	Not ascertainable, but not oak–birch heath forest of varied moisture content	
Number of comparisons	6	4	6	4	4	4	28
Prod. ratios Dougl. fir/Norway spruce							
Acc. to mean ht.	*1·35 : 1·00*	*1·27 : 1·00*	*1·15 : 1·00*	*1·17 : 1·00*	*1·14 : 1·00*	*1·07 : 1·00*	*1·20 : 1·00*
Acc. to tot. volume prod^n.	*1·48 : 1·00*	*1·34 : 1·00*	*1·15 : 1·00*	*1·18 : 1·00*	*1·13 : 1·00*	*1·02 : 1·00*	*1·23 : 1·00*
In dry weight	*1·59 : 1·00*	*1·45 : 1·00*	*1·24 : 1·00*	*1·27 : 1·00*	*1·22 : 1·00*	*1·13 : 1·00*	*1·33 : 1·00*

the rules governing the working of felling series. In the following chapter, some typical examples of average and extreme performances of native and exotic species in pure stands are given.

Growth performance of different species on European sites,
as extracted from yield tables

Table 64 once more displays the marked differences between the performances of the familiar tree species at given mean heights resulting from the varying local conditions and methods of treatment in different European countries. As a general rule, there is

TABLE 64

GROWTH PERFORMANCE OF DIFFERENT TREE SPECIES ON EUROPEAN SITES, ACCORDING
TO YIELD TABLES, Q. CL. I IN EACH CASE

Species	Country and yield table	For mean height (m)	At age	Total timber volume (m³)	m.a.i. (m³)	(%)
Common beech	*Germany* Wiedemann, 1931/mod.	30	90	729	8·1	100
	Denmark Mar:Møller, 1933	30	86	926	10·8	133
Norway spruce	*Germany* Wiedemann, 1936/42		47	480	10·2	100
	Vanselow, 1951		44	628	14·3	141
	Denmark Mar:Møller, 1933	20	40	640	16·0	157
	Great Britain Hummel and Christie		38	627	16·5	162
	Germany Wiedemann		81	987	12·2	100
	Vanselow		73	1265	17·3	142
	Denmark Mar:Møller	30	70	1259	18·0	148
Douglas fir	*Germany* Kanzow– Wiedemann	30	55	915	16·6	100
	Great Britain Hummel and Christie		42	912	21·7	131
Sitka spruce	*Great Britain* Hummel and Christie	30	42	999	23·8	
Scots pine	*Germany* Wiedemann, 1943	20	54	421	7·8	100
	Great Britain Hummel and Christie		46	573	12·4	159

an evident tendency towards larger total crop volumes for given mean heights in maritime areas. Apart from decreased frost danger, the earlier start to thinnings is likely to be decisive as affecting the mean height at an early age. Incidentally, the differences in performance become noticeably smaller at the mean height of 30 m. The record performance in Great Britain is held by Sitka spruce with a m.a.i. of $23 \cdot 8$ m³ at the age of 42 years.

In decided contrast are the low production figures of Scots pine and Norway spruce in north Sweden under sub-arctic, dry and cold conditions, as well as the modest yields of Scots pine in Germany on the poorest sands in the Lausitz; these are shown in Table 65.

TABLE 65

EXTREME LOW GROWTH PERFORMANCES OF SCOTS PINE AND NORWAY SPRUCE ON SWEDISH AND GERMAN SITES

Species	Country and yield table	For mean height (m)	At age	Total crop vol. of stemwood (S) or timber of dia. > 7 cm (D)	m.a.i. (m³)
Scots pine	*Sweden* (North-Sweden) Petterson, 1955	9·7	100	150 (S)	1·5 (S)
	Germany Qual. Class VI Wiedemann 1943	8·3	100	109 (D)	1·1 (D)
Norway spruce	*Sweden* (North-Sweden) Petterson, 1955	10·0	100	112 (S)	1·1 (S)
	Germany Wiedemann, 1936 Qual. Class V	17·2	100	396 (D)	4·0 (D)

Arising from incorrectly calculated volumes per unit area[1] (among others by Schmitz-Lenders, 1948), vague and, in most cases, exaggerated ideas are held in Germany about the productive possibilities of the numerous clones of poplars. Starting from the values which were calculated by Crocoll (1957) on the basis of trial plots of sufficient size under long-term observation in the Rheinauen (Rhine meadows) of Baden, we find increments which are impressive, not so much in their absolute value, but rather in the low age at which they were achieved, and the tree dimensions achieved. Crocoll quotes maximum current increments of 25 m³ timber over 7 cm in diameter. Among his trial plot data, we find maximum m.a.i.s of approximately 15 m³ (wood over 7 cm in diamater) which are achieved at the age of 45–50 years, with mean stems of approximately 65 cm diameter at breast height and 36 m height. In a draft yield table for *Populus Marilandica*

[1] The increment of poplar avenues cannot be related to an area which is limited by the crown projections. It is necessary to take into consideration the fact that the crowns in avenue trees have complete freedom on at least one side, and that the degree of liberation on that side is "infinite".

of Quality Class II in North Baden, spaced 5×5 m, the following data are given for the age of *50 years*:

$$m.a.i. = 12 \cdot 5 \text{ m}^3 \text{ (timber over 7 cm in diameter)}$$
$$h_m = 35 \cdot 7 \text{ m}$$
$$d_m = 64 \cdot 4 \text{ cm}$$

The current annual increment culminates at the age of 30–35 years with 17 m³.

Finally, some *peak performances of individual trees of the Silver fir (Abies grandis)* in Europe:

Site	Age	d.b.h. (cm)	Height (m)	Timber vol. (m³)
Leighton Hall Estate	68	113	48·8	16·6
North Wales	68	103	50·0	18·7
Holzhausen, Kr. Lübbecke northern Westph., medium slope, white Jurassic+loess loam	80	91	˙42	13·0
Ditto, water-collecting trough (after Burchard, 1960)	48		43	9·4

3. Disturbances in the Normal Trend of Increment

We find that in the smoothed increment trends shown in the yield tables, individual trees as well as stands exhibit considerable fluctuations which, over long periods of time, stand out particularly clearly in the sequences of annual rings on stem cross-sections and borings. For long past, changing climatic conditions from year to year have been recognized as being chiefly responsible for these fluctuations.

Climate, weather during the year, and increment

The sequences of annual rings of long-lived trees like *Pinus ponderosa* and especially *Sequoia gigantea* in the dry regions of North America were used by Huntington (1925), Antevs (1925) and Douglass (1929) for investigations into long-term climatic fluctuations and the climatic character of historical epochs. Douglass (1929) succeeded in connecting up the sequences of annual rings on cross-sections of logs of Indian dwellings (Pueblos) with those of freshly felled trees and thus determining the years of construction which lie 1000 and more years in the past. Huber (1941, 1953, 1958), together with his collaborators v. Jazewitsch, John, Müller-Stoll (1951) and Wellenhofer (1949), is endeavouring to construct an annual ring chronology for Central Europe. In this endeavour, the sequences of annual rings of oak from the Spessart have principally been used.

For the purposes of yield studies, we are more particularly interested in the extent of the increment fluctuations, the size of possible increment losses and the *different effects* of short-term changes of climatic factors *upon the individual habitats*. The fact, that a dry and hot summer has, for example, a variable effect upon height growth, according to the habitat and average local climate had already become apparent in the investigations of Cieslar (1907) and Hesselman (1904). From extensive material to hand, Burger (1926) was able to demonstrate the different effects of precipitation and temperature levels on height growth depending on site and species. Wiedemann (1923) found that the main cause of the considerable falling-off of growth by Norway spruce in Saxony on sites outside its natural range of distribution was the *increasing frequency of dry periods* (= months with rainfall below 40 mm). Flury (1926) used the increment measurements of Swiss research plots to prove climatic effects. He found specially high increment losses (40 per cent and over) occurring as a result of dry periods in pure crops of *Norway spruce* in the hill country, although beech proved to be less sensitive. Flury found also that upon mountain sites with a cool and damp climate, hot and dry years may have a favourable effect on the increment.

Owing to the intervals of 5 or more years between assessments, which may include years of variable or erratic weather, the periodic increments of sample plots are not very suitable for investigations of this kind. Moreover, any apparent fluctuations may be strongly distorted by errors of appraisal.[1] For this reason, measurements of annual rings on stem cross-sections and drillings are indispensable.

Informative results have become available from Knuchel's (1933) extensive examinations of stem discs. Characteristically, these were caused by peculiar reductions in increment in the Swiss selection forests of Couvet and Boveresse upon which Favre (1928 and 1931) reported and which Favre and Biolley rightly ascribed to climatic effects. On numerous discs cut from trees of several species from different parts of Switzerland it became apparent that the fluctuations of the width of annual rings and the reduced increments as a result of dry years were largest in the Jura, smallest in the high mountains, and relatively small for Silver fir and spruce in the Lower Alps. Figure 98 well illustrates this difference in fluctuation of the annual ring width of Silver fir from the Lower Alps, the Mittelland and the Jura. Knuchel proved beyond doubt that the striking reduction in increment during the management periods of 1915–20 and 1917–22 at Couvet and Boveresse respectively were caused by climatic effects.

In high alpine sites (Artmann, 1949; Brehme, 1951; Müller Stoll, 1951), as well as in high northern latitudes of Scandinavia and Finland (Eide, 1926; Mikola, 1950 *et al.*) where the climate is cool, a warm summer has a favourable influence, whilst during a cool summer only narrow annual rings are developed.

For the most thorough and accurate analytical studies upon annual rings made in Europe to date, we are indebted to Holmsgaard (1955) who took no less than 78,000 measurements of ring widths on increment cores, mainly of beech and spruce from Denmark. He succeeded in calculating, for a long sequence of past years, *mean annual ring indices*, free from age trends and thinning effects. These indices show clearly the *influences of climatic factors as well as thinning and mast years* on the different Danish sites.

Holmsgaard has exposed the relationships between climatic factors and annual ring width by means of correlation analysis. Among other things, he found that in *beech and spruce, the amount of rainfall during the months of May to July* is of decisive importance for the width of the annual rings, whilst in *oak and Silver fir* the summer *temperature* is more important. The winter and early spring temperature has a considerable influence on alder, Scots pine, Douglas fir and a lesser influence on ash. Among the *climatic*

---

[1] Permanent experiments which are meant to exhibit the influence of certain methods of treatment must contain at least two individual plots with different treatments, because only in this way is it possible to eliminate and allow for the contemporaneous climatic effects, which will operate in similar manner on each of the separate plots.

conditions of the previous year, it is mainly the *quantity of precipitation* which is effective upon the increment of *Norway spruce in Denmark*. This post-effect is the more marked, the older the stands are.

Thinning causes the widening of annual rings by 6–12 per cent for both the first and the second summers after thinning. In the index calculations, Holmsgaard removes these thinning effects by forming the mean of six to eight stands with different times of thinning in each case.

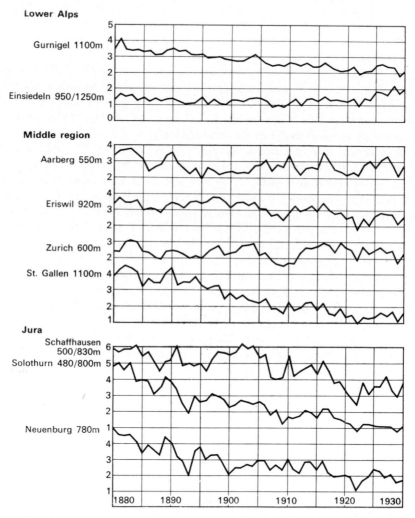

FIG. 98. Widths of annual rings of dominant Silver fir trees at different altitudes in Switzerland (*Knuchel*).

The annual ring indices deduced by Holmsgaard permit a conversion of the measured increments of arbitrarily chosen periods into "normal" increments by way of *climate corrections*. The calculation and use of indices for climate corrections in countries with relatively slight differences in the macro-climate, as in Denmark, is easier than in countries with large differences of climate, as for example Germany.

With what telling effect local peculiarities of site may modify the effects of macro-climatic variations on, for example, the height growth of Norway spruce is shown in Figs. 99 and 100. On the warm and dry Jurassic site in Härtsfeldhausen forest, the wet years 1954 to 1956 led to an almost incredibly rapid acceleration of height growth. In Fig. 99 a height growth curve was first drawn in order to show the particular height-

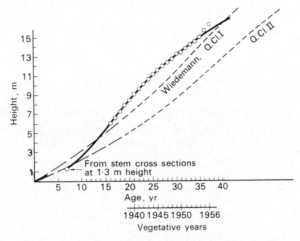

FIG. 99. Height growth curve for dominant spruce trees (mean of ten sample stems) on a dry Jura site, compared with yield table values by *Wiedemann*.

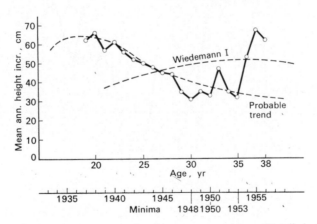

FIG. 100. Height increment curve for the same spruce stems. Details in the text.

growth trend, which deviates from the typical yield table trend of Wiedemann, and then this is used to support the increment trend curve in Fig. 100. It is obvious that the result of several wet years was a *singular advance in increment* on this site. A completely different reaction was shown by the—admittedly much older—Norway spruce trees on very fresh gravelly loam (high-terrace gravel) in Sachsenried forest (Fig. 101). The average amount of rainfall there, with a height above sea level of 850 m, amounts to a good 1250 mm per year. The increment fluctuations occurring there are relatively small, with slight depressions and peaks. Whilst the depression due to the dry years of 1947 and 1949 appears similar to that of the Jura stand, the damp and cool years of 1954 and 1956 have induced an opposite reaction in Sachsenried!

The numerous increment surveys, carried out by the author's own Institute in Norway spruce stands on sites with moderate water supplies, all agreed in yielding 15–35 per cent higher volume increments for the "wet" 5 years from 1950 to 1955 than for the "dry" 5 years from 1945 to 1950. The increase in younger and middle-aged stands was throughout larger than in the old stands.

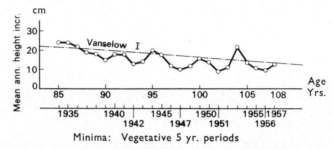

Minima: Vegetative 5 yr. periods

FIG. 101. Height increment curve (mean of fourteen dominant spruce stems) for a cool and humid site. Sachsenried Exp. Series (3).

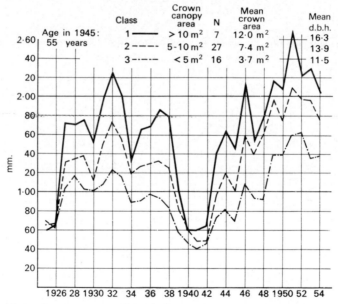

FIG. 102. Mean width of the annual rings of Sessile oak for different tree classes, 1925–54 *(Mayer)*.

In the Lower Saxony region Schober (1950) found, as a result of the dry years of 1947 and 1949, reductions in the breadth of annual rings for 1947–9 from 25 to 40 per cent as compared to those of 1946, which are considered normal. In agreement with Topcuoglu the most marked reductions in the width of annual rings showed themselves at 0·2–0·4 of the stem height, whilst those directly below the crown and at the butt-swell were insignificant.

Figure 102 according to the investigations of R. Mayer (1958) shows the striking influence of the cold winters of the years 1939–42 on the annual ring width of Sessile oak, which is exhibited in what might be called a collapse of the ring growth. As may be seen, the climatically conditioned variations of annual ring width are considerably larger in the dominant trees with large crowns than in the co-dominant trees with small crowns. In his analysis of the sequences of annual rings of Sessile oak in the Steigerwald, R. Mayer managed to show, alongside the marked influence of temperature in the previous year and the rainfall during the actual growing season, how extraordinarily intricate are the relationships between annual ring width and weather.

Seed development and wood increment

R. Hartig (1889) demonstrated with the help of examples the *influence of mast years on the increment of Beech stands*. After the extensive recent investigations of Holmsgaard (1955), the ring width of the over 100-year-old beech stands (capable of seed-production) in Denmark is markedly reduced by seed years. *In 130-and more-year-old stands the reduction in good mast years, which occurs every 6–7 years, amounts to approximately one half of the average ring width of unaffected years.* This increment reduction, as a rule, continues for another 2 years after a good seed year, because the trees must then replace their reserves.[1] Figure 103 clearly shows the strong influence of mast years on the increment

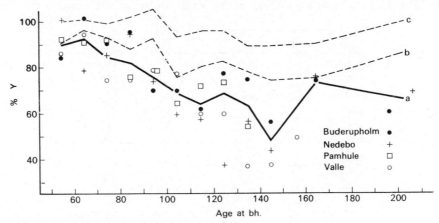

FIG. 103. The influence of the seed year on width of annual rings of Common beech in Denmark. *Abscissa:* mean age of stand at breast height; *ordinate:* relative width of annual rings. Curve *a:* width of annual rings in good mast years; *b:* in the following year; *c:* in the second year after seed harvest *(Holmsgaard).*

of Common beech. Smaller reductions of the ring width as a result of seed years (25–30 per cent) were found by Holmsgaard in 60-and-more-year-old *Norway spruce* stands. Reductions in the ring width as a result of a full mast in *Common beech* were found also by Schulz–Brüggemann (1947). Mikola (1950) observed considerable reductions in the width of the annual rings of *Norway spruce* in Finland during years when the trees produced large amounts of cones.

How strongly the consumption of assimilates for seed production reduces the production of wood has been proved by Rohmeder (1949) by measurements of numerous *male and*

---

[1] Gäumann (1935) discovered that 35 m high beech trees had stored reserves of carbohydrates and hemi-cellulose of not less than 87 kg. Of these, only 26 kg, i.e. only one-quarter to one-third, were used per year for the development of leaves and for the tree increment.

female ash trees in avenues and stands. The wood volume production of male ash trees showed a superiority over the female trees of approximately 40 per cent. This superior performance corresponds approximately to the consumption of assimilates by the female ash trees for seed production. This illustrates the drastic curtailment of wood production in those tree species which fruit frequently and abundantly. The falling-off of growth by our forest trees along with the onset of senescence following their fertile stages, is very likely connected not only with the using up of nutrient materials for fruit development but also with the redirection of hormones which influences the respiration in an unthrifty manner.

Increment reductions through pathological influences

About the increment reductions caused by insect and fungus damage we have unfortunately very little accurate information. H. Badoux (1918) calculated the increment loss in middle-aged Norway spruce stands in Höhragen (Switzerland), 430 m above sea level due to *damage from the Small spruce sawfly (Lygaeonematus abietum)*, to amount to 2·7 m^3 annually. Merker and Niechziol (1957) estimated the current increment losses caused by the same insect in the Mooswald near Freiburg at no less than 60 per cent of the volume increment. The picture of the ever-repeated increment losses caused over several years by attacks by *Grapholita diniana* in the larch forests of the Engadin, in Fig. 104,

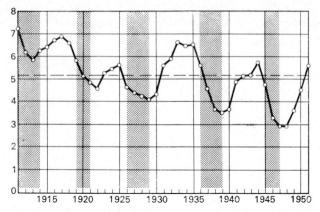

FIG. 104. Depressions of increment in Engadine Valley larch as a result of attacks by *Grapholita diniana* *(= Semasia dineana)*. The years during which the attacks occurred are shown by shading. Widths of annual rings in 1/10 mm *(Badoux)*.

taken from a work of E. Badoux (1952), is very impressive. Zimmerle (1952) estimated the *increment reduction due to an attack by Adelopus* in some Douglas fir trial plots in Württemburg for 4–9 year periods at 11–43 per cent, on average approximately 30 per cent. Notwithstanding the devastation of large areas of forest by known destructive insects, we should not overlook the extent of the increment losses which are caused by other noxious creatures which, although less lethal, do, however, cause damage for short periods or are endemic and attack repeatedly.

Astonishingly large are the *amounts of honeydew* occurring in forests as products of the metabolism of plant sucking *aphids* and, according to investigations of Zoebelein (1954, 1956), serve as a source of nutrition for numerous insects, and especially for wood ants and bees.

Zoebelein (1954) succeeded, by systematic observation and weighing of red wood ants, in estimating the honeydew production of individual spruce trees (attacked by *Physokermes* species) and the probable annual production of spruce stands. He arrived at a minimum amount of 700 kg of honeydew, corresponding to approximately 140 kg dry sugar, which is equal to a loss in timber production of, to say the least, 0·4 m³/ha. That kind of calculation, however, shows itself as short-sighted utilitarian thinking if one remembers the valuable functions of the red wood-ant in the forest biocoenose. Moreover, it is, after all, possible by way of bees to convert the honeydew of the forest into exceedingly valuable and healthy human nourishment, a circumstance which was pointed out by Zwölfer (1952).

Root investigations made by Wagenknecht (1960) and his collaborators proved that the decisive factor in the familiar phenomenon of "arable land sickness" which decimates afforestated stands of Scots pine on agricultural soils is, not the impediment to root development—the "Pflugsohle" (plough sole) is penetrated without difficulty—but the primary damage caused by *Fomes annosus*, which according to Wagenknecht "can be extraordinarily virulent on non-forest soils owing to the absence of hostile controlling agents". The roots of Scots pine which have been attacked by this fungus die as a result of overproduction of resin. The consequence is a heavy reduction of the height and diameter increment, which according to the examined example can cause a drop in height quality class from an original II (at the age of 20 years) to IV (at the age of 50–60 years). The fact that those pine trees which survived the attack, after recovery resumed their growth so rigorously that the height attainments expected for the site had been regained at the age of 100 years is remarkable. The increment losses caused by the extensive opening up of the stands are, of course, large.

4. Growth Patterns and Their Interpretation

The observation that many biological processes occur in a similar manner, showing unmistakable correspondences between certain measurements of the observed living beings and their age, has led to attempts to express these inferences in mathematical formulae. One spoke, and still does speak of "growth laws". By "law" in the physical sense, we mean the causal connection between events so that a certain event *a* must be followed by an equally certain event *b*. *The classic law concept in physics* is marked by the following characteristics:

1. There are *strictly* quantitative, i.e. *functional*, relations between the observed magnitudes or phenomena.
2. The *relations* formulated in the law apply *generally* under the assumptions which are made.
3. The mathematical formulation offers, at the same time, an *explanation* of the underlying circumstances.

In contrast, these biological regularities show the following peculiarities:

1. We have to deal with a body of *stochastic, more or less loosely connected data*. The observed, mathematically formulated, *relations* are *non-convertible* in other terms.
2. *Conditions for biological processes* are extremely *complicated* and change continually—we need only remember the continually changing structure of growth-

controlling factors upon an individual tree in a stand: they are therefore *never fully assessable* in individual cases.

Under these circumstances due reservation appears advisable in the use of the expression "growth *law*" for the "growth *patterns*" which we can observe.

Attempts to develop mathematical formulae from yield study observations

In his excellent work Peschel (1938) distinguishes between three stages in the mathematical formulation of yield study regularities:

(a) The description of arbitrarily selected biological relationships by an approximate function.
(b) The attempt at a description of growth processes by functions which are based on an energy concept.
(c) The attempt to formulate a growth law which has general validity.

Into stage (a) fall, for example, Schiffel's (1904) attempts, in his yield table constructions, to express certain known quantity relationships by formulae, or the inter-relationships found by Kopezky (1899) and Gehrhardt (1901) to exist between certain tree dimensions of even-aged stands. Whereas Schiffel was conscious of the character of such simplified mathematical constructions as *approximate functions for individual cases*, Gehrhardt believed he was dealing with genuine growth laws.

The attempts of R. Weber (1891) on the basis of energy concepts to express certain growth continuities by formulae must be regarded as belonging to stage (b). Assuming, for example, a growth dynamic which increases rapidly from the early years to the culmination of the increment, and then remains constant for a longer period, this energy must, as the tree dimensions become larger, gradually be consumed by *growing internal obstacles to the productive capacity of the tree*. If it is assumed that these obstacles increase in proportion with the increasing tree height, then the height increment must eventually become equal to zero. Thus, Weber arrives at the following formularization for the height growth of Norway spruce, in which the height h_a, attained at the age a, is regarded as a function of a constant growth energy p:

$$h_a = 20 p \left(1 - \frac{1}{1 \cdot 0 \, p^a}\right).$$

It is geometrically represented by an equilateral hyperbola of which one asymptote runs parallel to the x-axis at the distance of the maximum height achievable in each case. This formularization is unsatisfactory because it cannot give an approximate description of the height growth until the time of culmination of the height increment. Tischendorf (1925) later followed R. Weber along this path.

Attempts concerning stage (c) to form a general growth law are based on the familiar inferences about the progress of an increment curve as a function of the age with an initially slow, then rapid climb towards culmination and subsequent decline. An attempt of this kind by Robertson (1908) resulted in a symmetric increment curve, whilst the true curves are asymmetric. Original, but unsatisfactory, is the attempt of Kövessi (1929) to interpret the course of the increment curve as an a-periodically damped oscillation. Moreover, as shown by Baule (1920), the growth law of Mitscherlich cannot be used as a fully satisfactory growth law. Better adapted to reality is the growth law formed by Hugershoff (1936) which gives an asymmetric increment curve. But, just as in the growth law of Backman, which has already been explained with examples, this excellent formularization proves to be *too rigid* to be able to describe all possible growth patterns.

Growth laws or growth patterns?

At the end of his work Peschel expresses the hope that one day it may be possible to discover *a growth law of general validity*. In contrast to this, Assmann (1943) asks us to remember that the stochastic character of all hitherto observed correspondence allows little probability of finding a simple general solution. We are, after all, dealing with limited collectives which continually fluctuate in combination. For that reason, the analytical formulation of the average smooth trends, observed by us, will probably always have to retain the character of approximate functions.

In physics also, in the forming of laws about the movement of newly discovered elementary particles, penetration into the interior of the atom has arrived at similar uncertainties as those we meet in our attempt to express the behaviour of living beings in mathematics. The laws of nuclear physics are of a statistical character similar to the stochastic correlations in the realm of biology. Only the integration of immensely numerous individual phenomena can lead to the drawing of inferences of sufficient precision and strictness. Under these circumstances we shall have to be content with describing the oscillating processes of life by mathematical approximations which correspond suitably to the average behaviour of a great number of living beings. The expression "growth *pattern*" should probably be preferred because, compared to "growth *law*", it represents a cautious restriction. *The mathematical formularization, in any case, offers great advantages because it enables compressed statements to be made, and permits control over the certainty of statements by means of statistical methods.*

STRUCTURE, INCREMENT AND YIELD OF STANDS IN RELATION TO SILVICULTURAL TREATMENT

IN THE last section we have tried to obtain an insight into the natural laws which operate to control the composition and growth of stands. According to the production equation of Boysen-Jensen, there remains, out of the gross organic production of our tree crops, a comparatively modest 35–40 per cent constituting the net production in the form of timber and seed. From the point of view of silviculture we are interested mainly in the *timber growth*. If this is harvested by the felling of trees we refer to it as *yield*, which therefore represents the harvested increment. Now, the silvicultural techniques at our disposal are capable of exercising a considerable influence, *not only on the volume of out-turn, but also upon sizes and grades of produce*. We therefore have to take into account not only the volume yield, but also the *out-turn by assortments* in terms of the dimensions of convertible timber. Since a wholly satisfactory *comparison between different methods of treatment can only be conclusively reached by working out the values of the several different assortments in money terms* we must accordingly, examine the *financial yield* resulting from different methods of treatment.

I. CONCEPT AND SCOPE OF CULTURAL MEASURES IN STANDS

Under the general concept of *woodland and forest management* may be combined all measures designed to promote conditions favourable for production in woods. Managed forests are woods serving in the main an economic purpose. *By the cultural treatment of stands* we therefore mean *measures aimed at promoting and improving the natural*

TABLE 66

SIZE LIMITS OF SILVICULTURAL UNITS

Definition	Group	Clump	Small	Stand Medium	Large
Diameter in terms of tree-lengths (final crop height)	up to 1	1 to 2	2 to 5	5 to 10	over 10
Size of area with final crop height of	ar	ar	ha	ha	ha
25m	6	6–25	0·3–1·5	1·5–6·0	over 6
30m	9	9–36	0·4–2·0	2·0–9·0	over 9
35m	12	12–50	0·5–3·0	3·0–12·0	over 12
40m	16	16–65	0·6–4·0	4·0–16·0	over 16

Note: 1 ar = 100 square metres; 1 hectare = 10,000 square metres = 2·47 acres.

processes of timber production in stands, which are those parts of a wood that are homogeneous in character.

By a more precise definition, the word *stand* denotes a *well-demarcated portion of woodland having a uniform structure and sufficiently limited in extent to permit a certain thinning treatment to be independently applied.* According to Assmann (1954) the *"final crop height"*, i.e. the average length of mature trees when harvested, can provide a useful natural guide to the size limits imposed on *silvicultural units.* This will depend on the quality of site and the purpose of management (see Table 66).

Size restrictions upon silvicultural units

The dimensions reached *by trees* of the final crop are a measure of their spacial requirements, and the mean *height of trees at maturity, prior to harvesting*—the final crop height—may be used as a convenient and generally practicable *index of those proportions.* Their size determines the effect they bring to bear upon neighbouring trees, as well as the extent of favourable or unfavourable *influences upon the margins of tree communities,* for example, by protection afforded against sun and wind, by shade cast, by felling and extraction damage, etc. Within a minimum span of two final crop heights, it is possible to fell all trees belonging to a certain unit without causing damage to adjacent units. For this reason, the above distinction between the tree clump ("Horst") and small stands was chosen.

Let us assume a nearly square or circular shape. With a rectangular shape, the narrow side should be of length equal to the above minimum dimensions. If the length of the longer side exceeds that of the narrow side by more than double, we have a *strip system* for which special limits have to be devised.

Existing types of stands include single-, or even-aged stands, uneven-aged stands, stands consisting of one or several storeys, and pure or mixed stands.

We shall, to begin with, try to determine the effects of one particular *type of silvicultural treatment,* namely that which aims, *by means of thinning operations, to influence the further development of the remaining stock.* In the

Classification of cultural measures by thinning

we follow largely the ideas of Schädelin (1942).

In our present context, what Schädelin referred to as a "cleaning" operation must be regarded as just *part of the thinning programme*; in its wider aspects it is *applicable to all silvicultural operations* carried out *in close stands of strongly competing individuals.* A feature distinguishing it from former notions upon thinning is that the cultural motive now takes precedence over conversion out-turn. The commonly held strictures upon cleaning in the opinion of administrators that it brings in no remunerative return is unacceptable. Furthermore, there appears to be no occasion for exchanging the clear expression "thinning" for the vague euphemism of "improvement felling" (Pflegehieb).[1]

---

[1] There are without doubt fundamental differences between thinning as defined by Hartig and Michaelis, "thinning in the dominant quarter"; and yet Michaelis did not think of devising a new term for his method as an alternative for the old expression "thinning". Despite the considerable differences which exist between, let us say, a leg amputation by "Dr. Eisenbart" (a fictitious German quack) and a modern surgeon, no medical man would think of looking for a new expression for this operation.

TABLE 67

CLASSIFICATION OF SILVICULTURAL TREATMENTS

Type	Definition	Purpose
1. Tending of the young growth	*Intervention in stands which have not yet formed canopy*	Protection against hazards, cutting to improve shape, removal of undesirable trees, regulation of mixed growth.
2. Thinning	*Intervention in stands which have closed canopy.* Canopy of the upper storey is *only temporarily* broken so that the crop is always *fully productive*	Improvement of the quality of the current production of the stand by removing undesirable elements and favouring the best members of the stand
(a) Cleaning	*Slight, short-term* breaks in the top-storey canopy	Predominantly for the removal of undesirables and weaklings
(b) Selective thinning	*Moderate short-term* interruption of the upper-storey canopy	Freeing the better-shaped individuals
(c) Increment thinning (Lichtwuchs)	*Stronger* and *more lasting* interruptions of the canopy	Positive promotion of the best individuals
3. Regeneration felling, with isolation of the parent crop trees	Intervening to cause permanent breaking of canopy so that *full production of the upper storey is no longer* secured.	Raising of a new generation in a stand or of another productive storey

The successive phases of intensive cultural management of a beech stand with natural regeneration would roughly overlap as follows:

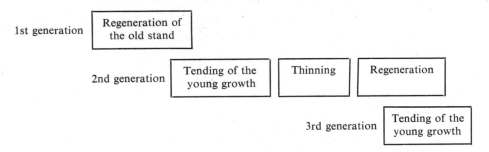

The intensive silvicultural procedure here makes a cycle which embraces the total duration of the life of the stand. Clearly, such an intensification of operations depends on certain economic preconditions. A hundred years ago, for example, only firewood and wood for charcoal were produced in beech stands. There was neither the technical necessity nor the economic justification for an intensive early thinning operation. The increase in the intensity of operations is a consequence of economic development and is therefore historically conditioned. We shall have to bear this in mind when we start to examine the possible effects of thinning on the volume increment and on the value production of our stands; in order to do this we shall have to evaluate before all else the *results of thinning experiments* conducted hitherto, some of which were started as early as the 1870's.

II. THE RESEARCH PROJECTS OF THE VEREIN DER FORSTLICHEN VERSUCHSANSTALTEN (ASSOCIATION OF FOREST RESEARCH INSTITUTES)

Since the beginnings of German experimentation in forestry, nearly 100 years have passed. Among the notable advocates and promoters of this development the following names should be mentioned: in forest science, Carl Heyer (1846); in forest administration A. v. Ganghofer (1881). The primary task of such experimentation was *to conduct scientific investigations into current problems of technique in forestry*, among them the *design of thinning experiments*. For this purpose, regular "working plans" (Arbeitspläne) were set up which were to ensure the uniform conduct of experiments. A first objective was to test out various thinning methods according to kind and severity.

1. Characterization of Thinning Methods

A thinning method can be characterized by the tree classes which are to be removed in any particular case. In the

Working plan of 1873

the oldest constructed working project, a *natural tree class division* based on social position was used and the following distinctions are made:

1. *Dominant* stems which, with fully developed crowns, form the *upper* canopy of the stand.
2. *Retarded* stems which lag behind in development and while still forming part of the canopy yet have their largest crown diameters at a lower level than those of the dominant trees, so that they form a second storey.
3. *Suppressed* stems (over-topped with submerged crowns), their apices being completely below the level of crowns of the dominating trees—stems which are bent down also belong to this category.
4. *Dying* or *dead* trees.

Directions about the tree classes which are to be removed determine the degree of thinning:

(a) in *light thinning*, only dead trees are removed;
(b) in *moderate thinning*, dying and suppressed trees are also removed;
(c) in *heavy thinning*, all retarded trees are finally also removed.

In a revision made in 1878, it was decided that *dying trees were to be removed in light thinning*.

The *underlying idea of this plan was to effect a timely removal of those categories of tree which are foredoomed to perish by natural processes if left in the stand and so utilize them before they become valueless, furthermore, to assess those additional yields which become available by such means.* There is no evidence of any emphasis upon positive measures to improve stem form. The absence of complicating technical objectives, on the other hand, renders it possible to conduct a purely scientific study. The tree class division and grading of the *Research Institutes* of *Switzerland* and *Württemberg*, which are still valid, are based directly on this experimental plan, which has been extended by one extra (D-grade) degree of thinning.

With the rapidly progressing industrialization towards the end of the nineteenth century, demand for utilizable timber of certain dimensions increased; new possibilities were opened up for the utilization of timber, especially from broad-leaved trees (e.g. beech), which made it worthwhile to raise trees with straight stems free from branches and with large diameters. The plan described above provided no opportunities for experimenting upon the techniques of timber production. Schwappach, who initiated the new experimental plan at that time, had to look on indignantly when, in newly laid-out beech thinning experiments, up to 75 per cent of the total number of stems were felled *without regard to their form or shape*, in a literal pursuance of book instructions. Not until after the death of Dankelmann did he succeed in drawing up and putting into effect a new experimental plan. This new

Work project of the Association of Forest Research Institutes drawn up in 1902

was based on a combined tree- and stem-quality-class grading system in which the biological aspects of social position and crown shape are combined with the technical and functional aspects of stem form. Below are the main provisions contained in the experimental plan of 1902:

(§ 2)

The members of a stand may be distinguished as follows:

I. *Dominant stems*. These include all those stems which form the upper crown canopy layer, consisting of:
1. Trees with normal crown development and good stem form.
2. Trees with abnormal crown development or poor stem form.

   To this category belong:

   (a) Trees which are cramped, or hemmed in.
   (b) Advance-growth of poor shape.
   (c) Other trees with faulty stem form, especially forked stems.
   (d) Whips, i.e. slender stems with underdeveloped crowns.
   (e) All kinds of diseased stems.

II. *Dominated trees*. These include all stems which do not find a place in the upper crown layer. Into this group belong:

3. Retarded stems which, however, are not directly over-topped. ⎫ Important to the
4. Suppressed stems which may constitute an under storey below ⎬ maintenance of soil
   the main canopy but which are still capable of survival. ⎭ and stand.
5. Dying and dead trees, no longer important for the maintenance of soil and stand. Thin bent-over stems also come into this category.

(§ 4)

The following types and grades of thinning are distinguished:

I. *Ordinary low thinning* ("thinning from below")

1. Weak thinning (A-grade). This is confined to the removal of dead and dying trees and weakly bent-over individuals (class 5) along with diseased stems. Its sole object is to supply comparative data for increment investigations.
2. Moderate thinning (B-grade). This is applied to the dead and dying, very bent and suppressed stems, whips, the more objectionable among the malformed advance growth if they cannot be rendered innocuous by pruning, and the diseased stems (classes 5, 4 and part of 2).
3. Heavy thinning (C-grade). In this grade all stems belonging to classes 2–5, as well as occasional individuals in class 1, are gradually removed so that only trees with normal crown development and good stem form remain. These should be distributed as evenly as possible, allowing them sufficient room on all sides to develop their crowns freely, but without effecting any *permanent* interruption of canopy.

The following additional rules apply for both B-grade and C-grade:

(a) In all instances where gaps are caused by the removal of dominant trees, suppressed or retarded trees which may be growing in these gaps can be left.
(b) The removal of healthy stems of class 2 because of faulty crown development or stem form should be done with some restraint and only after consideration of the general condition and extent of closure of the stand as a whole.

II. *Crown thinning* ("thinning from above")

This is an intervention in the dominant stand, aiming at giving special attention to the future final crop trees, whilst sparing on principle some of the dominated stems. Here it is necessary to distinguish between two grades:

4. Light crown thinning. This is limited to the felling of dead and dying trees as well as stems which are bent over, also badly shaped and diseased stems, forked trees, trees with spreading crowns, whips and those stems which must be removed for the purpose of breaking up groups of trees of equal value. Hence, it removes: class 5, a large part of class 2 and occasional stems of class 1. The removal of malformed advance-growth and other stems with faulty shape, especially forked stems, may, if such stems exist in fairly large numbers, be carried out on several different thinning occasions in order to avoid causing large gaps in the canopy. It is also advisable that stems of such description which still remain after the first thinning, should be made harmless for a time by pruning or by removing forked limbs. This grade is used mainly in young stands.
5. Heavy crown thinning. This grade aims at giving direct attention to a variously determined number of final crop stems. For this purpose, the trees removed are, in addition to the dead, dying, bent-down and diseased stems, also all those which impede the satisfactory development of crowns of final-crop stems, i.e. class 5 and some stems from classes 1 and 2. This grade appears to be suitable mainly for older stands.

The *mixing-up of biological and technical aims* in this "mixed tree class division" (cf. Section C, p. 92) has in classes 1 and 2 gone to such lengths that it is *no longer possible to define clearly* the trees characterized in this way, because one cannot decide whether a tree was classified as being in class 2 because of "abnormal crown development" or "poor stem shape". This, however, is an extreme disadvantage in the future evaluation of an experiment, because the initial situation has not been clearly established and any possible differences between the effects of treatments designed to improve the stem quality cannot be safely affirmed. Moreover, the differentiation between stem qualities in terms of "good" or "poor" is insufficient; it is necessary to distinguish between at least three, or better still, five quality classes. This failure cannot easily be excused, because in the design of the experimental plan the natural tree-class division of Kraft (1884) as well as the stem-class division of Heck (1898) were already available and a combination of these two divisions obviously suggested itself.

We distinguish between the two *types* of thinning, *low thinning* and *crown thinning* with three and two grades respectively and separate them by characterizing the tree classes which are to be removed.

The principle of strict low thinning is modified in that by the supplementary rule (a), it is permissible to leave suppressed or retarded stems which are growing in occasional gaps. This is also the reason for the expression "ordinary thinning".

The supplementary provision (b) is a marked restriction upon the dangerous prescription that with C-grade thinning, "all stems belonging to classes 2–5 must gradually be removed".

In *crown thinning* we distinguish between two grades, "light" and "heavy", although there are no clearly defined differences; with both grades trees belonging to classes 1 and 2 can be removed. One difference is given simply by the prescription that in "heavy" crown thinning "a variously ascertained number of final crop stems" are directly favoured by the removal of neighbouring individuals which hinder the development of good crowns. In actual fact—as proved by Assmann (1950)—there is no difference in the degree of thinning in the crown thinning experiments of the former Prussian Research Institute; the only difference lies in the early selection of definite future stems in "heavy" crown thinning.

In order to specify adequately a definite thinning régime, four main particulars must necessarily be stated: namely, the *kind, grade, beginning* and *frequency*. These we must now discuss in more detail.

The kind of thinning

The thinning carried out nowadays in practice is neither "pure low" nor "pure crown" thinning but "free" thinning for which reason one might contemplate dropping the classic differentiations. However, owing to their historical links they should be retained, apart from some small alterations. *Low thinning* is "nature's thinning method" (Assmann, 1953a) as a result of which the suppressed trees always die first (apart from some pathologically conditioned exceptions) from lack of light. However, there is nothing to prevent us from occasionally sparing some trees from the under- and middle-storeys when using a type of thinning which, on principle, works *from below* (hence low thinning!). In *high, or crown thinning*, the task of steering the growth processes in the dominant crown space in favour of our desired technical and cultural objectives by active felling is undertaken directly and without engaging in a small divertive tussle with the dominated tree classes. Such a definitive action, however, need not preclude our encroaching upon the middle-

or under-storey. These storeys must also be opened up, so that the under-storey is able to survive and to fulfil its protective functions. In common with Wiedemann (1931) who discriminated between the aims of single- or multiple-storeyed stands, we choose the following definition:

1. In low thinning, it is essentially the dominated tree classes that are removed first; the object is to achieve a single-stage structure of the stand as far as possible.
2. In high or crown thinning the primary attack is made upon the dominating stand, the under-crop is maintained and tended as required for soil and stem protection; the objective is a multiple-storeyed structure of stand.

Criteria of grading in measuring severity of thinning

The research project of 1902 *permits a clear characterization of the degree of thinning by naming the tree classes to be removed* in low thinning *only up to the B-grade; with the C-grade this is no longer possible. The extent to which we may encroach upon the dominating tree classes in individual cases cannot be determined in this way. In order to specify the intended, or actually practised, severity of thinning a quantitive measure is indispensable.* Assmann (1949) suggested the *periodic mean basal area* as such a measure.

The density of stocking depends on the number and diameter of the trees per unit area, i.e. the number of trees N per hectare and the mean diameter as measure of average tree dimensions. For a given breast-height diameter $d_{1.3}$ of an individual tree there corresponds a basal area $g = \pi/4 \times d^2$. The sum of the basal areas of all individual trees is given by the basal area per hectare: $g_1 + g_2 + \ldots g_n = G$. The mean basal area arises from $G/N = g_m$; this is accompanied by the mean diameter $d_m = \sqrt{4/\pi \times g_m}$ which we may take from a circular area table.

The basal area per hectare

$$G = N \times g_m = N \times d_m^2 \times \frac{\pi}{4}$$

thus contains the two components N and d_m. An idea about the number of trees which with a given diameter amount to 1 square metre basal area is given by the following figures:

Trees with a mean diameter of d_m	Corresponding to a basal area of g_m	Number amounting to *1 m^2* basal area
11·3 cm	0·01 m²	100 trees
35·7 cm	0·10 m²	10 trees
113·0 cm	1·00 m²	1 tree

Or: *a basal area of 50 m^2 per ha* may be made up by

5000 trees with   11·3 cm d_m
500 trees with   35·7 cm d_m
50 trees with 113·0 cm d_m

The fact that the *coverage ratio is an unsuitable measure for the determination of the density of stocking* has already been commented on (p. 110). For example, Kraft (1884) has shown that, after an increment felling in Common beech stands the full crown contact (degree of coverage 0·85) had been regained notwithstanding that only 0·6 of the basal area before opening up was regained. Besides, *the degree of coverage*, if measured some years after the last time of thinning, *is largely independent of the degree of thinning*.

It is therefore customary to determine the so-called *degree of stocking* as the ratio of the actual basal area of the stand per hectare to the basal area of some stand used as a basis for comparison. The basal area per hectare may be determined by calipering (perhaps on part-areas, circular plots, sample strips). The *Spiegel* (mirror) *relascope of Bitterlich* (1948) gives the basal area per hectare with *unequalled speed and facility* by a simple count of all the trees surrounding the observer which subtend at the eye an angle greater than a certain minimum.

The basic magnitude used in practice is the *basal area of a yield table* for a particular height quality class and the corresponding age. This may be questionable if the yield table is unsuited or contains construction errors (p. 150). In planned thinning experiments however, it is fortunately possible to *choose the basal area of very lightly thinned experimental plots as a criterion*. We thus obtain in every case the locally adapted *"natural stocking density"* which is always to be preferred to the doubtful stocking densities found in yield tables.

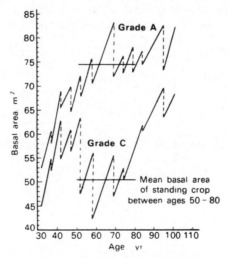

FIG. 105. Basal area development along with application of thinning grades A and C respectively in the spruce trial series, Sachsenried (2).

On given sites, the average growing space available to an individual tree in a stand *varies inversely with the number of trees* per hectare and *directly with the mean diameter* (d_m) of the trees, because with an increase of the tree diameter the average size of the crown roughly increases, as does the required growing space. *The larger the basal area* per hectare, *the higher the density of stocking, the smaller the average growing space* for individual trees of the stand and *the less favourable the increment prospects* for the average tree; conversely, *the smaller the basal area* per hectare, *the lower the density of stocking, the larger the average growing space* for the individual tree, and *the more favourable the average growth prospects*.

Thus Schwappach (1911) was of the opinion that "one obtains an incomparably better idea about the effects of a certain method of treatment from the *dimensions of stem basal area possessed by a stand* over a lengthy period of observation than by any specification of thinning grade or disengagement felling".

If we want to use the basal area per hectare as a measure of the density of stocking over any appreciable length of time, we should not take the average basal area of the crop left standing just *after thinning has taken place*, because by the time the next thinning comes round the increment will have caused a considerable increase of this reduced basal area. Figure 105 shows the strong upward spurts of basal areas put on in the A- and C-plots of the Norway Spruce research series No. 2 at Sachsenried, alternating with reductions at each thinning (broken lines). It is therefore evident that we must calculate the *mean basal area between each of two thinning occasions. The intervals between thinning,* however, *differ in length*; they vary between 5 and 11 years. In order to obtain the *correct mean value for a long observation period*, we must weight these mean values by the intervals between the thinnings. We thereby arrive at the following simple formula for

The mean basal area over a period (p.m.b.a.)

If g represents   the basal area at the beginning of an increment period,
  G   the basal area at the end of an increment period,
  m   the number of years of an increment period,

then, for the increment periods 1 to *n*, the

$$\text{p.m.b.a.} = \frac{\left(\frac{g_1+G_1}{2}\right)m_1 + \left(\frac{g_2+G_2}{2}\right)m_2 \ldots + \left(\frac{g_n+G_n}{2}\right)m_n}{m_1 \quad + \quad m_2 \quad \ldots + \quad m_n}.$$

EXAMPLE. *Beech thinning, experimental area 25 at Mühlenbek; observation period 79–104 years.*

Increment period from to	m	g (m²)	G (m²)	$\frac{g+G}{2}$	$\frac{g+G}{2} \times m$
79– 85	6	28·9	33·5	31·2	187·2
85–100	15	25·2	33·2	29·2	438·0
100–104	4	22·1	24·8	23·45	93·8
Total	25	76·2 /3	91·5 /3	83·85 /3	719·0 /25
Means		25·4	30·5	27·95	28·8 = p.m.b.a.

Obviously, 25·4 and 30·5 are unsuitable as averages, also 27·95, because the increment periods differ in length.

In Fig. 105 the mean basal areas are in each case shown for the age periods 50–80, after corresponding calculation. They appear to balance with the fluctuations of the basal area over the period.

The suitability of the above formula as an *expression for the strength of thinning actually applied, or density of stocking maintained during fairly long periods,* shows itself also in the example of the two yield tables for Common beech of Wiedemann, 1931, height Quality Class I. The following values apply for the age-period 50–80:

| With Table | and an interval between thinnings of years | the mean basal area | | the *mean basal area over the period* |
		before thinning (m²)	*after* thinning (m²)	(m²)
B "*Mod.* thinning"	5	33·6	30·2	*31·9*
A "*Heavy* thinning"	5	28·5	*25·1*	*26·8*
	10	32·0	*25·1*	*28·5*

If, with heavy thinning, the interval between two successive thinning occasions is extended from 5 to 10 years, then the average basal area does not change at all *after* thinning has taken place. It is, however, clear that with a longer thinning cycle the basal area must accrue to higher values (in this case 32·0 instead of 28·5). The figures provide a clear record of an increase of the periodic mean basal area from 26·8 to 28·5 m²; accordingly it reacts *to changes in the mean intervals between thinnings*, which is not the case with the average values of the basal area *after* thinning. The latter however, are employed especially by Wiedemann, as a means of identifying the strength of thinning.

The unequal productive efficiencies of the different social tree classes must, of course, be taken into consideration when we use the mean basal area over a period. This applies especially for those tree species for which crown thinning is suitable and normally practised, as for example with beech and oak. In such cases it is recommended *that the basal area data should be confined to Kraft's tree classes 1 to 4a inclusive.*

The increment put on by tree classes 4b and 5a is so small that their *positive* contribution to crop yield, may be neglected when the relationships between density of stocking and increment are under investigation. Indeed, on sites with only scanty moisture and nutrient supplies, their influence is decidedly *negative*. We may expect to find the clearest relationships in low thinning experiments, where in principle, the tree classes with the lowest increment are removed first. The effects of a crown thinning which has been started at an early age are more complicated and here a careful analysis of the tree class ratios[1] of the basal area of such stands is necessary.

The intensity of thinning; beginning and frequency of intervention

The cultural effect of thinning, especially upon stem quality and crown development, depends also on making an early start and the frequency of subsequent interventions. In addition, early thinning can induce favourable effects on increment by accelerating growth. Thus *the age at which thinning commences is of great importance.*

[1] In the publications of the former Prussian Research Institute an analysis of this kind is missing. The subsidiary crop ("Füllbestand") in a "heavy crown thinning" of beech, for example, represents a haphazard assortment of all social tree classes (from Kraft 1 to 5a). As a contrasting example, we can mention the model analysis of Haug's Norway spruce crown thinning experiment, given by Dieterich (1923) in *Allg. F. u. J. Ztg.*

The *mean time-interval between two thinning occasions*, the *cutting cycle*, is important because, with short intervals, a *better control of the growth processes* is possible and because the effects of fairly heavy thinning must be influenced by whether this is carried out in one operation or several.

If we express the number of years of the observed period as *n* and the number of thinnings including the first and last thinnings within this period as *z*, then the average *thinning cycle* is calculated as

$$\text{T.C.} = \frac{n}{z-1}.$$

EXAMPLE. Thinning at the ages 65, 70, 76, 90, 95 years.

$$n = 95-65 = 30; \quad z=5; \quad \text{T.C.} = 30/4 = 7.5.$$

Assmann (1950b) has suggested that the combination of the two aspects, viz. the beginning and the thinning interval, serves to distinguish between different degrees[1] of *thinning intensity*. The *beginning* may be specified, independently of age, *with the help of the mean height*. The *increment in mean height* provides a suitable biological measure for appropriate intervals in the life phases of the stand because the general lengthening of the leading shoots can be assumed to be proportional to the height increment, and both characterize the speed of the *growth processes which are to be controlled*. If we assume an approximate height increase of the growing stock of 1 meter for each thinning incursion, we arrive at a thinning time-table for beech stands Q.Cl. II (Assmann, 1950b) the intervals in which correspond roughly to the approved rules of "*Danish* thinning".

For *beech* and other broad-leaved species which demand treatment up to an age of 80 years, it has been possible to define the following:

Levels of thinning intensity

(1) "extensive"	Beginning at over 12 m mean height; average cutting cycle 5·1 and more years.
(2) "intensive"	Beginning at 8 to 12 m mean height, average cycle 3·1 to 5·0 years.
(3) "highly intensive"	Starting before mean height of 8 m has been reached; average cycle 3·0 years or less.

Considering the present official trend of opinion in German forestry which tends to disparage intensive treatment of broad-leaved crops, it may be said that an *early start* is *more important* in effect than frequent intervention.

Conflict between biological and technico-economic points of view

The foregoing numerical interpretation of the degree and intensity of thinning provides a simpler and more precise description of the methods of treatment actually practised than the definitions given by the research institutes, excepting that for the A-grade thin-

---

[1] Intensity must not be confused with the severity of thinning, as happens frequently (among others Künanz, 1950; also Schädelin, 1932; Assmann, 1953a). Heavy thinning may be "extensive", and moderate thinning "intensive".

ning. The *particular type of thinning* in any individual instance, and especially in the case of *free crown thinning* which is now customary, cannot be identified in this way. This last-named method is practised mainly for the purpose of *promoting those trees which possess boles of the highest quality with light branching and are of high technical value.* In many cases this leads to the elimination of vigorous trees with wide crowns and thick branches, the so-called wolf trees. Admittedly, these trees are *of inferior value in respect of their utilizable and saleable qualities*, but from a *purely biological viewpoint* they may be particularly *valuable*. Since they have reached a dominant position in the competitive struggle, we may as a rule, assume that *they are especially efficient in the production of organic substance and of wood volume.*

Merely designing a thinning experiment with the sole object of securing high-grade timber as regards dimensions and freedom from knots, thus *focusing the inquiry upon technical and economic problems, does not enable us to clear up basic biological questions.* In so doing, we subordinate all to utilization and economic objectives. An experiment of this nature must include at least some *control plots on which it is possible to record the growth and development resulting from purely natural processes of elimination.* We shall see later in the case of Common beech what a deplorable part this conflict between natural science and utilitarianism has played in the course of research work.

2. Experimental Methods and the Accuracy of Growth Determinations

The effects of different thinning methods on the increment, and thereby on the yield, can be correctly judged only if we succeed in finding significant differences in growth performance. This depends on the layout of the experiment, the method of procedure in the field and the method of evaluating the results.

(a) LAYOUT OF THE EXPERIMENTS

In contrast to the methods used in agricultural research, *replications* have *not* as a rule been provided in forest yield experiments; that is to say, a certain type of treatment is represented only once in each experimental series. This militates against obtaining statistically valid determinations. But in experiments which need continued observation until the stand has reached a great age, critical minimum sizes of individual plots are required, namely 25–100 ar,[1] depending on the tree species and the expected final dimensions. In order to ensure a broadly effectual smoothing out of the errors within individual plots, a minimum number of 100 trees are needed in each plot at the end of the experiment. By comparison, the number of trees per individual plot of 25 ar in 130- to 150-year-old beech stands drops to 20 or 30! With the given minimum size of individual plots, it is hardly possible to ensure even approximate similarity of the local site conditions for more than three plots in a series.

The interesting Norway spruce thinning experiment at Bowmont in Scotland (Hummel, 1947), which was begun in 1930, has four different treatments replicated four times. It has been possible to make an analysis of variance of the results of this experiment. However, in 1945, at the age of 35 years, the number of trees left on the most heavily thinned plots was only about forty.

[1] Roughly, 0·6–2·5 acres.

To each of the individual plots must be attached *a surround* which should be at least 15 m wide (for long-term experiments). In many older experiments, the surrounds of the lightly-thinned plots (which should receive the same treatment as the plots) have been opened up severely by the felling of sample trees. This leads to a marked disturbance of the experiment if the individual plots are small.

A temporary remedy for these difficulties may be found by dividing the individual plots of more recent experimental layouts into two or four sub-plots of equal size, measuring and assessing them separately for as long as the number of trees in the sub-plots makes this possible. This enables statistical inferences to be drawn with some precision, at least for the early decades of the experiment.

(b) METHODS OF FIELD INVENTORY AND COMPUTATION

The *numbering* of trees in permanent sample plots is indispensable, because the identity and diameter of lost or stolen trees could not otherwise be determined. For the purpose of accurate

Measurement of the basal area

it is necessary to apply *special bands or rings to trees* at *breast height*. Calipering which is still predominantly practised in Germany carries the danger of *systematic measurement errors* through the caliper being out of adjustment, for which reason it is necessary to check the calipers against some standard gauge (Assmann, 1938) before using in the field. If the caliper error is known, the calculated basal area may be corrected by simple percentage additions or subtractions (Assmann, 1957a).

EXAMPLE. Calipering of an experimental plot of beech 25 ar in extent with basal area of 6·00 m². The *true* 5-year *increment* amounts to 0·8 m².

If the first enumeration is made with an accurate caliper, but the second enumeration made at the end of a 5-year interval *with a caliper which on locking has a splay of 1 mm* (at 150 mm distance from the measuring scale), a *systematic increment error* of −5·7 per cent will be incurred.

In the calipering of trees with thick and rough bark and irregularly shaped cross-sections, considerable *random* errors may occur for *individual trees*. If, for example, the error incurred in the determination of the basal area of individual trees amounts to ±3 per cent then only by measuring up 100 trees can this percentage error be reduced to $\pm 3 \cdot 0 / \sqrt{100} = \pm 0 \cdot 3$ per cent.

Subjective measurement errors due to light or heavier pressures applied to the caliper are not to be underestimated. Owing to the considerable pressures which can be brought to bear by the narrow faces of the caliper arms (Kennel 1959), especially if dirt and resin on the inner edge impede easy sliding action of the moveable arm, these errors may reach noticeable proportions. The accuracy of measurement with the makes of caliper in common use today is indeed so poor that they have to be regarded as almost *primitive*. The most urgently needed modifications to any new caliper construction would be a separation of the bearing edge of the adjustable arm from the beam, together with the provision of ball-bearings permitting the former to run true and with a minimum of friction across the scale, which should have a magnifier attachment to ensure accuracy of reading with the avoidance of parallax. It should be mentioned that, according to Lars Tirén (1929), the process of "rounding down" to the nearest millimetre leads to a percentage error of circular area estimation amounting to as much as $-0·5$ to $-1·0$ per cent. The much-to-be-suspected mistakes which occur when measurements are called out to be recorded by a listener could be obviated in a first inventory by double-measuring, and from subsequent inventories by comparing the figures with the diameters recorded at the previous survey.[1]

Girth measuring with steel tapes, which the Munich Institut für Ertragskunde successfully employs in new experimental layouts instead of calipering (especially in fertilizer experiments on low-quality Scots pine sites with small increments), has the advantage of *greater uniformity of the measurement results* (Kennel, 1959) and with less liability to subjective influences. The work of Matern (1956) has shown clearly that *girth measuring provides the same value for the sectional area* (if this is calculated as area of a circle with the same circumference) *as the arithmetic mean of all diameters having to be calipered on the tree cross section.* In the special cases where there are strongly elliptical or oval (combination of circle and ellipse) cross-sections—not indeed, that they are by any means common—calipering of the largest and smallest diameter and reckoning by the formula for an ellipse: $(g = \pi/4 \times D \times d)$ will provide an absolutely accurate value for the cross-section; however, the systematic positive error in the circular area, if sectional area is calculated from girth measurements, is, as proved by Müller (1957b), considerably less than had hitherto been assumed. It amounts to only $+0·2$ to $0·5$ per cent instead of $+2$ to 5 per cent as previously thought and hardly exceeds, even with the most extreme diameter ratios $(d : D)$ which occur in practice, the value $+0·5$ per cent. The hitherto-assumed large positive differences by girth measuring as compared with calipering are caused by negative caliper faults (splaying of the caliper, excessive pressure of application of the caliper arm). With the commonly occurring non-elliptical shapes of cross-sections, the theoretical accuracy of girth measuring is higher.

Height measuring

In order to determine the height of the stem with the mean basal area from a fitted height curve with a mean error of ± 1 per cent it is necessary, in the case of coniferous trees, to take at least forty height measurements;[2] in the case of broad-leaved trees with dome-shaped crowns and no clearly defined apex, approximately fifty measurements are required. When primitive hypsometers, such as those of Weise or Christen, with a measurement error of approximately ± 4 per cent, are used, the number of required measurements increases by approximately one-third. Since the German research institutes have started using the Blume-Leiss hypsometer (from about 1936) and have increased the number of height measurements, the obtained results have become more reliable. However, even with present-day hypsometers, systematic as well as subjective errors are possible. It is thus not unusual for the mean heights of older stands to appear to have decreased within a period of 5 or 6 years, even though such a reduction is physically impossible (cf. Fig. 112, p. 256).

[1] Upon the assumptions made in the example on p. 223, if a tree with a diameter of 35·1 cm were to be mistakenly recorded as 45·1 cm in diameter during inventory at the end of a growth period, an error in the basal area increment of $+7·9$ per cent would be incurred.

[2] With the Blume-Leiss and "Haga" hypsometers the mean error of an individual measurement amounts to approximately ± 1 per cent. The *natural* variance about the height curve with even-aged spruce stands amounts to $\pm 4·5$–5 per cent.

Measurement of form factors

Even greater difficulties arise in determining the form factor. In pure spruce stands, approximately sixty to seventy sample stems, measured in sections, are required for the construction of the form-factor curve from which the form-factor of the mean basal area stem may be read with a mean error of ± 1 per cent. With broad-leaved trees, which have a strongly developed crown, the variance in the form-factor is even larger. Obviously, it is impossible to take the required number of sample trees from an experimental plot of 0·25 ha during a single inventory, except in the case of a first enumeration of a young plot under heavy thinning. Even if the slight shift of the form-factor curve, resulting from increasing age permitted us to use sample trees from several consecutive inventories in order to make up a common form-factor curve, it would only be possible in exceptional cases to arrive at form-factors for the trees of the standing crop with any assurance on the basis of local measurements.

In the former Prussian Research Institute, for example, plausible and indeed probable average form-factor values were obtained from the first inventories of newly laid-out experimental plots up to about the year 1911. From later inventories however, improbable and even impossible form-factor values appeared, caused by the *huge natural variance of the form-factors* and an insufficient number of locally examined sample stems. The new methods, developed by Krenn, Prodan, Dittmar, Assmann and others following upon Hohenadl, whilst causing heavy outlay on field work, do offer improved prospects for ascertaining, individual form, relationships on single plots. As already shown on p. 69, however, the most expedient and safe method at the present time is still the construction of volume or form-factor tables on the basis of numerous and successive examinations of sample stems to date. Such tables manifest the *systematic form-factor changes* which correspond to the possible combinations and changes of diameter and height. Even the use of common volume tables, despite the construction errors with which some of them are burdened, provides more reliable *increment* values, than the calculation of volumes based on unreliable local form-factor values.

Calculation methods

As a rule, the individual diameters which have been measured in millimetres are sorted out into 1-cm diameter classes, the basal areas being taken from "multiple tables of circular area". Apart from the frequent mistakes which such sorting into 1-cm classes renders unavoidable, this procedure on older experimental plots carrying only small numbers of trees causes "*random classification errors*" in contrary directions and of such magnitudes that from them increment errors of more than 1 per cent may result for 5-year periods. For this reason, at the author's institute calculation of basal area is always carried out tree-by-tree with modern computers[1] which allow of check by a system of double-reckoning. The summed result of the class-wise calculation (1-cm classes, which are combined into 3- or 5-cm classes respectively) is rectified by means of correction factors which are based on the individual stem calculation.

---

[1] $\Sigma d_1 \times d_2 \times \pi/4$ or $\Sigma c^2 \times 1/4\pi$. The amounts $d_1 \times d_2$ or c^2 which are summated in the accumulator are finally multiplied by $\pi/4$ or $1/4\pi$. Intermediate summations on each side facilitate the control.

In comparison with the former customary sample-stem methods of Draudt and Urich, the derivation of height and form-factor values from the corresponding smoothed curves such as those introduced in the former Prussian Research Institute by Schwappach and Fricke, represents a considerable advance, because it avoids the random element in sample tree selection being carried directly on to the volume calculation (Assmann, 1957a).

The directions given by Wiedemann (1930) and Erteld (1957d) should be referred to in connection with methods of procedure in research plots and calculations to be employed.

(c) Accuracy of the Increment Determination

The mean error incurred in the determination of the basal area on an experimental Common beech plot of 0·25 ha with a calipered basal area of approximately 6 m² is estimated by Assmann (1950a) at ± 0.3 to ± 0.5 per cent, which is fairly high.

In the following *example* we shall calculate with a mean error of ± 0.2 per cent: 80-year-old Common beech, 0·25 ha, for the growth period 80–85 years.

Age	Basal area (m²)	%	Mean error, absolute
80	6·00	± 0.2	$\pm 0.0120 = e_1$
85	6·80	± 0.2	$\pm 0.0136 = e_2$

Increment $i_G = 0.80$ m²; standard error of the increment $E = \sqrt{e_1^2 + e_2^2} = \pm 0.0181$. For these data therefore the *accuracy of the 5-year increment* amounts to 0·80 m²± 0.0181 ($= \pm 2.3$ per cent).

With this short increment period the increment error expressed as a percentage is roughly 10 times as big as the error arising in the calculation of the basal area.

If one compared two measured increment values of equal accuracy from adjoining experimental plots (possibly with different thinning), the difference D between the increment values would, with an increment error of ± 2.3 per cent, carry a standard error of $\mu_D = \sqrt{2 \cdot 3^2 + 2 \cdot 3^2} = \pm 3.25$ per cent.

As a general rule, a difference between two magnitudes involving error may be considered significant if it is at least 3 times as large as the amount which it can reach alone by random error fluctuations between the compared magnitudes: $D \geqq 3\mu_D$.

Under the assumed conditions, a *difference in increment production per cent* must amount to at least $3 \times 3.25 = 9.8$ per cent *to be significant*. This, however, applies only when a large number of measurements or samples respectively (at least 30) are available. With a small number of measurements, the probability that certain error limits will be exceeded is considerably greater than shown in a calculation by the Gauss integral for $n = \infty$. With only two measurements it is impossible to make any safe statement about the error probability beyond the confidence limits or anything else about them. In the well-known student's "*t*-test" the number of measurements beyond 1 are known as "degrees of freedom" and the probability with which a certain multiple of the mean error $D/\mu_D = t$ may still be exceeded, as *P*. If $n = 2$, the number of degrees of freedom by which the two values are to be compared, becomes $= n_1 + n_2 - 2 = 0$. With $n = 4$, i.e. with two similarly

treated experimental plots having one replication to each, the number of degrees of freedom would be 2. In this case, if

$$P = 5 \quad \text{per cent } t = 4 \cdot 3$$

and if
$$P = 0 \cdot 3 \text{ per cent } t = 19$$

and therefore, despite our having duplicated the experimental plots, the number would
have to be twice as large as assumed above for $P = 0 \cdot 3$ per cent with $n = \infty$.

The question whether in thinning experiments undertaken by us, every individual tree
measurement may be regarded as a sample and whether one can thus arrive at t-tests or
analyses of variance of our hitherto "single" layouts of thinning experiments, can be left
open. At this stage, a strict probability calculation does not appear to be feasible. We
must, for the present, base our proofs on the *uniformity of the results of several experimental series*.

Apart from the accuracy of the individual basal area calculations, the error of the
increment depends also very much on the *length of the observation period*. If, as a precau-
tionary measure, we assume the slightly higher inventory error of $\pm 0 \cdot 3$ per cent in the
basal area estimates, then for the average conditions in beech stands of Q. Cl. II, and
under the same conditions as before, we obtain the following increment errors:

Increment period	P_{iG}
60–70	$\pm 1 \cdot 6\%$
70–80	$1 \cdot 7\%$
80–90	$1 \cdot 8\%$
90–100	$1 \cdot 9\%$
60–100	$\pm 0 \cdot 6\%$

Only by adopting 40-year periods can we reduce the error of basal area increment to
$\pm 0 \cdot 6$ per cent.

Considerably *larger* is the *error* which is to be expected *for the volume increment*.
Assmann (1950a), for the same conditions as above, arrived at the following *probable
increment errors* for Common beech:

	For 10-year increment periods	For 40-year increment periods
For *basal area increment*	$\pm 1 \cdot 8\%$	$\pm 0 \cdot 6\%$
For *volume increment*	$\pm 8 \cdot 0\%$	$\pm 2 \cdot 4\%$

Consequently the basal area increment would be affected by an error which is only one-
quarter to one-fifth that of the volume increment.

It is to Näslund (1929, 1936) that we owe the most thorough statistical analysis hitherto
of yield study inventory procedure. With respect to the very carefully observed Swedish
pine thinning experiments he assigned the following mean volume increment errors:

for a single thinning period (= increment period of 5–7 years) ±15–27 per cent (!) and for three such periods (= 15–20 years) ±5–9 per cent.

With the help of an approximation formula devised by Krenn (1941) the relationships for the percentage volume increment error can be simplified:

If:

p_V represents the percentage error of the single volume determination,
V_m the volume at the middle of the increment period (arithmetic mean of the initial and the final volumes),
i_V the annual increment in volume,
n the number of years in the increment period, then

$$p_{iV} = \frac{p_V \times V_m \sqrt{2}}{n \times i_V}.$$

The percentage increment error therefore increases proportionately with the error of the volume calculation and is inversely proportional to the amount of the increment. *The smaller the increment in proportion to the increasing volume and the larger the error in the volume calculation, the longer must be the increment period chosen to achieve an acceptable accuracy of the increment calculation.*

Is the basal area increment suitable as a criterion of performance in thinning experiments?

The considerably greater accuracy with which the basal area increment may be determined would suggest its use as a measure of comparison in thinning experiments. This has been done up to very recent times and has led to *seriously faulty conclusions. With the differing densities of stocking* resulting from different grades of thinning, *the volume increment is no longer proportional to the basal area increment,* even if height and form-factor for the different experimental plots agree. This has been proved by Wiedemann (1931) and affirmed by Assmann (1950a). It may easily be proved with the help of the increment formula on p. 151:

$$i_V = i_G \times fh_e + i_{fh} \times G_a$$

because, even if the final form-height and the form-height increment of two stands are equal, *the stand with the larger initial basal area G_a, i.e. the less heavily thinned stand, must—with the same basal area increment i_G—have a higher volume increment,* because the second term of the formula becomes larger for this stand.

In addition to this, as shown on p. 236, *the total volume of the extracted material from heavy thinnings becomes considerably less per square metre of felled basal area than with weak thinning,* owing to the "reduced length of harvested stems".

Correction and smoothing out of faulty experimental results

It is usually the thinnings that can be measured up and their volume ascertained with the greatest reliability. The cut stems are useful, if for no other purpose, for the measurement of heights (since they now lie flat) but they can also be used for sectional measurements. Moreover, it is to be expected that, when the results of several consecutive thinnings are totalled up along with the sum of previous early yields, an averaging out of errors will be effected. The sum total of intermediate yields, which in some experiments amounts to 50 and more per cent of the total crop production, must be considered as the most reliable production figure.[1]

The situation is different for the "remaining stand", in which there resides a high potentiality for the introduction of error in determining heights and form-factors every time an inventory is made.

Height measurements from earlier assessments which were quite obviously subjectively biased, being too high or too low, cannot possibly be repeated and thus corrected. In cases where unmistakable errors have occurred, an acceptable expedient can be found by drawing a smooth curve through the *mean heights* (heights of mean basal area stems) *plotted over the corresponding diameters* of the mean stems.[2] Even if the progress of height growth is not proportionate to diameter growth, it is still to be assumed that growth periods during which the climate is favourable to diameter increment will also assist the height increment. Furthermore, the resulting "statistical shift" of the mean diameter which occurs alongside that observed with the mean height, must follow from heavy thinning from below, and is fairly well taken into account by this kind of smoothing process.

If the mean *form factors for the stand* are unreliable or obviously wrong, then the only solution is to use form-factors for the diameter and height of the mean basal area stem which are taken from form-factor or volume tables. In even-aged stands for which the volume line $V = f(G)$ is almost straight, the calculation of the volume by diameter classes deviates only very little from such a line derived from the volume components (g, h, f) of the mean basal area stem. Besides, any possible systematic errors are rectified in consecutive calculations for the main, or standing crop.

These corrections having been carried out, it is finally possible to *fit* the unreliable volume increments to the more reliable basal area increments, by plotting the total volume production curve against the total basal area production (Reinhold, 1926; Assmann, 1950a).

Fitting produces curves which are convex to the x-axis;[3] as a rule the curvature is slight, sometimes so slight that a straight line fit is possible. By calculating the differences between the adjusted figures of total volume production corresponding to their respective values of total basal area growth, we obtain volume increments for those respective growth periods which can then be *fitted* to the corresponding basal area increments. Of course, this method can result in correct volume increments for the particular increment periods only if the basal area calculations at the beginning and end of the increment period are accurate. By comparing the increment values for several sample plots in an experimental series, such errors are easily recognizable by the appearance of improbable deviations in the figures of certain plots, which are shown up by contrasting fluctuations over the following growing period. In some cases a check of the research records can bring

---

[1] In current and, especially, in newly laid out experiments, this should persuade us to measure *all* eliminated trees in sections. If, finally, this is done with the trees which remain at the end of the experiment, then the total yield would be exactly determined!

[2] The curve h_m over d_m for weak thinning must, in this case, always progress on a *higher* course because heavy thinning promotes the growth of diameter to a greater extent than height and systematically decreases the ratio $h:d$. Exceptions indicate differences in height quality class or age.

[3] A suitable approximate function for numerical fitting of such curves is the power $y = bx^a$, for which the parameters of the logarithmic transformation $\log y = \log b + a \log x$ are easily calculated by the method of least squares.

to light mistakes of calculation which were responsible for errors. Often, however, the errors are of a systematic nature which are incurred in the process of calipering and cannot subsequently be removed. Owing to this weakness in basal area estimation, it is, as a rule, not possible in older thinning experiments to draw comparisons of growth for periods covering less than 15 to 20 years. It is accordingly wise when making such comparisons, to select periods with limits which coincide with reliable inventories.

Only after a searching review and careful correction can the results hitherto obtained from thinning experiments be used for comparisons of growth performance. The reason for this is that incremental differences tend to be small on account of the relatively slight differences in treatment, the treatment itself being subject to change and only in exceptional instances seen to have been carried out uniformly and consistently.

III. THE EFFECTS OF DIFFERENT THINNING METHODS ON GROWTH AND YIELD

1. Typical Increment Reactions to Thinning

In order to be able to make a correct interpretation of thinning experiments we must first become familiar with some *typical growth reactions* in stands under different thinning régimes. These were revealed particularly clearly in the *Norway spruce thinning experiment No. 54 in Dalby, Sweden*, on which Carbonnier (1957) recently reported after 50 years of observations.

The experimental Norway spruce series at Dalby, Sweden

This experimental series is situated in South Schonen, in the Swedish state forest at Dalby. The climate at the nearest meteorological station in Lund is as follows: mean annual temperature $+7.2°$, mean annual rainfall exceeding 600 mm; oceanic climate with humid air. Clayey moraine soil mixed with clayey slate. Plantation on former pasture. Out of the four individual plots, No. I was not thinned at all (control), whilst II–IV had been submitted to low thinnings in an increasing order of severity. After 50 years observation, a heavy storm in January 1956 blew plot IV flat, severely damaged plot III, but plot II suffered little and plot I no damage at all. The situation during the latest assessment in 1955, *at the age of 81 years*, is shown in Table 68.

TABLE 68

Plot		N	G (m²)	Main crop			V (m³)	Total of thinnings (m³)	Total crop volume (m³)
				d_m (cm)	h_m (m)	h_o (m)			
I	no thinning	1396	64·9	24·3	26·8	29·0	917	305	1222
II	mod. low-thinning	600	43·2	30·3	28·1	29·4	608	590	1198
III	heavy low-thinning	336	34·3	36·1	27·2	29·3	437	739	1176
IV	"extra heavy low-thinning."	200	28·9	42·9	28·5	30·2	367	766	1133

The top heights (h_0) in this case are the mean heights of the class with the largest diameters respectively. From the point of view of local site factors the plots are directly comparable.

This is therefore an experiment which has been observed over a long time for several widely differing grades of thinning. The intermediate yield percentages (proportions of the thinning yield to the total crop volume) amount respectively to 25, 49, 63, 67 per cent. The total crop volumes up to the age of 81 years have the following ratios 100:98:96:93.

TABLE 69

PERIODIC MEAN BASAL AREAS, AND INCREMENTS, IN THE EXPERIMENTAL NORWAY SPRUCE SERIES AT DALBY, SWEDEN, AFTER CARBONNIER (1957)

Increment period	Number of years	Grade of thinning	Mean basal area	Periodic increment per year in basal area	increment in stem-wood		Relative figures for		
			(m²)	(m²)	(m³)	p.m.b.a.	i_G		i_V
31–42	11	I	49·4	1·34	19·3	(19·2)	100	100	100 (100)
		II	46·4	1·34	19·1	(18·8)	94	100	99 (97)
		III	45·1	1·62	20·6	(20·6)	92	121	107 (107)
		IV	44·8	1·51	19·9	(19·8)	91	113	103 (104)
42–51	9	I	56·8	1·00	17·3	(17·3)	100	100	100 (100)
		II	49·8	1·11	18·2	(18·1)	89	111	105 (105)
		III	44·5	1·27	19·2	(19·4)	78	127	111 (112)
		IV	36·9	1·46	18·9	(19·1)	65	146	109 (110)
51–61	10	I	62·8	1·08	21·6	(19·1)	100	100	100 (100)
		II	53·9	1·25	22·3	(22·2)	86	116	103 (116)
		III	43·0	1·47	18·8	(17·8)	68	136	87 (93)
		IV	35·4	1·50	17·7	(17·6)	56	139	82 (92)
61–71	10	I	64·7	0·74	16·8	(20·4)	100	100	100 (100)
		II	51·9	0·81	15·6	(15·8)	80	109	93 (77)
		III	38·1	1·08	15·0	(16·2)	59	146	89 (79)
		IV	29·6	1·02	14·3	(13·9)	46	138	85 (68)
71–81	10	I	64·4	0·86	20·4	(19·4)	100	100	100 (100)
		II	48·2	1·04	19·0	(19·3)	75	121	93 (100)
		III	37·0	1·05	16·5	(16·1)	57	122	81 (93)
		IV	31·7	1·08	16·5	(17·0)	49	126	81 (88)
31–81	50	I	59·46	1·010	19·10	(19·10)	100	100	100 (100)
		II	50·07	1·113	18·85	(18·85)	84	110	98·7 (98·7)
		III	41·56	1·304	18·05	(18·05)	70	129	94·5 (94·5)
		IV	35·84	1·315	17·49	(17·49)	60	130	91·6 (91·6)

The periodic volume increments are corrected; the figures in parentheses are the original values.

The relationships between the grade of thinning, measured by the mean basal area over a period, and the increment become apparent in Table 69 and Fig. 106.

During the first increment period from 31 to 42 years, when there were only small differences in the degree of thinning, we recognize *no clear reactions*. In contrast to this, the intensive thinnings in plots III and IV at the age of 42 years have caused during the growing period 42–51 years, considerable increases of the increment (up to 11 per cent). For the growth period between the ages of 51 and 61 years, we find that only plot II shows a slight positive improvement with more severe thinning (relative to plot I), whereas III and IV by this time already show noticeable *increment losses*. During the increment periods 61–71 years and 71–81 years, the completely unthinned plot I had taken the lead! The same applies also to the increment performance over the time of the entire experiment. We shall come across the same tendencies in other experiments.

Characteristic values of the basal area for different periods

The mean basal area over a period of years, employed as a measure of the strength of thinning, thus indicates *clear relationships* between the thinning grade and the increment. According to a suggestion of Assmann (1950a) it is possible on the basis of a well-planned thinning experiment to determine three characteristic values for a given site, namely:

(1) The *maximum basal area* (present value at a certain age) or *maximum basal area over a period* (mean value for an observation period), respectively. This refers to *the highest possible basal area of a site, or the maximum basal area over a period respectively, of living trees* per hectare. It may be determined for stands which have not been actively thinned, or in which only dying trees have been removed.

(2) The *optimum basal area over a period, by which the highest possible increment can be achieved during a given increment period.*

(3) The *critical basal area over a period by which alone just 95 per cent of the potential maximum increment for a site can be achieved.*

Figure 106 shows the volume increments plotted as percentages over the percentage values of the periodic mean basal areas, the values for the unthinned plot I in each case having been set equal to 100. *The abscissal values, which decrease from left to right, thus represent decreasing degrees of stocking per cent, corresponding to increasing severities of thinning.*

If the percentages for the increment are fitted by a curve which points towards the zero point (at the bottom right) in the system of coordinates, we shall very probably be able to state *the way in which Norway spruce crops* on this site will *react to increasing strength of thinning.* The maximum basal area during the age period 42–51 years amounts to 56·8 m². The peak value of the fitted curve lies at 75 per cent of that amount, reaching a little over 110 per cent of the increment of the maximum basal area in the period. Consequently the *optimum basal area for that period* amounts to 42·6 m²; the *optimum stocking density lies at 0·75.*

Ninety-five per cent of the optimum increment of 110·5 per cent are 105 per cent. Under the ordinate value of 105 we find the abscissa value of 59 per cent. Consequently the *critical basal area for that period lies at 33·5 m² or the critical stocking density amounts to 0·59.*

Analogous to this, we find the following characteristic values for the age period 51–61 years:

	Maximum	Optimum	Critical
Mean b. area in period	62·8	57·1	48·3
Nat. stockg. density	1·00	0·91	0·77

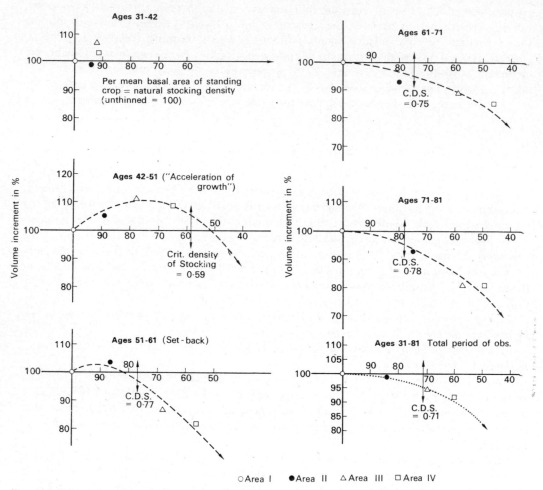

○ Area I   ● Area II   △ Area III   □ Area IV

Fig. 106. "Natural stocking density" and volume increment in the spruce thinning series at Dalby, Sweden.

With increasing age, therefore, *the absolute amounts* of the characteristic values of the basal area over a period *increase*. As they are nevertheless dependent on the site, it is probably difficult to state absolute values of the optimum and the critical basal areas for stands of different sites and different ages.

The prospects are better for the *relative amounts*, especially for the *critical* degree of stocking. *Whereas the optimum degree of stocking approaches the maximum, the critical degree of stocking changes but little.* Apart from an initial phase of exceptional growth reaction following the first occasion of thinning, which in this case coincides with the age period 42–51 years and for which the critical degree of stocking generally is especially low, its systematic increase with age is small. For the three periods of 10 years each in the age period 51–81 years, we find, in this case, consecutive values of 0·77, 0·75, 0·78. This is due to the *bend in the optimum curve which, with increasing age, becomes less acute. Thus the critical degree of stocking remains almost constant*, although the optimum degree of stocking approaches more and more closely the value 1·0.

The natural critical degree of stocking and the "optimum basal area"

In literary discussions of the problem of thinning the "optimum basal area" has so far played a decisive part, especially during the time when one was still inclined to believe in definite absolute amounts as, for example, Schwappach's *optimum basal area of between 21 to 25 m² per tree*, which was supposed to apply *generally to Common beech stands of the age of 70 years and over* (Schwappach, 1911). In reality, however, this amount is correct only for a few sites of quality classes I–II and for the first one to two decades after the first vigorous thinnings, i.e. approximately during the age period 50–80 years. Unfortunately, up to now there are only a few experimental series in existence which permit a sufficiently reliable determination to be made of the optimum basal area and other, characteristic quantities in absolute terms. On the basis of these experimental series Assmann discovered a fairly *narrow range of fluctuations in the natural critical stocking density*.

The values found in support of this,

0·60–0·70 for *Common beech*,   ∼0·75 for *Sessile oak*,

0·75–0·80 for *Norway spruce*,   0·80–0·90 for *Scots pine*,

display a kind of gradation which corresponds to the known ability of the different species to respond to opening up of the canopy. The *lower values*, incidentally, always apply to *younger stands* and the *higher values to older stands*.

With the help of these supporting values we are able to determine the *absolute size of the critical basal area*, provided that the *potential maximum basal area for a site*, maybe in a lightly thinned section of a stand or on the basis of observed figures, is known. A knowledge of the maximum possible basal area for a locality is, moreover, important for an accurate estimate of the yield level (cf. p. 165). We ought therefore to endeavour to apply only a light thinning to stand areas of 0·3–0·5 ha on all important sites in order thereby to be able to discover the maximum basal area which can be sustained over a period. *This is an ecologically important indicator value for sites, by which we are able to discover how many living trees of certain average dimensions a site can support.* Once we know this basic value, we can use the *natural degrees of stocking* for an easy determination of *the limits of the intensity of thinning with which it is still possible to achieve nearly full increment efficiency*. The ranges offered in this way are so wide that we can comfortably undertake the necessary thinnings for stand maintenance within their limits. Only in exceptional cases can these limits be determined on the basis of stocking densities derived from yield tables.

Wiedemann (1950) holds the doctrinal view that "the identifiable limits of the optimum basal area which produces the highest increment at all ages, from medium polewood to the harvestable stand" remains "nearly unchanged." "This optimum range differs for the various timber species and quality classes. On good soils it lies, for Norway spruce, between 40 and 55 m²; for Scots pine, between 25 and 40 m²; for oak, between 23 and 30 m²; and, for Common beech, even between 20 and 40 m². *Within these wide limits, therefore, the basal area can shift without any marked change in the basal area increment or, as shown later, in the volume increment per ha.*"

These figures of spread, although derived from numerous statistically supported communications, are comparable only to a limited extent and certain results are unreliable

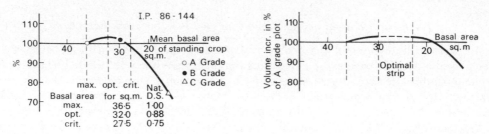

FIG. 107. Relationship between basal area of standing crop and increment in oak stands based on the results of the oak trial series at Freienwalde (left curve) and according to Wiedemann's hypothesis (right curve).

(on account of large increment errors!); but in this general context they are inconclusive even were we to concede a 5 per cent loss of increment and still more so if we assume that the highest increments were obtained. Accordingly they will need to be substantiated several times yet. Referring to the experimental oak thinning series *Freienwalde 172*, on the results of which Wiedemann's statements are based, it appears that according to Assmann (1956c) a drop to the lower limiting figure (23 m²) during the age period 125–144 years would cause us to expect *increment losses of between 20–25 per cent*. A basal area of 23 m² in that case would, according to the oak yield table of Schwappach-Wiedemann, be equivalent to a yield table stocking of 1·05, because the C-plot of this experiment between the ages 86 to 144 had a mean basal area of *20·1 m²* which on this site corresponds to a *natural degree of stocking of 0·60. The natural critical degree of stocking for the same age period lies at 0·75.* Figure 107 shows the true progress of the optimum curve of this experimental series compared to the progress which would have to be assumed according to Wiedemann's tenets.

An attempt to explain the progress of the optimum curve

Practical foresters generally subscribe to the opinion that thinning in all cases has an increment-promoting effect. They deduce this from the *apparently favourable reaction of the remaining trees.* But of course, as we have long recognized, it is not the increment of individual trees which is of decisive importance, but *the increment per unit area. How then is it possible that the removal of substantially effective members from a tree population can lead to a rise in increment?* Surely this is conceivable only if the remaining trees, in addition to taking over *the increment which is lost by extraction, can more than compensate this loss* by an extra rise in productive efficiency. We already know that with a given quantity of leaves the capacities for producing new growth by the suppressed and dominated trees are far smaller than those of the dominating trees (Burger) and that their respiration losses are larger than those of the dominants (Boysen-Jensen). According to Vanselow (1943a), they operate "less economically" than the dominants. In all cases where there is a *lack of those substances which are of primary importance to the assimilative activities of the trees, namely water and nutritive elements, the removal of suppressed and dominated trees will as a rule result in an enhancement of increment. An over-abundance of water and nutritive elements* is likely to be available *on only a few specially well-favoured sites.* There, even the dominated and suppressed trees can still be supported without difficulty. In such circumstances we must also reckon that even if the suppressed trees are removed, only trifling reductions of the increment will be incurred. In actual fact, the *shape of the optimum curve* of such sites *is seen to be particularly flat*. Apart from the first favourable reactions to thinning, the cause of which we shall have to regard further in more detail below, the optimum basal area over a period on such favourable sites very quickly approaches the maximum.

On the other hand, *on sites with scanty supplies of water and nutritive elements, a particularly sharp bend of the optimum curves*, lasting up to fairly high ages, is observable. Indeed, it may happen that the removal of co-dominant and sometimes also dominant trees entails no consequential loss of increment. But when in thinning we cut out dominant trees, it is, so to speak, to be compared with dismissing not only workers with notoriously poor out-turn (Pressler's "lazy fellows") but also the able and efficient. Clearly then the remaining workers, in our case the remaining trees, would be put under excessive strain. The result will be to aggravate increment losses, whereupon the optimum curve falls away. The reason for an initially slow drop lies in the fact that the remaining trees respond to the enlarged growing space, diminished root competition from neighbours and improved light conditions for the crowns by producing accelerated *increment* ("Lichtungszuwachs"). For as long as this enhanced increment due to increased light continues, the curve progresses in a trend concave to the *x*-axis. After this, when the provision of further growing space no longer evokes a rising growth-rate in individual trees, the volume increment per unit area must decrease in proportion with the decreasing basal area of the stand. From this "proportionality limit", the curve proceeds in a straight line to the zero point.[1]

The characteristic course of the optimum curve is due in the first instance to the favourable effects of thinning on the growth of the remaining trees. These effects begin with a *reduced competition* and an accelerated rate of *"humus turnover"* (Assmann, 1950a) resulting from the temporarily improved light and temperature conditions of the soil. In addition to this there is an accession of nitrogen supplies from the *decaying roots* of the felled trees (Romell, 1938).

For as long as these positive effects of thinning outweigh the negative effects which must accompany any removal of substance-producing trees, the optimum curve is on the ascent; when these effects balance, it reaches a peak; when the negative effects predominate the curve descends.

The acceleration of growth

This attempt at an explanation, however, is not sufficient to explain the initial and exceptionally rapid increases of growth which are observed when we intervene in young crops. *These exceptional reactions occur in stands which have not yet reached the peak of their current volume increment*, as in the experimental Norway spruce series at Dalby, Sweden, during the ages from 42 to 51 years. Assmann (1956a) explains this as an *"acceleration[2] of the natural growth process"*. The rate of progress is impeded not only by *overhead cover* (for example in a selection forest), but also, as shown by comparative

[1] More precisely, it reaches first a point for which abscissa and ordinate are determined by the basal area and volume increment of the last tree remaining on the hectare.

[2] There is a conscious connection between this expression and terms used in physics. The first derivative of the integral curve, distance covered as function of time, results in *speed*, the second derivative results in the increment of speed, in fact *acceleration*. By analogy, the first derivative of the growth curve supplies the *increment*, the second derivative the *acceleration of growth*.

observation of stands with close and wide spacing, by *side-shade thrown from competing neighbours*. If these hindrances are removed *early enough by vigorous thinning, an acceleration of growth by individual trees will ensue. so that these reach the culmination of their current volume increment within the shortest possible time.*

As to whether, and to what extent, this results in an added impetus to the stand increment in relation to ground area, depends on the extent to which the average ground-space occupied by individual trees $s = 10,000/N$ (cf. p. 156) increases at the same time. For as long as the number of stems remains large, the average extension of the available growing space capable of inducing the quickening effect is small; yet if at the same time the crown dimensions are still favourable to efficient production (i.e. crowns which are *slender*, fully covered with needles and without a bare interior), then the rate of the area-related volume increment must turn out to be high. Conversely, if the number of trees has already been fairly heavily reduced or has been low from the outset, if the crown measurements are less conducive to efficient production and the stand increment has in any case already moved close to the culminating point, then we can expect only a small speeding-up effect. In fact, if under these conditions the thinning carried out is too heavy, we shall have to expect increment losses.

From such considerations, it would follow still further that the gain in *increment* as a result of this impetus imparted to growth can be *only temporary, because a stand which has undergone early and heavy thinning reaches not only its peak growth-rate but also the decline of its increment curve at an earlier date so that a stand that has been thinned more lightly, or at a later age still has an opportunity to catch up with it.*

This becomes apparent in further Swedish spruce thinning experiments,[1] the results of which were published by Carbonnier (1954). The plots with natural thinning in the two older experimental series T_4 and T_{32} are, *from the age of 70 years onwards, clearly superior in total increment.*

The same phenomenon has been demonstrated in the Bavarian Norway spruce thinning series Ottobeuren 8 (Assmann, 1956a). The C-area there had been vigorously thinned already at the age of 27 years, *5 years before the beginning of the experiment*, with the result that *by the time the experiment started the plot showed 15 per cent superiority in total growth performance over the A-plot*. But by the age of 70 years the A-plot had caught up with the C-plot and overtaken it,[2] as is demonstrated by the curves of the average increment (by age) of all three plots in Fig. 108. That this in fact amounts to a *change in the rhythm of the growth-rate becomes apparent in the earlier culmination of the average increment for the C-plot*, which is reached approximately *5 years earlier* than in the A-plot.

Similar typical reactions occur in the Danish Norway spruce thinning experiment at Hastrup (Bornebusch, 1933) and in the Swiss thinning series at Olten as well as in further experiments with Common beech and oak, with which we shall have further acquaintance below. In addition, Dittmar (1959) has recently been able to demonstrate the *"growth-quickening effect"* in the Norway spruce thinning series Dietzhausen 78/79 (in the bunter-sandstone region in south Thuringia). In this instance it might be a stimulating exercise in the course of plant physiology investigations, to follow up the possibility of some likely underlying *connection with an augmented development of growth-promoting substances.*

---

[1] Owing to peculiarities of site and close spacing, the Swedish experimental Norway spruce series in the experimental area (near Halmstad) have an exceptionally *late culmination of the current volume increment*.

[2] If the C-area during the last 20 years had not been more lightly thinned than the A-area the present lead in efficiency of the A-area would be even larger.

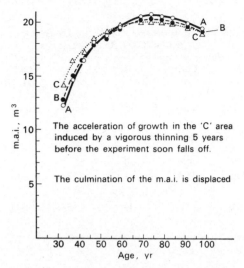

The acceleration of growth in the 'C' area induced by a vigorous thinning 5 years before the experiment soon falls off.

The culmination of the m.a.i. is displaced

FIG. 108. Mean annual increment curves for the three degrees of thinning in the spruce experimental area 8 at Ottobeuren.

From the yield study aspect, it is very important to demonstrate this growth acceleration, as it is thereby possible to prove the inaccuracy of many premature conclusions deduced from experiments which have been under observation for only a short time and to reduce exaggerated hopes for increment-promoting effects of thinning to the right level.

2. Typical Changes of the Average Tree Dimensions

The thickening of the stem

The *trees remaining in the crop* after thinning put on increased growth in diameter. This finds expression in the larger mean diameter (of the mean basal area stem) of a fairly heavily thinned research plot which at the same time exhibits a smaller number of stems. The view held by practising foresters about the favourable effects of thinning is founded on this obvious impression. How unimportant this diameter growth is in view of the *total production* however becomes apparent in Table 70.

The diameter difference between the most heavily thinned plot IV and the unthinned plot L in the Swedish experimental series at Dalby at the age of 81 years amounts to

+186 mm for the standing crop

+ 34 mm for the total production.

The corresponding differences between plots III (heavy thinning) and I (weak thinning) at the age of 104 years in the Bavarian experimental Norway spruce series, Denklingen amount to

+58 mm for the standing crop

+3·1 mm for total production.

TABLE 70

DIAMETER INCREASES FOLLOWING THINNING, INDICATED BY THE DIAMETERS AND DIAMETER DIFFERENCES
OF MEAN BASAL AREA STEMS

Definition	Plot I d_m (mm)	Plot II d_m (mm)	Diff. II−I (mm)	Plot III d_m (mm)	Diff. III−I (mm)	Plot IV d_m (mm)	Diff. IV−I (mm)
(a) Swedish spruce research series, Dalby							
Total production							
to the age of 31	98	108	+10	101	+ 3	111	+13
to the age of *81*	*142*	*163*	*+21*	*157*	*+15*	*176*	*+34*
Total thinnings							
Age 31−81	92	131	+39	135	+43	154	+62
Standing crop							
at the age of 31	118	127	+ 9	128	+10	131	+13
at the age of *81*	*243*	*303*	*+60*	*361*	*+118*	*429*	*+186*
(b) Bavarian spruce research series, Denklingen 5							
Total production							
to the age of 35	113	112	−1	114	+1		
to the age of *104*	*167·3*	*170·1*	*+2·8*	*170·4*	*+3·1*		
Thinnings							
Age 35−104	115	119	+4	127	+12		
Standing crop							
at the age of 35	135	144	+9	150	+15		
at the age of *104*	*373*	*424*	*+51*	*431*	*+58*		

These are sobering figures which show how much our judgment is biased by the standing crop.

Reduced length of the harvested stems

A hitherto neglected negative effect of thinning pointed out by Assmann (1956b) is the "reduced length of harvested stems". The example of the experimental series at Denklingen will help to explain how this arises. In Table 71 the total production to date of the series, up to the age of 104 years, is divided into 10 cm classes, the *mean heights* of all trees of the individual classes produced so far have also been calculated. Apart from the class 60–70, these values, with increasing intensity of thinning, are systematically less. The differences in disfavour of the heaviest thinning are in all cases particularly large in the classes 10–40 (values in italics): in the class 20–30 they amount to no less than +2·1 or 4·6 m respectively in favour of light thinning. The explanation is simple: as shown in Fig. 109 the height curve of a Norway spruce stand (here of plot II) displays a fairly large systematic shift with increasing age so that the height of trees of a given diameter, for example 28 cm, continuously increases with increasing age. A tree with a b.h.d. of 28 cm, harvested at the age of 45 years, has a height of 23·7 m; if, however, a tree with this diameter is not felled until the age of 104 years, then it will have a height of 29·6 m! The *heavier* the thinning, the *earlier* the trees of a certain b.h.d. are felled. As shown in Table 71, the trees belonging to the three diameter classes 10–40 under more heavy thinning in

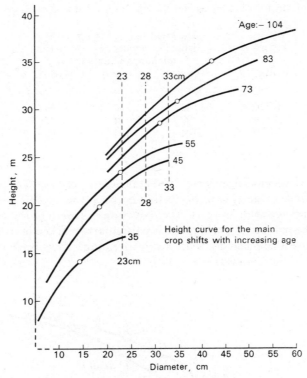

FIG. 109. Spruce experimental series, Denklingen (5). Shift of position of the height curves between ages 35 and 104.

TABLE 71

EXPERIMENTAL NORWAY SPRUCE SERIES, DENKLINGEN

(a) Distribution of the total production up to the age of 104 years to different diameter classes

b.h.d. class (cm)	I. Light thinning				II. Moderate thinning				III. Heavy thinning			
	Number of stems	Mean height (m)	Stem volume (m³)	%	Number of stems	Mean height (m)	Stem volume (m³)	%	Number of stems	Mean height (m)	Stem volume (m³)	%
up to 10	2928	8·1	48	3	3048	7·5	46	3	2860	7·4	41	3
20	1456	18·6	249	17	1564	17·5	242	15	1568	17·4	249	17
30	480	29·3	336	22	364	27·1	244	16	440	24·7	251	17
40	268	33·7	402	26	204	33·1	304	20	240	31·4	321	22
50	156	36·1	373	25	200	36·1	470	30	164	35·5	384	26
60	32	37·9	105	7	72	37·8	239	15	60	37·2	197	13
70					4	39·1	19	1	8	39·2	37	2
Totals	5320		1513	100	5456		1564	100	5340		1480	

(b) Mean harvesting age for the trees of some diameter classes

Class	The mean harvesting age with		
	light	moderate	heavy
	thinning amounts to		
(cm)	(years)	(years)	(years)
10–20	64	54	51
20–30	98	84	65
30–40	104	103	96

the experimental series Denklingen were felled at progressively younger ages. For example, the difference of the average ages of harvesting between the C- and A-grade in the class 20–30 amounts to no less than 33 years. The reduction in length of the harvested stems as a consequence of the reduced harvesting age is particularly marked in trees of the diameter class 10–40, because these classes, with heavy thinning, have been most severely encroached upon (cf. in this connection Fig. 110).

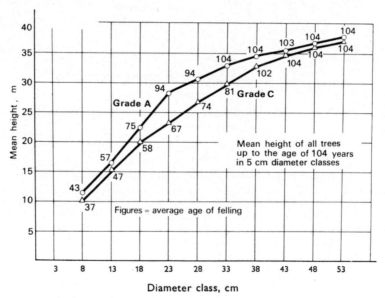

FIG. 110. Experimental area, Denklingen. Mean heights and mean ages of realization for all trees up to age 104 years.

As already mentioned (p. 225), it is probably this circumstance which is mainly responsible for the fact that *heavy thinning may be considerably less effective in volume yield than light thinning even though the former may give superior results in basal area growth*, because obviously the trees from heavy thinnings are not only shorter, but at the same time have smaller form-heights. This applies to all species.

*The change in the distribution of the total production by diameter
classes and grades of produce*

The table also shows distinctly a typical *change in the distribution of the total volume
production* as a consequence of heavier thinning. Whereas the percentage ratio of the
volume in the total production of the first two classes (up to 20 cm) changes only a little,
a noticeable shift to the diameter classes over 50 cm becomes apparent as a result of
heavier thinning. However, combined with this *superiority* of heavy thinning *in the
production of large-diameter trees, there are losses occurring in the middle size-classes*
20–40. At the same time there is a change in the distribution of the total production by
the separate assortment classes, as may be seen in Table 72.

TABLE 72

EXPERIMENTAL NORWAY SPRUCE SERIES DENKLINGEN

Percentage ratios of the different assortments in the total produce

Timber classes	Thinning grades		
	A	B	C
Firewood	4	4	4
Bolts, poles, etc.	12	12	12
Stemwood of the Heilbronn classes			
2	6	6	10
3	8	4	5
4	16	11	11
5	20	21	18
6	12	19	18
Sections	2	3	2
Bark and conversion losses	20	20	20
Total	100%	100%	100%

Comparing the C-grade treatment with the A-grade, there is an obvious shift of out-turn
towards the large diameter classes of stemwood, whilst at the same time, the quantities
in the middle stemwood classes are smaller. In the Heilbronn classification, which demands
certain minimum lengths together with fixed minimum top diameters (cf. p. 70), the
shorter converted lengths of stem given by the C-grade show to its disadvantage because,
with longer and less tapering stems, slightly lower b.h.d.-values will suffice to qualify for
a certain Heilbronn class.

3. Enlargement of Dimensions, Improvement of Timber Quality and Financial Yields

Along with increasing diameter and length of the trees their range of uses also increases.
These can be evaluated according to

external quality characteristics, viz. dimensions (diameter and length), straightness of
stems, absence of branches, and

internal quality characteristics, namely structure of annual rings, soundness, strength, colour, heartwood, cellulose content, etc.

By the interplay of supply and demand in the open market, as modified through political or planned economy regulations, the utility value of timber thus finds expression in the price.

Timber prices and price differentials

Whereas the average price level is subject to continuous changes depending on the market, the season, and on social and cultural conditions, the *relative differences between prices* for different standard timber grades are comparatively constant. This is expressed in the official index figures for timber valuation in Table 73.

This relates to timber of class B, "normal" quality. Timbers of Quality Class A = "excellent", or C = "faulty" will be valued respectively at higher or lower prices. Select grades with special quality characteristics, as, for example, oak veneer timber, claim top prices of 3500 DM per solid cubic metre and over.

Complications in connection with a *varying quality grade* will be neglected at this stage and we shall first of all consider only the consequences of dimensional increases on the financial yield, assuming mean timber quality (B) for all grades of thinning. For a price basis we assume 200 per cent of the measurement index—for example, 200 per cent of 32 = 64 DM for stemwood of Heilbr. cl. 2. For the firewood class, we choose a uniform 18 DM, for the mixed class of stackwood + poles + stemwood of cl. 1 an average of 52 DM per solid cubic metre (fm).

TABLE 73

EXCERPT FROM THE OFFICIAL INDEX FIGURES FOR TIMBER VALUATION
(stemwood cubic metre)

Norway spruce, Silver fir	Long logs		1	2	3	4	5	6	
Douglas fir	Heilbr. class		29	32	36	40	46	50	
	mid-diameter	1a	1b	2a	2b	3a	3b	4	5	6
	classification	29	33	37	40	45	48	50	52	54
Scots pine, Larch		1a	1b	2a	2b	3a	3b	4	5	6
Weymouth pine		25	28	34	40	47	55	65	75	85
Common beech			1	2	3	4	5	6	
			25	30	40	50	60	70	
Oak		1b	2a	2b	3a	3b	4a	4b	5	6
		35	40	60	80	100	130	160	180	200

In order to avoid long discussions about the problem of including other expenses which are not directly linked with harvesting we shall base our comparison of yields on income free from felling and extraction costs for the several timber assortments produced. The calculation of forestry costs has recently been undertaken by Speer (1959). He distinguishes between "direct" costs, as for example expenses for harvesting and extraction, and "indirect" or general costs. Of these approximately 30 per cent (among them expenses of administration) must be considered as "fixed" expenses whilst the remainder, for example cultural and road-making costs, are up to a degree variable and are related to the extent of timber utilization.

We shall furthermore exclude the question of interest on timber capital, which is lower with heavy thinning, in order not to encumber our comparisons with unreliable factors. The problem of interest and its link with the "natural volume interest" will be discussed later, in Section E.

TABLE 74

GROSS AND NET REVENUE PER FM OF TOTAL GROWING STOCK PRODUCED IN THE EXPERIMENTAL SERIES DENKLINGEN 5 ACCORDING TO DIAMETER CLASSES (WOODCUTTERS' PAY = 0·05 DM PER MINUTE, INCL. WELFARE CONTRIBUTIONS). SPRUCE

Diameter class (cm)	Gross value per fm (DM)	Harvesting expenses (DM	Net value (DM)	per fm gr.-stock (smoothed values)
3	16·3	21·6	—	—
8	33·2	20·7	12·5	10·–
13	41·2	18·8	22·4	22·2
18	48·0	15·2	32·8	33·0
23	54·0	11·5	42·5	42·2
28	59·5	9·9	49·6	49·5
33	63·9	9·2	54·7	54·7
38	67·7	8·8	58·8	58·5
43	70·3	8·6	61·7	61·5
48	72·4	8·6	63·8	63·6
53	73·8	8·6	65·2	65·1
58	74·6	8·6	66·0	66·0
63	75·0	8·6	66·4	66·4

Harvesting costs for thin stems are substantially higher than for medium- and large-diameter stems. How this affects the *net proceeds* which remain after subtracting harvesting costs from the *gross value yield*, is shown in Table 74, in which gross average values, harvesting costs and net timber values per festmetre[1] of growing-stock are calculated for increasing diameter size-classes.

The net income after deducting harvesting costs, which is of importance for management calculations, increases steeply up to the diameter class 28, then more slowly and beyond the class 58 remains practically level. The conversion of timber under 6 cm b.h.d., with present-day wages is bound to incur loss. And the production of Norway spruce of b.h.d. over 50 cm is nowadays clearly unrewarding owing to the low price differentials obtainable for large-diameter wood.[2]

Comparison of the value yields, with and without computation of future value of thinnings

The question now arises, whether or not we must, when comparing financial yields, include *the more or less early income from thinnings*, which is done in Faustmann's familiar formula for the *soil expectation value*:

$$S_e = \frac{Y_r + T_a \times 1 \cdot 0 p^{r-a} + \ldots + T_q \times 1 \cdot 0 p^{r-q} \ldots - C \times 1 \cdot 0 p^r}{1 \cdot 0 p^r - 1} - \frac{e}{0 \cdot 0 p} .$$

[1] 1 fm = 1 cubic metre solid.

[2] It is, however, to be noted that in a working section with a low rotation there will inevitably be a relatively large proportion of small-size timber fetching low prices but for which the *conversion costs are high*, and thus in many cases today they no longer yield positive net returns after harvesting. With a longer rotation period the proportion of such timber classes in the total production is reduced. It can, therefore, be an advantage to endeavour, with older stands, to achieve target diameters of more than 50 cm.

If we neglect expenses for planting and administration and the discount factor

$$\frac{1}{1 \cdot 0p^r - 1}$$

which supplies the soil expectation value as the capitalized value of a periodic income for all r years, our question becomes simplified and we have to decide whether we wish to calculate the total net value yield up to the rotation age of r

either as a simple sum $Y_r +$ sum of the thinning yields

or as $Y_r + T_a \times 1 \cdot 0p^{r-a} \ldots + T_q \times 1 \cdot 0p^{r-q}$,

that is, valuation with interest compounded to the age of r.

In the former case we would use as our value index the *continuing performance of a corresponding working section under sustained yield management* without computing interest on the timber capital. In the second case we adopt the point of view of an entrepreneur who is planting a piece of ground and calculates expenses and yields with the help of the Faustmann formula. Decisive for the question whether or not the thinning yields are allowed to accrue with compound interest is obviously the economic position of the woodland owner and his chosen objectives. The big woodland owner with large growing stocks will be hardly likely to calculate future values of thinning revenues, but instead, will probably direct his calculations towards the highest forest rental and neglect to make heavier thinnings which cause a lowering of timber stocks, keeping these meantime in view until he requires to release liquid capital for other purposes.

In contrast to this, a farmer who, for example, plants a piece of unfertile meadowland will understandably calculate by the Faustmann formula and assess his early yields higher accordingly. The calculations for larger land properties will have to be similar, if management for sustained yield is in the initial stages of being built up.

The attractiveness of heavy thinning is very greatly enhanced by virtue of accumulated interest because the earlier incomes will accrue to large final values. With $p = 3$ per cent and $r = 100$, a certain sum received from thinnings at the age of

40 years will, by the age of 100 years, have grown to 5·89 times,

50 years will, by the age of 100 years, have grown to 4·38 times,

60 years will, by the age of 100 years, have grown to 3·26 times.

And a sum credited 10 years ago will have increased by about one-third its value at the present time.

Comparison between the financial attractiveness of the various thinning régimes works out differently according to our initial assumptions as we find when we look at the example of the experimental series at Denklingen. If we assume *gross value returns*, the ratio A:B:C-grade behaves as 100:107:99; for *net value yields* we find *100:108:100; if we adopt future values for intermediate yields*, then the *C-grade with 100:116:128 is markedly superior.*

The variation in financial yield per fm of the total production is strikingly low: the value of the average festmetre produced in the C-grade is only 1 per cent (gross), *or 2 per cent* (net) *respectively higher than in the A-grade!*

The value performances of the heavily thinned plots in the Swedish thinning experiment at Dalby are weakened by up to 10·4 per cent (plot IV) by increasing attacks of red rot.

TABLE 75

FIGURES OF OUT-TURN FOR THE EXPERIMENTAL NORWAY SPRUCE SERIES, DENKLINGEN 5

Definition		A-grade abs.	%	B-grade abs.	%	C-grade abs.	%
Mean basal area over period from 35–104 years	m²	65·0	*100*	61·1	94	51·7	*80*
Mean ann. *increments* from 35 to 104 years in basal area	m²	0·921	*100*	1·019	*111*	0·973	*106*
in stem volume	m³	16·6	*100*	17·3	*104*	15·9	*96*
Total production up to the age of 104 years in *basal area*	m²	117·1	*100*	124·0	*106*	121·8	*104*
in volume	m³	1513	*100*	1564	*103*	1480	*98*
in *gross* value, total	DM	92,390	*100*	98,510	*107*	91,630	*99*
per fm	DM	61·1	*100*	63·0	*103*	61·9	*101*
Financial net yields excl. harvesting costs Total of thinnings	DM	15,980	*100*	18,930	*118*	21,770	*136*
per fm	DM	31·4		33·9		34·7	
Main crop	DM	58,740	*100*	61,640	*105*	52,640	*90*
per fm	DM	58·5		61·3		61·7	
Total net yield	DM	74,720	*100*	80,570	*108*	74,410	*100*
per fm	DM	49·4	100	51·5	104	50·3	102
Total for thinnings at 3% c.i.	DM	34,320	*100*	46,470	*135*	66,260	*193*
Total yield with accum. int. on early yields	DM	93,060	*100*	108,110	*116*	118,900	*128*

Carbonnier (1957) calculated the following performance ratios for the four plots:

	Plot I	II	III	IV
Total volume production	100	98	96	93
Net value production (under consid. of red rot)	100	113	114	115
Do. with thinning revenues at c.i.	100	131	155	169

The net value efficiency for heavy thinning in this instance is higher than in the Bavarian thinning experiment at Denklingen. This is due to the different grading of Swedish timber prices and the younger final felling age. With the experimental series at Denklingen a high proportion of the timber classes earning the highest incomes is already reached at the age of 104 years even where light thinning has been applied. Here again a comparison of performances for the age of 81 years would show slightly better figures for heavy thinning. On the whole, a comparison of the value out-turns in this experiment speaks *much in favour of moderate thinning*. The most important conclusion which emerges, however, is this: *If thinning does not succeed in exerting a positive influence on the average timber dimensions as well as on the timber quality, then the prospects for an increased value production by this means are disappointingly low.*

Selective and quality-promoting effects of thinning

Prospects for this kind of quality improvement are offered by the effects of selection (Assmann, 1953a) such as those achieved in an ideal manner by Schädelin's cleanings and selection thinning. The timely elimination of trees with poor shape causes a rise in the proportion of well-shaped trees and an improved quality of stem. Subsequent growth will contribute to greater excellence of stocking and more valuable timber, thus raising the *quality of the total production generally.*

The prospects for success by such selective thinning methods are the better, the more marked are the natural differences in stem quality and the earlier the start made in selection. The strong negative *geotropism of coniferous trees* with their natural tendency to straight growth, as instanced by Norway spruce, occasions but small differences in straightness of the stems. If they are planted and raised at sufficiently close spacing they will be clean-boled and develop fine branches. This is entirely different where the photo-tropically reacting broad-leaved trees are concerned; these, as for example oak and beech, tend to have crooked stems and to become strongly branched. Here then we find wide *natural differences in the quality of the stems* from the *point of view of straightness and branchiness.* Quite generally therefore the opportunities for improving the timber quality by a timely start of the selection are much greater for broad-leaved trees than for coniferous trees. As to whether it is possible to select out the most vigorous genotypes in the course of thinnings must remain doubtful. We must, on the contrary, count on the possibility, that, where technical objectives predominate, the vigorous trees (much-branched advance-growth and wolf trees), which more often than not are the more vigorous genotypes, will be systematically removed. The prospects for the rejection of alien ecotypes with undesirable characteristics are better, in so far as the externally recognizable characteristics correspond to genetically fixed characteristics. The linking of biologically and technically valuable properties, as for example rapid growth, resistance to pests and virus infections, fine branching, etc., is the task of intensive breeding. Remarkable possibilities in this field have been opened up following the researches and recent successes by Rohmeder (1954, 1955, 1960).

A further means of raising financial productivity is the *promotive effect of thinning to isolate the crowns of the trees with the finest boles,* by which the valuable quality increment is encouraged (Assmann, 1953). One could refer to this as a purposeful individual enlargement of the diameters of those trees with the best shape. Such desirable effects, however, need not lead us to overlook the question as to whether a too rapid increase of diameter might not result in some impairment to the internal quality characteristics. This, for example, is the case in Norway spruce where the strength of the timber is adversely affected by excessive width of annual ring. With ring widths such as those to be expected in the Swedish experimental plots III and IV at Dalby, one must reckon on decreasing specific gravity and lowered cellulose contents in the light of the studies conducted by Hildebrandt (1954). A lowering of the timber quality with increasing width of the annual rings is to be feared also in oak, for example. The qualification for veneer wood becomes doubtful with an annual ring width of over 1·8 mm (Mayer-Wegelin, 1950, 1952). If increment thinning for crown development is commenced too early, the length of clean bole may thereby be reduced and the proportion of branchy crown-wood increased at the expense of stemwood, with resulting loss in value.

IV. RESULTS OF THINNING EXPERIMENTS CARRIED OUT TO DATE IN PURE EVEN-AGED STANDS

The concept of the "even-aged" stand cannot be narrowly defined; in the case of artificially cultivated stands we must allow age differences of 5 up to a maximum of 10 years and in naturally reproduced (shade-tolerant) stands even differences of 10 up to a maximum of 20 years. The several individual plots of an experimental series must, however, if possible correspond exactly as regards their *average ages*.[1] If other species are to be mixed with the main species, maximum proportions of 5–10 per cent in basal area and up to 10 per cent of canopy cover seem permissible where felling of the additional components, would disturb the experiments and is impracticable for silvicultural reasons.

1. Common Beech

A brief characterization of the species Common beech

Common beech *(Fagus sylvatica)* is a typical shade-tolerant species with a late culmination of increment, and a long-sustained period of active growth which falls off only slowly in old age. According to the Y.T. of Wiedemann we may expect on sites belonging to height quality class I,

the culmination of the c.a.i. at the age of 60 years, with 12·2 fm,
the culmination of the m.a.i. not until the age of 140 years, with over 9·0 fm.

The greatest attainable age is only about 250 years, due to increasing fungal attacks. Common beech responds to liberation of the crown and admission of light by making considerable additions to growth. By the development of sun-leaves on the laterally exposed crown periphery the length of that part of the crown surface which is exposed to sunlight is increased. In addition to this, the crown can be "fanned out" by an increase of the initial angle of the branches with the stem. The ability to continue crown expansion lasts up to a fairly old age. We might speak of it as a "plastic" species which is capable of filling very variable types of growing space. The timber quality is dependent upon freedom from branches, whilst the annual ring width is unimportant. The development of red heartwood seems to increase with age, for which reason a fast diameter development is desirable. Owing to wide natural differences in stem quality with respect to straightness and freedom from branches, there is hope for succesful improvement by selection. The pathogenic danger of attacks by insects (woolly aphids, rose beetles, and pale tussoch moths) and fungi is relatively small; it can be almost entirely excluded, if silvicultural mistakes (lateral exposure, sudden opening up of the stand) are avoided. All in all, this species is particularly suitable for comparative thinning experiments.

---

[1] An age difference of 2 years can, in a stand of spruce pole-wood, completely veil any effects thinning may have had on the diameter.

The most important experimental thinning series

The following research institutes have, or have had, a fairly large number of experimental thinning series of Common beech:

1. The *former Prussian Forest Research Institute*

Twenty-seven series with a total of sixty-four plots, used as follows:

Low thinning series	four series with grades A, B, C, ten series with grades B and C,
Crown thinning series	one series with comparative A-plot, nine series with comparative B- and C-plots, one series without comparative low-thinned plots.
Selection thinning series	two series with comparative C-plots.

The most important publications are by Schwappach (1911) and Wiedemann (1931).

2. *Forest Research Institute of Württemberg*

(Württembergische Forstliche Versuchs-Anstalt)

Seven series with twenty-three plots, used as follows:

Six series, originally low-thinned at grades A, B, C on the site of the experiment of 1873, A-plots subsequently converted into E-grade plots (crown thinning after Lorey) and thereby changed into crown thinned series with low thinned comparative plots. One original crown thinned series with two E- and D-grade plots each.

Publications by Dieterich (1925) and Zimmerle (1938b).

3. *Forest Research Institute of Baden*

(Badische Forstliche Versuchs-Anstalt)

Nine series with twenty-five plots, used as follows:

Low thinned series	four with A, B, C-grade.
Crown thinned series	five with B, C-grade or comparative C-plot respectively.

Two series include added mixtures of Silver fir and Norway spruce.

Publications by Wimmer (1914), Wohlfarth (1938), Mitscherlich (1951).

4. *Bavarian Forest Research Institute*

(Bayerische Forstliche Versuchs-Anstalt)

Seven series with twenty-one plots, used as follows:

Low thinned series	six with grades A, B, C.
Crown thinned series	one with comparative B- and C-plots.

Publications: Reinhold (1926). In five of the low thinned experimental series there are differences between quality classes or sites, disturbing their comparability.

5. *Hessian Forest Research Institute*

   (Hessische Forstliche Versuchs-Anstalt)

   Seven series with twenty-one plots, used as follows:

Low thinned series	three with grades A, B, C.
Crown thinned series	four with grades A, B or B, C, or B comparisons.

   Publications by Schober (1937).

6. *Swiss Forest Research Institute*

   (Schweizerische Forstliche Versuchs-Anstalt)

   Five series with seventeen plots, used as follows:

Low thinned series	two with grades B, C, D.
Crown thinned series	three with grades B, C or B, C, D comparisons.

   Publications: Flury (1903), Engler (1924), E. Badoux (1939).

Owing to the broad scope of the experiments at the former Prussian Research Institute we should accord special weight to their results. Nevertheless, some of the general conclusions which have been drawn so far from these experiments must now be set aside.

Outdated conclusions from former experimental results

As a result of observations up to 1911, Schwappach concluded that it was possible to achieve *a considerable increase in volume production* by way of thinning. His presupposition in ascribing to the yield table for *heavy thinnings* (Table A) a yield superior by nearly 20 per cent over that obtained by moderate thinnings (Table B) has been shown to be incorrect. He was persuaded thus by the *powerful upsurge of growth following upon the first occasions of heavy thinning*. These, however, were due mainly to the "acceleration of growth" which we have already observed, and they were later compensated by setbacks, as we shall presently see. Schwappach, furthermore, leaned his assumption on the *basal area increment*. This, however, is by no means proportional to the volume increment.

Wiedemann corrected these conclusions in 1931, but himself maintained that *basal areas can be altered within wide limits—in the case of the Common beech between 20 to 40 m²—without causing any "conspicuous change" of the increment*. The incorrectness of this view has in the meantime been demonstrated by Mitscherlich, Erteld and Assmann.

Baader, in 1935, tried to answer the question about the influence of thinning on the increment by a *statistical mean* of all the results from German and Swiss experiments published up to that time. His comparisons, based on total crop volumes to date in Common beech, culminated in the following percentage figures, in which case the B-grade is set equal to 100:

	Low thinning				Crown thinning		Open stand thinning (Lichtung)	
Grade	A	B	C	D	light	heavy	gradual	sudden
	94	100	102	102%	99%	97%	98%	80%

According to these figures, a *production optimum* would have to be expected *in the C-and D-grades*. The untenable nature of such a comparison, the weaknesses of which incidentally are pointed out by Baader himself, becomes apparent by the following facts:

1. The *grade definitions of the different experimental institutes are not identical* (cf. p. 211), and even if they were identical, beyond the B-grade they become uncertain.

2. Most of the assessed experimental series contain *no A-plots*. These latter plots, however, provide the only useful basis for comparison.

3. Faultless comparisons are possible only if
    (a) *all individual plots* of a particular series *occupy equivalent site conditions* which can be claimed only for a few series, and if,
    (b) for the purpose of comparing general averages, we assemble in the same context only *"composite" series* which are bound to contain at the same time *all compared thinning methods*.

4. Even if this is done, we still have to make allowance for the fact that *the same types and grades of thinning* may have different effects, depending on the site, age phase and the condition of the stand.

5. The answer to the question, which thinning method would supply the highest volume yield, depends decisively on the *age period* which is to be examined or evaluated in each particular case.

In these circumstances therefore, the only answer to the problem must be found by analysing individual experimental series. This will be undertaken in the following subsection.

(a) VOLUME AND VALUE EFFICIENCIES IN LOW-THINNING EXPERIMENTS

Thinning of A-grade plots, not in accordance with plans

Of the four experimental series of the former Prussian Research Institute containing grades A, B and C, the experimental series Oberscheld 18 alone has an A-plot which was treated absolutely according to plans. In other series, some of the A-plots have several times suffered thinning in excess of the planned degree, as the Table 76 shows.

The most outstanding case in the experimental series Kupferhütte is one of several illustrating the lack of understanding upon the problems of scientific research on the part of many practical foresters.[1] The blame for other instances of thinning beyond the intended grade probably lies with the research institutes; the probable reason for this was a *concession to the thinning concepts employed in practical forestry*. The commendable endeavour of Schwappach (1911) "always to remain in close touch with the practical side of work and *in projecting aims and methods, to indicate its proper development*" (italics by the author) has on several occasions involved him in conflicts with the scientific

---

[1] In this connection, an anecdote from agricultural research, said to be of recent origin, which characterizes this attitude: A farmer, realizing at the beginning of May how splendidly the manured parcels of a clover field in a fertilizer experiment responded, speedily proceeded to apply fertilizer in the unfertilized "zero-parcels"!

TABLE 76

THINNING BEYOND THE PLANNED DEGREE IN THE A-PLOTS

Exp. series	Age or year respectively (in brackets)	Extractions in *basal area* per ha as % of the basal area *before* thinning		Mean diameter of the removals
		(m²)	(%)	(cm)
Freienwalde 195	73 (1896)	4·83	10	12·9
Freienwalde 188	82 (1890)	5·39	13	14·1
	88 (1896)	4·74	12	17·6
	105 (1913)	3·64	9	21·5
	118 (1927)	3·44	8	29·0
Kupferhütte 25	91 (1898)	5·22	11	16·9
	103 (1910)	4·64	10	19·6
	118 (1924)[1]	8·55	18 (140·8 fm)	24·5

* Mainly removed by authority of the local forest administration during the First World War.

aims of the experiments, whilst he was fully aware of their higher importance.[1] Looking back today, we cannot help feeling that this has regrettably prejudiced the informative value of many long-term experiments. Research and treatment if directed according to wholly scientific objectives would by now have yielded more extensive information. Wiedemann, since 1928 the esteemed Director of the Prussian Research Institute, endeavoured by planned treatment of the A-plots to differentiate clearly between the degrees of intervention necessary in the B-, C-, and crown-thinned plots. Unfortunately he let himself be influenced by the yield table basal areas for moderate and heavy thinnings which along with the arbitrary and partly unnatural basal area frame of these tables (cf. p. 182), were bound to lead to insoluble contradictions. This, among other instances, is demonstrated by the exp. ser. Battenberg 81 (cf. *Die Rotbuche*, 1931, p. 34).

Periodic mean basal areas and volume increments of some typical low-thinned series

Some typical reactions to increasing grades of low thinning will be demonstrated on the basis of four experimental series which have provided results of exceptionally long-term experiments.[2] They are the experimental series Freienwalde 195, Freienwalde 188

[1] As Schwappach reports in his *Rotbuche*, 1911, p. 2, the Alsatian Oberforstmeister Ney (known by his humorous writings) in 1892 made the following statement on the occasion of an inspection of the experimental series at Freienwalde: "If one of my foresters left a tree of this kind standing, I should demand from him a fine of 10 Marks." We are not likely to make a mistake in assuming that this criticism from a practical forester may have given rise to the removal of the worst "offenders" from A-plots. Schwappach found an original way out of this dilemma in the crown-thinned experimental series Dalheim 116, laid out by himself, where by his instructions every tree in the comparative plot under low thinning (A-grade), which according to the notions of silvicultural tending should have been removed, was encircled with a double ring in white oil paint! This plot, apart from the A-plot of the experimental series Oberscheid 18, is the only one which was spared irregular thinning. This, being a comparative plot in a crown-thinned experimental series, has provided us with particularly instructive possibilities for comparison (cf. p. 271).

[2] The author once more expresses his cordial thanks to Prof. Dr. Erteld, Eberswalde, who supplied him with the results of the two experimental series at Freienwalde until 1957, as well as to the former Director of the Austrian Federal Research Institute, Min.-Rat. Dr. Horky, who provided the author with some previously unpublished figures of yield for the experimental series at Laabach. By kind permission of Prof. Dr. Wiedemann, the author was enabled to collect measurements of the research series Kupferhütte and thereby to obtain figures for the period after 1931.

and Kupferhütte 25 of the former Prussian Research Institute, as well as Laabach which belongs to the Austrian Federal Research Institute (in this connection see also Assmann, 1957).

Brief site-description of the research series

1. *Freienwalde 195*. East German diluvium, end-moraine; 80 m above m.s.l., level or gently sloping towards N. Loamy sand over boulder clay loam. The A-plot, where the growth has been retarded by a fairly thick cover of sand and local topography, today belongs to a lower height quality class than the B- and C-plots.

	Temperature (°C)	Rainfall (mm)
Annual mean	8·3	560
May–August	16·0	240
"scarce water supply"		

2. *Freienwalde 188*. As above; 50 m above m.s.l.; undulating landscape; C-plot favoured by topography. Climatic figures as above: "scarce water supply".
3. *Kupferhütte 25*. Southern Harz; 450 m above m.s.l.; steep SE. slope; Wissenbach slate (rich in lime); deep grounded fresh gritty loam.

	Temperature (°C)	Rainfall (mm)
Annual mean	6·3	1100
May–August	13·0	500
"good water supply"		

4. *Laabach*. Vienna woods, 430 m above m.s.l.; leaning to steep NNE. slope, Viennese sandstone, very deep fresh loam. Four plots from I–IV, with increasing degrees of open-stand thinning (Lichtung), II at a disadvantage regarding position, III and IV favoured.

	Temperature (°C)	Rainfall (mm)
Annual mean	8·4	900
May–August	14·4	490
"adequate water supplies"		

The experimental series under increment thinning at Laabach is suitable for our purpose, despite the fact that the most lightly thinned plot I is officially considered as "heavily thinned". Apart from one occasion of medium heavy thinning at the age of 72 years, this plot up to the age of 110 years was treated practically in the same way as an A-grade plot. Heavy thinning at the age of 110 has had an influence only during the last 6 years of the whole observation period to date.

TABLE 77

MEAN BASAL AREA AND GROWTH IN THE EXPERIMENTAL SERIES FOR DIFFERENT OBSERVATION PERIODS

Experimental series	Observation period from/to	Grade	Mean basal area over a period		Ann. incr. of wood over 7 cm in diameter		Remarks
			abs. (m²)	rel. (%)	abs. (fm)	rel. (%)	
1. Freienwalde 195	64–73	A	33·2	100	8·6	100	Acceleration of growth
Height Q.	(1887)	B	30·1	91	11·3	131	following initial heavy
Cl. = I.4		C	26·6	80	11·8	137	thinning
(Beech)	73–84	A	32·8	100	12·0	100	A-plot thinned
		B	29·1	89	13·2	110	
		C	25·6	78	11·8	98	
	84–103	A	36·1	100	9·3	100	Fresh burst of increment
		B	31·9	88	10·3	111	
		C	25·2	70	10·4	112	
	103–133	A	41·6	100	9·7	100	Ditto
	(1957)	B	33·3	80	10·6	109	
		C	24·3	58	9·5	98	
	64–133	A	37·6	100	9·83	100	A-plot belongs to a lower
		B	31·8	85	11·03	112	Q. Cl.
		C	25·1	67	10·43	106	
2. Freienwalde 188	76–88	A	38·2	100	8·0	100	Acceleration of growth as
Height Q.	(1884)	B	35·4	93	10·3	129	in series 195
Cl. = I.7		C	29·1	76	12·0	150	
(Beech)	88–99	A	36·2	100	12·5	100	Disturbed:
		B	32·3	89	12·2	98	A-plot thinned
		C	26·6	73	13·7	110	
	99–118	A	39·7	100	11·8	100	Set-back
		B	33·6	85	11·1	94	
		C	25·4	64	9·4	80	
	118–148	A	44·4	100	11·3	100	Ditto
	(1957)	B	34·5	78	11·3	100	
		C	25·2	57	10·5	93	
	76–148	A	40·9	100	11·07	100	Ditto
		B	34·4	84	11·24	102	
		C	26·1	64	10·97	99	

(continued)

TABLE 77 *(cont.)*

Experimental series	Observation period from/to	Grade	Mean basal area over a period		Ann. incr. of wood over 7 cm in diameter		Remarks
			abs. (m²)	rel. (%)	abs. (fm)	rel. (%)	
3. Kupferhütte 25	86–103	A	44·1	100	9·1	100	Acceleration of growth
Height Q.	(1892)	B	37·2	84	10·2	112	
Cl. = I.7		C	27·2	62	10·5	115	
(Beech)	103–118	A	39·9	100	9·7	100	A-plot heavily thinned
		B	35·2	88	9·4	97	
		C	26·0	65	8·3	86	
	118–127	A	39·9	100	8·3	100	Set-back
		B	34·9	87	9·0	108	
		C	26·5	66	7·9	95	
	127–136	A	41·8	100	8·2	100	Set-back
	(1942)	B	32·0	77	7·3	89	
		C	23·8	57	6·1	74	
	86–136	A	41·7	100	8·9	100	Set-back
		B	35·2	84	9·2	102	
		C	26·1	63	8·6	96	
4. Laabach	60–72	I	34·1	100	14·3	100	Acceleration of growth
Height Q.	(1893)	II	28·0	82	16·7	117	
Cl. = I.4		III	23·6	69	17·8	124	
		IV	18·8	55	16·5	115	
(Beech)	72–88	I	36·1	100	12·4	100	Thinning pause,
		II	33·7	93	12·5	101	approach in stocking
		III	32·3	90	11·8	95	densities, set-back
		IV	27·9	77	11·4	92	
	88–103	I	43·4	100	11·7	100	New thinnings, suitably
		II	34·7	80	11·1	95	graduated weaker
		III	30·7	71	12·2	103	reaction
		IV	24·6	57	9·4	80	
	103–116	I	45·2	100	11·7	100	New set-back
	(1949)	II	37·1	82	10·8	92	
		III	32·8	73	10·9	93	
		IV	27·4	61	9·1	78	
	60–116	I	39·7	100	12·46	100	
		II	33·5	84	12·62	101	
		III	30·1	76	12·96	104	
		IV	24·9	63	11·43	92	

Table 77, along with Fig. 111a–c, illustrates the typical growth-reactions very clearly. We can recognize equally in all four series the conspicuous bursts of increment after the first occasions of heavy thinning, which point to a "growth impulse".

In view of the exceptionally late culmination of the c.a.i. of volume in beech, this phenomenon might in the circumstances be expected to occur even at such a deferred age as

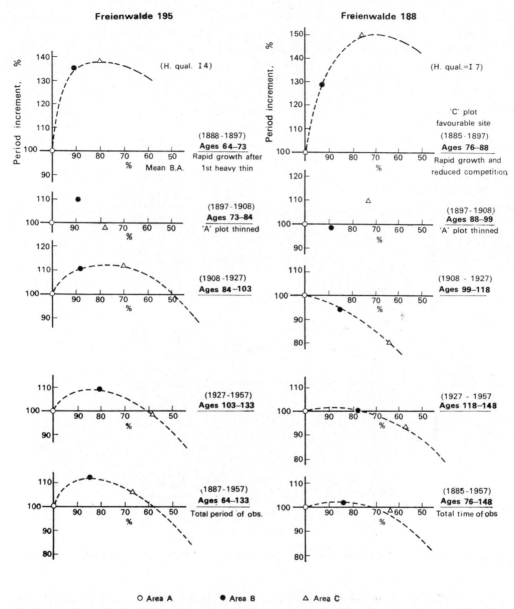

FIG. 111a. Mean basal areas and volume increments for the beech trial series 195 and 188 at Freienwalde.

80–100 years. The bursts of increment of + 37 per cent and + 50 per cent in the C-plots of the Freienwalde series are particularly strong. This may perhaps be associated with the macro-climatic conditions of this warm and dry site, which despite the favourable type of soil, has a "scarce water supply". On such sites, the favourable effect of reduced competition may well play a part alongside the actual growth impulse. The growth reactions of the ensuing observation period were disturbed by thinnings at variance with plans. Concerning the further growth reactions in series 195 it should be noted that the *A-plot* suffers from a local disadvantage and *the height quality class today is inferior by a half-stage*!

The striking new burst of increment during the period 84–103 and the impressive superiority in growth of the B- and C-grades over the whole period of approximately 70 years' observations upon this series are mainly ascribable to the inferiority of the A-plot. Series 188, we notice, suffered "set-backs" and the A-grade *succeeded in achieving superiority* during the corresponding two contemporary observation periods. The optimum curve for the total observation period proceeds on a remarkably level course. The relative performance of the three grades of thinning remains typical, though differences are small.

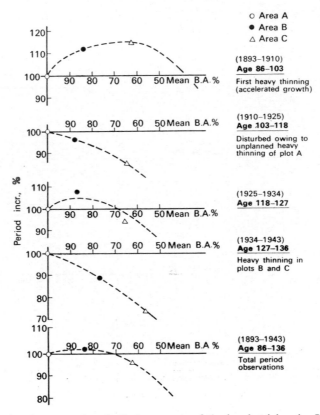

FIG. 111b. Mean basal areas and periodic increments of the beech trial series Kupferhütte (25).

The parallel behaviour of the two experimental series at Kupferhütte and Laabach is noteworthy if we bear in mind the somewhat untoward disturbances suffered by the experiment at Kupferhütte, particularly during the second observation period. *The first powerful accretions of increment*, which were mainly due to the acceleration of growth activities, *were followed by set-backs*. In general, the optimum curves become more level with increasing age, whilst at the same time the culminating point approaches the maximum basal area.

On the whole, this result agrees with the important work by Badoux (1939). From the résumé of his investigations the following passage is quoted here: "Very heavy thinning ... reduces the volume increment of the total stand very noticeably by as much as 20 per cent. Occasionally it causes a *temporary stimulation* to the current increment. But this

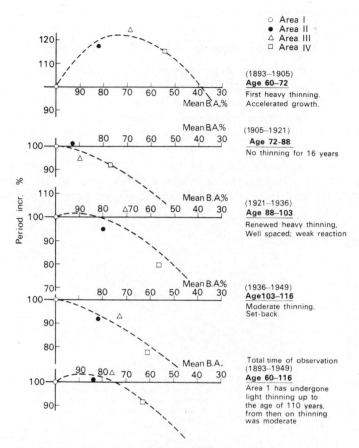

FIG. 111c. Mean basal area and periodic increment for the beech heavy thinning series at Laabach (Vienna Woods).

is only a 'whip lash' and has no lasting effect." In the same connection Wiedemann also talks of a temporary "stimulating effect" of thinning.

The A-grade in the experimental series *Oberscheld* 18 of the former Prussian Research Institute shows a clear optimum of the increment. This site has good supplies of water and base nutrients on diabase, at 574 m height above sea level. The mean height quality class is II.4. The most important figures for the observation period from 73 to 114 years (1886–1927) are:

Thinning grade	Mean basal area		Per. mean ann. inct. timber over 7 cm diam.	
	abs. (m²)	rel. (%)	abs. (m³)	rel. (%)
A	46·0	100	9·8	100
B	38·4	83	9·6	98
C	31·5	68	9·5	97

The same implications are found also in the

Results of the Bavarian low-thinned beech series

Unfortunately, in the Bavarian experimental Common beech series, the individual stems were not numbered until shortly after 1900. Owing to numerous unrecorded losses, especially in the Spessart, the increment calculations prior to that time are not usable. However, even after 1900, the inadequacies of a calculation by sample stem form-factors and the systematic measuring errors of many height measurements show themselves in a typical manner, as illustrated by Fig. 112 on the basis of mean height values of the exp. ser. Fabrikschleichach, collected during surveys to date. Only a person not acquainted with the difficulties of obtaining exact height measurements in beech stands will be surprised by the fact that, in four cases, the mean heights after 5 years were lower by 0·2–0·7 m.

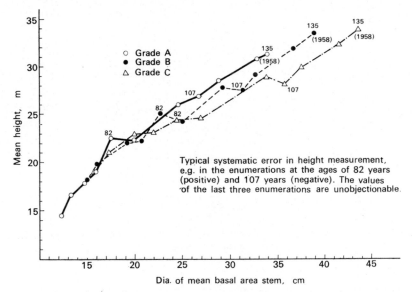

FIG. 112. Development of mean height plotted over the diameter of the mean basal stem in the beech thinning experiment at Fabrikschleichach.

Table 78 furnishes the most important results of six low-thinned series subsequent to the stem-by-stem numbering of trees. Except for the series Fabrikschleichach, the geological formation of which is of Semionoten-sandstone, the sites of the experimental series consist of upper and medium bunter-sandstone. The existence of unquestionable differences between the experimental series, which manifest themselves during long observation periods by differences between the quality classes, is proved by the comparison of height quality classes in the last two columns of Table 78.

It should be noted that with increasing severity of thinning, the heights of the mean basal area stems must increase also, i.e. from A to C. The differences are particularly marked in the young and middle ages and disappear at older ages because in Common beech the shift by calculation of mean diameters and heights is lessened with the broadening of the crowns and the decrease in vertical height growth. The height curves for beech also level out in older crops. The two last-mentioned circumstances moreover, cause a

TABLE 78

RESULTS OF THE BAVARIAN LOW-THINNED EXPERIMENTAL BEECH SERIES

Experimental series	Observation period		Thinning grade	Per. mean basal area		Average ann. increments in basal area		Wood over 7 cm in diameter		Qual. cl. comparison Mean percentage ratio of the heights of all surveys		Remarks
	From	to		abs.	rel.	abs.	rel.	abs.	rel.	Mean heights (%)	Top heights (%)	
				(m²)	(%)	(m²)	(%)	(m³)	(%)			
Fabrikschleichach Final Q. Cl. I.9 satisfactory water supply	82–135	= 53 yrs.	A	41·9	*100*	0·432	*100*	9·4	*100*	100	100	A not as good as B and C
			B	36·8	88	0·521	121	10·5	*112*	109	101	
			C	26·3	63	0·454	105	9·4	*100*	112	103	
Rothenbuch Final Q. Cl. I.9 well supplied with water	83–134	= 51 yrs.	A	41·1	*100*	0·432	*100*	9·5	*100*	100	100	C slightly poorer than B or A
			B	35·5	86	0·431	100	9·2	97	104	100	
			C	26·5	64	0·408	95	8·2	86	103	98	
Lohr-West Final Q. Cl. II.5 (C-plot good) water supply	100–142	= 42 yrs.	A	43·7	*100*	0·442	*100*	8·4	*100*	100	100	C considerably better than B and A
			B	32·7	75	0·427	97	8·3	99	111	102	
			C	25·8	59	0·431	97	8·2	98	117	105	
Hain/Spessart Final Q. Cl. I.2 satisfactory water supply	73–115	= 42 yrs.	A	36·7	*100*	0·455	*100*	9·1	*100*	100	100	A considerably poorer than B and C
			B	30·7	84	0·460	101	9·4	*103*	117	106	
			C	32·1	63	0·419	92	8·5	93	120	107	
Mittelsinn Final Q. Cl. III.4 scarce water supply	77–122	= 45 yrs.	A	33·8[1]	*100*	0·494	*100*	7·5	*100*	100	100	A better than B and C
			B	27·9	82	0·392	79	6·0	80	105	96	
			C	24·3	72	0·450	91	6·3	84	106	94	
Elmstein-Nord Final Q. Cl. II.0 scarce water supply	84–129	= 45 yrs.	A	38·6	*100*	0·429	*100*	8·8	*100*	100	100	
			B	25·0	65	0·354	83	6·7	76	103	99	
			C	18·9	49	0·324	76	6·2	70	107	99	
All. exp. series except Mittelsinn Mean Q. Cl. I.9			A	40·4	*100*	0·438	*100*	9·0	*100*	100	100	
			B	33·8	84	0·439	100	8·8	98	109	102	
			C	24·1	60	0·407	93	8·1	90	112	103	

[1] By thinning not in accordance with plans, approximately one-third of the crop growing on the A-plot was removed during the First World War.

tendency in the older experimental beech series for the *top height* (height of the mean basal area tree of the 100 stoutest trees per ha, taken from the height curve) to diminish, along with increasing severity of the thinning.

Accordingly, *in five out of six series there are differences between the quality classes* which must be taken into consideration in a comparison of the yields.

Whilst the original values of increment obtained from older volume calculations often result in impossible figures—owing to unreliable height values and confused fluctuations of locally obtained form factors—the corrected values for volume increment[1] in Table 78 are in complete agreement with the concurrent basal area increments, after due consideration is taken of known regularities and quality class differences.

If we regard the production ratios under these conditions, the *inferiority of the C-grade* stands out particularly clearly. The occurrence of an optimum in the B-grade of the series Fabrikschleichach and Hain, Spessart, is caused by prejudicial site-factors in the corresponding A-plots.

In Bavaria the A-plots have been subjected to repeated unregulated thinnings; in the Spessart, the local population, which exercises rights to cut wood, has played a similar part in this unplanned thinning. During the First World War the local forest administration utilized about one-third of the crop on the A-plot of the Mittelsinn experimental series! For that reason this experimental series is excluded from the summary comparison made of Table 78.

This comparison shows an overall optimum for the A-grade plots (of which one has been favoured by local site conditions but two have suffered check) a not improbable outcome on account of the fairly advanced ages reached at the end of the observations. One might accordingly reckon on a natural critical stocking density of 0·70, which could be reduced to 0·64 if we were to raise the periodic mean basal area of the A-plots throughout by 10 per cent to allow for the unregulated removals. This would then give us approximately the true potential maximum basal area.

The four more closely analysed experimental series have above all shown that reactions to thinning are dependent to a great extent *on the age*, and that unregulated thinnings which are not carried out according to plan distort the results. Further evaluations indicate that it is absolutely essential to take into account *the frequent differences between quality classes* and to *correct any calculation errors. The contradictory and indifferent results of statistical evaluations to date are explainable on these grounds.*

Results of Danish thinning experiments

That in the long-term and with older crop ages, the more lightly thinned stands of beech should develop some superiority of growth, would lend colour to our discussion upon fundamental relationships on p. 230.

Thus, the interesting experiment of the Danish Forest Research Institute at *Brahetrolleborg*[2], on the island of Fünen, where a heavily thinned stand is compared to a completely unthinned stand ("urskoven") shows the superiority of this unthinned plot. The height

---

[1] The volumes of extracted timber have been used without alterations; only the calculations for the remaining crops at the beginning and end of the 40–50-year observation periods have been corrected.

[2] My cordial thanks are expressed here to the Director of the Danish Forest Research Institute, Dr. Holmsgaard, and Forstmeister Dr. Henriksen for their kindness in allowing me to use some results of the experiments.

quality class of the two compared plots at the age of 109 years is I.0 according to Mar: Møller, or I.2 according to Wiedemann.

The values for the age period 60–109 amount to:

		Per mean basal area	Annual basal area increment	Annual volume increment (tot. tree vol.)
For the unthinned plot	abs.	45·92 m²	0·575 m²	13·8 m³
	rel.	*100%*	100%	*100%*
For the heavily thinned plot	abs.	24·78 m²	0·614 m²	13·1 m³
	rel.	*54%*	107%	*95%*

The superiority in increment of the unthinned plot, which becomes evident approximately from the age of 80 years, is likely to increase even further with continued observation beyond the age of 100 years.

Of special interest to us are the results of a new thinning experiment in a young stand of Common beech on Zealand, in *Bregentved* forest, which belongs to Count Moltke, *Waldort Totterup*.

In this experiment, the A-grade (no thinning) is represented by one parcel, the increasing grades B and C by three parcels each, the D-grade by 2 parcels and the heaviest grade F (Lichtung) by one parcel. The increment values for 5 growing periods of 2 years each and one 3-year period making up a total observation period covering ages from 19 to 32 years, show an *optimum of the basal area increment in the D-grade*. The average figures of the different grades are as follows:

		Grades					
		A	B	C	D	E	F
Mean b. area over period	m²	20·0	19·6	15·0	14·6	12·6	10·6
	%	100	98	75	73	63	53
Basal area increment	m²	1·70	1·58	1·83	1·89	1·84	1·69
	%	100	93	108	111	108	99
Volume increment	m³	15·7	14·5	14·5	15·3	14·2	13·1
	%	100	92	92	97	90	83

Owing to the uneven number of parcels and a fairly large variance of the increment values discovered by Henriksen (measuring errors and local influences), this result is not absolutely clear. Unexpectedly indeed, the *optimum volume increment* for such an early development occurs already *in the A-grade*.

All the more informative are the increment values which Henriksen calculated for each year on the basis of an analysis of ten stems each of four individual parcels and for which he further made "climatic corrections", which freed the individual annual increments from climatic aberrations. These corrected increments are assembled in Table 79 for 2-year periods and illustrate the regular influences of the natural growth pattern, the acceleration of growth and the reduction of stem numbers and basal areas as we

TABLE 79

COMMON BEECH THINNING EXPERIMENT TOTTERUP, BRAGENTVED FOREST

MEAN PERIODIC BASAL AREAS AND TREE VOLUME INCREMENTS OF FOUR SEPARATE PARCELS FROM STEM ANALYSES (TEN EACH) AND CORRECTED TO APPLY FOR AVERAGE CLIMATIC CONDITIONS, BY H. A. HENRIKSEN

Exp. parcel	Definition		Increment periods						
			19–22	22–24	24–26	26–28	28–30	30–32	19–32
No. 3 B-grade	Mean b. area	m²	13·1	17·4	20·1	22·4	21·6	22·2	18·96
		%	100	100	100	100	100	100	100
	Ann. incr.	m³	10·2	13·5	14·7	15·7	16·0	**17·4**	14·2
		%	100	100	100	100	100	100	100
No. 9 C-grade	Mean b. area	m²	10·9	14·0	15·1	16·1	16·0	15·7	14·37
		%	84	80	75	72	74	71	76
	Increment	m³	11·8	13·7	16·4	17·8	**18·0**	16·9	15·5
		%	115	102	111	113	112	97	109
No. 8 D-grade	Mean b. area	m²	12·1	14·7	14·8	14·5	14·3	12·7	13·71
		%	92	84	66	65	66	58	72
	Increment	m³	13·9	16·0	17·0	17·9	**18·3**	16·6	16·4
		%	136	118	116	114	114	96	115
No. 7 F-grade	Mean b. area	m²	10·1	10·6	9·7	9·9	9·2	6·8	9·45
		%	78	61	48	44	43	30	50
	Increment	m³	12·4	12·9	14·5	**15·4**	14·1	10·5	13·2
		%	122	96	99	98	88	60	93

The highest volume increment values are in **bold** type.

would expect them on the basis of all the available information. The fact that a B-parcel has to serve as basis for comparison is of little concern, because the mean basal area of these parcels up to the age of 24 years amounted to approximately 100 per cent, from 24 to 28 years about 98 per cent and from 28 to 32 years about 83 per cent of the A-parcels. The volume increment of the B-parcels increased up to the age of 32 years in a regular manner.

The *impetus imparted to growth in C and D causes an early culmination of the volume increment.* The reactions of this young beech stand reveal the power of very early and severe thinnings to alter the natural trend of development. We might almost regard the temporary positive increment changes as a direct result of a disturbance to the natural growth rhythm. However, already during the last growing period from 30 to 32 years, the increasing strength of thinning in C and D enabled the B-plots to take the lead. The extreme severity of thinning in the F-plot during the last increment period even went to *a natural stocking density of* 0·30, and already during the period from 22 to 24 years had led to reduced production. *This experiment shows convincingly the value of systematic yield study experiments.*

Recent attempts at a total statistical evaluation

Besides the above C. Mar:Møller (1954b, c) has evaluated numerous experimental and comparative measurements in Danish stands of beech and Norway spruce thinned to differing grades. He combined his results in a comprehensive representation by means of curves. From this, the critical degree of stocking for both species is to be found not below about 0·50. This aberrant result is based mainly on the fact that the majority of increment values apply to young and middle-aged stands in which accelerated growth is still effective. Moreover, in Denmark there are no sufficiently long-observed experimental beech series comprising a lightly thinned A-plot, at least not to the knowledge of the author (with the exception given above!).

In a more recent attempt at a total statistical assessment, Mitscherlich (1954) used an original graphical method, based on similar principles to those used in the construction

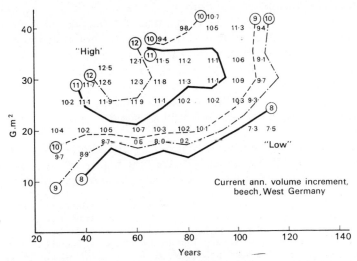

FIG. 113. Annual volume increment of beech stands of Quality Class I in relation to age and basal area (*Mitscherlich*).

of lines of constant atmospheric pressure, or isobars, in our familiar weather charts. In a system of co-ordinates with the abscissae representing age and the ordinates basal area (at the beginning of the increment period), the volume increments (c.a.i. of timber over 7 cm diam.) are plotted at each point of intersection of the grid co-ordinates of age and basal area, as shown in Fig. 113. The lines connecting equal increment values create contoured areas, defining regions with high ("High") or low ("Low") increments. We find a "High" increment region for the age 40–70, with basal areas around 30 m². The shape of the "relief-map contours" demonstrates that the basal areas giving optimum yield rise steadily with increasing age and that performance declines fairly rapidly when basal areas are appreciably reduced. By separate plotting according to quality classes, Mitscherlich made allowance for the influence of the site, and by using age as abscissa, he included the influence of age. *The result* is fairly clear and is *broadly in keeping with Assmann's experimental results.*

In contrast to this, convincing proof is lacking from the result of a more recent comprehensive statistical comparison by Schober (1957) based on 72 experimental series of "European research institutes" (mainly the experimental series listed on p. 246) remains unconvincing because, apart from other aspects (cf. p. 248), the *decisive influence of age* was not taken into consideration.[1]

Optimum and critical basal areas in Common beech

Confining our interest in the first instance to pure volume production, it becomes clear that in that case, the observance of an "optimum basal area" makes sense only if thereby an economically important improvement of the timber volume production can be achieved. But obviously there is little prospect for this in the case of Common beech. In contrast to Norway spruce, the production periods for beech cannot be shortened to any great extent and certainly not under 120 years. *By that age, however, the considerable increase of increment production from heavy thinning has had to yield place to a steadily increasing superiority induced by light thinning.*

It is much more important, on the other hand, to know the critical basal area for a certain period or the natural critical degree of stocking. The question whether 95 per cent or 90 per cent should be chosen as limit of the achievable optimum increment can await future settlement. The limit of 95 per cent, suggested by Assmann, already offers a fully sufficient flexibility for the thinning of young crops. Under these conditions, and on the basis of the above experimental results, the natural critical degree of stocking in Common beech can be estimated as 0·6–0·7 of the maximum potential basal area or basal area over a period, 0·6 applying to younger and 0·7 to older stands.

These values are deduced from experiments, in which the A-plots have on several occasions undergone thinnings not conforming with plans and the true maximum periodic basal areas may, as a result, be about 5–10 per cent higher. *From experience we know that the maximum basal area in over 100-year-old beech stands on good sites* (quality classes

---

[1] In Fig. 1 on p. 392 of the *AFZ*, Schober used *absolute* periodic basal area values as abscissae, and increment values of quality class I–III as ordinates, thus providing a wide variance in height and width. If he had used relative values for the periodic basal area and the increment (in which case the values of the lowest grade in each case could be set equal to 100) the optimum curve would have presented an equally clear picture as in Fig. 2 which gives Mitscherlich's results for the age of 80 years. Regarding Schober's further expositions, compare the reply by Assmann (1957) on p. 486, and following pages in the *AFZ*, 1957.

I to II) *lies between 45 and 50 m²*. Thus, if we use the basic magnitudes of 0·6 to 0·7 as critical natural degree of stocking, we have allowed for a certain *safety factor*. If we use as basis the previously mentioned absolute maximum values of 45 to 50 m², which are suitable for a rough calculation of the critical basal area in older stands, we can occasionally and temporarily go down to a natural degree of stocking of 0·5–0·6. How far we can reduce the natural degree of stocking in practice depends mainly on the value yields and their changes due to thinning; these must now be the next subject for discussion.

Changes in value efficiency due to low thinning

Wiedemann, in his work *Die Rotbuche 1931*, was the first to undertake a comprehensive discussion upon comparative value yields for different types of thinning on the basis of long-term observations. He explained convincingly that a *comparison of yields* must not be restricted to the "remaining stand" but instead *should be based on the total production*, including all extracted produce.

Wiedemann's division of the total production of the classic low-thinning series Freienwalde 195 into 5-cm diameter classes (*Rotbuche*, p. 98) shows the same typical shift to higher diameter classes due to heavy thinning which we found earlier in the example of the Norway spruce research series, Denklingen (p. 236). The percentages of the total crop with diameters over 40 cm b.h.d. up to the age of 102 years are as follows:

With light thinning	26%
With heavy thinning	39%

In this case again, an increase in the number of large diameter trees is bought at the expense of a decrease in numbers of medium diameter trees (20–35 cm). Thus, the mean diameter of the total crop after heavy thinning is larger by only 6 mm (!) than after light thinning. On the basis of this altered distribution Wiedemann calculated the value of the total crop with the help of average festmetre values (based on Mayer-Wegelin), which showed only moderate differences in prices[1].

For his comparison of value production, Wiedemann used the values of seven more low-thinned series, five of which, however, had no A-plot. The total crop volumes which he used as a basis are furthermore unreliable owing to differences between quality classes within the series, errors of volume calculations, and, in some cases unassessed early yields. In the comparison below, based on Wiedemann's figures, only the three low-thinned series with A-, B-, and C-grades are used.

The enhanced average values per fm in the next but last line (without compound interest) indicate the *effect of heavier thinnings on the timber value*, without the—here uncertain—changes of the volume production. *Equal assortment prices are assumed for all three grades of thinning*. Again, as already proved in our Norway spruce example (p. 243), we find that *the increases in value production must be disappointingly small, unless we achieve an improvement in the timber quality by way of thinning, so that higher prices can be demanded for timber of equal dimensions*.

---

[1] The following prices in Reichmarks were used as foundation:

b.h.d.	5–10–15–20–25–30–35–40–45–50–55–60–65–70	
price per fm	4 6 7 9 11 13 15 17 20 23 26 30 34	RM

TABLE 80

COMPARISON OF VALUE YIELDS OF THREE EXPERIMENTAL LOW-THINNING SERIES
AFTER FIGURES BY WIEDEMANN (1931)

Exp. series	Age	Total production in volume			Total production in value		
		A- (fm)	B- (fm)	C-grade (fm)	A- (RM)	B- (RM)	C-grade (RM)
Kupferhütte 25	122	983	967	898	12042	17030	18455
Freienwalde 195	103	718	774	781	11823	14467	15982
Oberscheid 18	117	843	775	772	10521	10527	13210
Total		2544	2516	2451	31231	32193	32504
Value per fm of					12·28	12·80	13·26
the total production					*100 :*	*104 :*	*108*
With computation of interest							
at 3%, these ratios change to					*100 :*	*112 :*	*126*

In these experimental series, possibilities for improving the stem quality as regards straightness and freedom from branches according to the provisions of the experiment were non-existent for the A-grade, limited for the B-grade and adequate only in the C-grade. *However, we have to remember that these potentialities were not utilized until the turn of the century and then only occasionally by way of active improvement of stem form.* This becomes apparent also in Table 81 where the remaining stand of the experimental series Kupferhütte at the age 136[1] is divided into stem quality classes[2].

Neither a selection effect, which would have to show itself in a number of better-formed stems on the B- and C-plots, *nor* a definite *outcome of favouring conditions,* which

TABLE 81

EXPERIMENTAL SERIES KUPFERHÜTTE 25; EXISTING CROP IN 1950, AT THE AGE OF 136 YEARS, DIVIDED
INTO STEM QUALITY CLASSES

Quality class	A-grade				B-grade				C-grade			
	Number of trees	Basal area (m²)	 (%)	Mean diam. (cm)	Number of trees	Basal area (m²)	 (%)	Mean diam. (cm)	Number of trees	Basal area (m²)	 (%)	Mean diam. (cm)
1+2*	66	8·38	20	40·2	33	5·42	22	45·8	24	4·28	21	47·5
3	184	18·25	44	35·5	84	11·47	45	41·7	75	13·29	64	47·5
4+5	162	14·83	36	34·1	60	8·32	33	42·0	18	3·20	15	47·6
Total	412	41·46	100	35·8	177	25·21	100	42·6	117	20·77	100	47·5

* 1+2 = "very good" and "good".

[1] Thanks to kind permission by Professor Wiedemann, the author was able in the year 1950 to make a survey of the experimental series Kupferhütte. The catastrophic gale in June 1946 left the 0·50 ha A-plot completely undamaged, but severely opened up the B- and C-plots, both of which are 0·333 ha in area.

[2] The demands on quality, used for this division, are those of the classification key on p. 90, Table 29.

should become evident in considerably larger diameters among the well-shaped trees, at any rate in the C-grade, is recognizable. The astonishingly high mean diameter value in quality classes 1+2 on the A-plot is due to a single large ash tree with 56 cm diameter at breast-height and a fine bole, which was classified with beech. The basal area percentage ratio of best-shaped trees is nearly the same on all three plots.

Somewhat more favourable results are obtained by a comparison of the value yields on the Bavarian experimental low-thinning series *Rothenbuch*.

TABLE 82

EXPERIMENTAL SERIES ROTHENBUCH 26; RATIOS OF HECK'S QUALITY CLASSES IN THE BASAL AREA OF THE STANDING CROP AT THE AGE OF 134 YEARS (KRAFT TREE CLASSES 1–3)

Quality class	Number of trees N	A-grade Basal area (m²)	(%)	d_m (cm)	N	B-grade Basal area (m²)	(%)	d_m (cm)	N	C-grade Basal area (m²)	(%)	d_m cm
α "very good"	8	1·0	3	39·0	17	2·5	7	44·1	25	4·6	15	48·4
β "medium"	108	13·1	33	39·2	111	13·3	38	39·0	122	15·8	54	40·5
γ "poor"	253	25·4	64	35·3	175	19·3	55	37·5	70	9·1	31	40·8
Total	369	39·5	100	36·9	303	35·1	100	38·4	217	29·5	100	41·6

The increase in numbers and basal area of good stems, as well as their increasing proportions alongside progressively heavier thinning grades here express a certain *success in active improvement of stem form*. The demands in quality required for class α, incidentally, are stricter than those for class 2, which in the example of Kupferhütte was combined along with stem quality class 1.

A calculation of the total production to date of this experimental series has with great distinctness illustrated a phenomenon which we have already demonstrated in Norway spruce, namely the

Reduction in average length of harvested stem

In Table 83, under (a), the mean height and form height of those diameter classes are tabulated, which were particularly affected by thinning. The *reduction in the length of harvested stems in the 28-cm class* (25·5–30·5 cm) in the C-grade compared to the A-grade amounts to no less than *5·4 m*! At the same time, the *mean form-height in the C-grade is lower by approximately 19 per cent* than in the A-grade. Accordingly, the total volume of this class for a given crop basal area is lower in the C-grade than in the A-grade. *One can judge from this the kind of false conclusions a comparison of yields from different grades of thinning must lead to if derived solely from the basal area production.*

In the *distribution of the volume of the total production* we see the familiar *shift to larger diameter classes* as a result of heavier thinning. As the size classes up to 30 cm supply practically only stackwood, and sundry uncontrolled fellings prior to numbering of the stems prevent a closer sub-division, the total production of trees with a b.h.d. under 30 cm has been given collectively.

TABLE 83

EXPERIMENTAL COMMON BEECH SERIES ROTHENBUCH 26; HEIGHT QUALITY CLASS = 1·9. AGE AT VALUATION 134 YEARS

(a) *Reduction of the length of mean harvested stems*

Mean heights and form-heights of total timber production in those diameter classes which have been influenced most by thinning

Diameter classes (cm)	A-grade h (m)	A-grade fh (m)	B-grade h (m)	B-grade fh (m)	C-grade h (m)	C-grade fh (m)
18	24·1	11·98	21·9	10·84	21·2	10·40
			−2·2		−2·9	
23	28·1	14·13	25·8	12·93	23·3	11·63
			−2·3		−4·8	
28	30·9	15·70	29·6	15·01	25·5	12·85
			−1·3		−5·4	
33	32·1	16·44	32·0	16·38	29·7	15·21
			−0·1		−2·4	

(b) *Distribution of the total production to diameter classes*

Diameter classes (cm)	A-grade wood > 7 cm dia (fm)	A-grade (%)	B-grade (fm)	B-grade (%)	C-grade acc. to records (fm)	C-grade (%)	C-grade* "adjusted values" (fm)	C-grade* (%)
Up to 30	357	37	313	33	229	28	305	35
40	306	32	307	33	267	33	267	30
50	218	23	281	30	235	29	235	26
60	76	8	39	4	83	10	83	9
Total	957	100	940	100	814	100	890	100

* To correct for underestimated yields at the beginning of the experiment, caused by unrecorded thinnings. Only diameters under 30 cm$_{b.h.d.}$ can have been used in this category.

Value performance in the experimental series, Rothenbuch

For the comparison of value performances which follows below, the average incomes of the Hessen-Land forest administration (Hessen owns the largest stocks of Common beech) for the financial year 1958 have been used, whilst the harvesting expenses have been based on the wage conditions of the winter 1959/60. Thus, the following prices and harvesting costs, including social expenses, have been assumed:

Timber assortment	Price	Harvesting costs per festmetre	Net values
	(DM)	(DM)	(DM)
Stackwood and firewood	25·–	15·–	10·–
Sleepers			
Stemwood 2 b	50·–	10·–	40·–
Stemwood 3 a	74·–	6·–	68·–
Stemwood 3 b B	86·–	6·–	80·–
Stemwood 3 b A	101·–	6·–	95·–
Stemwood 4 B	99·–	6·–	93·–
Stemwood 4 A	116·–	6·–	110·–
Stemwood 5 B	108·–	6·–	102·–
Stemwood 5 A	128·–	6·–	122·–

The price intervals for the stemwood assortments with larger diameters are therefore smaller than the measurements suggest; also, the values for stemwood of quality A are only about 18 per cent higher than for quality B. These price conditions are due to the present situation in the market with ample supplies of competitive tropical timbers (okoumé and limba).

Table 84 gives under (a) the distribution of the total production to the different timber assortments. We observe that *the absolute, as well as the percentage quantities of the higher priced stemwood classes 3b–5 increase with increasing strengths of thinning grade.*

As shown in Table 84(b) the total money yields free from harvesting costs differ but little, if there are no A-timbers to take into account, because of the poorer volume production in the C-grade. Nonetheless, the average per festmetre value for the C-grade is *11 per cent* higher than for the A-grade. Taking into consideration the better stem quality in the C-grade, which has been proved in Table 82, *the value of the average produced cubic metre in the C-grade is higher by 16 per cent than in the A-grade.*

TABLE 84

EXPERIMENTAL COMMON BEECH SERIES ROTHENBUCH 26

(a) *Distribution of the total production up to the age of 136 years to different timber assortments*
(Assortments table of Mitscherlich)

Timber assortment	A-grade		B-grade		C-grade "adjusted values"	
	(fm)	(%)	(fm)	(%)	(fm)	(%)
Stackwood and firewood	524	55	496	53	468	53
Stemwood						
Class 2b	86	9	67	7	48	5
Class 3a	63	7	81	9	83	9
Class 3b	88	9 ⎫	101	11 ⎫	55	6 ⎫
Class 4	48	5 ⎬ 16	61	6 ⎬ 18	101	12 ⎬ 20
Class 5	21	2 ⎭	8	1 ⎭	15	2 ⎭
Harvesting, measuring and bark losses	127	13	126	13	120	13
Total	957	100	940	100	890	100

TABLE 84 *(cont.)*

(b) *Financial value efficiency under different conditions*

Definition	A-grade		B-grade		C-grade "adjusted values"	
	(DM)	(%)	(DM)	(%)	(DM)	(%)
Total value without A-timbers:						
gross,	36,650	100	37,333	102	36,591	100
free of harvesting costs,	26,654	100	27,768	104	27,595	104
ditto *per fm.*	27·9	*100*	29·5	*106*	31·0	*111*
Total value, taking into consideration the proportions of quality A:						
(a) *gross,*	37.075	100	38,146	103	38,286	103
(b) *free of harvesting costs,*	28,444	100	30,096	106	30,774	108
(c) do. *per fm*	29·7	*100*	32·0	*108*	34·6	*116*

On the basis of local stem quality concepts, the following percentages of quality A were assumed for the stemwood upwards from class 3b: for the A-grade 15 per cent, for the B-grade 30 per cent and for the C-grade 60 per cent.

The figures in Table 84(a) display the important fact that the *proportion of stemwood in festmetres of felled timber under bark amounts to only from 32 per cent* (A-grade) *to 34 per cent* (C-grade) *of the total production of growing stocks in m³ over bark,*[1] in fact, *that the proportion of stemwood which is at all capable of increasing in value,* upwards from class 3b, *lies only between 16 and 20 per cent. This low proportion of stemwood in the total production of a Common beech stand,* or—what amounts to the same thing—a complete working section of Common beech, *cannot be arbitrarily increased.* This has been emphasized by Assmann (1953) and Mitscherlich (1954).

In contrast to Norway spruce which, from a b.h.d. of 20 cm starts to supply timber earning high net incomes, in Common beech we have nowadays no timber fetching reasonably profitable prices (stemwood 2b) below 30 $cm_{b.h.d.}$; in any case, timber capable of yielding value increments requires *breast height diameters of over 40 cm* (stemwood 3b). *The most profit-earning timber with a high proportion of A-quality comes at breast-height diameters upwards from 50–60 cm.* This is proved in Table 85 in a comparison with the figures in Table 74 on p. 241.

Furthermore, by far the major proportion of the net value production in Common beech lies in the main crop. Thus, in the C-grade in Rothenbuch, the value free from harvesting

expenses of the total production so far amounts to	30,744 DM =	100 per cent
Of this, the amount *from the main crop* is	25,421 DM =	83 per cent
and *from thinnings so far*	5323 DM =	17 per cent

This is due to the fact that the early yields contain a preponderating quantity of stackwood assortments, which with present wage and price conditions, yield only very small net incomes.

Therefore it is necessary

(a) to increase the proportion of higher-priced stemwood assortments in the total production,

(b) to raise the worth of those stemwood grades which are at all susceptible of a value increment to the largest possible extent.

[1] In terms of festmetres of felled timber over bark the percentage is 37–39 per cent.

TABLE 85

AVERAGE VALUES, FREE FROM HARVESTING COSTS, PER FESTMETRE OF
THE TOTAL PRODUCTION TO DATE IN THE EXPERIMENTAL COMMON
BEECH SERIES ROTHENBUCH

B.h.d. inc. bark (cm)	A-grade without A-timber	A-grade with A-timber	C-grade with A-timber
10	–	–	–
15	3·–	3·–	3·–
20	7·50	7·50	7·50
25	13·–	13·–	13·–
30	21·–	21·–	21·–
35	31·–	31·–	31·–
40	41·–	43·–	44·–
45	49·–	53·–	58·–
50	53·50	59·–	63·–
55	57·–	62·50	66·–
60	58·–	65·–	68·–

In respect of (a), there are but limited possibilities for *allowing* the stands *to go to advanced ages* with only *moderate thinnings*. We will then obtain very long stems free from branches, and only small amounts of crownwood. This course is recommended by Olberg (1951). On the other hand, qualms must certainly be felt about the development of dark heartwood which increases with age and reduces the value of the wood (Freist, 1961). A contrasting measure, in a sense, is the forcing of a diameter increase by *excessively heavy thinning*, as is recommended by v. Arnswaldt (1953). The danger in this case lies in the fact that the length of clean-boled stem is drastically reduced and the proportion of crownwood is *increased* at the expense of the stemwood.

For (b), the endeavour must be to achieve a high proportion of *quality A* timber. By a timely selective process, the number of trees with good boles can be increased, and by the favouring effect of crown isolation, the diameter development of those trees with the best stems may be speeded up. What possibilities there are in this respect, we shall see presently from the information gained from crown-thinning experiments.

The increase in value of A-quality timber depends on prices and markets. According to Mitscherlich (1954), the increase in value must remain a *modest* one, even if today's very small price differentials between quality A and B were considerably increased. For example, if one assumed that all C-grade stemwood at Rothenbuch, from 3b upwards, were of quality A, and that this earned 150 per cent of the B-quality prices, then the value of the total production, free from harvesting costs, of the C-grade stemwood would increase to *131 per cent* and the average value per festmetre to *141 per cent of the A-grade*. However, such a big increase is impossible because, according to recent investigations[1] by Freist (in the Institute of the author), the proportion of A-quality stemwood which is susceptible of a value increment (class 3b and larger) does not as a rule reach more than 40 per cent, and because, with more severe crown isolation, one must expect the C-quality stemwood, which is knotty and less valuable, to increase by at least 10 per cent. The natural limitations in this case cannot be exceeded, as was convincingly set forth by Mitscherlich (1954) with constructed examples using unattainable assumed values.

[1] Published 1962, *Fw. Cbl.*, No. 17, special edition.

(b) Volume and Value Yields with Crown-thinning Experiments

From two typical examples in Section C (p. 96) we have already become acquainted with the peculiar structure of crown-thinned stands of Common beech. This is characterized by a relatively large basal area of trees belonging to Kraft class 5a (5–15 per cent), which as a rule are completely absent from low-thinned stands. Clearly, the removal of a large number of dominant trees and the retention of trees of low efficiency in the lower and middle storeys, as is customary in crown thinning for the protection of the soil and stems, must on principle have *a negative influence on the growth performance.*

Volume yield in crown-thinning experiments

Contrary to the slightly premature and favourable conclusions, arrived at by Engler (1924) on the basis of the Swiss experiments, Dieterich (1924/5) proved from the experiments in Württemberg that the volume production of the crown-thinned plots was 1–5 per cent lower than that of the low-thinned plots. This inferior performance does not apply to the basal area increment; Dieterich explained this as being due to the appreciably smaller heights and form-heights of trees in the middle and lower storeys which accordingly for a given basal area increment must have a considerably smaller volume increment than those in the upper storey. In making a comparison between crown- and low-thinned plots of the seven experimental series of the former Prussian Research Institute, all of which contain comparable plots of both methods of treatment, Assmann (1950b) found that the *average loss of production by crown-thinning amounted to only a little more than 1 per cent.* If one remembers that in these experiments, *belated felling of "Protzen"*, i.e. trees with large crowns and vigorous growth, used to be the rule and that very heavy thinning was permitted among the dominants, then this loss of production seems surprisingly low. It is evidence of an excellent resilience in the growth of Common beech. We can assume that timely and intensive crown thinning, corresponding to the doctrines of present-day silviculture, will achieve higher increments, because it obviates:

1. the belated felling of wolf-trees, which especially concerns trees of extra rapid growth;
2. belated and excessively severe thinnings which are common in stands where treatment was not started early enough;
3. too thick a closure in the lower and intermediate storeys resulting in the premature death of those trees in the underwood which would be most suitable for stem shading. If by timely thinning, broad-leaved trees were encouraged in the understorey, a far smaller number of these would suffice to provide ground and stem cover than, for example, by weakly lower- and intermediate-storey trees with narrow crowns (Assmann, 1950b). For this purpose, a "lower storey cover-screen" (Wiedemann, 1931) with a low water and nutrient demand, would be sufficient.

Changes in value yield with crown thinning

A well-conceived thinning from above can have a gratifying effect on the value of the out-turn, as will be shown in the following typical example.

Experimental crown-thinning series of Common beech, Dalheim 116

The valuable records relating to this series, which were put at the disposal of the author by kind permission of Prof. Wiedemann in 1947/8, furnish the data given in Table 86 along with Figs. 114 and 115.

FIG. 114. Beech experimental plot 116, Dalheim. Light low thinning. Trees to be removed in cultural thinning are marked by double rings. Enumerated at age 101 years.

FIG. 115. Experimental series, Dalheim. Light crown thinning (without selecting stems of the future). Enumerated at age 101 yrs.

Site

Elevated area at Paderborn, 300 m above sea level, almost level; middle chalk (Turonian), shallow to moderately deep gravelly loam, degraded rendzina. Climate: damp and cool; annual rainfall approximately 850 mm (vegetative period 350), mean temp. during the vegetative period (according to Ölkers), approximately 13·6°C. Height quality class: II.0.

Lay-out plan

Light low thinning (0·10 ha), "light" and "heavy" thinning (each 0·25 ha), put into effect by Schwappach in 1898 at crop age of 53 years.

Treatment

I. "*Light*" *crown thinning*. Continuous tending of a fairly large number of good dominant trees without making any definite choice of stems of the future.

II. "*Heavy*" *crown thinning*. Strong disengagement of the crowns of 188 selected stems per ha at the age of 53 years; the mean height of these trees amounted to 17·4 m, the clean-boled stem length to approximately only 7 m. Repeated release of these selected stems of the future, which at the age of 102 years still amounted to 180 trees per ha and in 1948 they had again closed up on all sides. Thinning to loosen contact in the lower and middle storey was neglected until the age of 87 years.

III. *Light low thinning*. Only removal of dead and dying trees.

TABLE 86

PERIODIC INCREMENT OF THE EXPERIMENTAL SERIES DALHEIM

Exp. plot	Incr. period from–to	Years	*Mean basal area*		basal area		P.M.A.I timber volume (a)		(b)	
			(m²)	(%)	(m²)	(%)	(fm)	(%)	(fm)	(%)
I	(1898)		32·9	92	1·228	114	14·8	103	13·4	125
II	53–58	5	32·0	90	1·332	121	16·4	114	16·2	151
III			35·7	100	1·102	100	14·4	100	10·7	100
I			32·1	78	0·930	102	11·4	95	10·9	80
II	58–78	20	31·6	76	0·923	102	11·3	94	10·9	80
III			41·4	100	0·909	100	12·0	100	13·6	100
I			28·6	60	0·736	110	9·1	105	11·0	153
II	78–87	9	29·3	62	0·704	106	8·7	100	10·0	139
III	(1933)		47·4	100	0·667	100	8·7	100	7·2	100
I			31·3	74	0·923	106	11·3	98	11·3	98
II	53–87	34	31·0	73	0·924	106	11·4	99	11·4	99
III			42·2	100	0·874	100	11·5	100	11·5	100

(a) After smoothing by a special method.

(b) After the original calculation by the Research Inst. The dubious volume increments (which occur in several places) are in each case compensated for during ensuing periods by deviations in the opposite sense which proves that they arise from errors of calculation.

Despite therefore the vigorous interventions in the dominant upper storeys of plots I and II[1] their periodic volume increments over the 34 years were only 1–2 per cent smaller than in the comparative plot III with light low thinning.

The effect of these methods of treatment on the social stratification has been shown earlier in Table 32 and Fig. 50 on p. 98. *The effect on the proportions of stem quality classes* may be seen in Table 87.

[1] The periodic mean basal area of the two crown-thinned plots includes approximately 2 m² in each which belongs to the under storey, where there was practically no increment. The grade of thinning in plots I and II therefore was heavier than expressed in the relative figures for the mean basal area.

TABLE 87

PROPORTIONS OF THE STEM QUALITY CLASSES BY BASAL AREA, LIMITED TO TREE CLASSES 1–4

Class	I. "Light" cr.-thinning				II. "Heavy" cr.-thinning				III. "Light" low thinning			
	N	Basal area (m²)	(%)	d (cm)	N	Basal area (m²)	(%)	d (cm)	N	Basal area (m²)	(%)	d (cm)
1	—	—	—	—	—	—	—	—	—	—	—	—
2	68	9·57	33	42·3	64	7·98	28	39·8	80	5·59	11	29·9 (!)
3	132	15 35	53	38·5	116	12·51	44	37·1	340	21·84	43	28·6
4	48	3·98	14	32·5	108	8·13	28	31·0	430	23·06	45	26·1
5	—	—	—	—	—	—	—	—	10	0·32	1	20·2
	248	28·90	100	38·5	288	28·62	100	35·6	860	50·81	100	27·4

"Stems of the Future"

Cl.	N	Basal area (m²)	(%)	d (cm)
1	—	—	—	—
2	64	7·98	39	39·8
3	88	9·86	48	37·8
4	24	2·66	13	37·5
5	—	—	—	—
	176	20·50	100	38·5

The fact that stem quality class 1 is not represented at all is due to an apparently local tendency towards twisted growth ("Renkwuchs").

If we compare the mean diameters of the tree classes 1–4 (plot I = 38·5, plot III = = 27·4 cm) we find that in the main crop at age 101 years an appreciable general *filling out of diameter dimensions* has been achieved.

On the other hand, a *selective effect*, which would need to manifest itself in a larger number of trees of quality grade 2 in plots I and II[1], is not noticeable. After the relatively late start at the age of 53 years, such an effect is not to be expected, because the number of trees with good boles could certainly not be *increased* at that stage.

Very considerable, however, is the improvement effected by the *freeing of crowns in the process of crown thinning*. This shows itself (a) on the two crown thinning plots in the noticeable diameter *difference in favour of trees with better stem form* and (b) in the difference in mean diameters achieved by stem quality class 2 as a result of crown thinning in comparison to low thinning (cr.-thinning plot I = 42·3, low-thinning plot III = 29·9 cm).

The average annual *diameter increments* of the trees still standing at the age of 101, reproduced in Table 88 for the age period 52–101, show *large differences between the annual diameter increments* within the plots from the lower to the upper storey, as well as between crown thinning and low thinning. *The diameter increment of a significant number of dominant trees* (in plot I these amount to *132 trees per ha*) *exceeds the diameter increase of the mean basal area stem of the main crop in each case, including the shift due to calculation.* This important fact needs to be borne in mind.

[1] If we remember that plot III covers only 0·10 ha and that therefore the number of 80 trees of quality 2 derives from a multiplication of 8 by 10 (!), then presumably, the original number of trees with good stems per ha was equal in all three plots.

TABLE 88

EXPERIMENTAL COMMON BEECH SERIES, DALHEIM 116

Average annual diameter increment of the trees still standing in 1947 (aged 101) during the age period 52–101

Social ranking	Diam. class 1947 (cm)	I. "Light" cr.-thinning		II. "Heavy cr.-thinning (a) Future stems plus aux. crop		(b) Future stems only		III. Light low thinning	
		Trees per ha	Ann. diam. incr. (cm)	Trees per ha	Ann. diam. incr. (cm)	Trees per ha	Ann. diam. incr. (cm)	Trees per ha	Ann. diam. incr. (cm)
Under storey (Kraft 5)	9	8	0·03	16	0·03	—	—	—	—
	12	52	0·04	64	0·04	4	0·01	—	—
	15	40	0·07	48	0·07	—	—	—	—
	18	24	0·12	12	0·12	—	—	—	—
Intermediate storey (Kraft 4)	18	8	0·12	8	0·14	8	0·25	—	—
	21	8	0·18	20	0·18	—	—	—	—
	24	4	0·24	4	0·21	—	—	—	—
	27	4	0·30	8	0·25	—	—	—	—
	30	—	—	8	0·28	—	—	—	—
Upper storey (Kraft 1–3)	24	—	—	—	—	—	—	40	0·21
	27	—	—	16	0·32	8	0·32	180	0·25
	30	8	0·34	20	0·34	—	—	130	0·28
	33	20	0·38	32	0·38	20	0·38	120	0·31
	36	56	0·42	52	0·42	40	0·42	70	0·35
	39	36	0·46	48	0·46	44	0·46	10	0·38
	42	40	0·50	32	0·50	28	0·49	—	—
	45	28	0·54	24	0·54	16	0·53	—	—
	48	20	0·58	12	0·58	12	0·56	—	—
	51	8	0·61	—	—	—	—	—	—

For comparison: average annual diameter increment of the *mean basal area stem* of the main crop in each case (age period 52–101) incl. the "statistical shift"

	0·43	0·42	0·33	cm

The trees with the largest diameters on the particularly outstanding "free" crown-thinned plot I show annual diameter increments at breast height of over 6 mm. In the course of the 49 years, from 52 to 101 years, the following increments have been achieved on this plot:

the *100 trees with the largest diameter per ha* had an average diameter increment of *0·54* cm,

the *120 trees with the largest diameter per ha* had an average diameter increment of *0·51* cm,

the *160 trees with the largest diameter per ha* had an average diameter increment of *0·50* cm.

The *sixty-eight trees per ha of 2nd quality timber* in the standing crop show an average diameter increment of *0·50* cm, covering a range from 0·43 to 0·62 cm.

TABLE 89

CLASSIFICATION BY ASSORTMENT GRADES AND VALUE FREE OF HARVESTING COSTS, OF THE REMAINING STAND AT THE AGE OF 101 YEARS, RESTRICTED TO TREE CLASSES 1–4, WITH LIGHT LOW THINNING I.E. NO ACTIVE TREATMENT (PLOT III) AND WITH MODERATE CROWN THINNING (PLOT I)

Definition	Plot III		Plot I	
	abs.	%	abs.	%
Timber volume o.b. in fm	730	100	415	100
Divided into				
Stackwood, fm (felled) incl. bark	519	71	170	41
Stemwood cl. 2b, qual. cl. B,				
fm (felled) under bark	86	12	27	6
cl. 3a, qual. cl. B	40	5	37	9
cl. 3b, qual. cl. B	—	—	41	10
cl. 3b, qual. cl. A	—	—	39	10
cl. 4, qual. cl. B	—	—	20	5
cl. 4, qual. cl. A	—	—	22	5
Harvesting, measuring and bark losses	85	12	59	14
Total value, without harvesting costs, DM	11,350 = 100%		16,480 = 145%	
Average value, without harvesting costs per fm of growing stocks	15·6 = 100%		29·7 = 190%	

If we remember that the largest proportion of the net value production lies in the remaining stand, which today contains 116 trees/ha with a b.h.d. over 40 cm, forty-eight of which belong to quality class 2, the success of crown liberation, which provides such favourable conditions, becomes obvious. On the other hand, we recognize also what is still lacking from the success that can be gained by the treatment. With good stem quality in the initial crops and early start of treatment, it should be possible to achieve the result that all 116 trees over 40 cm b.h.d. are of class 2 quality at least.

The *success of treatment by free crown thinning* in plot I, compared to the largely unthinned plot III, is revealed in Table 89. According to this, only 126 fm of felled timber under bark (= *17 per cent*) of the 730 fm growing stock in the remaining stand have become stemwood assortments by *light low thinning* whilst, with *"free"* crown thinning, as much as 186 fm of harvested timber under bark (= *45 per cent*) of the smaller amount of 415 fm in the growing crop have been converted into stemwood assortments, among them 61 fm harvested timber (= *15 per cent*) *into A-quality*. Free crown thinning surpasses low thinning in total value, free from harvesting costs, by 45 per cent, and in *average value per fm by as much as 90 per cent*. This superiority is mainly due to the fact that, with light low thinning, the major part of the crop consists of stackwood sizes. A comparison 30–40 years later would show the superiority of crown thinning to be considerably smaller, and mainly due to a higher proportion of A-quality trees. But even if one declines to adopt calculations on the basis of soil expectation values, one still has to acknowledge the *favourable consequence* from the fact that *the production period for favourable price-earning timber sizes has been reduced by 20 years and that the average annual value per ha of timber out-turn free of felling and extraction charges* over this period has been *very appreciably enhanced*.

Disadvantages of the early and inflexible selection of "future stems"

The "*heavy*" *crown thinning*, practised in plot II, did not do so well. *Crown thinning with an early selection of definite Z-Stämme (future stems)*, as practised under that definition by the former Prussian Research Institute, should be renamed "future stem crown thinning". One would have thought that the 47 (= 188 per ha) early selected prodigies, the crowns of which were isolated repeatedly and "ruthlessly" (Wiedemann, 1931), would be superior, at least in diameter attainments, to those receiving free crown thinning. A look at Table 88 advises us that this is not the case, in fact, that the so-called "auxiliary stand", which consists of a mixture of all tree classes, contains some even more efficient dominant trees which surpass the performance of the prodigies.[1] Table 87 shows, moreover, that *only sixty-four* of the 176 Z-stems per ha (without tree class 5) still in existence, belong *to stem quality class 2*, whilst twenty-four even belong to class 4. Liberal crown thinning would have got rid of this ballast long ago. In many cases the endeavour to achieve uniform distribution has evidently made the selection of future stems of only moderate stem quality unavoidable.

We must regard the *rigid preference for a high number of Z-stems* as a further silvicultural error. Having regard for the crown dimensions of continually favoured dominant trees, which at the age of 101 years already throw a ground cover of 70–90 m², *the growing space on one hectare is sufficient for no more than approximately 120 trees at the age of 100 years, and approximately 100 trees at the age of 120 years.*

Crown isolation started when the length of the clean-boled portions of stems exceeded no more than approximately 7 m (Assmann, 1950b)[2] with the result that the thickness of the branches in the lower part of the crowns increased considerably on both crown thinning plots. As the result of *renewed contact between these strongly branched crowns* under a Z-stem crown thinning régime some stout green branches in the lower parts of the crowns died; this introduces the risk of dead knots, stem-rot and dark heartwood development. The length of stem free of green branches in the dominant trees of both crown thinning plots was on average reduced only to 13·5 m as compared with 16·7 m by light low thinning. According to investigations by Assmann (1950b), free crown thinning caused shorter zones of dead branches than Z-stem crown thinning. Once a start has been made to liberate the crowns, it is necessary to prevent the re-establishment of close contact and to continue consistent "open stand (Lichtwuchs) thinning" according to the doctrine of Schädelin (1934) in order to prevent the risk of stem-rot in consequence of the die-back of stout living branches.

In an *early* selection of future final-crop stems one would have to bear in mind their later crown dimensions and accordingly the number of trees per hectare which are possible in a mature harvestable stand. But even then, uncertainty about their subsequent development would argue against adopting rigid rules for future treatment and the undue anticipation of future decisions. *Obviously, it is much better to follow Schädelin's (1942)*

---

[1] One of these future stems (No. 37) has increased its b.h.d. in 49 increment years from 12·1 to 12·7 cm, i.e. by all of 6 mm (!) and today belongs to tree class 5.

[2] According to statements by Schwappach (1911) in other experiments of the former Prussian Research Inst. the isolation of the crowns started when the trees were still fairly small in height and the clean-boled stem length did not exceed 5 m. Schwappach's complaints about "wide ugly crowns" (Fischbach 106) or "downright-hateful spreading crowns" (Johannesburg 62) and Wiedemann's unfavourable criticisms are a necessary consequence of silvicultural mistakes. The results of such "experiments" are all the more valuable!

counsel *"to work out with each thinning a closer ... selection of candidates"* from the originally large number so as eventually to produce an *"élite"* of mature harvestable trees. But early marking of the best-formed trees, even at the pole-stage (with paint marks or rings), is certainly useful. It facilitates decisions at later thinnings and offers some protection against damage, although it must not be regarded as finally determining.[1]

If our target is to have about 100 dominant élite trees with full crowns per hectare at the mature rotation age we must have for beech crops about twice as many candidates at the pole-wood stage in order to provide against unavoidable hazards and so as to achieve a reasonably uniform distribution of valuable trees at the time of harvesting.

The question arises, can we by intervening early enough achieve an effective increase of the number of élite trees in the final stand of the type advocated by Schädelin? The results of a recent crown thinning experiment (Wieda 49/50), which will be discussed later, suggest that we can.

Before proceeding, it must be stressed that the experimental series at Dalheim is the *only crown thinning series of Common beech*, at least to the author's knowledge, *containing an A-plot which had been treated strictly as* laid down in the experiment plan. Thus, in its results, it offers the entire range of potential changes in value yield. This confirms forcefully the necessity, again and again stressed by Assmann (1957d, 1959b), for providing in all experimental series A-plots as a basis for comparison. Also, it becomes clear that general conclusions about the suitability of certain silvicultural methods, for example "heavy crown thinning in Common beech stands", can be drawn from thinning experiments only if we take into consideration the *methods of treatment* which were *actually* used in the individual experiments.

The results of the important publications of Dieterich (1924/5) and Zimmerle (1938b) about the beech thinning experiments in Württemberg are in agreement with the conclusions drawn so far. The value of the information derived from the crown thinning experiments in Württemberg is reduced by the fact that the crown thinning plots (Lorey's E-grade) were originally A-grade plots which, in some cases, were not converted to crown thinning treatment until they were over 70 years old and had grown under closed-stand conditions for 20–25 years. Thus the experimental series were robbed of their most important comparative plots. Besides, crown thinnings which started under such unfavourable conditions cannot provide information about their true potential.[2]

The experimental crown-thinning series at Wieda

This experimental series was laid out by the author during the years 1946–51 for the purpose of observing the effects of intensive crown thinning.

Situation. South Harz, approximately 400 m above sea level, on a slope with an E. aspect; compt. "Knicking" 49/50.

---

[1] Ölkers (1932), who in his work *Waldbau* recommended the selection and marking of uniformly distributed stems of the future, allowed for some subsequent removals. His rule is: "One ought to examine each Z-stem individually and decide whether it can remain as such."

[2] None the less, it is astonishing what Heck (1931) made of the "rival plot" for "free crown thinning" (106 F) despite a late start (at the age of 81 years). This plot had been laid out by himself in the experimental series Geislingen, and subsequently received consistent favouring treatment of the still existing upper-storey trees with the best stems. In Sept. 1948 this F-plot showed up so favourably in comparison to the E-plot of Lorey (106 E), that the author said to the head of the Research Inst. of Württemberg, at that time Landforstmeister Dr. h.c. Zimmerle: "The hand of the master is unmistakable."

Climate. Mean rainfall per annum = 1100 mm, during the vegetative period (May–August) 350 mm.

Soil. Decomposed diabase; moderately deep gritty loam, freshly deposited on the slope; mesotrophic, little-developed brown earth; mull.

The quality of the site is favoured by the position of the three plots at the foot of a slope; it changes with the variable micro-relief. Because of the somewhat unreliable ages, the *height quality class* cannot be accurately determined; it rises from I.8 according to Wiedemann (mod. thinning) on plot 2 through I.4 on plot 1 to I.1 on plot 4. Plot 3, a plot with a mixed stand and a different experimental object, is not relevant to our present discussion.

The three experimental plots, and the surrounding stand, now 70 to 80 years old with varying proportions of high-grade timber, were subjected to *moderately heavy thinnings* every 3 years *from the age of 40 years onward, after early cleaning operations at approximately 30 years.* They produced, on average, about 20 fm/ha of felled timber. From the age of about 55 years, when the dominant trees had achieved a *clean-boled stem length of nearly 10 m, the crowns of the trees with the best stems in each case were systematically isolated.*[1] Such an initial heavy crown isolation produced in the winter of 1942/3 equal amounts of 58 fm growing timber per hectare on plots 1 and 2!

All three plots received the same treatment until 1947. Since then, *plot 2 has not been thinned at all* (only removal of dead and dying trees), whilst *plot 1 continued to undergo heavy crown thinning* and *plot 4 moderate crown thinning.*

In consequence of familiar obstacles due to lack of time, the experimental series could only gradually be numbered and thus kept under reliable permanent control (plot 1 from spring of 1947, plot 4 from 1950 and plot 2 from 1954).

The *small basal areas of the under storey* in 1960 are traceable almost entirely *to unauthorized removals* (the experimental plots are situated directly adjacent to the village). In this connection, see Table 91(b.) Thus the under storey in plot 1, which is indispensable for soil and stem protection, suffered a reduction from 634 stems and 3·4 m² basal area in 1947 to 389 stems with 2·53 m² by 1960. Although these latter suffice for the purposes of soil cover, with the total ground cover still remaining at 2764 m², the circumstance is regrettable because it supports the mistaken view of many practising foresters, that even if crown thinning starts early enough the under storey of beech stands on active soil will not be able to survive.[2] In this connection, see Fig. 116.

Table 90 contains the essential data to provide an insight into the *present-day structure of the stands* of the three plots. The ground-cover data suggest that *despite heavy thinning,* the *vertical contact* of the three storeys is satisfactory, the total ground cover of the upper storey + middle storey on plot 1 still remaining at 9509 m².

The proportion of high-grade broad-leaved trees (ash, maple, hornbeam) is significant only for the growth conditions on plot 4. Up to the present their production ranks equal to that of beech, so that in further calculations they can be counted along with beech.

When judging the *growth performances* of the three plots in Table 91(a) it should be noted that plot 4, besides being older and of higher quality class than plots 1 and 2 is

---

[1] The commendable activities of the unfortunately early deceased Haumeister Ernst Jörn of Wieda are remembered here with gratitude; during the war he was entrusted with the deputizing for forest officials called away and splendidly carried out their duties.

[2] Even in the crown thinning series Dalheim 116, the author found in 1947/8 that a large proportion of the losses in the under storey were due to unauthorized removals (theft) during the war and the post-war period.

FIG. 116. Beech stand after heavy crown thinning directly adjoining trial area No. 1 at Wieda. Inventory made in May 1948 when the stand was 62 (57–67) years old.

more favoured by local factors. The volume increment of the heavily crown-thinned plot 1 falls off more sharply as compared with the unthinned plot 2, more so than the existing differences between the mean basal areas would lead us to expect. This is presumably due to a "set-back" following upon a spell of accelerated production. The volume increment of 13·6 fm during the preceding 7 years was relatively high, despite a low natural degree of stocking. Incidentally, in the cool climate of the Harz, the vegetative years 1954–7

TABLE 90

BEECH EXPERIMENTAL SERIES, WIEDA. REMAINING STANDS IN THE SPRING OF 1960 ACCORDING TO MEASURE-
MENTS BY FREIST (1961)

(a) *Exp. plot 2:* On average *74-year-old* beech (98% beech, 2% quality broad-leaved spp.)
Height qual. cl. *I.8.* "No thinning" since 1946

Definition	Number of stems	Basal area (m²)	Diameter Mean (cm)	Diameter Range (cm)	Mean height (Lorey) (m)	Timber volume (m³)	Canopied area (m²)
Upper storey (Kraft 1–3)	673	31·29	24·3	15–40			8025
Intermediate storey (Kraft 4)	242	3·32	13·2	9–16	23·3	377	775
Lower storey (Kraft 5)	325	1·95	8·7	6–12	12·3	8	1575
Total stand	1240	36·56				385	10375

(b) *Exp. plot 1:* On average *74-year-old* beech (91% beech, 9% quality broad-leaved spp.)
Height qual. cl. *I.4.* "Heavy crown thinning"

Upper storey	374	21·64	27·1	15–40	24·8	286	7730
Intermediate storey	132	2·33	15·0	11–20			1779
Lower storey	389	2·53	9·1	4–14	13·7	13	2764
Total stand	895	26·47				299	12273

(c) *Exp. plot 4:* On average *78-year-old* beech (79% beech, 21% quality broad-leaved spp.)
Height qual. cl. *I.1.* "Moderate crown thinning"

Upper storey	416	24·95	27·6	18–42	27·1	363	7677
Intermediate storey	76	2·61	20·9	13–22			1290
Lower storey	473	3·57	9·8	2–18	16·2	23	1557
Total stand	965	31·13				386	10524

TABLE 91

(a) Mean basal area and increment of the upper and intermediate storeys (Kraft 1–4), 1954–60

Experimental plot	Mean basal area/period (m²)	Mean basal area/period (%)	Mean ann. increment in basal area (m²)	Mean ann. increment in basal area (%)	Mean ann. increment in timber volume (m³)	Mean ann. increment in timber volume (%)
No. 2 "no thinning"	32·3	100	0·774	100	13·8	100
No. 1 "heavy crown thinning"	24·1	75	0·688	93	11·5*	83
No. 4 "moderate crown thinning"	27·3	85	0·796	107	14·5	105

(*continued*)

* 1947–54 = 13·6 m³.

TABLE 91 *(cont.)*

(b) Thinning out-turn of plot No. 2 and 1

Time	Thinnings in fm growing wood over 7 cm in diam.		Remarks
	Plot 2	Plot 1	
1943 Spr.	58·2	58·1	
1946	24·5	20·3	
1948	—	27·2	
1950	—	1·1	
1954	—	37·0	
1954–9	3·9	1·3	Unauthorized removals from under storey.
1959 Spr.	—	28·2	Planned removals
Total	86·6	173·2	

produced slow growth of beech. As thinning in the comparative plot 2 ceased only 13 years ago, this plot does not have quite the local maximum basal area for the observation period 1954–60; this, one would guess, lies at approximately 40 m² so that the natural degree of stocking on plot 1 amounted to approximately 0·6.

The success of 40 years intensive management is proved in Table 92. The large number of trees belonging to stem quality class 1 and 2 on all three plots amounting to nearly *200 "high-grade trees" with good stems per hectare*, proves the *selective effects of an early start to crown thinning.*

If part of this success is possibly due to the good form of growth of the ecotype, native on this site,[1] the striking *selective effect* is entirely to the credit of systematic management.

TABLE 92

AVERAGE ANNUAL DIAMETER INCREMENTS (I_d) OF ALL TREES BELONGING TO KRAFT CLASSES 1–3, WHICH WERE STILL IN EXISTENCE IN THE SPRING OF 1960, SEPARATED INTO STEM QUALITY CLASSES

(Increments of identical trees, without "statistical shift")

Stem qual. classes	Expl. pl. 2 "no thinning"			Exp. pl. 1 "heavy crown thinning"					Exp. pl. 4 "mod. cr. thinning"		
	N (per ha)	d_m 1960 (cm)	I_d 1954–60 (mm)	N (per ha)	d_m 1960 (cm)	I_d 1947–54 (mm)	I_d 1954–60 (mm)	I_d 1947–60 (mm)	N (per ha)	d_m 1960 (cm)	I_d 1954–60 (mm)
1 "Very good"	39	27·5	4·6	30	32·6	6·8	5·0	5·9	34	31·1	5·4
2 "Good"	150	26·9	3·6	162	28·0	5·2	4·0	4·6	172	29·7	4·6
3 "Moderate"	368	24·0	2·9	159	25·4	4·6	3·7	4·2	141	28·3	4·0
4 "Poor"	116	21·4	2·2	23	24·8	4·0	3·1	3·6	30	26·6	3·9

The percentage proportions of quality classes 1+2 in the basal area of the upper storey amount, in 1960 to   34%   58%   58%

---

[1] On the basis of observations of pressure-damage and breakage caused by falls of wet snow, which are frequent at these altitudes, a selection of narrow-crowned beech trees over fairly long periods of time seems probable.

The figures in Table 92 show that *the trees with the better stem form* in each case today have the largest diameters and *have achieved a considerably larger diameter increment than those with a poorer form.* Particularly striking are the differences in plot 1 during the period 1947–54, following the first, particularly severe isolation of the crowns; the annual diameter increment of the thirty trees with the best stems amounts to 6·8 mm compared to only 4 mm in the twenty-three trees with poor forms. After timely felling of the badly shaped dominant trees, crown isolation also enables the trees with the best stems to achieve the largest diameter increment in each case. Heck (1931) tried to express this phenomenon in his "rule of beauty" according to which the "most handsome" trees (with the best stems) are also supposed to have the largest increment.

The *proportion of trees belonging to stem quality class 1 and 2 in the basal area of the upper storey in plot 1* increased as follows:

From 50% in spring of 1947 (absolute = 9·53 m²/ha)

to 58% in spring of 1960 (absolute = 14·49 m²/ha).

Today, nineteen trees per hectare have diameters over 35 cm. In contrast to this, the proportion of trees with good stems in the *comparative plot 2*, which has not been thinned since 1947, amounts to only

34% in spring of 1960 (absolute = 10·80 m²/ha),

despite the fact that both plots received the same intensive treatment until 1947, which fact is proved by the nearly equal number of high-grade trees in the upper storey today (189/ha compared with 192/ha on plot 1). However, the favouring of the best-formed trees ceased in 1947, for which reason their actual basal area proportion increased only slightly whilst their *percentage proportion even dropped* considerably.

The high-grade trees on *plot 1* today represent nearly two-thirds of the volume of the upper storey, and it is already possible to foresee, that *in approximately 30 years, the upper storey will contain only trees with faultless stems.* If the high-grade trees are further selected and favoured and their further growth in diameter promoted by reduction of numbers the 120–130 individuals at the age of 100 years could have a mean diameter of approximately 45 cm. *The 100–110 high-grade trees, still in existence at the age of 120, will then be mature and harvestable with a mean diameter of nearly 55 cm* and their clean-boled lower butt sections will supply at least *150 fm felled stemwood of classes 4 and 5 with A-quality.* A possible price drop of 5–10 per cent of the potential volume increment bears little weight in comparison to this increase.

If the number of high-grade trees with a mean height of 20 m, and good to very good stem quality in the upper storey amounts to 200, as was the case on the plots of the experimental series Wieda, the question whether or not *the really possible maximum of A-timber is produced* in such a beech stand depends on continued purposeful felling activities (isolation of the crowns and uniform spacing of the high-grade trees). This actually enables us to achieve "highest yield of high-grade timber", indicated by Olberg (1951, 1954). However, *the appearance of the pole-wood in the early growth and thicket stages and the treatment required to obtain this number of dominant trees with good stems* are different questions. It is certain that the early start of management in Wieda, 20 years earlier (at the age of 30 years) than in Dalheim (at the age of 50 years), considerably increased the number of dominant trees with good stems which existed at the outset of the experiment. Besides, the observations of Schädelin (1942) and Kurth (1946), which strongly support

Schädelin's doctrine, as well as the recent analyses of diameter increase by Köstler (1952) have made it highly probable that by an early start of intensive treatment in the early growth and thicket stages we can achieve a decisive increase in the number of future élite trees. However, there are as yet no exact results to supply information about the long-term effects of such measures, which can be varied in diverse ways with regard to type and intensity. Safe results of this kind depend entirely on long-term observation of differently treated, although originally comparable, initial stocks, i.e. on planned experiments. None the less, there are a number of facts, which speak in favour of Schädelin's doctrine. These we shall now discuss.

Prospects for success by treatment in the early growth and thicket stages according to Schädelin's doctrine

In his doctrine of thinning, Schädelin shifted the emphasis of management from the tree-wood and pole-wood stage to the hitherto neglected thicket and early growth stages which he rightly defines as the "critical stages of development". The rapidly advancing growth process and consequent changes from storey to storey at these stages ought to be controlled at the earliest opportunity. Quite obviously, the species *Common beech* has served *as a model* in this case. Its *silviculturally important characteristics* can be seen as typical for broad-leaved crops, though, in many respects, they are *fundamentally different from the characteristics of coniferous trees*, of which *Norway spruce* is a good example. Therefore, let us compare the silviculturally important differences between the characteristics and the natural development of these two species.

	Common beech	*Norway spruce*
Stem form:	*Owing to phototropic sensitivity* and a ready reaction to local site influences (e.g. shallow soils), *more or less bent.*	*Owing to pronounced negative geotropism, always straight*, without noticeable deviations whether grown in isolation, in open or closed crop conditions.
Branching:	Rapid branch thickening and ramification in response to greater isolation, seriously reducing timber value. Pruning a practical impossibility.	Branches thicken with increasing isolation; however, the ensuing loss of quality becomes serious only under open stand conditions. Pruning of the dry branches (and to a lesser extent when green) is possible.
Crown:	Capacity for rapid lateral projection; the crown is capable of revival and renewed growth even at an advanced age.	Limited capacity for lateral projection; limited capacity for renewal in old age.
Proportions of assortments in the total production.	A maximum proportion of 50 per cent stemwood is achievable; the proportion of stemwood and high-grade timber depends largely on the mode of upbringing.	About 95 per cent stemwood is achievable; the influence of cultural upbringing is relatively small.

This comparison clearly shows *a much greater need of cultural tending in broad-leaved crops* (cf. also Dieterich, 1923), but at the same time, there are better prospects for success by suitable management in broad-leaved and mixed crops. Whilst a reasonably closed young spruce stand or a mixed Norway spruce–Silver fir regeneration, or even a spruce crop planted at medium spacing, is capable of developing into a valuable mature stand without active thinning, this is inconceivable for a patchy regeneration of beech interspersed with much heavily branched untidy adventitious growth. Admittedly, many excellent and uniform closed beech regenerations of the last century have produced polewood of quite satisfactory stem quality without having received treatment in the juvenile or pole-thicket stages; however, the timely removal of untidy advance growth from uneven regeneration, such as is usual nowadays for various reasons, must be carried out by tending operations. The longer we put off this task, the greater the risk that the better-shaped components will be smothered and repressed. Early alteration is similarly indispensable for the regulation of growth in mixed crops such as we find commonly today.

Early thinning at the thicket stage as demanded by Schädelin could meet with two main objections:

1. that it may *prevent self-pruning* and encourage the development of thick branches; and
2. that it would be wrong to interfere with a *natural development*, which, as a rule, would lead to an automatic selection of the most vigorous trees.

The importance and correctness of these objections may be judged on the basis of the prospective development of stem numbers and growing space in beech thickets. On quality class II sites this provides the following averages.

The figures *for the dominant trees* are:

at the age:		15	20	30	40
Stem number per ha		32,260	14,280	4,500	1,850
Mean height	m	4·0	6·0	10·5	14·5
Mean width of crown	m	0·6	0·9	1·6	2·5
Mean growing space	m²	0·31	0·70	2·22	5·41
The ratio of the mean growing space with increasing age therefore amounts to		*1·0 :*	*2·2 :*	*7·2 :*	*17·4*

The earlier the time when extraction of undesirable trees can be begun, the smaller will be the gaps caused. When after the regeneration has been uncovered and a closed thicket has formed at about the age of 15 years as shown above, the peak rate of height-growth sets in at ages between 20 and 30 years. Accordingly up to the age of 30 years, the gaps created in the canopy by the removal of badly shaped dominants are not only unimportant but will also quickly close up again *because of the rapid increases in shoot-length!* It is this particular age period from 15 to 30 years which Schädelin has in mind for his cleansing. The removal of a large number of dominant young trees during this development period cannot be detrimental to self-pruning, because, on the whole, the loosening of crown contact is slight and temporary. The consequences of thinning from the age of 40 years, which up to the present has been the usual age to start thinning, are more severe because gaps which are caused at the age of 40 years are nearly 8 times as large as those at the age of 20 years!

It is by early thinning with relatively small interruptions of canopy, that a *uniform,* if perhaps slightly loose, *contact between the competing dominant members* is obtained, so that the population consists of a large number of individuals which are offered equal growing chances. At this early stage, then, we remove a limited number of vigorous young phenotypes with undesirable form of growth (bent stems or many branches) in the justifiable expectation that we can secure their satisfactory replacement by trees of more desirable qualities in the dominant storey from which they have been removed.

If, however, we postpone this negative selective thinning until the pole-wood stage, the prospects of obtaining vigorous, well-shaped trees in the dominant storey become consistently less.

It is an urgent task of research to discover the best means of dealing effectively with the young growth and thicket stages of beech crops, in common also with mixed broadleaved crops, while avoiding excessive expense. In all cases the basic conditions are: *a well-closed initial regeneration, and the subsequent maintenance of a somewhat looser but even form of cohesiveness in the upper storey until the start of increment thinning.* Today, both of these aspects are insufficiently taken into account because of an unsuitable application of the rules for regeneration and raising of mixed stands of Silver fir–Norway spruce–Common beech (or even the ideal of a selection forest) to the completely different natural growing conditions and cultural necessities of broadleaved crops.

Beech stands on good sites, which have undergone treatment according to Schädelin's doctrine, will provide an elite of fully tended, mature harvestable trees at the age of 110–120 years. Up to that age, a good understorey prevents the development of ground vegetation, which would prevent regeneration. After successfully completing "crop tending" it is then possible to switch completely to "regeneration".

How to obtain quality timber at favourable prices in older beech stands with slender stems will be discussed later in the chapter on "Open stand and high forest with reserves system in Common beech".

(c) Summarizing Conclusions about a Suitable Thinning Technique for Common Beech

1. *The "natural critical degree of stocking" of Common beech* by which it is possible to reach 95 per cent of the potential optimum production, *fluctuates between* 0.6–0.7, the lower figure applying to younger and the upper one to older stands. As the optimum curves, which represent the relative volume growth-rates as a function of the natural degree of stocking, level off with increasing age, the optimum density of stocking simultaneously approaches a maximum; this circumstance allows *no prospects for achieving economically important gains in increment by using an "optimum basal area" or an* optimum degree of stocking. The importance of the natural critical degree of stocking is the greater because it allows sufficient scope for necessary tending operations, especially if these start early enough.

2. At present-day wages and prices in West Germany it is not possible to earn an acceptable net income for beech timber with breast-height diameters of less than 30 cm. Stem timber fetching a value increment requires a minimum breast-height diameter of 40 cm. *As a result, even if the proportion of thinnings amounted to 50 per cent at the age of 120 years, by far the bulk of the total value production after deducting harvesting expenses, namely approximately 80 per cent, lies in the remaining stand.*

After 60 years' treatment by liberating the crowns of favoured trees (assuming good sites with quality classes I and II) the dominants in the upper storey of this remaining stand have reached crown diameters of 10–11 m and mean ground cover areas of 80–100 m², so that only between 85–105 of them can be contained on one hectare. With a mean b.h.d. of 55 cm, corresponding to a basal area of 23–26 m²/ha, these trees alone would supply approximately 150 fm of felled stemwood of classes 4 and 5 in A-quality, provided all of them had first-class stems, not reduced in length by premature early crown isolation.

3. This conceivable maximum in net value return can be achieved only under the following conditions:

(a) Complete initial regeneration; removal of all heavy-crowned advance growth by tending of the young stands.

(b) Early cleaning as advocated by Schädelin and subsequent selection thinning in the pole-wood stage at a height of 20 m *can ensure that approximately 200 trees with good stems per hectare are secured in the dominant stand.*

(c) The subsequent opening up for increment, which ought not to start before clean boles of 9–10 m have been obtained, freely favours these 200 or so high-grade candidates by crown isolation, and a further selection up to the age of 120 years with the greatest possible uniformity of distribution in the stand leaves approximately 100 high-grade trees as the mature harvestable élite.

4. With an early start of crown thinning, a fully sufficient number of broadleaved under-storey trees (Kraft 5a), suppressed from an early stage, remains capable of survival and can, in an ideal manner, take care of soil and stem protection. This function they can fulfil more satisfactorily and with less hindrance to the volume increment than co-dominant trees with small crowns (Kraft 4 a and b), the proportion of which ought to be kept small.

5. An intensification of treatment can increase the net value efficiency in Common beech more effectively than, for example, in Norway spruce. However, such an increase is limited by the necessarily high proportion of stackwood assortments (firewood, pulp-wood) and small-diameter stemwood (class 2) in the total production. Even if the present small price differences between stemwood A- and B-quality (120 : 100) were to increase considerably, the net value production cannot be increased at the same ratio within normal rotations, because the proportion of A-quality stemwood in the total production of working sections cannot reach more than 15, up to a maximum of 20 per cent.

6. The rotations of approximately 140 years hitherto required for the production of large-diameter timber can be reduced by some 20 years to 120 years by intensive free and heavy crown-thinning. The loss of 5–10 per cent in volume increment, which must be expected as compared with moderate low thinning under a longer rotation, can be afforded, especially as losses in value due to the development of dark heartwood in old age are simultaneously reduced.

2. Norway Spruce

Brief characterization of the species Norway spruce

Norway spruce *(Picea excelsa)* is a half-shade-tolerant species with a much earlier culmination of the current and mean volume increments than the shade-tolerant species Common beech. According to Wiedemann's yield table for moderate thinning, the culminations for quality class I occur as follows:

	At age	m³
Current volume increment	35–40	17·4
Mean ann. volume increment	90	12·2

The ability of Norway spruce to respond to increased light and to react to liberation fellings is considerably below that of Common beech. The capacity of the crown for lateral extension is much smaller and therefore its ability to develop in old age is limited. Once the crown length is reduced as a result of the lower branches dying off in a closed stand, the assimilating crown surface can be elongated only by further upward growth, i.e. by height increment. At greater ages, however, this requires more time, because by the age of 80 years the rate of height growth on good sites has already dropped to 20 cm and less per annum. Open-stand treatment causes an increase generally in branch diameters and delays self-pruning, so that artificial pruning must be resorted to. The timber quality is reduced by the greater width of annual rings.

Injuries from disease or climatic causes play a significant rôle, particularly when the species is introduced in regions beyond its natural distribution and on unsuitable sites. Among insect pests we mention the following: the Nun moth *(Lymantrica monacha* L.), the small spruce sawfly *(Lygaeonematus abietum* Htg.), *Laspeyresia pactolana* Zll. and the great spruce bark beetle *(Ips typographus)*. Among fungi, *Polyporus annosus* Fr. becomes disagreeably evident by causing red rot. The susceptibility of Norway spruce to damage by gales and snow breakage is well known. It is therefore not surprising that numerous Norway spruce thinning experiments have suffered such extensive damage from disease and weather disturbances that they have had to be terminated prematurely or written off as no longer able to supply clear information.

The most important experimental Norway spruce thinning series and their treatments

According to Wiedemann (1937) the former *Prussian Forest Research Institute* had a total of over 110 Norway spruce thinning plots, thirteen of these being single plots without controls for comparison and therefore having little value. The remaining ninety-seven plots are distributed over *thirty-seven experimental series.* Of these

six experimental series contain the low thinning grades A, B, C,
fifteen experimental series contain an A-grade plot.

The remaining *sixteen series have no A-grade plot, i.e. no definitive control plot.*

Three of the above-mentioned *six* experimental series with A, B, C-grades *are not suitable* for a clear assessment of the effects of thinning, because they are at the same time experiments in spacing, their individual plots having been *laid out with variable spacing.* This means that there are differences in the initial circumstances, especially in the physiological age of the individual plots at the start of the experiment. Thus, the separate effects of initial spacing and thinning treatment on the growth-rhythm interact and become confused. Another series (Carlsberg 148) was laid out at the age of 69 years and at the age of 81 years was destroyed in a catastrophic gale. *The only two series remaining for comparison are Schleusingen and Hinternah in the Thüringer Wald.*

In *Schleusingen 123/24,* measuring of heights did not start until the crop was 66 years old; some considerable earlier thinning yields were not assessed.

Hinternah 146 suffered considerable damage by snow breakage, so that the differences in the density of stocking and the degree of thinning are slight, as in Schleusingen.

Thus the thinning yields recorded by the Research Institute in the exp. series Hinternah during the period 1913–30 (age 68–85) amount to

> 157·6 fm (!)   in the A-grade,
> 136·8 fm   in the B-grade,
> 87·2 fm   in the C-grade.

The most important results of both series follow:

Schleusingen. Observation period 66–111 years

		A	B	C-grade
Periodic mean basal area	m²	39·7	37·9	36·9
	%	100	96	93 (!)
P.m.a.i. of timber volume	m³	8·1	9·0	8·9
	%	100	111	110

Hinternah. Observation period, age 44–89

		A	B	C-Grade
Periodic mean basal area	m²	44·4	40·7	37·1
	%	100	92	84
Increment	m³	11·5	11·3	10·7
	%	100	98	93

The superiority of the B- and C-grade in Schleusingen is—notwithstanding an earlier attempted explanation by Assmann (1953a)—probably due to some inferiority of local site conditions of the A-grade plot, because such strong differences between the performances seem scarcely possible with such small differences in the degree of thinning. The C-plot is definitely favoured, because in 1872 the basal area amounted to

$$G = 30·63 \text{ m}^2 \qquad \text{with } N = 1450$$

whilst in the A-plot

$$G = 31·60 \text{ m}^2 \qquad \text{with } N = 3204.$$

The comparison between all mean heights, measured up to the age of 111 years (cf. p. 257) results in the following relation:

$$
\begin{array}{ccccc}
A & : & B & : & C \\
\text{as} \quad 100 & : & 105 & : & 110(!)
\end{array}
$$

which indicates a *considerable inferiority of A*, at least *in comparison to C*.

Despite the large number of individual plots, the former Prussian Research Institute has *no experimental series under sufficiently long observation* with A-, B- and C-grade plots *by which we could convincingly demonstrate the effects of graduated strengths of low thinning on the volume increment.*

Of particular interest are the investigations made in those experimental series, where *heavy thinning* started at an early stage; Schwappach refers to this as "Schiffel thinning" (cf. Schiffel, 1904, 1906) and Wiedemann, borrowing from Bohdanecky and Gehrhardt, calls it "rapid growth" thinning. There are fourteen series of this type, ten of them laid out in the years 1904–9 and four during the period from 1924 to 1930. Of these series seven have a comparative plot with A-grade. Also, of more recent origin, are the six experimental series with a crown thinning plot.[1] The results of some "rapid-growth experiments" will be discussed in more detail later in this chapter.

[1] One of these series, namely *Dalheim 97*, which was laid out in 1928, was inspected by the "Yield Study Section". From a guide-book issued on that occasion, the author gathers that the *A-plot* of this series at the age of 66 years had a mean height of 24·9 m (corresponding to quality class I.4) and a *basal area of 59·10 m²* which far exceeded the yields given in the yield table of Wiedemann (mod. thinning). And, as might have been expected, the volume increment in the period so far (age 42–66) is also higher than those produced by "light crown thinning" and "heavy low thinning". Again a proof of the indispensability of A-plots!

The Bavarian thinning experiments in Norway spruce stands, which are reported by Gutmann (1926) and Reinhold (1926) as well as Vanselow (1943) and Assmann (1954c), originally consisted of thirteen series with A-, B-, and C-grade and three series with B- and C-grade. Of the thirteen complete series, two have prematurely become useless as a result of calamities; two further series contain fairly large admixtures of Silver fir; in one of the experimental series there are such large local differences that it has become useless for a comparison of performances. The results of the remaining eight series are critically evaluated below. The experimental thinning series have either escaped altogether from disasters due to climatic extremes and disease, or have been only slightly damaged; they have received uniform treatment throughout, and only during the period 1940–6 was there some disturbance to four A-plots through unregulated thinnings. These are practically the only Norway spruce research series which have been observed over a sufficiently long period in the whole of Germany, from which the effects of low thinnings at different strength can be clearly demonstrated.

The former *Research Institute of Württemberg*, for example, has only a few long-observed Norway spruce thinning experiments the B-grade plots according to the research plan of 1873 being the most lightly thinned, accordingly there are no A-plots. Below we shall discuss one of these experimental series which was evaluated by Dieterich (1923). The same obtains for the former *Research Institute of Baden* which used as its most lightly thinned controls *B-grade* plots according to the experimental plan of 1902, so that the comparative performances in these series are even more difficult, if not impossible, to straighten out.

On the other hand, the results of the *Swedish Norway spruce thinning experiments*, laid out by Schotte (1912) since 1906 and reported by Carbonnier (1954, 1957), are of great interest, because all six experimental series contain a completely unthinned plot.

In the Swiss Norway spruce thinning experiments again, as in those of Württemberg, the B-grade represents the lightest thinning grade. We shall later discuss one of these experiments, as well as the *Danish* experimental series at Hastrup and Ravnholt and the new experiment at Bowmont in *Great Britain*.

(a) VOLUME AND VALUE YIELDS OF NORWAY SPRUCE UNDER DIFFERENT THINNING RÉGIMES

From a few examples we can inform ourselves about some typical reactions to thinning by Norway spruce. By analysing such long-term experimental series as have escaped appreciable disturbance we shall be able to uncover some further points of interest.

Periodic basal area content and volume increment in the Bavarian experimental Norway spruce series

Table 93 gives a brief summary of the climatic and local site conditions of these series. The two series on low terrace are in sharp contrast as regards quality class and m.a.i. at 80 years with the peak series in Oberschwaben, whereof Denklingen 5 is a strikingly poor performer. In this connection, see also p. 165. Figures 117–20 illustrate the conditions of stocking in the leading experimental series Ottobeuren 8.

So as to examine the *comparability existing within each of the series*, Table 94 presents the total *stem numbers at the beginning of the experiment* and also according to numbers above 15 cm and 20 cm b.h.d. respectively.

TABLE 93

BAVARIAN NORWAY SPRUCE RESEARCH SERIES: POSITION, CLIMATE AND SOIL

Res. series	At age 80 — Height qual. cl.[1] (Wiedemann)	At age 80 — m.a.i. timber over 7 cm diam.	Elevn. above m.s.l. and slope	Climatic data — (a) Annual temp. (°C)	Climatic data — (b) May–Aug. rainfall (mm)	Soil description
Eglharting 72	II·0	11·0	530 m level	(a) ~7·4 (b) ~15·1	(a) ~940 (b) ~450	Low terrace; loamy sand mixed with gravel which increases with depth; top layer free from gravel, inclined to compactness, strongly acid; oxyphilous flora. *Rooting depth over 1 m.* No differences due to soil in all six plots. Old forest soil.
Eglharting 73	1·7	11·0	do.	do. "scarce water supply"		
Denklingen 5	I·0	14·5	740 m almost level	(a) ~6·7 (b) ~14·7 "adequate water supply"	(a) ~1100 (b) ~450	Loamy high-terrace rubble; loam mixed with gravel and coarse grit; top layer up to 5 cm duff mull. Flora with oxyphilous constituents. *Depth of rooting only up to about 25 cm.* Old forest soil.
Sachsenried 2	0·5	17·9	820 m level	(a) ~6·3 (b) ~14·3	(a) ~1250 (b) ~550	Loamy high-terrace rubble; fresh loam mixed with gravel; duff mull, well populated by earthworms; favourable flora. Depth of rooting to 1 m. Series 2 on old garden and housing site; series 3 on former agricultural soil.
Sachsenried 3	0·6	15·9	do.	do. "ample water supply"		
Sachsenried 67	0·2	16·5	840 m level	as above		High terrace rubble near terminal moraine, surface layer of light loam; mull-moder; favourable flora; depth of rooting 50–70 cm. Former agricultural or grazing land.
Sachsenried 68	0·4	16·0		"ample water supply"		
Ottobeuren 8	0·0	19·6	830 m 1·5° SSW.	(a) ~6·4 (b) ~14·4 "good water supply"	(a) >1000 (b) ~500	Fissured morainic material, fine loam surface layer over rock debris compressed into a conglomerate of limestone and bacis material. Luxuriant flora. Depth of rooting to 1·1 m. *Former grazing land.*

[1] Mean of the three individual plots in each case.

TABLE 94

BAVARIAN EXPERIMENTAL NORWAY SPRUCE SERIES

Examination of the initial stands by a comparison of stem numbers, stem number distribution and top height at the beginning of the experiment
(stem numbers per ha)

Exp. series	Age at start	Comparative values	A-grade	B-grade	C-grade	Remarks
Eglharting 72	36	*Stem number* Total	(a) 8472	6888	7640	B has the lead
		> 15 cm dia.	(b) 104	288	108	
		> 20 cm dia.	(c) 8	4	—	
		Top height, m	13·5	13·7	13·3	
Eglharting 73	41	Stem number	(a) 3012	3472	3720	A and B in advance of C
			(b) 1188	1088	1012	
			(c) 208	188	144	
		Top height, m	17·9	17·8	17·8	
Denklingen 5	35	Stem number	(a) 5320	5456	5340	
			(b) 1168	1144	1228	
			(c) 244	292	264	
		Top height, m	15·6	15·8	15·7	
Sachsenried 2 Planted	32	Stem number	(a) 5356	5252	5132	B and C in advance of A
			(b) 1188	1244	1156	
			(c) 84	144	164	
		Top height, m	15·7	15·9	15·6	
Sachsenried 3 Broadcast sown	33	Stem number	(a) 19268	19312	18748	
			(b) 320	348	332	
			(c) 20	44	16	
		Top height, m	13·7	14·2	14·2	
Sachsenried 67 Sown	43	Stem number	(a) 4044	3692	4352	Pronounced lead by C and B over A
			(b) 1088	1340	1384	
			(c) 293	508	600	
		Top height, m	20·4	21·2	21·8	
Sachsenried 68 Planted	42	Stem number	(a) 3960	3216	3472	Pronounced lead by C and B over A
			(b) 1368	1340	1448	
			(c) 400	492	560	
		Top height, m	19·9	20·1	21·1	
Ottobeuren 8	32·5	Stem number	(a) 5948	5596	4352	Noticeable lead by C which was thinned 5½ years earlier than B and A
			(b) 1160	1196	1384	
			(c) 104	144	304	
		Top height, m	16·8	16·9	17·1	

The striking lead of the B- and C-plots in the series 67 and 68 is probably the result of vigorous thinning before the main crop was taken in hand. As in the series Ottobeuren 8, this stimulated faster growth.

The occurrence of a fairly large number of trees of more than the started minimum diameters suggests that there must be a *lead in growth or productivity* enjoyed by that particular plot. This might be due to an *advantage of age*. So far, however, no appreciable differences in age have been discovered as between the different series.[1] If there are no age differences, then it is possible that certain site conditions may be more favourable then others. Finally, there is the possibility that the plot in question has, *owing to an earlier start of thinnings, experienced an acceleration of growth and thus gained a lead in production.* This has been already illustrated on p. 234 for the C-plot of the experimental series Ottobeuren 8. The striking lead in performance of the series 67 and 68, which is also expressed in a corresponding superiority of top heights, can most likely be explained in the same way.

FIG. 117. Spruce research area at Ottobeuren. A-grade in summer 1953. B. area = 79 m², V_s = 1265 fm/ha.

Despite many endeavours, it has unfortunately been impossible to trace how the crop was handled prior to taking it under control. However, it is reasonable to assume that thinning had been carried out in the B- and C-plots some 5–10 years before the numbering and control of the standing crops was started and that this was recorded and booked as yield at the beginning of the experiment. This is indicated also by the similar leads of B- and C-plots in both series. Moreover, the differences between the initial numbers of stems in sown and planted areas are remarkably small as compared to Sachsenried 3 (sown) and 2 (planted). Unless we assume that germination in the series

[1] The winding up of an older experimental series, as for example the series Sachsenried 3 which has been going on for the last 4 years, is accompanied by a careful determination of the age of all trees.

67 was very patchy, a large number of unrecorded stems must have been felled (in the A-plot also) before the start of the experiment.

The procedure of *"compared diameters"*[1] used by Reinhold (1926), if applied to the crops at their initial state, produces similar results, although the shift of diameter distri-

FIG. 118. Ottobeuren, B-grade, b. area = 74 m², V_s = 1180 fm/ha.

bution towards the larger end occasions an automatic increase of the "compared diameter". The use of the "compared height" is more dubious because this depends at the

---

[1] The sectional area and diameter of the mean basal area stem are calculated as for the *number of stems of that plot which contains the smallest number* of individuals (the most heavily thinned plot), by a count from the larger end. The corresponding heights, read off the height curve, are the "compared heights".

FIG. 119. Ottobeuren, A-grade. A view of the crown space. Fine branches rendered invisible owing to strong top light, conveying illusion that crowns of trees are beginning to dry out.

FIG. 120. Ottobeuren, C-grade. A view of the crown space.

same time on the accuracy of height determination. This applies especially to some later inventories which were at times carried out by people with insufficient practice or by means of imperfect instruments. *As the length of the experimental period increases* the ratio of the "compared diameters" also *loses its value as a test criterion because it is likely to change as a result of the different types of treatment.* Quite definitely this is the case with the "compared height", because the ratio *h : d alters systematically* with heavier thinning, to which fact Assmann has drawn attention (1943/4).

It is evident that even when diameter growth obtained a noticeable lead at the start, the initial top heights within the different series (with the exception of series 67 and 68) show relatively small differences, although mostly similar in direction.

Local observations, examinations of the soil profiles, consideration of the relative positions and assessment of growth behaviour so far, all combine to indicate that only the B-plot of the series Sachsenried 2 enjoys any noticeable advantage as regards *local site conditions.*

Another reasonably objective guide to comparability is *the average of all hitherto measured mean and top heights of the individual plots* in the experimental series. A look at the curves of mean height over diameter of the mean basal area stem for all surveys to date proves that the obvious systematic height-measurement errors of the individual assessments as a rule agree in kind. If we take into consideration the fact that the heights of the mean basal area stems must show reasonably positive graduations from "A" to "C" grade, which is not the case with the top heights (apart from the effects of an initial growth stimulus), and further that the position of the B-grade stands evidently promotes height development, this "comparison of heights" suggests a distinct and permanent inferiority only in the C-plot of the series Eglharting 73. Table 95 gives a summary result of the height comparison along with separate data for the three series with a moderate water supply and the five series with a good supply. As may be seen, the *superiority of top height in the B-grade plots is particularly pronounced in the three series with a moderate water supply.* Presumably this is associated with the specific ecological conditions of these sites, which are probably effective to an optimum degree in the B-grade.

TABLE 95

BAVARIAN EXPERIMENTAL NORWAY SPRUCE SERIES

Quality class comparison on the basis of the mean values of all hitherto measured mean and top heights of stands

Mean values for		A-grade		B-grade		C-grade	
		Mean height	Top height	Mean height	Top height	Mean height	Top height
All 8 series	m	24·3	27·6	25·3	28·0	25·4	27·6
	%	100	100	104	101	104	100
3 series with *moderate* water supply	m	21·8	25·1	23·1	25·8	22·5	25·0
	%	100	100	106	103	103	99
5 series with a *good* water supply	m	25·8	29·1	26·6	29·3	27·1	29·1
	%	100	100	103	101	105	100

Is the total growth performance a suitable measure for comparisons?

Owing to the aforesaid lead in development and production of certain individual plots at the beginning of the experiment, the *total crop volume* under different thinning grades is obviously not a practical *basis for comparison*, if the treatment before the start of the experiment and the yields thereby are not known and assessed with absolute certainty. If, for example, the C-grade at the start of the experiment possessed a superiority in total crop volume and this by virtue of an imparted stimulation to growth, a "raised assessment" of the A-grade, as suggested by Reinhold (1926), would be a disadvantage to the C-grade, because the physiologically younger stand of the A-plot has a superiority in potential growing power, which enables it to overhaul the lead of the C-plot.

For this reason comparative performances must be judged on the *increments accruing over the whole experimental period*. Owing to the unavoidable and fairly large mensurational errors which occur in standing crop inventories, the basic increment periods must be of adequate length (at least 15–20 years) and sufficiently reliable enumerations of the growing crop should be made at the beginning and the end of these periods. Although the volume increments can be smoothed out to conform with the more reliable basal area increments by the method shown on p. 226, this device must fail if the basal area determinations of the remaining stands are very faulty, which happens not infrequently. Yet again, the assessment of volume growth *must not be restricted to timber dimensions ("Derbholz") alone*; first thinnings of Norway spruce are by no means valueless and much could be lost to sight—a loss especially likely to be felt by C-grade—were the smaller sizes not brought into account. Moreover, any such restriction *would distort growth relations at the particularly interesting phase of waxing increment prior to full vigour*. We should therefore use stem-wood values. It would, of course, be better still to use total tree-wood quantities, if these can be supported by careful measurements of branch-wood.

The three characteristic periods of treatment of the Bavarian experimental Norway spruce series and their yields

In the Bavarian experimental series individual stem numbering unfortunately did not start until 1900. The resulting uncertainties therefore make it necessary to calculate the results of the observation period *up to the time of numbering* separately. This 20-year observation period is characterized by moderate thinning and is shown in Table 96 in line (a).

The 20–33 year observation period following this is distinguished by *heavy thinning in the C- and B-plots*. The increment results of this important period are shown in line (b) of the table and are italicized for emphasis.

During the third observation period lasting 16–22 years, *thinning in the C- and B-plots was weak*, in fact in some cases there was no thinning at all. What is more, removals from the A-plots were proportionately greater throughout, a fact clearly demonstrated by the relative *increase in the percentage figures for the basal areas* in the C-grade plots during this period, designated (c) as distinct from (b). Even closer evidence of this is provided by the average percentage removals in terms of basal area (p. 302, further below).

The considerably lower production figures of all C-grade plots during period (b) is unmistakable; the mean of all eight series reaches only 91 per cent of the A-plots.

The B-grade plots of the series 72 and 73 on low terrace rubble with limited moisture supplies, on the other hand, show *considerably higher productions of 8 and 11 per cent respectively as against the A-grade plots.* As explained by Assmann (1954c), a thorough examination of the soil and survey of the plots failed to reveal any indications of locally favouring conditions for any of the plots in either series.

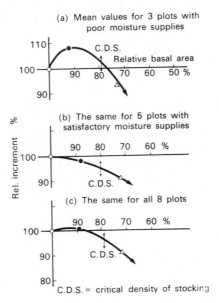

FIG. 121. Bavarian spruce trial plots. Natural stocking density and increment during the period of heaviest thinning.

The increased yields of the B-grade must be considered the result of thinning treatment. Increment reactions to moderate thinning—resulting from reduced competition—seem perfectly credible on this site. The slightly smaller positive reaction of the B-plot at Denklingen 5 (+5 per cent) which, judging by the scant rooting (depth of rooting only 25 cm!) seems to have only moderate moisture supply, is in agreement with this also. The small increase in efficiency of the B-plot at Sachsenried 2 (+3 per cent) is probably due to favourable site conditions.

With the well-accounted for exception of Sachsenried 2, the A-grade plots of the 5 experimental series with a good water supply display optimum yields.

If we summarize the results of observation period (b) for the three series with a short water supply and the five series with a good water supply, as in Table 96, we find an average reaction in agreement with the local conditions of the sites and the particular natural age phases, corresponding to theoretical expectations.

Figure 121 represents the optimum curves for observation period (b), for the two groups of sites and all eight plots. Despite the different bend of the curves the *critical degree of stocking* for both groups lies *at approximately 0·8 of the maximum periodic basal area*, represented by the A-grade plots. This figure stands in agreement with the figures stated on p. 231.

During the third observation period (c), the current increment in the C-plots of the series Sachsenried 2 and Ottobeuren 8 is catching up noticeably, in fact the performance

TABLE 96

MEAN BASAL AREAS AND VOLUME INCREMENTS (STEM-WOOD)

Observation periods: (a) up to the time of individual stem numbering   (d) total observation period
(b) heaviest thinning in the B- and C-plots   (e) total growth at the beginning of the experiment
(c) weak thinning in the B- and C-plots   (f) total growth at closing age

Exp. series	Observation periods Age	Rel.	A-grade B. area (m²)	(%)	A-grade Increment (m³)	(%)	B-grade B. area (m²)	(%)	B-grade Increment (m³)	(%)	C-grade B. area (m²)	(%)	C-grade Increment (m³)	(%)
Eglharting 72¹ Planted at close spacing 0·9×0·9 m	—	(a)	—	—	—	—	—	—	—	—	—	—	—	—
	36–69	(b)	49·0	100	17·1	100	45·8	93	18·5	108	34·7	71	15·4	90
	69–85	(c)	59·0	100	14·9	100	57·9	98	14·8	99	46·0	78	11·3	76
	36–85	(d)	52·3	100	16·4	100	49·7	95	17·3	105	38·4	73	14·1	86
	Total growth	(e)			191	100			226	118			207	108
		(f)			993	100			1074	108			897	90
Eglharting 73² Planted at wide spacing 1·2×2·0 m	—	(a)	—	—	—	—	—	—	—	—	—	—	—	—
	41–75	(b)	53·5	100	14·6	100	48·1	90	16·2	111	39·0	73	13·5	92
	75–91	(c)	59·6	100	10·3	100	56·5	95	13·1	127	46·1	77	9·6	93
	41–91	(d)	55·4	100	13·2	100	50·8	92	15·2	115	41·3	75	12·3	93
	Total growth	(e)			353	100			362	103			340	96
		(f)			1014	100			1122	110			954	94
Denklingen 5 Planted 1·4×1·4 m	35–55	(a)	58·3	100	20·8	100	54·1	93	21·3	102	53·2	91	20·3	98
	55–83	(b)	63·7	100	16·7	100	58·8	92	17·5	105	46·9	74	15·7	94
	83–104	(c)	73·2	100	12·5	100	70·9	97	13·2	106	56·6	77	12·0	96
	35–104	(d)	65·0	100	16·6	100	61·1	94	17·3	104	51·7	80	15·9	96
	Total growth	(e)			367	100			371	101			380	104
		(f)			1513	100			1564	103			1480	98
Sachsenried 2 Planted 1·4×1·4 m	32–52	(a)	64·0	100	24·3	100	61·5	96	25·9	107	56·2	88	25·1	103
	52–79	(b)	74·8	100	20·7	100	66·3	89	21·3	103	50·5	68	19·8	96
	79–101	(c)	77·1	100	14·1	100	72·5	94	16·0	114	63·9	83	14·1	100
	32–101	(d)	72·4	100	19·7	100	66·9	92	20·9	106	56·4	78	19·5	99
	Total growth	(e)			408	100			420	103			384	94
		(f)			1765	100			1865	106			1732	98

Series	Period												
Sachsenried 3 Broadcast sowing	(a) 33–53	55·9	100	23·6	100	51·8	93	24·1	102	44·8	80	23·2	98
	(b) 53–80	65·7	100	22·4	100	56·2	86	21·3	95	43·2	66	19·2	86
	(c) 80–102	75·9	100	16·2	100	68·5	90	15·4	95	57·6	76	14·0	86
	(d) 33–102	66·1	100	20·8	100	58·8	89	20·3	98	48·3	73	18·7	90
	(e) Total	—	—	272	100	—	—	302	111	—	—	267	98
	(f) growth	—	—	1705	100	—	—	1699	100	—	—	1557	91
Sachsenried 67 Broadcast sowing	(a) —	—	—	—	—	—	—	—	—	—	—	—	—
	(b) 43–75	65·2	100	25·1	100	60·3	92	24·2	96	51·6	79	23·1	92
	(c) 75–92	73·9	100	17·7	100	72·2	98	16·6	94	63·8	86	14·9	84
	(d) 43–92	68·2	100	22·5	100	64·4	94	21·5	96	55·9	82	20·2	90
	(e) Total	—	—	438	100	—	—	525	120³	—	—	563	128³
	(f) growth	—	—	1543	100	—	—	1580	102	—	—	1555	101
Sachsenried 68 Planted 1·4×1·4 m	(a) —	—	—	—	—	—	—	—	—	—	—	—	—
	(b) 42–74	66·5	100	24·5	100	58·1	87	23·5	95	51·0	77	22·7	93
	(c) 74–91	74·2	100	18·6	100	68·4	92	18·5	99	65·3	88	15·7	84
	(d) 42–91	69·2	100	22·4	100	61·7	89	21·8	97	56·0	81	20·3	91
	(e) Total	—	—	447	100	—	—	472	106³	—	—	517	116³
	(f) growth	—	—	1547	100	—	—	1540	100	—	—	1510	98
Ottobeuren 8 Planted 1·4×1·4 m	(a) 32·5–53	68·8	100	29·1	100	64·0	93	27·5	95	59·9	87	27·3	94
	(b) 53–79	78·3	100	24·1	100	68·4	87	23·7	98	57·3	73	21·3	88
	(c) 79–98	80·6	100	14·5	100	72·7	90	14·4	99	64·9	81	15·4	106
	(d) 32·5–98	76·0	100	22·9	100	68·3	90	22·2	97	60·3	79	21·5	94
	(e) Total	—	—	397	100	—	—	414	104	—	—	456	115⁴
	(f) growth	—	—	1896	100	—	—	1868	99	—	—	1862	98
Mean values for obs. per. (b) (heaviest thinning)	*All 8 series*	64·6	100	20·65	100	25·7	89	20·78	101	46·8	72	18·84	91
	3 series with scanty to adequate water supply	55·4	100	16·13	100	50·9	92	17·40	108	40·2	73	14·87	92
	5 series with good water supply	70·1	100	23·36	100	61·9	88	22·80	98	50·7	72	21·22	91

[1] Thinning contrary to plans in the A-plot at age 75 with 150 fm/ha.
[2] Thinning contrary to plans in the A-plot at age 81 with 120 fm/ha.
[3] Probable acceleration of growth as result of thinning *before* control of the remaining stand.
[4] Acceleration of growth as result of heavy thinning 5½ years before beginning of the experiment.

in series 8 is 6 per cent above A-grade. This can be explained as a consequence of the distinctly light thinning of the C-plots and their favourable relative basal areas during this period. At the same time we have further evidence of the widely divergent methods of treatment hiding under the equivalent grade definitions of the different research institutes.

The average percentage reduction in basal area as a
quantitative measure of thinning

Petterson (1954), in his highly important work, used the percentage reductions to characterize the degrees of thinning in Swedish coniferous forests. These figures can be related either to the number of stems, the basal area or volume. A percentage which is easy to use in practice and gives a good characterization is that of removals of basal area. If we relate this to the basal area of the stand prior to each particular thinning occasion, obviously we must take into account the particular period of time which has passed since the last occasion of thinning, as well as the period until the next occasion. If the first period is defined as t_1 (= last interval) and the second as t_n (= next interval), the arithmetic mean of both $(t_1 + t_n)/2 = t$ is the mean interval between the three occasions of thinning, the one during which a particular thinning operation is to be carried out lying in the middle. If the basal area of the stand before this operation equals G and the basal area to be removed equals g, the corresponding removed percentage is calculated by the following statement:

$$p_r = \frac{g/t}{G} \times 100 = \boxed{\frac{g}{G \times t} \times 100}.$$

If, for example, $t_1 = 6$, $t_n = 4$, then $t = \dfrac{6+4}{2} = 5$ years.

If $G = 54$ m^2, and $g = 8$ m^2,

then
$$p_r = \frac{8 \cdot 0}{270 \cdot 0} \times 100 = 2 \cdot 96 \text{ per cent.}$$

For *longer periods of time* with values of $t_1, t_2 \ldots, g_1, g_2 \ldots, G_1, G_2 \ldots$, we can calculate a mean reduction percentage:

$$P_r = \frac{g_1 + g_2 + g_3 + \ldots g_n}{t_1 G_1 + t_2 G_2 + t_3 G_3 + \ldots t_n G_n}.$$

The table which follows offers the mean reduction percentages for some Bavarian experimental series.

As mentioned earlier (p. 298), *thinning during the observation period (c) was heaviest in the A-grade plots and lightest in the C-grade plots.*

Clearly, the *percentage of removed trees must become smaller with increasing age* and decreasing basal area growth, if the basal area of the stand is not to be forced below a "critical" level. For the growing conditions of the above four experimental series we may deduce *an average percentage removal for optimum efficiency of production.* In order to be able to transfer this to other stands also, the following optimum P_r-values are given according to mean annual height increments of the stand. These preliminary basic values (assuming low-thinning) amount to:

Mean ann. height incr. of stands (m)	P_r (%)
0·50	1·8
0·40	1·6
0·30	1·3
0·20	1·0
0·10	0·5

TABLE 97

AVERAGE PERCENTAGE OF BASAL AREA REMOVED (P_r) FOR THE CHARACTERISTIC PERIODS OF TREATMENT OF SOME BAVARIAN EXPERIMENTAL NORWAY SPRUCE SERIES

Exp. series	Observation period		Mean percentages of removals		
			A-grade (%)	B-grade (%)	C-grade (%)
Denklingen 5	35–55	a)	0·83	1·54	1·54
	55–83	b)	1·12	1·29	2·34
	83–104	c)	0·49 (!)	0·26 (!)	0·22 (!)
	35–104	d)	0·87	1·12	1·69
Sachsenried 2	32–52	a)	0·92	1·51	1·69
	52–79	b)	1·19	1·64	2·39
	79–101	c)	1·01 (!)	0·83 (!)	0·63 (!)
	32–101	d)	1·06	1·34	1·70
Sachsenried 3	33–53	a)	1·61	2·42	2·84
	53–80	b)	1·14	1·68	2·42
	80–102	c)	0·72 (!)	0·56 (!)	0·40 (!)
	33–102	d)	1·12	1·53	1·95
Ottobeuren 8	32·5–53	a)	1·37	1·69	2·48
	53–79	b)	1·16	1·53	1·66
	79–98	c)	0·99 (!)	0·84 (!)	0·91 (!)
	32·5–98	d)	1·17	1·37	1·69

Thus, for example, with a thinning cycle of $t=4$ years in a Norway spruce stand of 28 m mean height, $G=65$ m², volume of stemwood $=845$ fm ($fh=13·0$ m) and an *ann. height increment of 0·25 m*, the following values would be produced:

mean ann. $p_r=1·15$, therefore for 4 years $=4·5$ per cent, and consequently
$g=3·0$ m², which if $fh=11·5$ m (13·0–10 per cent) corresponds to a *thinning yield of app. 35 fm growing crop* (stem-wood).
For $t=6$, this would be 52 fm growing stem-wood.

We will suppose that the average rate of volume production from final crop and thinnings of a spruce stand during its 100-year span of life (or, what amounts to the same thing, of a felling series on 100-year rotation) comes to 3 per cent; then, assuming that some 35 per cent of the t tal yield comes out in thinnings, the *thinning reduction per cent as an average of all thinnings* must be $3.0 \times 0.35 = 1.05$ per cent. Because the trees removed in low thinnings are mostly thinner and smaller than the average of the stand, the corresponding percentage of basal area removed may be estimated to be 10 per cent higher. A look at the felling percentages in our common Norway spruce yield tables proves that these are sometimes not in keeping with the natural progress of growth and so force—in some cases unnecessarily—the natural degree of stocking down to values well below 0.8.

It is good practice to base the percentage of removals upon some natural measure of growth (height increment or basal area increment), because this leads to smaller actual quantities being removed in thinnings in cases where, for instance, severe earlier thinnings have already reduced the basal area to a low level of stocking. Estimation of basal area with the Bitterlich relascope and calipering of the thinned trees with the tree angle-caliper of Mayer (1959) simplify the application of this method. Thus, measurements of typical stands can furnish valuable supporting figures and aids to practising foresters who do not wish to depend solely on eye-estimates.

In order to get away from the rigid and often locally unsuitable yield table data, further research into extraction percentages should be worthwhile. This might supply useful basic values for the different species and sites and especially values at the margin, corresponding to the natural critical degree of stocking.

In a method concerned with growing space factors, developed by Becking and Hart (1953), the ratio of average distance apart of trees in a stand as a percentage of the top height is used to find optimum stem number conditions. This method is not so suitable for the determination of the thinning grade, because the ratio of crown diameter to height changes systematically in the course of the life of a stand and in a manner which has so far been insufficiently investigated, as has been shown by Assmann (1960). The idea of this method started from Köhler (1919) who tried to deduce ideal stem numbers as a function of the mean height of the stand. Köhler's stimulating approach to the problem of thinning is partly based on hypotheses which are today no longer sustainable.

Periodic basal area and increment in experimental Norway spruce series of other countries

Results of the Swedish research series

Of these we have already quoted the experiment at Dalby to demonstrate typical reactions to thinning. Carbonnier (1954) reported the results of five other experimental series. These are situated in the experimental forest park *Tönnersjöheden*, north-east of Halmstad, not far from the west coast of Sweden, 90–130 m above sea level, in a cool and damp oceanic climate (annual temperature $=6.7°C$, annual rainfall$=1040$ mm) on sandy moraine. Soil: podsolic brown earth with a surface layer of 5–11 cm raw humus. The stands were close-planted at 1.0–1.25 m square spacing and are notable for their very slow rate of progress. The culmination of the current volume increment in quality class II/III according to Wiedemann had still not been reached at the age of 70 years and is likely to take place some 20–30 years later than is assumed in this table. On account of local conditions, development was slow during the early years, and the first of heavy thinning incursions (at ages between 31–48 years) took place *at the phase marking the natural onset of full vigour*, long before the culmination of the increment. Large initial numbers of stems helped to obtain a uniform distribution of the crop and so avoided the too-rapid diminution in productive capacity per hectare of the remaining trees (cf. p. 233). The m.a.i. at present is 30–40 per cent more than the values of Wiedemann's table.

In all five series, natural self-thinning ("självgallring"; trees which die naturally are simply recorded, but not removed) is compared to heavy and very heavy low thinnings and crown thinning (see Fig. 122). Some of the series contain broad-leaved trees which in the series T_{10} are so numerous as to exert a disturbing influence on the experiment.

FIG. 122. Swedish trial series T_4. *Right:* natural thinning, *left:* heavy low thinning.

Here, with well-defined and consistently maintained differences in the severity of thinnings, we find that although the heavily thinned plots show superior growth in the first instance they are eventually surpassed by the naturally-thinned plots which reach the highest yields when given sufficient length of time. In series T_4 and T_{32}, which have been observed over 40 years, this is already the case, whereas in series T_1, T_{16} and T_{19}, there is still, after only 25–30 years' treatment, the moderate or slight superiority of volume increment under heavy low thinning, which has been evident since the beginning of the experiment. Table 98 illustrates this by the example of series T_4 and T_{19}.

Here we have substantial *proof of the existence of an accelerated growth-rate which then slows down consequent on a change in the natural growth rhythm.* Whilst in the series T_4 a clear superiority of natural thinning has already established itself, this had only just

TABLE 98

MEAN PERIODIC BASAL AREA AND VOLUME INCREMENT IN THE SWEDISH EXPERIMENTAL NORWAY SPRUCE SERIES T_4 AND T_{19} (CARBONNIER, 1954)

Obs. period (age) from–to	Definition	Natural thinning	Low thinning heavy	very heavy
		Exp. series T_4		
31–46	mean b.a. m² and %	53·0 = 100	32·7 = 62%	
	Incr. m³ and %	11·3 = 100	13·6 = **120%**	
46–61	mean b.a. m² and %	57·2 = 100	29·1 = 51%	
	Incr. m³ and %	16·9 = 100	16·3 = **97%**	
61–71	mean b.a. m² and %	58·7 = 100	33·0 = 56%	
	Incr. m³ and %	21·9 = 100	17·2 = **79%**	
31–71	mean b.a. m² and %	56·0 = 100	31·4 = 56%	
	Incr. m³ and %	16·1 = 100	15·5 = **96%**	
		Exp. series T_{19}		
40–56	mean b.a. m² and %	45·4 = 100	27·1 = 60	22·0 = 49%
	Incr. m³ and %	11·8 = 100	13·1 = **111**	12·1 = **103%**
56–66	mean b.a. m² and %	48·5 = 100	27·9 = 58	22·4 = 46%
	Incr. m³ and %	13·9 = 100	14·4 = **104**	12·7 = **91%**
40–66	mean b.a. m² and %	46·6 = 100	27·4 = 59	22·2 = 48%
	Incr. m³ and %	12·6 = 100	13·6 = **108**	12·4 = **98%**

started in the series T_{19}. Figure 123 shows how the mean increment (m.a.i.) of the naturally thinned crop gradually overtakes the lead initially established by the heavily thinned crop on the series T_4.

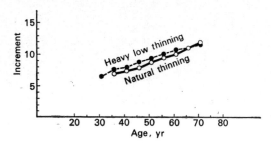

FIG. 123. Swedish spruce trial series (T_4). Progress of the average increment.

Another fact to be mentioned is that according to observations made by Carbonnier the *crown-thinned plots* in all four series show significantly lower volume increments as compared with the low thinning plots.

The Danish thinning experiment at Hastrup

Phenomena of equal significance are apparent in the *Danish thinning experiment at Hastrup*, reported by Bornebusch (1933) and the subject of a difference of opinion between Wiedemann (1933) and Gehrhardt (1933, 1934). This is one of the typical "plantations" in Jutland, 65 m above sea level; ann. temperature = 6·7°C, ann. rainfall = 680 mm; loamy sand over coarse sand; "heath podsol"; afforested pasture land (formerly cultivated land, prior to that heathland). This stand which suffered severely under red rot has, according to information from Dr. Holmsgaard, Director of the Danish Research Institute, since perished. The most important figures are given in Table 99.

TABLE 99

MEAN BASAL AREA AND INCREMENT IN THE NORWAY SPRUCE THINNING EXPERIMENT AT HASTRUP ACCORDING TO DATA OF BORNEBUSCH (1933)

Obs. per. (age)	Definition		Thinning grades			
		A-grade	B-grade	C-grade	D-grade	L-grade
30–42	mean b.a. m²	41·4 = 100	37·5 = 91	32·8 = 79	27·2 = 66	26·4 = 64%
	Incr. m³	14·3 = 100	16·0 = 112	16·3 = 114	14·8 = 104	13·7 = 96%
42–52	mean b.a. m²	53·0 = 100	45·7 = 86	34·0 = 64	28·5 = 54	26·5 = 50%
	Incr. m³	19·3 = 100	19·6 = 101	20·6 = 107	17·7 = 92	16·5 = 85%
30–52	mean b.a. m²	46·7 = 100	41·2 = 88	33·3 = 71	27·8 = 60	26·4 = 57%
	Incr. m³	16·5 = 100	17·6 = 107	18·3 = 110	16·2 = 98	14·9 = 90%

As clearly seen, the speeding-up of growth in the B- and C-plots during the first observation period had already slackened during the second observation period, whilst the performances of the D- and L-plots are in fact inferior. According to opinion in Gehrhardt's days, the undeniably improved out-turn by C-grade and its economic importance were held to confirm his thinning doctrine. *Today we know that this superiority can only be temporary.*

During an inspection in spring 1954 the author became acquainted with the results of the Danish thinning experiment at Ravnholt where the effect of the speeding-up of growth does not stand out so clearly, because in this case the only plot for comparison is a moderately thinned "B" grade area. None the less the D-plot, which at the age of 38 was superior in total crop volume, was overtaken by the B-plot during the next 9 years. Moreover, this is a top-quality site with annual volume increments of over 30 fm.

The results of a new thinning experiment in *Great Britain* are of special interest to research into this problem in Germany.

The thinning experiment at Bowmont

Results to date of this experiment have been reported by F.C. Hummel (1947). The experimental series is in a position south-east of Edinburgh, not far from the Scottish east coast at about 170 m above sea level. It was laid out in 1930 by J. A. B. Macdonald, with four plots each for three low thinning grades and one crown thinning grade, making a total of sixteen plots, in a "Latin square" arrangement. Each plot is about 4 ar in area. Volume control is restricted to timber over 7 cm in diameter, so that clarity of the results is slightly obscured by the recruitment of timber over 7 cm in diameter and the disappearance of thinning yields under 7 cms b.h. diameter.

TABLE 100

PERIODIC BASAL AREA AND INCREMENT OF THE THINNING EXPERIMENT AT BOWMONT AFTER FIGURES
BY HUMMEL (1947)

Observation period (age)	Definition		B-grade	Thinning grades C-grade	D-grade	L.C.-grade (cr. thinning)
20–25	mean b.a.	m²	44·9 = 100	42·0 = 94	36·5 = 81	38·2 = 85%
	Incr.	m³	13·5 = 100	15·4 = 114	15·9 = 118	14·2 = 105%
25–30	mean b.a.	m²	52·1 = 100	47·8 = 92	34·8 = 67	38·6 = 74%
	Incr.	m³	14·9 = 100	16·9 = 113	22·0 = 147	19·3 = 150%
30–35	mean b.a.	m²	56·2 = 100	52·3 = 93	36·5 = 65	41·6 = 74%
	Incr.	m³	16·8 = 100	14·5 = 86	17·5 = 104	17·6 = 105%
20–35	mean b.a.	m²	51·1 = 100	47·4 = 93	36·0 = 70	39·5 = 77%
	Incr.	m³	15·1 = 100	15·6 = 103	18·4 = 122	17·0 = 113%

On the whole, however, the results in Table 100 correspond to theoretical expectations. *The most heavily thinned D-plot still leads* in volume efficiency; but, the considerable *setback* during the observation period 30–35 coming after the powerful acceleration of growth, already forecasts the future shift of the productivities and the eventual superiority of the B-plot can already be predicted. Since thinning in the B-grade quite obviously went beyond the removal of dying trees, the maximum periodic basal area must be estimated at least 10 per cent above that of the B-plots, so that the natural mean degrees of stocking should amount to approximately

$$0.91 \quad 0.84 \quad 0.64 \quad 0.70.$$

The poorer showing of the crown thinning plot alongside the D-plot is in accordance with the expectation.[1]

The Swiss Norway spruce thinning series at Olten

An interpretation of the results of this series has already been attempted by Assmann (1956).[2] It has a B-grade (according to the 1873 plan) as its most lightly thinned plot, to which a C-plot and a D-plot are compared. After an initial growth-spurt in the C- and D-plots resulting from early thinning, the increment performances later levelled out,

---

[1] Mackenzie (1962) has since published further results of this particularly valuable experiment for a total experimental period amounting to 30 years by now. The author's cordial thanks are expressed here to Mackenzie who generously put particulars of this experiment at his disposal. Assmann (1964) has thus been enabled to form an opinion of the further experimental results which confirm his theory of the periodic basal area and the decisive influence of the acceleration of growth. During the last 10-year increment period, from the age of 40–50 years, the increment values of the plots B:C:D:L.C, after conversion into stemwood values and smoothing, were in the ratios of 100:101:85:85.

[2] The author's cordial thanks are once more expressed here to Prof. Dr. E. Badoux who on several occasions very kindly furnished results of this experimental series and willingly gave more detailed information.

which in view of the very small differences between the actual degrees of thinning is quite probable. For the total period of observation so far, i.e. from 22 to 89 years, and 24–89 years respectively (1955) we have the following values:

	B-grade	C-grade	D-grade
Mean b. area m² and % respectively	52·9 = 100	46·7 = 88	43·1 = 81%
Ann. incr. in volume m³ and % respectively	19·1 = 100	18·8 = 98	19·8 = 104%
Ann. incr. in basal area m² and % respectively	1·292 = 100	1·234 = 96	1·311 = 101%

If we assume that the maximum possible basal area lies 5 per cent above that of the B-grade the natural degrees of stocking of the three plots will be as follows:

$$0·95 : 0·84 : 0·78.$$

The superiority of the D-grade is ascribable to the improbably low form-factor values for the standing crop on the B-plot at the last assessment. By strenuous efforts the Swiss Research Institute determined the form-factors for standing trees. But here again, the natural variance of the breast-height form-factors is uncomfortably large and even when many measurements have been taken, form differences may appear misleadingly to disfavour certain plots. If the mean timber form factors for the stand, as calculated by the Swiss Research Institute for the three plots for the period since 1892 are plotted over the corresponding diameters of the mean basal area stems, the resulting values, for example, those from the 1925 assessment, are still plausible. But the values of the B-plot for 1940 as well as 1955 are very much too low. If smoothed form-factors derived from curves, in the manner mentioned earlier were used, the resultant performance ratios would harmonize much better with the basal area increments:

$$\begin{array}{ccc} B & C & D \\ 19·8 = 100 & 18·6 = 94 & 19·6 = 99 \text{ per cent} \end{array}$$

The reason for the unusual inferiority of the C-grade cannot be examined here.

Crown thinning in pure Norway spruce stands?

In all experimental Norway spruce series containing crown thinning plots, we have noticed the poor out-turn of crown thinning in comparison to low thinning. The already-mentioned *crown thinning series of the Research Institute of Württemberg*, which was laid out by Haug (1894, 1897, 1899) in 1892[1] and supplemented in 1896 by the Research Institute of Württemberg by the addition of a B- and C-grade plot each, was analysed in exemplary fashion by Dieterich (1923). Dieterich gave the results of three of Haug's total of five plots, which are compared with the yields of the B- and C-plots. Haug's guiding thought was, so to regulate the stem numbers in the "main stand" by early thinning

---

[1] According to statements by Haug (1894), this is a 27-year-old Norway spruce stand, 500 m above sea level in the Black Forest region which belongs to Württemberg, between Enz and Nagold near Bieselsberg, level to gently sloping toward S. It has grown on afforested former agricultural and forest meadow areas, in rows with close spacing (distance between rows 0·6–0·9, distance within the rows 0·3–0·5 m).

whilst preserving the "secondary (dominated) stand", that with full crown contact and an even distribution of the "main stems" optimum increments are achieved. In order to discover the most favourable stem number for the main stand he selected different numbers of best main stand stems, which he marked and tended by the removal of oppressive trees in main and middle storeys. The numbers of "main stems" selected at the beginning of the experiment, when the crop was 27 years old, were graduated as follows:

> Plot I: app. 1200 corresponding to app. 3·0 m spacing.
> Plot II: app. 2000 corresponding to app. 2·2 m spacing.
> Plot III: app. 2400 corresponding to app. 2·0 m spacing.

In plots I and III, most of the trees removed to favour main stems were upper storey trees with large diameters whilst the rather less vigorous trees in the intermediate and lower storeys were spared. In plot IV on the other hand, the trees removed to favour main stems were those of lesser and smallest diameters in the upper storey. The stand structures after 30 years, at the ages of 57 and 56 years respectively, are shown in Table 101.

Thus, *with crown thinning, the proportion of unthrifty stems in the intermediate and lower storeys*, where soil biology and stand climate have, at the most, a very doubtful effect, *amounted to 18–21 per cent of the stand basal area.* The inefficiency of crown thinning for volume production is not surprising therefore. During the observation period from 32 to 57 years and 31 to 56 years respectively the relevant figures are:

		Low thinning		Crown thinning		
		B-grade	C-grade	I	II	III
Per. mean basal area*	m²	53·2	48·4	47·9	49·1	54·3
	%	100	91	90	92	102
Mean ann. incr. (total tree vol.)	m³	28·0	25·4	22·5	23·2	25·9
	%	100	91	80	83	92
Basal area of the main crop in tr.cl. 1–3 at the age of 57 and 56 respectively amounted to	m²	46·5	43·2	34·0	36·4	40·0
	%	100	93	73	78	86

* The mean periodic basal area of the upper storey (Kraft 1–3) unfortunately cannot be calculated and stated here without a study of the original data.

If we bear in mind the basal area values of the upper storey, the connection between thinning treatment and volume increment is perfectly obvious. *The comparative inefficiency of crown thinning in this case reaches critical dimensions.* Moreover, as shown in Table 101, the mean dimensions achieved by the dominant trees give no evidence of a superiority of crown thinning which might reduce this deficit. Thus, the numbers and dimensions of dominant trees (Kraft 1+2) for comparison are as follows:

> In the crown thinning plot III   468 trees with $d_m = 28·0$ cm.
> In the low thinning plot B   644 trees with $d_m = 27·2$ cm.

At the same time, the trees remaining after crown thinning in the middle storey and more especially those in the lower storey produced little or no measurable diameter increment. Furthermore, Dieterich discovered that the crown-thinned plots had developed *unfavourable humus conditions* and assumed rightly that in this case the usually "parasitic effect of the auxiliary stand", which is to be anticipated on sites with low soil- and air-humidity, was less severe only because of high rainfall.

TABLE 101

PROPORTIONS OF TREE CLASSES IN HAUG'S CROWN THINNING SERIES ACCORDING TO FIGURES BY DIETERICH (1923)

Exp. plot	Tree cl. (Kraft)	Stem number	Mean diameter (cm)	Basal area	
				(m²)	(%)
B-grade (157)	1 and 2	644	27·2	37·42	71
	1–3	924	25·3	46·48	88
	4–5	288	17·0	6·52	12
	Total stand	1212		53·00	100
C-grade (158)	1 and 2	664	26·0	35·26	77
	1–3	948	24·1	43·23	94
	4–5	144	16·2	2·97	6
	Total stand	1092		46·20	100
Cr. thinning I (159)	1 and 2	512	26·4	28·01	67
	1–3	704	24·8	34·00	82
	4–5	340	16·8	7·50	18
	Total stand	1044		41·50	100
Cr. thinning III (161)	1 and 2	468	28·0	28·83	62
	1–3	680	26·1	36·38	79
	4–5	480	16·1	9·72	21(!)
	Total stand	1160		46·10	100
Cr. thinning VI (162)	1 and 2	612	26·6	34·03	69
	1–3	788	25·4	39·95	82
	4–5	476	15·5	9·05	18
	Total stand	1264		49·00	100

The experiment proves once again that in Norway spruce stands, as generally in coniferous stands with pointed crowns, the raising of trees with deep and heavy crowns can produce *no* lasting *improvement in growth-rate.* For one thing, one would have to sacrifice too many vigorous increment-producing dominant trees. Besides, the surfaces of the part of the crowns exposed to sunlight are reduced in stands receiving such treatment and the crown measurements of the trees left standing are modified with adverse effects on the yield in relation to growing space. The reasons have already been discussed in detail in Section C, II, p. 125.

On the other hand the surprising *adaptability of growth* which we find in *Common beech,* even after heavy crown thinning, is due, among other factors, to the *shape of the crown.* With full contact, the mean length of the arched, hemispheric or semi-ellipsoid shape of the part of the crown exposed to sunlight amounts to only one-third of the total length of the crown. After a crown isolation felling, the proportion of crown surface which is exposed to sunlight may be relatively quickly enlarged by a readjustment of the leaves on the crown periphery from shade to light habit, so that the original surface area of the parts of the crowns exposed to sunlight for the whole stand is soon restored. In Norway spruce, on the other hand, after crown isolation, this surface area, which in closed stands already amounts to two-thirds of the total crown length, must be extended mainly *by growth in an upward direction*, which requires more time. Thus, the advantage of a pointed crown to the physiology of assimilation, a feature which is peculiar to Norway spruce as well as other coniferous trees regarding the optimum utilization of growing space, can only be fully utilized in well-closed stands with large numbers of stems.

Changes in the total volume and value production as a result of a medium early start of low thinning

In Section D, subsection III, we learned from the example of the experimental series Denklingen 5 about the typical changes in value yield consequent on different grades of low thinning. In this connection it was astonishing how *minimal* was the *value increase achieved per average cubic metre of out-turn by heavier thinning*. A detailed classification of thinnings to date in the experimental series Sachsenried 2 and Ottobeuren 8 gives further proof of this. The gross values of the produced average festmetre behave as follows:

	Final age	A	:	B	:	C-grade
Exp. series Denklingen 5	104	100	:	103	:	101
Exp. series Sachsenried 2	101	100	:	103	:	101
Exp. series Ottobeuren 8	98	100	:	—	:	104

The gross- and net-value yields of the respective thinning grades at younger rotation ages must be expected to show a wider differentiation, because timber assortments which command good prices and earn acceptable net incomes can be produced earlier and more rapidly by heavy thinnings. In order to examine these relationships, the crops of the experimental series Eglharting 72 and 73 have each been separated out into assortments for two different rotation ages.

In the preceding chapters we have examined how the different thinning methods can alter the *current increment* and correspondingly the mean annual increment over long observation periods. Local site differences might lead to erroneous impressions but even so, it would hardly be possible for age differences of 1 or 2 years. A comparison of value yields, however, must be based on the recorded total crop volumes and the tree sizes attained. Both of these may be considerably affected by an advantage of age and development alone, especially in young stands. This should be borne in mind when considering the figures of the experimental series Eglharting 72 and 73. At the beginning of the experiment, the B-plot of the series 72 had an advantage in growth, equal to 1 or 2 year's lead in age, possibly as the outcome of young advance-growth which had become established in gaps. Incidentally, when comparing *current* increments, a possible lead in age of the B-plot must, if at all, be reckoned a *disadvantage*. If, in spite of this, plot 72/B proves to be superior in current increment and the same superiority is displayed by plot 73/B, whilst any local site advantage enjoyed by these plots can be excluded, we are then justified in ascribing the superior productivities of the B-plots on this site to thinning treatment. In this case it consisted of moderate low thinning giving a natural degree of stocking of app. 0·9 (if we take into consideration the unplanned removals in the A-plots) along with a thinning out-turn at the age of 90 years ($h_m \cong 30$ m) of barely 35 per cent.

The proportions of timber sizes in the produce shown in Table 102 are subject to typical changes. The B-plots are doing best of all, whilst at higher rotation ages, the A-plots draw remarkably close. The fact that the C-plots have done badly is due mainly to too heavy thinnings and the considerable reduction in the mean length of harvested stems[1] in consequence.

The total value yields (gross and net) emphasize the superiority of the B-plots in volume production, with higher net yields of up to 27 per cent. The C-plots, on the other hand, are demonstrably inferior; only in series 72 at age 69 has the C-area shown a slight superiority in net value production over the A-plot.

A noticeable temporary advantage of heavier thinning is to be found in the series 72, at age 69, in this case for the average net value (free of harvesting costs) of one cubic metre of produce. The series 72 is younger than series 73, not only in its actual age, but also, owing to close initial spacing, in physiological age. It seems that we have to consider even younger ages than this in order to find a noticeable lead in value production by stands under heavier thinning. This we shall do presently, in the discussion upon "rapid growth experiments".

If our hand is not forced by economic circumstances (financial emergencies, establishment of sustained management, small-scale management without sustained economy) or requirements in stand hygiene and security (for example, danger from snow breakage), there is no apparent reason in sustained forestry management for heavy thinning to be carried out in pure spruce stands. With the common rotation periods, the highest average net value efficiency is achievable, even on sites with less than adequate moisture supplies by moderate thinning, i.e. with natural degrees of stocking of approx. 0·9 and thinning yield percentages of about 35.

Changes in the volume and value efficiency with early low thinning: "Rapid growth management"

Significant and rapid increases of the average tree dimensions may be produced in Norway spruce stands by way of an *early* start of vigorous thinning. Practised with success by Bohdannecky at Worlik as far back as the eighties of last century and accorded theoretical support and encouragement by Schiffel (1904, 1906), this type of early heavy thinning became known as "rapid growth treatment". Gehrhardt (1925, 1928, 1932) also adopted the same term for a thinning method which he thought applicable to all tree species: it consisted in an early start to thinning (at tree heights of 4–6 m) with moderate interventions repeated at short intervals, but adding up to a heavy total effect. This aimed at obtaining trees of larger dimensions and enhanced value, but also greater volume producers. At the age of 40–50 years, Bohdannecky after a successful struggle against the dreaded "Kronenschwund" in the thicket and in the young pole-wood, considerably reduced the degree of thinning which had been heavy until then; Gehrhardt, on the other hand, demanded the consistent continuation of heavy thinning. In his C-table for Norway spruce 1st quality, Gehrhardt expected to get an additional volume out-turn of 18 per cent

---

[1] The applicable calculations and tables cannot be published owing to high printing costs. The reductions reach slightly smaller absolute quantities than in the exp. series Denklingen (cf. p. 237, Table 71), extending, however, over a wider diameter range.

TABLE 102

EXPERIMENTAL NORWAY SPRUCE SERIES EGLHARTING 72 AND 73

Distribution of the total production by timber assortments and value of the total production at different final ages

(price basis = 200 per cent the index number)

Definition	Experimental series 72 (close spacing)						Experimental series 73 (wide spacing)					
	up to 69 years			up to 85 years			up to 75 years			up to 91 years		
	A	B	C	A	B	C	A	B	C	A	B	C
1. Timber assortments in per cent of the tot. production of fire-wood, pulp-wood, pit-props and stem-wood	8	6	8	7	5	7	4	5	5	4	4	5
Stem-wood cl. 1	27	20	28	20	16	21	14	15	22	12	13	18
cl. 2	30	23	18	15	11	10	17	13	14	13	9	10
cl. 3	12	20	17	12	13	14	17	16	20	10	6	12
cl. 4	4	11	9	22	23	22	23	26	18	26	30	18
cl. 5	—	1	1	3	12	6	5	5	1	13	17	15
cl. 6	—	—	—	1	—	—	—	—	—	1	1	1
Sections Bark and harvesting losses	19	19	19	20	20	20	20	20	20	20	20	20
2. Total production volume m³	755	838	716	993	1074	897	850	913	800	1014	1122	954
%	100	111	95	100	108	90	100	107	94	100	110	94
3. Ditto in gr. value DM	35,410	42,400	34,510	51,140	59,390	47,090	46,150	49,390	41,040	57,900	65,190	52,950
%	100	120	97	100	116	92	100	107	90	100	112	91
4. Ditto in value without harvesting costs DM	24,340	31,000	24,770	38,190	46,510	36,010	36,000	38,320	31,260	46,400	52,520	42,040
%	100	127	102	100	122	94	100	106	87	100	113	91
5. Value per fm of the total production (a) gross DM	46·9	50·6	48·2	51·5	55·3	52·5	54·3	54·1	51·3	57·1	58·1	55·5
%	100	108	103	100	107	102	100	100	94	100	102	97
(b) net (without harvesting costs) DM	32·2	37·0	34·6	38·5	43·3	40·1	42·4	42·0	39·1	45·8	46·8	44·1
%	100	115	107	100	112	104	100	99	92	100	102	96

at rotation age of 100 years. This value is essentially based on an inadmissible generalization of the so-called "Eichhorn law". According to information based on more recent thinning experiments, an additional yield of this percentage magnitude is possible only for a limited period of 10–20 years. It is due to the not very lasting effect of the induced growth acceleration.

Today, effects of "rapid growth management" may be reliably judged on the basis of information of experimental series under long-term observation.

Some of the experimental "Schiffel" or "rapid-growth" series of the former Prussian Research Institute, which were laid out by Schwappach and Wiedemann, are useless for production comparisons owing to fairly large differences between the sites: thus, for example, the experimental series Tzulkinnen, Dietzhausen 90, Güntersberge 120[1] and Padrojen. The fact that the volumes and important stand characteristics on the first occasions of thinning have in some cases not been assessed is disturbing. The volume data are restricted to wood over 7 cm in diameter instead of stem-wood, thereby obscuring the volume increments of the decisive growth periods following on the first thinning interventions. This is a thorough handicap to the rapid growth plots, whose initial yields are thus largely "thrown down the sink". The typical effect of the acceleration of growth which is to be expected after the first thinning, therefore, in some cases, does not become clearly noticeable, because the experiments have been started too late (at mean heights of 10 m and over) or because the initial number of stems was too small.

Typical reactions may be found in the experimental series Dietzhausen 78/79, about which Dittmar (1959) recently supplied information.

Position: Thüringer Wald, 480 m above sea level, W. slope. Annual rainfall app. 800 mm. Slightly loamy sand; podsol to podsolized brown earth; deeply rooted. The rapid growth plot lies on the middle part of the slope, the comparative plot on the upper slope. Site differences in favour of the rapid growth plot are, none the less small. The initial stand with a large number of stems (at the age of 21 years, about 12,000 stems, 4–5 m high) originates from patch sowing. Height quality class II/III.

After carefully checking, and in some cases correcting, the experimental results Dittmar has shown that the rapid growth plot, which up to the age of 40 years was greatly superior in volume attainments, was overtaken by the dense comparative plot, approximately from that age onwards. In order to show quite clearly the peculiar changes in the growth pattern, Dittmar converted into stem-wood the data for timber over 7 cm in diameter, by means of the form factors of mean stems, and plotted the resulting total stemwood growth figures over the total basal area growth. This produced the following total stemwood volumes for the two plots, the initial volumes having been equalized:

Age	Comparative plot (fm)	Rapid growth plot (fm)	(%)
21	52	52	100
27	87	103	118
39	221	254	115
48	364	398	109
56	469	498	106

[1] Contrary to earlier statements of Ganssen, a more recent examination of the sites by Schilling, reported by Erteld (1959), has revealed a considerable local site improvement in the rapid growth plot at Güntersberge.

In a very similar manner to the example of Ottobeuren (p. 235) we see the acceleration effect fading and the lightly thinned plot catching up. The following percentage ratios appear for the current stemwood increments:

Periods	Increment ratios in per cent (comparative pl. = 100)
21–27	146%
27–39	112%
39–48	101%
48–56	95 (!)%

This means that, during the last increment period, the lightly thinned comparative plot is already superior. Dittmar concludes rightly, that the strength of thinning in the rapid growth plot should have been reduced from about the age of 40 years, if the increased growth already achieved was not to be wasted. The average basal area of the rapid growth plot during the increment period 39–48 amounted to 76 per cent of that of the comparative plot and to 66 per cent of this during the increment period 48–56. The mean periodic basal area of the two plots during the total observation period amounted

to   24·95   :   31·64 m²

= 79 per cent : 100 per cent

(the comparative plot perished in 1946 as a result of an attack by bark beetles). Bearing in mind that thinning in the comparative plot also exceeded the A-grade, we arrive at a *mean* natural degree of stocking for the rapid growth plot of app. 0·72.

The considerable increase in dimensions with rapid growth management becomes apparent in an impressive way from Dittmar's data, especially from the total production of trees with a b.h.d. over 7 cm (see Table 103).

TABLE 103

EXPERIMENTAL SERIES DIETZHAUSEN 78/79

TOTAL PRODUCTION OF TREES OVER 7 CM IN DIAMETER UP TO THE AGE OF 46 YEARS, THE SUMMATION BEGINNING WITH THE LARGEST DIAMETERS. AFTER DATA OF DITTMAR (1959).

TOTAL OF STEM NUMBERS PER HECTARE

Diameter class	Light thinning	Rapid growth
31–35	—	2
26–30	6	44
21–25	168	269
16–35	794	884
11–35	2234	1949
7–35	4276	4012

The rapid growth plot supplied forty-six trees/ha with a b.h.d. over 25 cm, whilst in the comparative plot there were only six.

Similar reactions are found in the *rapid growth experiments* which were laid out *by Gehrhardt himself*. On the experiments in Kattenbühl forest, inadequate funds prevented him from providing suitable plots for comparison with the rapid-growth plots. Even later, the provision of such a plot was possible only in one case, because meanwhile the stands in the immediate surroundings had also been heavily thinned, in fact some of them more heavily than the rapid growth plots. The results of the experimental series Kattenbühl 64/68 unfortunately are severely disturbed by snow breakage and windblow. In contrast to this, the Norway spruce rapid growth experiment Adelebsen in the Freiherrlich von Adelebsenscher Forest at Bramburg supplies very clear results. A description of the experiment follows:

Site: Solling; 320 m above sea level, level to gently sloping towards E; mean bunter-sandstone with a shallow top layer of loessic loam. Annual rainfall app. 850 mm. The stand was established in 1917 with various kinds of 3-year-old spruce. The initial position and site conditions are equal for both the rapid growth plot and the comparative plot.

The rapid growth plot was strongly thinned for the first time in 1932, when the trees were 18 years old (incl. age at the time of planting) and had a mean height of only 5·0 m. The comparative plot which was laid out 4 years later (age 22), in a stand which had previously not been touched, underwent moderate thinning for the first time at the age of 30 years and thereafter repeated occasions of heavy thinning. As a result of war and post-war influences the control in this plot was inadequate.

With gratitude we remember here the woodland owner Georg Freiherr von Adelebsen (†1957), who proved his understanding by promoting the experiment, and his officers, Revierförster Malesinski and Revierförster Schütz, who took much trouble with the laying out and supervision.

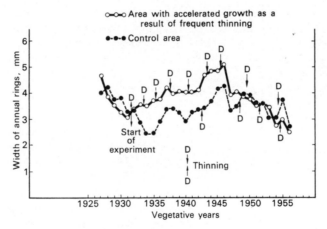

FIG. 124. Experiment at Adelebsen for producing accelerated growth in spruce by frequent thinning at short intervals. Mean width of annual rings, from borings of twenty-two dominant trees from each area.

Figure 124 shows the mean annual ring width of twenty-two dominant trees on each of the two plots, based on an analysis of increment cores for the years 1927–56. A considerable increase of the diameter increment of the trees on the rapid growth plot, immediately after the start of the experiment, is to be noticed; for 12 years the annual ring width there was nearly 1 mm larger than in the trees on the comparative plot. After this period the growth-rate slackened; the trees of the comparative plot, which was thinned for the first time in 1942/3, started to catch up and finally, after three interventions by heavy thinning or enforced removals on account of snow breakage or windblow they became even superior.

Owing to the unreliability of the volume increment values for the comparative plot we shall demonstrate the growth-acceleration effect by the mean dimensions of the 100 trees with the largest diameters per hectare:

Age	Exp. plot	Mean *diameter*		Mean *height*		Mean stem *volume*	
		(cm)	(%)	(m)	(%)	(fm)	(%)
22	Rapid growth	11·3	115	9·7	109	0·052	144
	Comp. pl.	9·8	100	8·9	100	0·036	100
43	Rapid growth	25·7	107	22·6	106	0·593	119
	Comp. pl.	24·1	100	21·4	100	0·497	100

The average annual stem-wood increment of the rapid growth plot during the increment period from 22–43 years amounted to 19 fm. At the age of 22 years, the total stem-wood production on the rapid-growth plot was already 31 per cent higher than on the comparative plot. The main crop data for the plots in 1956 (autumn) at the age of 43 years are as follows:

	Stem number	Basal area	d_m	Mean height after Lorey	Volume (stem-wood)
		(m²)	(cm)	(m)	(m³)
Rapid growth	1036	30·95	19·5	20·5*	328
Comp. pl.	1408	29·84	16·4	19·0*	297

* The corresponding height quality classes according to the Y.T. of Wiedemann are:

Exp. plot	Heavy thinning	Moderate thinning
Rapid-growth plot	0·6	0·4
Comparative plot	I.0	0·8

The final quality classes, to be expected at the age of 80 years, are likely to be I.5 at most, but judging by the site and the adjacent stands, probably only II.0.

Even more pronounced is the superiority of the rapid-growth plot in regard to the assortment out-turn of the remaining stand in 1956, which was classified on the basis of the Mitscherlich's table, timber prices = 200 per cent of M.I.; Heilbronn classification of stemwood:

Assortments	Rapid-growth plot fm felled timber	Comparative plot fm felled timber
Firewood	10	9
Pulpwood, pit-props		
Stemwood class 1	56	96
Stemwood class 2	173	124
Stemwood class 3	24	11
Total	263	240
Gross value	DM 15,960 = 114%	13,990 = 100%
Value less harvesting expenses	DM 13,750 = *119%*	11,560 = *100%*

Krenn (1942) reported the results of another experiment, laid out by Gehrhardt himself in 1931 in the municipal forest of Freiburg/Breisgau. Therein he explained the "advantages of early thinning in Norway spruce stands" in conformity with Wiedemann's positive findings (1937). The outset figures for the rapid-growth plot 7^{V} [1] at age 23 years were $N = 5034$, $G = 32\cdot7$ m² and $h_m = 9\cdot3$ m. The superiority of this plot over the unthinned comparative plot 7^{VI} [1] 9 years later at age 32 years amounted to $3\cdot4$ m in mean height of standing crop and to 60 m³ ($= 20$ per cent) of total timber volume. And the superiority in gross value out-turn, according to a classification carried out at the author's seminar, amounts to no less than 24 per cent.

According to Zimmerle (1951), parallel results were obtained from a rapid-growth experiment which was laid out by the author in 1934 in Biberach forest, Württemberg, according to instructions by Gehrhardt; this experiment was later taken over by the Forest Research Institute of Württemberg. The rapid-growth plot (plot 268), character- ized by initial values at the age of 18 years of $N = 5308$, $G = 27\cdot7$ m², $h_m = 8\cdot8$ m, was originally intended for comparison with a plot which had undergone normal thinning (plot 287). This was a technical mistake; an "A" plot would have served the purpose better. The mistake became apparent when, after only 7 years, the "normal plot", which was older by 1 year, underwent *heavier* thinning ($11\cdot67$ m² $G = 60\cdot4$ m³ wood > 7 cm dia.) than the rapid-growth plot ($10\cdot7$ m² $G = 55\cdot4$ m³ wood > 7 cm dia.). Despite this and the fact that it was younger, the rapid-growth plot at the age of 32 years had a lead in mean height (h_m) of $1\cdot1$ m and in mean height of the dominant trees of 1 m. According to recent results very kindly put at the author's disposal in an excursion guide by Land- forstmeister Hausser, the height of the 100 trees with the largest diameter per hectare in 1954 (aged 38 and 39 respectively) amounted to $21\cdot7$ m as compared to $20\cdot8$ m—a superiority of $0\cdot9$ m. Bearing in mind the age, therefore, even after 20 years the dominant and predominant trees have a genuine lead in height increment of about 1 m. At the same time, the total crop volume of wood over 7 cm in diameter amounts to 540 m³, compared to 560 m³ of the normal plot, which means that after due allowance is made for the age difference, the total volume performances are equal. The mean natural degree of stocking of the two plots so far may be estimated as $0\cdot70$ as compared to $0\cdot80$ (normal plot).

The continually recurring and striking lead in height attainments of the early thinned rapid growth plots show clearly that this is due to a genuine acceleration of growth, i.e. an alteration in the natural smooth growth-trend rather than to increased production arising from a more favourable choice of site. The most important conditions for imple- menting an acceleration of growth are an early start to thinning (at a stand height of 5–10 m) and large initial stem numbers. If the desired result is an increase in volume in- crement, the thinning must not be too heavy. The liberating effect on future growth of individual trees by the removal of competitors and isolating crowns can improve the stand performance per unit of ground area only if this does not involve an excessive increase in growing space for the individual trees, i.e. if too heavy demands are not made upon their growing capacities. If and whilst the stem numbers are large and the mean growing space available for each tree is accordingly small, the conditions are favourable. In stands which have been established with wide spacing, and where growth is more rapid anyway, the extra growth-rates can only be moderate and temporary and a decrease

[1] Prof. Dr. Mitscherlich, Freiburg, verbally denied the ecological comparability of the two plots. The yields shown by Krenn, however, are within the probable limits; possible ecological advantages enjoyed by the rapid-growth plot should not cause any very decisive increase; undoubtedly, they are mainly due to early thinning.

of the area-related volume increment with early, heavy thinning is to be anticipated. Therefore, all foresters who are in favour of rapid-growth management agree in their demand for large initial stem numbers (for example, Gehrhardt demands 1·3 m to a maximum of 1·5 m square spacing for Norway spruce).

The capacity of young Norway spruce stands to react readily is attributable to power of the crowns to extend upwards rapidly by big annual height increases. This was pointed out by Schiffel (1904). The fact that Gehrhardt, who tried to put rapid-growth management on a scientific basis, recognized the physiological connection is proved, amongst other things, by his expression "potentiality for accelerated growth" ("Wuchsbeschleuni- gungsmöglichkeit") which he used in his fundamental work *Über Schnellwuchsbetrieb* in 1932.

Advantages and disadvantages of rapid-growth management

By rapid-growth treatment of Norway spruce stands, timber sizes able to command good prices, especially of stem-wood belonging to the Heilbronn classes 2 and 3, may be produced within a considerably shorter time than is possible if thinning is postponed to a later stage. At the same time, stands which have been so treated, show themselves proof against snow breakage, which, after all, is no more than can be expected with a uniform development of crowns. Stands raised in this manner, moreover, develop a special resistance to the effects of wind, as proved by root investigations of Wagenknecht (1960); these proved that spruce trees possessing good crowns have specially deep root systems and effective development of supporting roots. On the other hand, and contrary to Gehrhardt's expectations, rapid-growth stands are probably more susceptible to attacks by red rot *(Polyporus annosus)* than lightly thinned stands, as proved by a study of Henriksen and Jørgensen (1953) and according to Carbonnier (1957) has also become apparent in the Swedish experiment at Dalby (see p. 227).

A disadvantage is the lowering of the timber quality as a result of considerably wider annual rings. As apparent from Fig. 124, the average width of the annual rings of the dominant trees in the experiment at Adelebsen is 3·5–5 mm; top values of 7–8 mm have been measured in individual trees. Mayer-Wegelin (1950) proved with the help of his "Härtetaster" (a device for testing hardness) that fast-grown sprucewood is soft and weak in texture and wide rings of alternate spring and summerwood cause contrasts in hard- ness with loss of uniformity in the timber. Von Pechmann (1958) declared: "Very rapidly grown spruce timber has no great compressive strength as building timber; it never ful- fils the demands made on quality class I building timber. Also, when converted for chem- ical purposes such a product yields very small quantities of cellulose and affords little satisfaction for two reasons: the timber with its wide rings and therefore low green weight not only contains little lignin substance but also comparatively little cellulose, because the cellulose-containing summerwood walls are only weakly represented."

With such rapid growth in the early years the branches on the lower part of the stem become coarser and later, when self-pruning is delayed, a less valuable black branch- zone develops, as shown by Pechmann and Schaile (1955).[1] Although these branches can

---

[1] In this work, the high quality of 122-year-old Norway spruce trees is determined by analysis, which proves it to be due to the fine branches and the low proportion of black branches owing to a long time of crown covering during the early years. In contrast to this, the analysis proves the inferior quality of 37-year-old Norway spruce (pole-wood), rapidly grown with coarse branches and wide spacing on an

TABLE 104

COMPARISON OF THE VOLUME AND DRY-SUBSTANCE PRODUCTION IN SOME EXPERIMENTAL NORWAY SPRUCE
THINNING SERIES OF THE FORMER PRUSSIAN RESEARCH INSTITUTE

AFTER FIGURES BY HILDEBRANDT (1954)

| Exp. plot | Incr. Period | Mean per. basal area | Per. mean ann. incr. in | | | | Mean specific gravity of the incr. (kg/fm) |
| | | | timber > 7 cm dia. | | wood dry weight | | |
			(abs. fm)	(%)	(abs. t)	(%)	
Benneckenstein							
Mod. thinning	46–73	*31·0*	9·15	100	3·87	100	423
"Rapid growth"	44–71	*21·3*	7·41	81	2·93	76	395
Güntersberge							
Mod. thinning	32–64	*46·5*	16·60	100	6·48	100	390
"Rapid growth"	32–64	*35·5*	17·24	104	5·88	91	341

be removed by timely artificial pruning as recommended and practised by Gehrhardt, labour shortages and rising wages today render it increasingly difficult in practice to carry out such an operation repeatedly on a large number of trees.

Hildebrandt (1954), who examined the specific gravity in the experimental rapid growth series Benneckenstein and Güntersberge of the former Prussian Research Institute, found the mean specific gravity of Norway spruce timber on the rapid growth plots significantly much lower than that of the experimental plots for moderate thinning. Table 104 gives a comparison of the volume and dry timber weight increments, after verification by Hildebrandt. This proves that notwithstanding the superior volume production by rapid growth treatment (which admittedly in the case of the Güntersberge research series is due to an ecological advantage of the rapid growth plot), the yield in dry substance is nonetheless considerably inferior. From Hägglund's studies upon the cellulose content of woods of different specific gravities, Hildebrandt rightly inferred that *spruce timber* from rapid-growth stands furnishes smaller yields of cellulose than that from moderately thinned stands.

The question whether or not to practise rapid-growth treatment in any individual instance will have to depend on the economic situation of the forest in question, the general conditions of the timber market in the country concerned and upon local requirements in forest conservation techniques. In Germany we must expect that future timber prices, will be linked more closely with quality than during times of shortage and economic boom.

Small woodlands which are unsuitable for sustained management (for instance, small parcels in farm holdings) and, by way of contrast, also larger, understocked tracts to be brought under control (Köstler, 1943) may benefit remarkably from rapid-growth treatment. In countries with a shortage of timber, such as Great Britain, Denmark and the Netherlands, there must be a strong disposition to practise intensive thinnings in young

---

afforested clear felling area. The old spruce trees required 63 years but the pole-wood only 37 years to grow to a height of 21 m. Clearly, such potentials for rearing quality timber must be utilized, wherever the structure of the stands, the site and the economic position make this possible.

stands on all forest properties including the large state-owned forests. When we consider the admirable work of forest establishment carried out by the Forestry Commission in Great Britain, we must admit that the type of early and very heavy thinning practised there in newly afforested coniferous stands may be absolutely right, even if it incurs considerable losses in volume increment, i.e. raw-material production, because the early net income helps to finance and thereby advance the expensive work of afforestation.

In Germany, in situations where there is danger from snow breakage, a suitable method of treatment appears to be the one defined by Wiedemann as "staged thinning", i.e. early and initially heavy thinning, modified later to moderate thinning.

(b) Summarizing Conclusions for Suitable Thinning Techniques in Norway Spruce Stands

1. Owing to its limited ability to produce open-stand increment and to renew stunted crowns, the natural critical degree of stocking in Norway spruce is as high as 0·75 to 0·80.

Early thinning, at a stand height of 5 up to a maximum of 10 m, can induce an acceleration of growth, which, in stands with large stem numbers (initial stem number if possible not below 5000/ha) causes a considerable superiority in volume increment (15 per cent and more) in comparison to unthinned stands. Lightly thinned stands, however, soon catch up with this lead and later surpass the heavily thinned stands in total crop volume. An increase in volume production by way of "rapid growth treatment" according to Gehrhardt, therefore, is achievable only with short rotations, or at all events, by an early change-over to moderate thinning (staged thinning according to Wiedemann).

With a scanty supply of water, the optimum curves (relative volume increment/relative periodic basal area) are acutely rounded up to an old age, so that by adhering to an optimum degree of stocking (0·95–0·90), it is possible on sites of this kind to achieve extra yields of from 5 to 10 per cent, even with a rotation of 80–100 years. The optimum curves for sites with a good supply of water, on the other hand, are so flat that the possible additional yields amount to only a few per cent. Besides, the degree of stocking for optimum increment soon approaches the value 1·0. The highest total volume yields on such sites is achieved by stands at fairly advanced ages (100 years and more) which have gone generally without active thinning and where no attempt has been made to forestall mortality from natural causes.

2. (a) The diameter increase resulting from heavy thinning is small if the thinning has started at a late stage. The increased production of large-diameter stems by heavy thinning is counter-balanced by a lower production of trees in the medium diameters. Heavy thinning has the further effect of considerably reducing the average length of harvested stems.

Early and heavy thinnings, especially under "rapid-growth treatment", produce strikingly large-diameter increases so that stem dimensions fetching good prices (Heilbronn classes 2 and 3) may be reached within an amazingly short time. But then, wide annual rings are apt to lower timber quality and cellulose content.

(b) With the present small price differentials for fairly large-diameter sprucewood, the average gross value per cubic metre of standing timber rises little beyond 45 cm b.h.d. An appreciable increase in value beyond this diameter is achievable only if clean-boled high-grade timber of large dimensions can command special prices. But if the total yields from the different thinning grades are converted into money by allotting appropriate prices for assortments of given dimensions while ignoring possible additions for quality improvement, the average value per cubic metre at final age of 100 years will not vary by more than 1 to 4 per cent! Owing to the smaller lengths of converted stems associated with heavy thinning, the value increase for the C-grade (nat. degree of stocking 0·75–0·80) of 1 to 2 per cent is actually smaller than for the B-grade (natural deg. of stocking 0·90–0·95) with 3–4 per cent. Accordingly an approach to the critical degree of stocking would, on account of the ensuing decrease in total crop volume by 5 per cent, also lead to a slight decrease in total gross value yield. Even at a younger final age of 70–80 years, the optimum values, both gross and free of harvesting expenses, are found to lie *with moderate thinning*. If, however, the income from thinnings is reckoned by compound interest at 3 per cent, heavy thinning gives superior total monetary returns. The superiority of early heavy thinning can be realized effectively only by using a short rotation (50–60 years) or by the compounding of incomes from thinnings.

Owing to the fact that rapid growth management causes a considerable decrease in timber quality, the question whether or not this method should be employed will have to depend on the economic circumstances of the individual forest, and on the over-all position in the timber market of the country concerned.

3. *Crown thinning in pure Norway spruce stands*, in contrast to low thinning always causes losses of volume increment which are the greater the more severe is the encroachment into the dominant tree classes. Contrary to the current widely held view, the "layering" of stands incurred thereby in this case reduces the area-related volume growth. The trees remaining in the under storey produce practically no increment and on most sites retard the breakdown of litter.

The most important effect of early and intensive thinning of pure Norway spruce stands in a manner compatible with their local ecological and climatic conditions is the improved health and resistance to hazards achievable by this type of stocking, which in many other respects is to be regarded with a critical eye.

3. Scots Pine

Brief characterization of the species Scots pine

Scots pine *(Pinus sylvestris)* clearly distinguishes itself as a light-demanding species by the early culmination of the current annual volume increment which is followed by a rapid drop of increment. According to Wiedemann's yield table for moderate thinning the culmination of current and mean annual volume increment in height quality class I is as follows:

	Age		fm
Current annual volume increment	30		12·0
Mean annual volume increment	75		8·1
Current annual volume increment falls off			
by age	100	to	6·4 fm
by age	140	to	4·2 fm

The *height increment* culminates much earlier than the volume increment and under the above conditions the height increment of unshaded trees culminates at the age of 15 to 20 years and by the age of 70 years it has fallen to an annual amount of 20 cm. With the given conditions for height quality class I, *the natural process of elimination and passage from storey to storey* which runs parallel to the height development accordingly *finishes one to two decades earlier than in Norway spruce.* During the stage of early growth which is decisive for the future timber quality, the trees, in as far as they have achieved a dominant or even predominant position, are inclined to develop coarse branches and widely projecting crowns, but by the time they begin to produce timber their capacity for projection is small. This limited capacity for crown development and lateral projection at medium and older ages is coupled with an inadequate ability to develop lateral roots. Scots pine is much slower in utilizing the available rooting space in the surface soil after competing neighbouring trees have been felled than, for example, Common beech or Norway spruce. Scots pine therefore has only a modest ability to respond to opening up by putting on increment for which accordingly we have to wait much longer than in Norway spruce, to say nothing of Common beech which so readily produces open stand increment.

Despite the xerophytic characteristics of Scots pine Wiedemann (1948) observed a particularly sharp falling off of growth during drought periods in the dry regions east of the river Elbe.

Trees grown at wide espacements during early years develop numerous strong branches, which render them incapable later of producing high-quality timber; a correction of this fault is possible only to a limited extent, by timely pruning. In localities where snow breakage is common the development of wide branches means certain death or at any rate malformation at a later stage. This points to the value of local races with fine branches and pointed crowns (upland form).

Scots pine is particularly susceptible to attacks by various pests. Among parasitic fungi must be mentioned: *Lophodermium pinastri* (causes pine needle cast), *Peridermium pini* (causes pine needle rust), *Trametes pini* (causes pine red heart rot and has a specially devastating effect in the pine regions east of the river Elbe), *Trametes radiciperda* (butt rot), *Sparassis crispa* (destructive of the valuable basal sections of the stem). Young crops in the open are threatened by the larvae of *Melolontha hippocastani* (chestnut chafer). An account of the numerous harmful, though not deadly, beetles is not required here. Among moths which can destroy forests or at least inflict serious damage the following must be mentioned: *Bupalus piniarius* (pine looper), *Panolis flammea* (pine beauty), *Dendrolimus pini* (pine moth), *Evetria buoliana* (pine shoot moth), the web-spinning pine sawflies *Acantholyda nemoralis* and *erythrocephala* as well as the pine sawfly *Diprion pini.*

Damage through disease and climate have occasioned many disturbances and losses of thinning experiments. Incidents of heavy snow breakage in the year 1886 have rendered Scots pine thinning experiments in Württemberg (Zimmerle, 1933) very nearly useless.

Shortcomings and disturbances of Scots pine thinning experiments

Under these conditions it is not surprising that at present there are only a few Scots pine thinning experiments containing A-, B- and C-grade plots which have been relatively unaffected by external factors and which have been treated according to experimental plans for a long period to enable safe conclusions to be drawn from them about the behaviour of the increment in Scots pine with increasing grades of low thinning.

Among the *fifteen experimental thinning series of the former Prussian Research Institute* of which Schwappach (1908) published preliminary results, only four are complete with A-, B- and C-grades. Their A-plots, however, have without exception undergone heavy thinning, i.e. 10 per cent and over of the growing crop have been removed. The question as to what extent these heavy encroachments were enforced by disease or climatic damage remains unanswered. Wiedemann's (1948) comprehensive monograph contains only a few isolated figures relating to the further results of these experimental series in which Toma (1940) carried out some valuable investigations (cf. p. 120). We must therefore welcome with gratitude the fact that after thorough research Erteld (1960) recently published the total long-term results of eight thinning series, among them three complete series, as well as two experimental open stand (Lichtung) series on East German diluvial sites.

Of the seven *experimental thinning series of the Hessian Forest Research Institute*, the results of which were summarized by Baader (1934) five are complete with A-, B- and C-grades, whilst the remaining two of them contain only B- and C-plots. To make up for that, two of the series each contain two B-grade and two C-grade plots respectively. On no less than ten of the total twenty-four occasions when the A-grade plots of the five complete series were thinned, 10 per cent or more and in extreme cases even 23 per cent of the total production of wood over 7 cm in diameter was removed. In addition to this, the fact that only the timber volume was measured has led to considerable distortions of the true increment for the observed ages. In such circumstances, these experiments can furnish no definite clarification of the underlying relationship that doubtless exists between the grade of thinning and volume increment in Scots pine.

Still worse in this respect are the conditions for the Scots pine experiments in Baden. Among the numerous experimental plots observed by Mitscherlich (1955/6) are two experimental thinning or open stand series respectively, with a B-grade plot as the most lightly thinned plot. A look at the relevant data shows us that these plots are not true B-grade plots in the sense of the experimental plan of 1902 but possibly C-plots with the present natural degree of stocking of 0·6 and less.

The absence of A-plots also reduces the value of four out of the total of five Bavarian experimental Scots pine series, about which Fabricius (1930) reported. In his opinion, the inclusion of A-grade plots is of little importance in the case of Scots pine, because the rapid death of the accessory or dominated crop would automatically make it very similar to a B-grade plot. This argument could be accepted, if the so-called B-grade plots were not actively thinned; this, however, is regular practice. In the only series containing A-, B- and C-grade plots (Zentbechhofen) there are differences in age of up to 4 years. The author has till now had no opportunity to make a critical assessment of this experimental series.

Mean basal area and volume increment in Scots pine, based on examples

The different growth reactions in the two Hessian Scots pine thinning series Alsfeld 15 and Eudorf 17 were explained by Assmann (1953) as being due to local site conditions, in particular the better supply of water in Eudorf 17. A recent investigation proved that *the small differences between the intensity of thinning in the A- and B-grade plots of series 15* are due to the fact that the A-grade plot had been thinned several times removing 12 per cent and thus partly obscuring the growth reactions in this series. As shown by Table 105, the periodic mean basal areas of the A- and B-grade plots in series 15 differ very slightly. Thus the proportion of total *basal area* production of the A-plot taken in thinnings amounts to 46 per cent compared to 49 per cent of the B-plot. On the site of series 15, which is inferior in height quality class and soil conditions, an optimum production seems obtainable at a natural degree of stocking of 0·8–0·9 during the observation period 39–82 years, whereas the production optimum for the much better site of Eudorf 17 can be expected to be near the maximum density of stocking. Taking into account the thinnings that have taken place in both of the A-grade plots, approximately 15 per cent must be added to the mean periodic basal areas in series 15 and approximately 5 per cent to series 17 in order to obtain the *probable values for the natural degree of stocking* given below:

	A-grade	B-grade	C-grade
Series 15	0·88	0·84	0·69
Series 17	0·95	0·84	0·66

Erteld's (1960) latest evaluations of the long-term experimental Scots pine series of the former Prussian Research Institute prove that the *natural optimum degree of stocking in Scots pine* for observation periods extending to older crop ages of 100 years or more *approaches very closely the value 1·0*, whilst the *natural critical degree of stocking increases to over 0·8*. The most important data concerning the complete series are reproduced in Table 106. They provide a clear illustration: even though the thinning of the A-plots on several occasions was heavier than planned, so that the relative values of the mean periodic basal area are higher than the true natural degrees of stocking, the optimum yields of these sites in the East German diluvium with a short supply of water (small amounts of rainfall, very warm summer temperatures) for a final age of 100 years and more are achievable by light thinning. *The natural optimum degree of stocking evidently lies near the value 1·0, whilst the natural critical degree of stocking must be expected to exceed 0·8, with an estimated value of approx. 0·85.*

TABLE 105

BASAL AREA AND INCREMENT IN TWO HESSIAN EXPERIMENTAL SCOTS PINE THINNING EXPERIMENTS, AFTER DATA OF BAADER (1934)

THE VOLUME INCREMENTS WERE CORRECTED BY BALANCING WITH THE BASAL AREA INCREMENTS

Exp. series Height qual. cl. Obs. period	Thinning grade	Average basal area during period		Mean ann. increment in			
				basal area		volume (timber)	
		(m^2)	(%)	(m^2)	(%)	(m^3)	(%)
Alsfeld 15	A	39·1	100	0·69	100	7·1	100
H.Q.Cl. = II.4	B	37·6	96	0·74	107	7·4	104
Obs. p.: 39–82	C	30·9	79	0·77	112	7·3	103
Eudorf 17	A	48·4	100	0·97	100	10·3	100
H.Q.Cl. = I.9	B	42·7	88	0·97	100	9·7	94
Obs. p.: 36–77	C	33·5	69	0·89	92	9·1	88

During the first 10 years of the experimental series at Falkenberg (which were established early at 21 and 26 years old respectively) the B- and C-grade plots showed a remarkable temporary superiority of basal area increment owing to the effect of an acceleration of growth. In Scots pine stands this effect is possible *only if the experiment has started early*; moreover, the critical degree of stocking is likely to become only slightly lower and this only for a short time.

The *Swedish Scots pine thinning series*, about which Näslund (1936) and Carbonnier (1959) have reported on the basis of very extensive material, confirm the above results in that the naturally thinned plots always display *the largest production in volume increment* for the total observation period to date, whilst the comparative plots with heavy and very heavy low thinning respectively show poorer increment production by up to 36 per cent.

TABLE 106

AVERAGE BASAL AREA AND INCREMENT IN THE EXPERIMENTAL SCOTS PINE THINNING SERIES OF THE FORMER PRUSSIAN RESEARCH INSTITUTE

AFTER ERTELD (1960)

Exp. series height qual. cl. obs. period	Thinning grade	Mean basal area during period		Mean annual increment in			
				basal area		volume (timber)	
		(m²)	(%)	(m²)	(%)	(m³)	(%)
Falkenberg 106/7	A	35·8	100	0·572	100	5·6	100
H.Q.Cl. = II.9	B	31·2	87	0·557	97	5·0	89
Obs. p.: 39–101	C	27·9	78	0·518	91	5·1	91
Falkenberg 142/3	A	31·5	100	0·472	100	5·1	100
H.Q.Cl. = II.8	B	29·8	95	0·463	98	4·9	96
Obs. p.: 36–106	C	27·6	88	0·447	95	4·8	94
Panten 131	A	43·4	100	0·552	100	7·6	100
H.Q.Cl. = I.8	B	38·4	89	0·529	96	7·0	92
Obs. p.: 49–104	C	33·8	78	0·543	98	6·9	91

The period used for calculating the basal area increment in Erteld's original table for the two series at Falkenberg was 10 years longer than that used to calculate the volume increment (according to the experimental files, presumably due to inadequate measurements of the volume increment). The values of mean basal area increment in the above table were recalculated using the same period as was used to calculate the volume increment.

The maximum periodic basal areas to be expected in Scots pine stands on sites with fairly high rainfall and adequate warmth are of a considerable size as proved by the *Swiss experimental open stand* (Lichtung) *series in the Letzholz near Chur*, in the canton of Graubünden (cf. Flury, 1932; Badoux, 1952; Assmann, 1953a), where the B-grade plot 17 B in the age period 61–83 years has a mean basal area of no less than 63 m². The absence of a complete series with an A-grade plot on sites in south Germany in this connection is particularly unfortunate.

To sum up, an increase of volume production of Scots pine by way of thinning is possible only in exceptional cases in very young stands as well as on sites with a scanty moisture supply provided the crop there is felled before the trees are very old. Once again the following statement of Wiedemann (1948) is confirmed: "On the whole, all interventions in excess of moderate thinning, if continued over a long period cause a reduction of the basal area increment per hectare, whereas surprisingly, the increment did not diminish when the stands were over-dense."

Often the effects of disease and climatic damage force us to apply a more severe degree of thinning than is required purely for technical reasons. The gradual opening of Scots pine stands which usually begins at tree-wood age causes such noticeable losses in increment that it becomes an urgent necessity to under-plant or add a shade- or half-shade-tolerant species. The additional volume and dry matter production achievable by such treatment will be the subject of a discussion in a later section.

Thinning and value production of Scots pine

The capacity of Scots pine for producing open-stand increment is so small that any possible increases in value due to *diameter increase* will be certain to be compensated for by simultaneous losses in volume increment. A *selective effect* can produce results *only if the treatment of the early growth and thicket stage starts extremely early*. Wiedemann (1948) did not find that the heavier grades of thinning produced a superior number of well-shaped dominant trees; on the contrary, he often found more well-shaped dominant trees in lightly thinned plots than in heavily thinned ones. In his opinion a number of well-shaped trees have been sacrificed in the breaking-up of groups by heavy thinning. He admitted that the existing *experiments were started too late*, because in a light-demanding species such as Scots pine with its rapid early growth all may have been decided by the age of 30. Since pine reacts so hesitatingly to crown isolation the *promotive effect* of this allows no hope for decisive results unless the volume losses in the opened top storey are counteracted by under-planting.

On the basis of data of the former Prussian Research Institute Wiedemann (1948) also constructed money tables for his new yield tables. In these he assumed a direct increase of the proportion of high grade timber with increasing intensity of thinning. The different high-grade timber proportions are estimated as follows:

Stemwood with moderate thinning   20 per cent
heavy   25 per cent
open stand (Lichtung)   30 per cent

For height quality class I at the age of 140 years he made the following calculations:

	Wood over 7 cm diam.		Financial value without c.i.	
	(fm)	(%)	(DM)	(%)
Moderate thinning	982	100	21,091	100
Heavy thinning	966	98	21,542	102
Open stand thinning	915	93	21,307	101

This disappointing result applies to thinning which started late and which was not very intense. The tiny extra production by heavy and open stand thinning is due solely to the assumed increase in high-grade timber yield.

Olberg (1950), in his work *Durchforstung der Kiefer*, described how and to what extent the financial value production of Scots pine stands may be increased. Supported by ample practical experience and his own experiments he developed a program of treatment which is intended to increase the practical value of the produced stemwood assortments by providing increased proportions of timber for masts and flooring. sawing blocks and veneer wood in place of pit-props and building timber. He calculated the potential increase of the total value production with the help of Wiedemann's yield tables height quality class II, for a rotation of 140 years. In this calculation he compared a potential high-grade timber yield (case (a)) to the average yield produced today (case (b)). In case (a) he assumed the largest possible yield of potential high-grade timber, i.e. complete suitability of the final yield and suitability of one-half of the early yields for high-grade timber. Case (b) assumes that only one-half of the final yield is suitable for high grade timber and none of the early yield. On this basis he calculated the following financial values in DM for *moderate thinning*, based on the (low) timber prices of 1950:

| | Case (a) | | Case (b) | |
	(DM)	(%)	(DM)	(%)
Early yield	5532	113	4898	100
Final yield	9198	124	7411	100
Total yield	14,730	*120*	12,309	100

According to Olberg, this 20 per cent production increase is founded on the following stipulations: first-class, dense, evenly closed stands, reared from natural regeneration, sowing or close planting; the timely exclusion of all advance-growth, if possible by weedings of the young crop, and definitely not later than during the first cleaning operation in dense pole stage crop; repeated cleaning at short intervals during critical phase of youth between the ages of 10 and 30 years; correction of inadequate self-pruning by timely pruning of dead or dry branches; under-planting of opened stands after the change-over to open stand thinning. As in the case of Common beech therefore the possibilities for gaining an increase in value lie, *not so much in increasing intensities of thinning but rather in a genuine intensification of stand treatment.*

Kunz (1953) deduced noteworthy conclusions for raising Scots pine for high grade timber production from his own investigations in dense young natural stands and a critical study of the literature to date.

Summary of conclusions for a suitable thinning technique in Scots pine stands

1. A definite light-demanding species with a low potential for poor crowns to re-develop and a limited ability to utilize vacant rooting space, Scots pine is capable of only a small production by *open stand increment;* therefore increment losses due to the removal of dominant trees can be compensated only to a limited extent. *The natural critical degree of stocking of 0·80–0·85 is a little higher than that of Norway spruce.*

Owing to the extremely early culmination of the current annual volume increment, an acceleration of growth may be expected only if thinning is started very early.

On sites with a limited supply of water, *the natural optimum degree of stocking approaches the value 1·0* by the age of 100 years. During the period when a sharp falling off of the increment occurs, commencing at late pole-wood ages, all interventions exceeding light or, at most, moderate low thinning lead to a reduction of the volume production.

2. Owing to the decline of the increment, which beginning at middle age is accentuated by the liability to disease induced by natural thinning, crops on suitable sites must be under-planted with shade- or half-shade-tolerant species or converted into two-storeyed types of stand.

3. All the thinning experiments to date, which without exception were started too late, have failed to establish any significant increase in value production resulting from heavier grades of thinning. This is to be expected, because

(a) it is possible to get a thickening of diameters during observed age-periods only by applying an open-stand type of thinning which would lead to a decrease in volume increment;

(b) a selective effect cannot now be presumed operative apart from the elimination of diseased trees, because the quality of the lower portion of the stem has already been decided during the youth phase;

(c) substantial improvement in growth can be effected only by completely isolating the crowns, which causes considerable losses in increment.

4. An increase of the financial yield can be achieved only by *intensifying* treatment during the decisive youth phase which to date has been neglected in most forestry practice. A further stipulation for future value production is close density of initial regeneration or the closest possible spacing in plantations. Under these conditions and assisted by pruning of the dead or dry branches the increase in value production as calculated by Olberg of approximately 20 per cent over ordinary treatment may be achievable.

5. Even from the point of view of the highest possible value production, a pure even-aged Scots pine stand as from middle age is an unsatisfactory type of stocking.

4. Oak

In yield research, the two oak species Sessile oak *(Quercus sessiliflora)* and Pedunculate oak *(Q. pedunculata)*, both native in Germany and her European neighbours, together with their numerous hybrid forms, have up to now been considered as one. As explained earlier in Section C (cf. p. 184) we must expect the two oak species to have a different growth behaviour. The growing conditions of the two species during the phases of youth and prime vigour (for example, wide spacing in coppice-with-standards, close spacing during the early years in high forests) must have such a decisive influence on the growth behaviour and the shape of individual trees, that they have to be taken into account in the construction of yield tables as well as in questions concerning ordinary and open stand thinning.

The following general characterization will be based on the features and dangers common to both species, whilst the *investigation of thinning effects will* — owing to the scarcity of the available data — be restricted to stocks of Sessile oak, sown or close-planted with a dense thicket stage.

Characterization of oak

In the light-demanding species oak both the current height and volume increments culminate fairly early, although later than in Scots pine. According to the yield table of Schwappach–Wiedemann (1920/46) the culminations with Q. Cl. I occur as follows:

	Age	fm
Current annual volume increment	45	10·2
Mean annual volume increment	100	7·0

The current annual volume increment drops

by the age of	100	to	6·8 fm
	150		5·8
	200		4·6

In contrast to Scots pine, the slow falling off of the current annual volume increment and its long persistence are characteristic features of oak, in keeping with the long physiological life-span of this species.

Conformably with the growth in height, which according to values given in the above table must reach its peak rate by the time the crop is 20–25 years of age, progress through the juvenile stages, so crucially important for silviculture, is rapid also.

The capacity for crown projection in the youth phase is equally as strong as in Scots pine, although persisting for a longer time. Oak is *pronouncedly a phototropic species*, and the effects of phototropism may be studied in middle-aged and mature Common beech stands containing individual Sessile oak trees which have not received special encouragement by freeing their crowns. In such stands we may notice almost grotesque bends in the oak stems because the trees have "screwed" themselves into every available gap in the crown canopy. These two characteristics throw light on the importance of the thicket stage for future stem development and accordingly value production. Here again is seen the necessity for ensuring uniform closure during the youth phase.

The capacity of oak for reacting to a complete freeing of the crowns for the production of open-stand increment lies between that of Scots pine and Common beech.

Trees which have endured close spacing for too long during the pole-stage can only slowly recover vigour in their crown development, by early maturity; and a sudden opening up leads to a marked development of *epicormic shoots*.

The quality of the timber depends on the site (hardness and colour of the timber) and on the *width of the annual rings*. If the width of the rings exceeds 1·8 or 2·0 mm it will doubtfully qualify as veneer wood. Pruning is possible to a limited extent and does not carry the same risks as in the case of beech where fungal attack may ensue.

There is relatively little danger from pathological causes. The familiar green oak roller moth *(Tortrix viridana)* causes heavy increment losses, although it does not become lethal until the attacked stands are physiologically weakened by other causes, such as the lowering of the ground-water level. In such an event oak mildew *(Microsphaera quercina)* could also have a lethal effect. Oak is known for its resistance to wind-throw and there is little risk of damage by other climatic factors.

Mean periodic basal area and volume increment of Sessile oak

The *experimental series Freienwalde 172* in the East German diluvium is the only existing thinning series in Sessile oak stands that is complete and has been measured for a long period. We are indebted to Erteld (1956) for our knowledge about the results of long-term observations upon this series. Erteld's figures, part of which had been published and others communicated separately, were used by Assmann (1956) after smoothing, in order to demonstrate a regular connection between the degree of thinning and the increment in Sessile oak stands. Information about this experimental series is given below.

Site. East German diluvium, 70 m above sea level, undulating ground and end moraine; fine loamy sand over loam which changes to marl, rich in carbonates from 40 cm; mull; brown earth, cool and moist in spring, becoming dry in summer; roots descend to 80 cm: "Rich common beech–Sessile oak forest". *Climate:* annual precipitation $=560$ mm, May/August $=240$ mm; annual temperature $=8.3°C$, May/August approximately 16°C.

Layout plan. In 1878 three experimental plots of 0·25 ha were laid out in the then 67-year-old Sessile oak stand. All plots were *underplanted with 2-year-old beech*. In addition to this there was an underwood and an intermediate storey of hornbeam of approximately the same age as the oak.

Treatment. Low thinning to A-, B- and C-grades according to the experimental plans of 1873 and of 1902. Thinning treatment was very uniform but, as the earlier thinnings were not measured, a comparison of increment is possible only from 1897 when the trees were 86 years old.

Height quality class: at the age of 140 years $=$I.0.

In Table 107 the mean basal areas and the increments derived from the above-mentioned contribution by Assmann (1956) are here abridged and concentrated into three long observation periods. The very heavy, open-stand type of thinning conducted in the C-grade resulted in a natural stocking density of barely 0·50 (!) and led to *considerable increment losses* which for the whole observation period amounted to *25 per cent as compared with the A-grade* and 26 per cent as compared with the B-grade. During the first

TABLE 107

MEAN PERIODIC BASAL AREA AND INCREMENT OF THE EXPERIMENTAL SESSILE OAK SERIES FREIENWALDE 172

Observation period	Thinning grade	Mean basal area		Mean annual increment in			
				basal area		volume (over 7 cm dia.)	
		(m²)		(m²)	(%)	(m³)	(%)
86–103	A	30·6	100	0·486	100	8·0	100
	B	26·1	85	0·526	108	8·4	105
	C	21·1	69	0·478	98	7·3	91
103–125	A	36·1	100	0·414	100	8·7	100
	B	30·1	83	0·458	111	9·6	110
	C	18·9	52	0·347	84	6·2	71
125–144	A	41·7	100	0·422	100	9·2	100
	B	31·9	76	0·402	95	8·2	89
	C	20·5	49	0·295	70	6·3	68
86–144	A	36·3	100	0·438	100	8·7	100
	B	29·5	81	0·459	105	8·8	102
	C	20·1	55	0·368	84	6·5	75

In addition to this, annual *increments in the under storey* (Common beech and hornbeam)

in the A-grade	0·25
in the B-grade	0·71
in the C-grade	1·11 m³

two observation periods, the "optimum" increment, achieving bursts of up to 10 per cent, was put on in the B-grade, with stocking density between 0·85 and 0·90, but in the last period (125–144 years) the optimum passed into the A-grade, with density approaching 1·0.

The natural critical degree of stocking during the first two periods *lay between 0·74 and 0·78 and* during the last period *it rose to approximately 0·83. The average for the 58-year observation period was app. 0·75*, which signifies a latitude in the growth of Sessile oak, comparable roughly with that of Norway spruce.

It is also worth remarking that the peak values of the current annual volume increment occur in the C-grade during the age period 86–103 years, in the B-grade during the age period 103–125 years and in the A-grade during the age period 125–144. Even the expectedly early culmination in the C-grade plot thus occurs 50 years later than that given in the yield table of Schwappach–Wiedemann. This is a yet further illustration of how very widely the growth pattern of closely established and maintained Sessile oak crops[1] deviates from that of the yield table.

A cutting which reduced the basal area in the C-grade plot to an extent considerably below the critical point has not only led to the above-mentioned *increment loss of a full quarter of the possible optimum* but *it is also seen to be neither necessary nor advisable for the purpose of securing high value yields.* According to the results of Erteld's investigations, the C-grade is *by no means superior in the production of large diameter trees and average quality of the stems* to the B-grade. The open-stand type of thinning in the C-grade amounts to an absolute waste of growing space. The degree of thinning in the B-grade (app. 0·8 nat. stocking) is quite sufficient to achieve the entire treatment effect possible. Besides, the sacrifice of valuable oak increment, which after all amounts to 2·3 fm per annum, is not in the least compensated for by the very small additional increment of 0·4 festmeter of the almost valueless beech under storey in the C-grade (value after deducting harvesting costs is negative). And the under storey of approximately 41 fm in the B-grade (compared with 65 fm in the C-grade) is quite adequate both for stem and ground protection. This experiment is thus instructive in several respects.

The increment data of the two other experimental series, Eberswalde 3 and Grumsin 55, where in each case a "heavy crown thinning" is compared with a "heavy low thinning", have so far furnished no definite conclusions about different increment production. It is generally agreed that *Sessile oak stands must in all cases be crown-thinned.* Regarding the intensity, one would not need to go below a natural stocking density of 0·8. The safest method to achieve regularly developed crowns of a moderate size, whilst at the same time avoiding the development of epicormic shoots, is by thinning to moderate intensity with a gradual isolation of the crowns. Incidentally, Erteld proved that, in the Eberswalde experimental series, a sharp encroachment in the year 1904 (crop age 41) in the plot under heavy low thinning was responsible for the very marked development of epicormic shoots in this plot.

Confirmatory results have emerged from the *younger experimental Sessile oak series in Waldleiningen forest.* This was established in 1934 by Fabricius for the purpose of clarifying assumptions concerning the influence of different types of thinning on the

---

[1] In the experimental Sessile oak plot 59, Lohr-West forest in the Spessart (heavy thinning with a naturally and artificially added under storey of Common beech), which has been observed from the age of 67 to 127 years (from the age of 120 years height quality class I.0) again the culmination of the current annual volume increment does not occur until the age period 101–113, in other words, not until after the age of 100!

development of epicormic shoots. From 1953 the series was continued by the Institute of the author as thinning series (two A-plots, two B-plots, two plots with a heavy crown thinning) with a simultaneous observation of the development of epicormic shoots. Preliminary results of this series were reported by R. Mayer (1958) who made specific investigations in these plots.

Situation. Pfälzer Wald, 420 m above sea level, gently rising to moderately steep NNW. slope with ridges and hollows. Upper bunter-sandstone (Trippstadt or Karlstal layers).

Climate. Average temperature = 7·5°C, May/August = 14·5°C, annual precipitation = 800 mm, May/August = 240 mm.

This stand of well-shaped trees, raised from sowing and having an average age of 48 years in 1934, has six plots each of 0·21 ha in adjacent positions and at the same elevation. By this arrangement, some of the plots are situated mainly on a ridge whilst others have a local advantage by being in a hollow. Table 108 below gives the more important growth statistics of three ecologically comparable plots; these are plot 5 (A-grade), plot 4 (B-grade) and plot 3 (heavy crown thinning).

TABLE 108

MEAN PERIODIC BASAL AREA AND INCREMENT OF THREE PLOTS OF THE EXPERIMENTAL SESSILE OAK SERIES WALDLEININGEN OBSERVATION PERIOD 48–72*

| Thinning grade | Mean basal area | | Mean annual increment in | | | |
| | | | basal area | | volume (over 7 cm diam.) | |
	(m²)	(%)	(m²)	(%)	(m³)	(%)
A	28·3	100	0·605	100	10·4	100
B	24·1	85	0·619	102	9·8	94
Heavy cr. thng.	20·9	74	0·570	94	8·8	85

* The height quality class of the plots at Waldleiningen measured by the yield table of Schwappach–Wiedemann rises from approximately 1·0 at the age of 50 years to approximately 0·0 at the age of 70 years. Similar conditions are found in the nearby yield control plot 62, which is on a similar site in the neighbouring forest of Elmstein-N., and has so far been observed from the age of 38 to 96 years. The volume increments, measured so far on this plot culminate at the age of 60 to 70 years, i.e. again considerably later than in the above Y.T. The mean increment of this plot is expected to culminate at approximately 130 years, yielding approximately 7·8 fm wood over 7 cm in diameter.

During the first 8 years of the total observation period of 24 years, the *effect of accelerated growth* becomes apparent by an increase in the volume production of the B-plot, amounting to 8 per cent as compared to the A-plot. The A-plot, with an early thinning yield of 18 per cent, was thinned slightly more heavily than planned. Thus the natural degree of stocking for heavy crown thinning must be estimated at barely 0·7, which with due allowance for those parts of the under- and intermediate storeys which were retained explains the 15 per cent inferior production of this plot. Some vigorous encroachments in accordance with ideas held by Oberforstmeister Schreiner have, on the other hand, led to the development of particularly deep and wide crowns.

Further observations on the development of *epicormic shoots* in this series confirm the earlier statements of Fabricius (1932, 1933), Rohmeder (1935) and Schreiner (1933). According to these, the main cause of epicormic shoots should be sought in an unbalanced relationship between the productive capacities of crown and roots, possibly due to the fact that the crown is powerfully restricted by lateral pressures or that sudden isolation so stimulates evaporation that the crown mass of the tree becomes insufficient. Trees in the upper canopy classes have on average *fewer* epicormic shoots and longer lengths of stem devoid of them. Exceptions to this rule may be explained by the *sudden isolation* of individual trees or by some hereditary disposition to this habit.

Here again, *moderate crown thinning*, corresponding to a natural stocking density of at least 0·8 is adequate to produce dominant trees with good stems and even, medium-sized crowns and it should be possible thereby to avoid loss of volume increment and the development of epicormic shoots. As demonstrated by Mayer (1958), the *width of the annual rings* in trees with large crowns must be expected to *fluctuate* particularly widely, whilst certain maximum widths are not exceeded even after complete crown isolation. Thus Sessile oak is quite unable to utilize an excess of available growing space. Remembering that according to Mayer–Wegelin, annual ring widths exceeding 1·8 mm render veneer quality doubtful, we surely have sufficient proof that only the most compelling reasons should persuade us to exceed moderate thinning (nat. deg. st. $\geqq 0\cdot8$) in valuable Sessile oak stands. The number of dominant oak trees, which must later be felled in order to enable a few individual beech trees to grow up from the intermediate storey into the upper canopy, so as to ensure sufficient regeneration for the protection of soil and stems, will have to depend on local conditions and the stand structure.

The excellent average quality of these and other Sessile oak stands in the Pfälzer Wald and Spessart is due mainly to their close initial spacing either by natural regeneration supplemented by successful broadcast sowings (under a canopy). A happy choice of sites and accomplished cultivation techniques give witness of the great ability of the foresters to whom we owe these promising stands.

Thinning treatments and financial production of Sessile oak stands

The official index figures in Table 73, p. 240, are based on the condition that oak timber of quality B has two to three times the average value of beech of the same dimensions and that the increase in prices for oak stemwood from class 3 to 6 is much steeper. The difference between quality A and B is also much wider than in beech. As a rough average we can today assume values for the relation A:B:C equal to 150:100:50. Oak veneer wood claims extremely high prices. At auctions in 1957, veneer oak from Waldleiningen forest fetched top prices of 4400 DM per festmeter and in 1958, 3500 DM. At the big veneer oak auctions in *Würzburg*, where in each case 1500 to 2000 fm of oak stemwood from the Spessart and the Fränkische Platte were auctioned, the following *average* values were obtained per fm of the different types of veneer:

	Full veneer quality (DM)	Partial veneer quality (DM)	Full and partial veneer quality (DM)
In December 1957	1835	548	1166
In March 1958	1778	555	1155

The highest price at the same time was in the region of 4100 DM. The production of veneer wood therefore can increase the financial production of oak stands to an extraordinary degree.

A calculation made by Wiedemann on the basis of the oak yield table of Schwappach–Wiedemann for height quality class I with a 180 year rotation, puts the total gross value production of a working section, assuming the prices of 1938, at the following figures:

	DM
With veneer production	27,814
Without veneer production	18,115

therefore

with veneer production
an additional amount of   *9699 DM = 53 per cent.*

Mascher (1953) calculated the yield of an oak working section under veneer wood management with a very long rotation of 300 years, and compared the gross and net amounts of this to those of a Norway spruce working section with a 90 year rotation. Undoubtedly using cautious figures he arrived at the following mean annual yields per hectare:

	Veneer oak (DM/ha)	Norway spruce (DM/ha)	Veneer oak as per cent of Norway spruce
Gross yield	759·–	567·–	134
Total expenses	111·–	136·–	82
Net yield	648·–	431·–	150
Management coefficient*	15%	24%	

$$* \text{ Management coefficient} = \frac{\text{G.Y.} - \text{N.Y.}}{\text{G.Y.}} \times 100.$$

Once established, a veneer oak working section is thus even better than Norway spruce in sustained pure yield!

In our present discussion we are interested mainly in assessing the extent to which the financial production of oak working sections may be improved by silvicultural tending. In order to demonstrate the whole range of possible variations in production we will take for consideration a Sessile oak working section with a rotation of approximately 200 years, basing our calculations on the proportions of the different stem-wood quality grades in two extreme outside cases together with two intermediate cases for which the produce can be assessed in stem-wood classes above class 3b.

For this rough calculation (an exact classification is impossible anyway) we assume the following value relations, based on present-day prices:

	Stem-wood, not capable of a value increase +utilizable logs +firewood over 7 cm dia.	Stem-wood, capable of a value increase (upwards from class 3)			
		quality class C	B	A	veneer quality
Value marks	30	50	100	150	500

The proportion of assortments, not capable of a value improvement, in the total production of a working section can be assumed to remain unchanged and to amount to 50 per cent. By a multiplication of the percentage proportions of the different stem-wood qualities used in the four assumed cases below, we then obtain the following relations for the value production:

	Value products*	Value relation (%)
Case 1. Stemwood susceptible of value improvement, *100% quality C*	400	100
Case 2. *50% quality C, 50% B*	525	132
Case 3. *20% C, 60% B, 10% A, 10% veneer*	825	206
Case 4. *10% C, 30% B, 20% A, 40% veneer*	1475	370

* In all four cases, the value product for stemwood, not susceptible of improvement + firewood, etc., remains unchanged at $30 \times 50 = 150$.

Case 3 ought to represent the average in moderately well-tended veneer oak stands, case 4 the attainable extreme. There are consequently quite exceptional opportunities for improving values by increasing the proportions of veneer wood. Such can be achieved by a thorough going technique of establishment ("ladder" sowing under a canopy), intensive tending in the young growth and thicket stages and cautious crown treatment with a moderate degree of thinning. The intensity of treatment applied to the young crops will be of special importance when beech has been mixed in with the original sowing for soil protection and to get clean stems.

In forest regions stocked extensively with veneer oak, especially in the Spessart and Pfälzer Wald, we find a discontinuity of age-structure. There are no stands 100–120 years old. The highly valuable 250–350-year-old stands in the Spessart must be harvested without too much delay in order to avoid losses in value. The existing gaps in the age-class structure could be closed rapidly provided a mean annual ring-width of 1·8 mm could be accepted without risking considerable reduction in veneer quality. According to Mayer-Wegelin (1950) we need have no qualms about using such a ring width. With intensive treatment of the thickets and moderate crown thinning, the trees on typical Spessart sites require 60–70 years to develop a mean breast-height diameter of 20 cm. Trees with a mean annual ring-width of 1·75 mm at breast height, corresponding to 3·5 mm annual diameter increase, require only 140 years to achieve a breast-height diameter of 70 cm over bark (taking into account the bark increment). Thus, *veneer oak of about 60 cm mean diameter under bark at mid-length of an 8-metre butt log could be produced within a rotation of 200–210 years.*[1]

Oak concludes this account of the small number of species upon which longterm experiments allow us to express opinion regarding their reactions to thinning. An important general outcome of these experiments is the realization that the possible effects of thinning have been *overrated* in the past. A genuine *intensification* of thinning promises to raise value production more effectively than the seeming preoccupation hitherto with an

[1] In an age of extremely rapid technical development and industrial mass-production it may seem absurd that foresters should count on production periods of 200 and more years and seriously base their long-term plans on these. Thanks to the perspicacity and unselfishness of our forefathers we still have the material conditions for producing sustained yields of such prime timbers. Let us then take care not to allow the continuity of the tree generations to be disrupted and let us close the gaps as quickly as possible!

increased severity of intervention. Such intensification, on the other hand, need not go to the extent of "forest gardening". *In statu nascendi*, minimum doses are sufficient for a powerful effect. What can be achieved in proper time by a slight touch of the finger will not be possible later on even if we should employ horsepower to do it. On the other hand, it is evident that in some cases it does no harm to allow fairly long intervals between thinnings. The resilience of growth which is characteristic of our forest trees provides plenty of scope for economy in management.

V. THE INFLUENCE OF METHODS OF ESTABLISHMENT AND PLANT SPACING ON PRODUCTION

A basic stipulation for the highest sustained yield is a close uninterrupted sequence of the production processes in the forest. This is preferably achieved by way of natural regeneration. Where this is impossible, artificial measures by sowing or planting take its place, in which case it is important to know which of the two methods will produce future yields within the shortest possible time and by what choice of spacing the highest volume and value production can be achieved on different sites.

The object of extensive cultivation and spacing experiments established in Germany in the sixties and seventies of the last century was mainly to discover which types of formation and planting distances would be the most economic under given conditions, i.e. how to secure the highest cash returns with minimum establishment costs. Thinning in these experimental plots started as soon as it was economically rewarding; intensities were approximately the same, that is to say "moderate", on all plots. Since 1912, the severity of thinning in the classic Norway spruce experiment at Wernsdorf (Saxony) has been noticeably increased. And after 1930, Wiedemann (1937) began to thin the older, as well as the newly established, plots of the former Prussian Research Institute at *different* intensities, these being generally more severe the wider the original spacing. As already mentioned (p. 288) the value of these investigations as thinning experiments is doubtful because the effects of the initial spacing and differences in subsequent treatment have become so merged that it is difficult to isolate definite causes of the recorded effects. At the same time, their value as spacing experiments is likewise reduced.

In yield research today we are interested mainly in examining the influence which the different initial densities of the growing crop bring to bear upon the growth pattern, height and diameter development and volume production. In order to present the problem in a more scientific manner it seems desirable that each method of establishment should have not only a plot subjected to a moderate thinning consistently applied throughout but also one which is not actively thinned at all ("light" thinning). This would enable us to observe the effect of the original density of stocking throughout the whole development of the stand. Also, it would enable a uniformity of thinning intensity on the other plots to be orientated by the undisturbed development of these "A-plots".

The Norway spruce cultural trials at Wermsdorf

This experiment was laid out in 1862 in the Saxony hill country, east of Leipzig, at approximately 200 m above sea level, with an annual rainfall of only about 650 mm, i.e. outside the region of natural distribution of Norway spruce. In this experiment, three types of sowing, twelve kinds of individual and group planting at different square spacings, as well as four plantings in rows at different spacing are compared in nineteen plots of 0·27 ha each.[1] The results were reported by Kunze (1889, 1895, 1907), Borgmann (1915), Fritsche (1919), Busse and Jaehn (1925).

Table 109 contains the more important data for broadcast sowing and three different square spacings at increasing width. The differences in d_m and h_m between broadcast sowing and planting at the widest square spacing (1·98 m) are surprisingly large. At the age of 60 or 62 years respectively, these differences amount to:

	d_m		h_m	
For broadcast sowing	11·2	$= 7·9$ cm	12·7	$= 5·0$ m!
For planting, 1·98	19·1		17·7	

In comparing these figures, we must bear in mind that thinning in the sown plot started 10 years later than in the planted. The tendency of over-dense natural regeneration and sowings of Norway spruce to stay in check is a familiar phenomenon which can be seen even on better sites (cf. p. 343). This imperfect capacity for selective elimination in Norway spruce might picturesquely be compared with the inability of undernourished and half-starved boxers to deliver the knock-out in a contest. This slowness of sown crops to get away could be remedied by timely weeding and early cleaning though perhaps at a high cost.

TABLE 109

NORWAY SPRUCE CULTIVATION EXPERIMENT AT WERMSDORF;
EXCERPT FROM THE FIGURES OF BUSSE AND JAEHN (1925)

No.	Definition	Age	Stem number	Remaining stand				Total thngs.	Total yield vol.	val.	Cultivation costs
				G (m²)	d_m (cm)	h_m (m)	V_s^* (m³)	V_s m³	(m³)	(M)	(M)
I.	Broadcast sowing 25 kg/ha	39	11969	23·8	5·1	5·7	93	40	133		
		60	2144	20·7	11·2	12·7	148	142	*290*	1030	560
IV.	Planting at sq. spacing 0·85 m	29	8460	23·6	6·0	6·8	97	2	99		
		62	1214	26·4	16·6	16·0	229	174	*403*	1707	140
VIII.	Ditto 1·42 m	29	3722	18·6	8·1	8·5	87		87		
		62	965	25·5	18·3	17·0	234	121	*355*	1628	55
XII.	Ditto 1·98 m	29	2078	13·9	9·2	8·7	65	1	66		
		62	864	24·7	19·1	17·7	234	82	*316*	1493	30

The first row in each case shows the figures of the first enumeration; this took place 10 years later in the sown plot.

* Stem-wood.

[1] According to a careful examination of the sites by Kunze (1895) the whole experimental layout is largely on sandy glacial loam and partly also on quartz porphyry (plots I, III, XVIII and XIX) with weathered soil which is inclined to dry out. Groundwater is out of reach. Plots IV, VI and partly also III and V lie on a hill-top, XVI and XVII have the advantage of being situated in a hollow position.

The characteristics d_m and h_m for the stand, as well as the total stem volume production at the beginning of thinning and at the end of the observation period, show quite unmistakable differences which are correlated with the initial crop densities on establishment. *The differences in the average amount of growing-space, available for individual trees during the development of the stand apparently had a decisive influence on the rate of growth.* This, however, has been compensated by thinning to the same intensity over the last 32 years. Any distinct remaining differences can be expected to disappear progressively. Busse and Jaehn have proved this by analyses of the diameter increment over the last 10 years of the twenty trees with the largest diameter in each of the extreme plots I (broadcast sowing) and XII (1.98×1.98 m). These analyses produced the following mean diameter increment percentages:

$$\text{Broadcast sowing} \quad 17.5\% \pm 1.2\%$$

$$\text{Planting} \quad 11.6\% \pm 0.7\%$$

Without any doubt, the physiologically younger sown crop is in the process of catching up with the lead in growth of the widely spaced planted crop.

None the less, the *differences in total crop volume of stemwood are still considerable.* If the production of the closest spacing, which is also the highest production of all individual plots, is set equal to 100 per cent, then the production percentages of the other two mentioned spacings are only 88 per cent and 78 per cent respectively and that of broadcast sowing only 72 per cent. Larger still are the differences in money yield which were based on the revenues free of harvesting costs for 1913/14 (smoothed).

Knotty stems have a decisive influence on the later yields. The number of knots increases directly with wider initial spacing. Busse and Jaehn carefully investigated the frequency and diameter of branches and the percentage of knotty area on planks. They found:

	Percentages	
	of branches over 22 mm dia.	of knotty area in plank area
With broadcast sowing	—	0.41
0.85 m sq. spacing	2.2	0.59
1.98 m sq. spacing	4.2	0.79
1.13×3.40 spacing in rows	12.9	1.04

The proportion of value-reducing coarse branches increases strikingly with wider spacing, especially between rows. Incidentally, in the latter case the *eccentricity of the stem cross-sectional areas* at breast height is also extremely marked. The *percentage of thinnings with red rot* was *lowest with sowing* and highest with wide spacing. According to Busse and Jaehn this is due to the retarded growth of sowings. On the other hand, Vanselow (1937) found that, in the experiment on the Köcherhof in Baden, the percentage of Norway spruce with red rot among thinnings of the year 1935 was lowest in the sown plot and in the two plots stocked with untransplanted trees (5 per cent and 6 and 9 per cent respectively), whilst it was twice to three times as large (15–16 per cent) on the plots established with 4-year-old transplants. Root damage caused by planting and transplanting, which is avoided in sowing, evidently promotes red rot.

In contrast to the classic experiment at Wermsdorf, where the closest espacement (0·85 m square spacing) achieves the highest volume production, the converse occurs in the former Prussian Research Institute's

Norway spruce spacing experiment Dietzhausen 37.

Situation. Thuringia, not far from Meiningen, 480 m above sea level, moderately steep slope, bunter-sandstone, fairly shallow, very stoney, somewhat loamy sand; podsolized brown earth. Annual precipitation approximately 700 mm.

Experimental layout. Established in 1877 with 3-year-old Norway spruce transplants; six plots each with three different square and row spacings of graduated widths. From the age of 31 thinned at equal intensities (moderate); from the age of 54 thinned to different grades.

According to Wiedemann (1937) there is no doubt about the ecological comparability of plots 1–3 with square spacings. Prior to fencing in 1889 (at age 13) plots 2 (1·25×1·25 m) and 3 (1·50×1·50 m) suffered such severe damage by *cattle grazing*, that extensive *replanting* was necessary; *on plot 3* this amounted to *approximately 60 per cent.*

TABLE 110

NORWAY SPRUCE SPACING EXPERIMENT DIETZHAUSEN 37;
EXTRACT FROM THE FIGURES OF WIEDEMANN (1937). THE VOLUMES OF WOOD OVER 7 CM IN DIAMETER WERE CONVERTED TO STEMWOOD VOLUMES BY THE FORM FACTORS FOR THE MEAN STEMS

No.	Definition	Age	Stem number	Main crop				Total of thngs. V_s	Total crop vol. V_s	Incr. since laid out	Cultural costs
				G	d_m	h_m	V				
				(m²)	(cm)	(m)	(m³)	(m³)	(m³)	(m³)	(M)
1	Planting at 1·0 m sq. spacing	31	6277	26·4	7·3	8·2*	125	20	145	369	142
		58	2191	38·6	15·0	18·5	380	134	514		
3	Ditto at 1·5 m sq. spacing	31	2908	27·9	11·1	11·5*	174	10	184	477	90
		58	766	34·9	24·1	24·2	432	229	661		

* Wiedemann (1937) convinced himself by stem-analysis of dominant trees on plots 3 and 1 that plot 3 at age 50 years had acquired an advantage in height amounting to approximately 5 m (= 25 per cent).

Table 110 proves that despite a patchy initial condition, plot 3 with the widest spacing *was far ahead* of the densest plot 1, *not only in height and diameter development but also in volume production.* At the age of 58 years the superiority in total crop volume still amounted to 147 fm = 39 per cent!

Obviously the *local habitat conditions* of this site must be *extreme*. The path along the slope below the experimental series bears the characteristic name "Hungerleiterweg" (i.e. "Starvation Lane"). From this we can justifiably conclude that the site has a particularly scanty water supply, and that the effect of competition on densely stocked stands is to retard growth, even in a plantation. In Fig. 125, the mean heights of the initial crops in plots 4–6 with row spacing show a straight-line increase, along with diminishing numbers of stems at outset; among plots 1–3 with square spacing, plot 2 is an aberrant instance. The small mean height of the initial stand on plot 1 is very probably due to the marked density of the initial stock. In view of the extremely low availability of water supplies on this site, it is the density of the crop rather than the varying quality of the site which has retarded growth to such an extent that this unusually inferior production in the closely spaced stand inevitably followed.

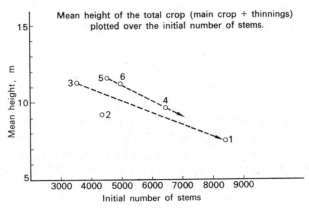

FIG. 125. Spruce spacing trial at Dietzhausen.

In the *other spacing experiments of the Prussian Research Institute "at greater altitudes"* with higher rainfall and more abundant supplies of water, the different types of spacing produced *only small differences in height and diameter development*. At the age of 50 to 60 years, the total crop production of wood over 7 cm in diameter was practically equal; this would represent a *superiority of stemwood production in the closely spaced stand*. Unfortunately these experiments have suffered in some parts such severe disturbances by snow breakage, bark damage and game browsing in the early years that we cannot draw any definitive conclusions from them.

South German Norway spruce spacing experiments

The results of the *experiment on the Köcherhof*, published by Vanselow (1937), correspond to those of the experiment at Wermsdorf.

In 1941 Vanselow took over a new and very generously laid-out *spacing experiment* in Graf Toerring's forest *Wessling*, when it was 32 years old, and reported it in 1942, 1950 and 1956. In 1910 this optimum site on young moraine deposit, divided into plots of 0·72 ha each, was planted up in all possible square spacings from 1·1 to 2·0 m, with 0·1 m graduations as well as an extremely open square spacing of 4 m using 4-year-old Norway spruce transplants.

An extract of the most important figures from Vanselow's extensive data, giving only four different spacings in Table 111, shows that the heavy natural losses up to the first thinning had caused a smoothing out in the stem numbers, which was subsequently further improved by the uniform thinning applied since 1941. Apart from the extreme 4-m spacing, the differences in the present-day diameter and height development are very small. The *total crop volume of wood over 7 cm in diameter* has a distinct *maximum for close*

TABLE 111

NORWAY SPRUCE SPACING EXPERIMENT WESSLING;
EXCERPT FROM THE FIGURES OF VANSELOW (1950, 1956)

| Square spacing, length of sides | Natural stem number development | | | Main crop (aged 44) | | | | | Total crop vol. | Cultural costs |
	Orig. 1910	Losses by death	Before 1st thng. 1943	Stem number	G (m²)	d_m (cm)	h_m (m)	$V*$ (m³)	1954 $V*$ (m³)	(%)
1·2	6945	2352	4593	1563	43·2	18·8	21·1	479	658	100
1·5	4444	666	3778	1474	41·8	19·0	21·1	450	588	68
2·0	2500	175	2325	1267	43·4	20·9	21·6	500	560	24
4·0 +replanting	625	31	594	576	36·2	28·2	21·9	385	387	10
1·0×1·0	9375	7746	1629	—	—	—	—	—	—	—

* Wood over 7 cm in diameter.

spacing at 1·2 m (the 1·1 spacing is not comparable as regards site). From 1·3 m spacing upwards, volume production becomes clearly less the wider the planting distance.

Such an excellent site is capable of supplying adequate nutrients for a large number of individuals. Although the initial growing space is small, we observe a rapid natural elimination of surplus trees without noticeably retarding growth. The advantage gained in height and diameter development on the wide spacing plots is soon defeated. If we are endeavouring to achieve the highest volume production, initial spacing on such a site has to be close (not over 1·3 m).

With regard to value production, wide spacing must be expected to produce *more knotty stems*; this was confirmed by Vanselow on the basis of measurements of sample stems (1941):

	Mean branch length (cm)	Mean branch diameter at the base (mm)
At 1·1 and 1·2 m sq. spacing	18	8–9
2·0 m sq. spacing	57	—
4·0 m sq. spacing	174	22 (!)

From these branch measurements and measurements of the length of the green crowns, which is nearly equal on all plots, Vanselow deduced a permissible maximum of 1·6 m plant spacing.

The extent to which growth of over-thick broadcast sowings can be retarded as compared to planting, even on an optimum site, is proved by the *experiment Sachsenried 2 (planting) and 3 (sowing)* of the Bavarian Forest Research Institute, which is at the same time arranged as a thinning experiment with A-, B- and C-grades, the results of which have already been discussed in a different context (p. 292). Table 112 gives a comparison of top heights and the total crop volumes in stemwood of the A plots of the two series.

The sown plot had initially the enormous number of 19,268 stems per hectare compared to only 5356 in the planted crop. *At the age of 58 years the seedling plot had already caught up upon the big lead in top height of the planted crop. While the total crop volume of the sown area had lagged earlier by a full third, at the age of 102 years, it had nearly caught up with that of the planted area.* The total crop volume of the sown plot A amounts to 91 per cent of that of the most productive B-plot of the planted series.

TABLE 112

COMPARISON OF THE TOP HEIGHT DEVELOPMENT AND TOTAL CROP VOLUME BY SOWING AND PLANTING (1·4 m SQ. SPACING), AS ILLUSTRATED IN THE A-PLOTS OF THE EXPERIMENTAL SERIES SACHSENRIED 2 AND 3

| Age | | Top height | | Total crop volume of stemwood | | |
Planting (2A)	Sowing (3A)	Planting (m)	Sowing (m)	Planting (m³)	Sowing (m³)	Sowing as % of planting %
32	**33**	**15·7**	**13·7**	**408**	**272**	**67**
37	38	19·5	17·1	521	382	73
42	43	22·8	20·9	697	515	74
47	48	24·6	22·9	767	615	80
52	53	25·7	24·9	894	744	83
58	**59**	**26·8**	**26·9**	**1050**	**872**	**83**
69	70	30·1	30·6	1281	1157	90
74	75	31·4	32·5	1366	1241	91
79	80	33·4	34·7	1454	1348	93
84	85	34·7	36·3	1537	1439	94
95	96	36·6	38·5	1675	1622	97
101	**102**	**37·6**	**39·3**	**1765**	**1705**	**97**

This experiment shows clearly that from the yield study aspect the method of establishment and choice of spacing distance are virtually equivalent in their effects to a *modification in the rhythm of the growth process, which is evoked by the provision of varying amounts of growing space.* Stands which have initially lagged behind in their development, possess a latent physiological potential for growth power which enables them on good sites to catch up with crops that were in the first instance more liberally provided with growing space and which accordingly get ahead.

In the extensive *Scots pine cultivation experiments* of the Saxon Research Institute in *Markersbach and Reudnitz,* about which Kunze reported several times between 1882 and 1918 and Busse and Weissker finally in 1931, the *sown crops had the highest volume production,* differing in this respect from Norway spruce. Busse and Weissker considered this to be due to the greater capacity for crown projection of Scots pine in the young stages. The original differences in height and volume production in these two experimental series have largely levelled out in the course of 65 years, but distinct differences have remained in the mean diameter. Owing to the outstanding importance of fine branching to the future quality of Scots pine timber, very close spacing will have to be stipulated for the production of high grade timber.

From Vanselow, the following *scale of plant spacings*, will serve to provide clear definitions:

Growing space for individual plants (m²)	Length of sides in square spacing (m)	Number of plants per ha	Definition
Up to 1·0	Up to 1·0	10,000 and over	Very close
1·0–1·7	1·0–1·3	6 to 10,000	Close
1·7–2·6	1·3–1·6	4 to 6000	Medium wide
over 2·6	over 1·6	under 4000	Wide

Summary of conclusions from cultivation and spacing experiments

1. By spacing at wider or closer distances we provide an *average growth pattern for the individual plant*. This decides the *speed of the future progress of growth* and has a "*formative*" *effect*, noticeable for a long time in the mean diameter and height development.

2. On poor-quality sites with a limited water supply, young trees have little vigour, so that stands initially densely stocked are incapable of making acceptable growing space by self-reduction of numbers. Impediments to development in growth result in a lower level of performance as compared to that of a stand which has been formed at wide espacement. This applies especially to broadcast sowings and over-dense natural regeneration of Norway spruce, but not to Scots pine, which has a striking capacity for reducing its surplus numbers in the juvenile stages.

Even with little initial growing space, individual plants on the better sites have, as a rule, sufficient competitive strength to gain the ascendancy and so better their chances of survival by improved growth. But even on the best sites, over-dense young stocks from broadcast sowing or natural regeneration, which have not been thinned out in time, may experience considerable setbacks in growth and thereby incur large economic losses in overall performance by comparison with planted crops.

3. In the long term there appears to be a strong *tendency for the yields of crops* established at different planting espacements *to level out;* but often the much reduced yields of over-thickly populated stands which were not thinned out at appropriate times can never make good the loss, even if these stands grow to an advanced age (80–100 years).

Variations from the average size and shape (mean diameter, height, crown ratio) are apt to continue over long periods on poor- and medium-quality sites, while on good sites they soon become less obvious and, in consequence of moderate or heavy thinnings, usually disappear completely in old trees.

4. The growth conditions in young crops are clearly *analogous to the relationships between the basal area* (= density of stocking) *and increment in medium-aged stands*. While over-dense young stocks on sites with a limited supply of moisture undergo checks in their growth development with loss of increment, which could be avoided by timely thinning, the highest productivity on sites with an ample supply of water seems to depend on a high density of stocking, even in the early years.

5. Within limits which allow of full increment attainments, we should regulate the stem numbers in young stands so as to achieve optimum value yields.

On good to very good sites and with good marketing possibilities, spacing should be very close and cleaning should take place at an early stage. If the marketing position is poor, medium spacing is to be preferred, in order to avoid expensive beating up. Planting on poor sites should be at medium to close espacements if the market permits early cleaning; alternatively, if timber quality does not have to be considered, the spacing should be wide.

6. Considering the better and more uniform utilization of growing space obtainable by *triangular spacing, this should be practised wherever it is locally and technically possible.*

VI. INCREMENT AND YIELD OF MIXED STANDS WITHOUT LARGE AGE DIFFERENCES AND IN UNDERPLANTED STANDS

1. Fundamental Problems of Growth in Mixed Species

Unlike the pure stands which have been discussed up to this point, mixed stands pose a number of problems which cannot be solved until much further experimental work has been carried out.

The different light requirements of the species participating in a mixture may produce an increased assimilation efficiency in comparison to pure stands. This is to be expected, especially if the upper storey consists of light-demanding species, and the intermediate and lower storey of shade- and semi-shade-tolerant species. These latter are capable of satisfactorily "utilizing the light which has been transmitted through the crowns of light-demanding species in the upper canopy and thus, according to Krenn, producing an "additive increment". *Unlike pure stands of light-demanding species,* such as Scots pine or larch, *this additional increment can certainly be expected because the organic production of the* mostly profuse *surface vegetation of such stands* (for example, bilberry) *can be converted into wood.*

The different natural growth rhythms of the species participating in a mixture introduce new complications into the concept of production. These natural rhythms undergo certain variations with age, the method of formation, the kind of mixture, and the methods of thinning practised. For example, let us assume that the upper storey consists of a rapidly growing, light-demanding species, such as Japanese larch, and the under storey of slower-growing underplanted shade- and semi-shade-tolerant species such as Silver fir, Common beech, Norway spruce, *Thuja plicata* or *Tsuga heterophylla;* or alternatively a semi-shade-tolerant species in the upper storey occupying an initially dominating position (e.g. Norway spruce) and a shade-tolerant species in the under storey (e.g. beech) in an initially retarded state; in both cases *the different growth rhythms can be utilized by way of suitable thinning methods in order to enable the maximum* volume and dry matter *production to be achieved.* Certainly, we must expect a considerable variation in performance, depending on the timing, degree and type of thinning, and the cultural methods employed.

If the mixed species demand *different root horizons,* the sites can be utilized more satisfactorily. The species with strong roots, such as oak, Silver fir or alder (Kreutzer, 1960) are capable of opening soil layers in which rooting is difficult, enabling the whole stand to enjoy an improved nutrient supply by way of the litter from such mixed species. Generally it is to be assumed that the deepening and expansion of rooting in the soil will increase productivity, because it enables a larger soil space to be penetrated by air, increases water storage, and renders it accessible to the soil fauna.

The *character of the litter* from mixed species, especially litter which is rich in protein and easily decomposed (cf. Wittich, 1953 *et al.*) can improve productive conditions by way of stimulating the soil fauna. And the amount of rainfall which is capable of penetrating into the soil, as well as the temperature of the surface soil layer, also depends on the species. Thus the addition of a broad-leaved species whose branches are bare in winter into a coniferous crop can improve the soil biology.

As we know, plants can have favourable as well as unfavourable *effects*. The experts talk of *allelopathy* and *allelophily* wherein root secretions and the effects of litter-casting play a part. We have as yet no information about the influence of these on the increment of our forest trees.

The *structure of* mixed *stands* is as a rule more *stable* than that of pure stands. Also, a more liberal silvicultural treatment is frequently possible. Whereas the greater stability affects the yield favourably, we must on the other hand count on *higher costs of silvicultural treatment* during the early years.

In order to make a quantitative assessment of the increment processes of mixed stands, and to compare them with those of pure stands, it is necessary to provide the following conditions which have received too little attention in the past:

(a) Knowledge about the *performance in pure stands of species participating in mixture*. This can be reliably achieved on a given site by simultaneous observation of such *pure stands along with the mixed stand*.[1]

(b) Knowledge about the *true ratios* of the species participating in the mixture. These are by no means identical to the basal area or volume ratios. An acceptable approximation is offered in the *ground-cover area proportions* found by vertical measurements of the crown projections. But even the ground-cover area ratios can be used only within each particular *storey*. In a heavily layered structure consisting of three or more storeys, the comparison of efficiencies becomes difficult, because we do not yet know enough about the extent to which the efficiency of the intermediate and lower storeys in reduced by the upper storey.

(c) A *comparison of the efficiencies* of the different species *based on volume production* is technically not free from objection because of the often considerable *differences between dry wood weights*. The volume production of Norway spruce with its low specific gravity (0·390) is not comparable to that of beech with a high specific gravity (0·560). The conversion figures of Trendelenburg (cf. p. 79) represent average values of a widely fluctuating range, and the true specific gravities fluctuate from site to site and between individual trees as well as between stands; because of this, *local measurements of the specific gravity* will be indispensable. Nevertheless, for the present we should be able to use with advantage Trendelenburg's averages, especially as it may be assumed that these reflect correctly at least the average specific gravity conditions for different species.

(d) The frequently changing growth patterns and processes of individual trees in mixed stands, each according to the degree of shading and lateral competition encountered, the type of mixture, and the manner of its formation are further strongly related to shifts of phase in the growth-rhythm. For example, an 80–100 years old beech

---

[1] In a more recent mixed oak–beech stand experiment, established by Wiedemann in 1929 in Dalheim forest (dept. 117/19) with five partial plots, one of the plots under observation consists of pure oak. The experimental results which the author obtained from an excursion guide of the Nethersaxon Research Station are inadequate for a safe comparison.

within a mixed Silver fir–Norway spruce–Common beech stand may be within the same natural growth phase as a 20–30 year-old beech in a natural regeneration which has just been freed from cover. On the other hand, the passage of physical time and therewith the actual age of crop cannot be neglected when comparing the performances of uneven-aged mixed stands.

If it is not easy to discover the laws of growth in pure stands, the difficulties of assessing this for mixed stands seem almost insurmountable. Because of the vast number of potential combinations (e.g. according to participating species, type of mixture, method of formation, age intervals) we can at best hope to clarify the relationships *of some typical types of mixed stands* within the foreseeable future.

If we wish to examine not only the volume and dry matter production, but also the *production in value* the following considerations are of importance:

(a) Owing to the marked *phototropism of broad-leaved trees, their stem form in mixed stands is considerably poorer than* may be expected on the same site *in pure, broad-leaved stands* (Burger, 1925, 1941b).

(b) Thus, in mixed stands we must count on particularly *large differences in the value* and range of timber of the same dimensions.

(c) The necessity for directing the different growth patterns and the different values of the participating species complicate the techniques of treatment and demand a high *intensity of intervention*. The actually achieved and the attainable results vary accordingly. It is therefore necessary to pay attention simultaneously to the differing degrees of vigour, varying growth-rates and light requirements, and the changing powers of crown overhang, as well as the contrasts between the technical and biological value!

2. Results of Experiments in Mixed Stands

Wiedemann and his collaborators have tried to lay down different yield tables for mixed stands, based on the observations to date of growth in mixed stands on experimental plots of the former Prussian Research Institute. But in the form devised, these have in the meantime proved unable to withstand criticism. In the following parts of this chapter therefore an examination of actual experiments in mixed stands will be made using the above-mentioned tables for possible comparisons.

(a) COMBINATIONS OF LIGHT-DEMANDING AND SHADE-TOLERANT SPECIES

(i) *Mixed stands of oak and Common beech*

These are mixed stands, with oak in the upper storey and a natural or artificial under storey of beech, hornbeam, lime and possibly even Silver fir, grown from a mixed regeneration, or from later underplanting; the result is either a more or less even-aged crop or a mixture of different ages.

From thinning experiments in pure oak stands we are already acquainted with figures of out-turn available from a beech and hornbeam under storey. The question in this instance is whether or not the volume and dry matter production of pure oak stands can be increased in this way. In the Freienwalde series the *increment accruing in the beech and hornbeam under storey of the C-grade plot was only 0·86 fm, and this was insufficient to compensate for the poor growth put on by the oak upper storey,* which was in fact 2·2 fm less than that attained by the A-grade plot. But then again, in the top-yielding B-grade with 8·8 fm annual increment since the age of 86 years, the under storey has after all produced an increment of 0·71 fm, which clearly shows that this latter produce must be considered in the light of a supplementary or *additional* yield. Thus it is certain that while a moderately thinned Sessile oak stand with a beech under storey has a larger volume and dry matter production than a pure oak stand, we may nevertheless take warning that on this comparatively dry East German diluvial site, any lowering of the yield from the upper storey oak in consequence of drastic opening up is unlikely to be compensated for by a correspondingly increased productivity of the shade-bearing under storey.

Mitscherlich's (1953) investigations in oak stands in the foothills of the Black Forest have proved that one must also expect a reduction in increment to result from competition caused by the under and intermediate storeys. Frequently on the mentioned sites an under and intermediate storey of Silver fir has developed, which not only is less useful for stem protection than, for example, beech, or even hornbeam and lime, but also has noticeably *reduced the increment of the oak upper storey.* Mitscherlich calculated that the oak upper-storey increment was annually reduced by 0·2 fm for every 10 fm/ha of the existing Silver fir under storey. Besides, Mitscherlich is of the opinion that only two-thirds of the increment of this under storey can be considered as "additive increment" in the sense used by Krenn.

Wiedemann's (1949) yield table for mixed oak–beech stands, the first outline of which was made by Christmann in 1939, assumes height Quality Class I of the yield table of 1920/46 for oak. At the age of 30 years the oak occupies only 20 per cent of the basal area of the mixed stand; by the age of 200 years this has been increased to 55 per cent (final ratio: 18·4 m² oak and 14·5 m² beech). By the age of 200 years the mixed stand has produced

in m.a.i. of oak and beech	8·1	fm
in dry matter	4·63	t

In contrast to this, the production to be expected according to the yield table would be

	for oak, Qual. Cl. I	*for Common beech*, Qual. Cl. I
in m.a.i.	4·8	~8·9 fm
in dry matter	2·78	~5 t

This comparison is questionable because (a) the yield table which is being used is doubtful and (b) the yield of Common beech in a pure stand on the same site is unknown. *Beyond doubt, the mixed stand is superior to the pure stand in volume and dry matter production,* equal periodic basal areas being assumed in oak in both cases. But on sites in the West German mountains at high altitude where Common beech is native and therefore high-yielding, a pure shade-bearing stand of beech would probably be superior to a mixed stand. On such a site it is likely that the reduced volume increment in an oak upper storey will be compensated by increased increments in the beech under and middle storeys.

The *value production* is a different question. In Wiedemann's yield table for mixed stands, these yields are laid down for experimental plots with a *late start of tending* operations and where the quantitative and qualitative proportions of oak at the beginning of treatments are apparently unsatisfactory. If treatment in the thicket-stage starts at the right time it ought to be possible from the beginning to ensure a proportion of 80 per cent of oak.

This table probably has been modelled mainly on the *experimental plots with mixed stands in Johannesburg* forest, the results of which were reported in great detail by Wiedemann (1931) and more recently by Bonnemann (1956).

On three pairs of plots (districts 61, 63, 57) the *favourable effect of tending the oak in a mixed stand* is compared with *untended oak*. In both cases "future stems" have been selected and marked. The success of active treatment is manifested in a higher proportion of oak in the treated plots, in the better shape of the stems and crowns as well as a higher annual diameter increase with large final diameters. After a careful grading and assessment of the total produce so far, Bonnemann made a comparison of the financial yields. This was based on prices obtained in 1930 and 1952. As the price ratios of oak and beech timber of equal dimensions from 1930 to 1952 changed in favour of oak—since then a counter-development has set in—Bonnemann calculated on 1952 prices, that the net value production of the "tended" mixed stands was superior by only 2–16 per cent (assuming incomes free from harvesting costs).

These not entirely satisfactory results of careful tending can be explained as being due to the small proportion of oak at the beginning of the experiment (especially on plot 63) and a late start. Furthermore, the age of the stands at the end of observations (100–125 years) was too young. At such ages oak which has been tended only just begins to develop profitable diameters and qualities. Remembering this, the consequent tending of oak in such mixed stands must unquestionably be regarded as rewarding.

In general, the allowable proportions between the species and the cutting techniques will have to depend on the site and the timber values attainable in the two species. With Sessile oak on sites which are capable of producing veneer timber, it would be economically mistaken policy to have a large proportion of beech. A larger proportion of oak in the mixture and of superior form and quality is achievable by the application of good cultural techniques to the juvenile and thicket stages rather than by belated heavy thinning.

(ii) *Mixed stands of Scots pine and Common beech*

Regarding this type of mixed stand, which may have been created by subsequent underplanting of an originally pure S. pine stand or by sowing and interplanting in a sparse regeneration of beech (former coppice woods), there are fortunately several existing experiments which have already supplied valid results. Most of these have been established by the former Prussian Research Institute. We may begin by looking at two of these experimental series in the East German diluvium, the results of which were reported in detail by Erteld (1953).

Scots pine open-stand thinning experiment with underplanted beech, Eberswalde 16

Site. 53 m above sea level. Ground moraine of the later diluvium; loamy sand (A_2 and B_1), below this sandy loam (B_2). Boulder clay with a low base-content (C) beginning at 130 cm.

Climate: Av. annual temperature $= 8\cdot1°C$; temperature during the vegetative period $= 16\cdot2°C$; annual precipitation $= 510$ mm.

Experimental layout. The experiment was established in 1886 in a fully stocked vigorous polewood stand of S. pine, underplanted in 1878 (47 years old) with beech. There are four plots of 0·25 ha each, plot I moderately thinned and II–IV taken to 0·8 of the basal area of I in 1886.

Height quality class. Wiedemann's moderate thinning of S. pine = I.5.

The mean annual increment according to Wiedemann's yield table for moderate thinning for the same age period is 6·8 fm with a mean periodic basal area of 31·7 m². Consequently the periodic basal area of the "moderately" thinned plot I is larger by 6 per cent and the increment is larger by 7 per cent. Despite this average stocking density of 1·06 for the S. pine in the upper storey of plot I, the under storey beech with a mean periodic basal area of 10·8 m² has produced an *additional increment of 2 fm.* And this additional beech increment was only 16 and 12 per cent respectively smaller than on the severely thinned plots II and III. The next but last column in Table 113 shows the corresponding *dry matter production* of the S. pine and beech. This, we find, is highest on plot I. *The increment losses incurred by open-stand thinning in the upper storey of S. pine therefore in this case have not been compensated by increased production of the shade-tolerant under storey!*

TABLE 113

PERIODIC BASAL AREA AND INCREMENT PRODUCTION IN THE EXPERIMENTAL SERIES EBERSWALDE 16 IN THE AGE PERIOD 55–111 YEARS

ACCORDING TO (PARTLY SMOOTHED) FIGURES BY ERTELD (1953)

Plot	Mean periodic basal area in			Mean annual increment in					Ann. production of dry matter			
	S. pine		C. beech	basal area of S. pine		wood over 7 cm diam.						
						of S. pine		of C. beech	S. pine	C. beech	together	
	(m²)	(%)	(m²)	(m²)	(%)	(fm)	(%)	(fm)	(t)	(t)	(t)	(%)
I	33·6	100	10·8	0·550	100	7·29	100	2·04	3·06	1·14	4·20	100
II	24·8	74	11·5	0·494	90	6·25	86	2·43	2·63	1·36	3·99	95
III	24·3	72	12·0	0·515	94	6·55	90	2·32	2·75	1·30	4·05	96
IV	26·1	78	8·5	0·481	87	6·21	85	1·62	2·61	0·91	3·52	84

If the annual production of S. pine in plot I is taken as an index of the possible dry matter produced from a pure crop of pine on this site, amounting to 3·06 metric tons (instead of 2·86 tons as shown in the yield table), then the enhanced production of dry matter under mixed stands can be assessed according to the following percentages:

Plot	I	II	III	IV
Increased production	+37	+30	+32	+15%

If we take into consideration that the beech under storey probably reduces the increment of Scots pine, and that according to Erteld's (1953) observations in the experimental series 21/22 (following below) this reduction can be estimated at approximately 10 per cent of the Scots pine increment, then the still considerable *increased productivity of the mixed stand amounts respectively* to:

$$+24 \quad +14 \quad +19 \quad +4\%$$

in comparison with the pure light-demanding stand.

Mixed Scots pine–Common beech experiment, Eberswalde 21/22

Site and climate. As in Eberswalde 16.

Experimental layout. The experimental stand originates from afforested agricultural land on soil impoverished by bad management. The experimental series, which was established by Fricke, was originally intended to investigate the influence of root competition. In 1929 Wiedemann arranged the series as an experiment in underplanting:

Plot I   heavy thinning of the *S. pine without* beech underwood.
Plot II   heavy thinning of the *S. pine with thinning of the underplanted beech.*
Plot III   heavy thinning of the *S. pine without thinning of the underplanted beech.*
Plot IV   heavy thinning of the *S. pine, the original beech underwood having been removed in 1929.*

Plots II–IV are ecologically slightly favoured in comparison to I, because their clay content lies at a lower depth. The height quality of the S. pine on plot I is approximately one-quarter quality class lower.

The removal of the beech under storey on plot IV resulted in an *increase of the increment of the S. pine in the upper storey.* Erteld (1953) proved this beyond doubt by analyses of the annual rings of ten dominant S. pine trees in each of the plots IV and II.

Table 114

PERIODIC BASAL AREA AND INCREMENT PRODUCTION OF THE EXPERIMENTAL SERIES EBERSWALDE 21/22 OF S. PINE AT THE AGE OF 70–88 YEARS AND OF THE BEECH UNDER STOREY AT THE AGE OF 37–54 YEARS ACCORDING TO (PARTLY CORRECTED AND SMOOTHED) FIGURES BY ERTELD (1953)

Plot	Mean periodic basal area of			Annual increment in					Ann. production of wooden dry matter				Corrected
	S. pine		Beech	basal area S. pine		wood over 7 cm diam. S. pine		Beech	S. pine	Beech	Together		
	(m²)	(%)	(m²)	(m²)	(%)	(fm)	(%)	(fm)	(t)	(t)	(t)	(%)	
I S. pine without underwood	30·1	100	—	0·514	100	7·61 (+0·35)	100	—	3·20	—	3·20 (+0·15)	100	3·35 t 100%
II Beech under storey thinned	29·2	97	8·2	0·475	92	6·94	91	3·53	2·91	1·98	4·89	153	146
III Beech under storey unthinned	29·4	98	10·5	0·480	93	7·11	93	3·76	2·99	2·10	5·09	159	152
IV Beech under storey removed	31·3	103	—	0·614	119	8·67	114	—	3·64	—	3·64	114	109

If the production of the pure S. pine stand without underwood on plot I in Table 114 is raised to correspond with the difference in height quality class, by 0·35 to 7·96 fm or by 0·15 t to 3·35 t dry matter, the lower *production in pure S. pine* of plots II and III amounts to 13 and 11 per cent respectively (instead of 9 and 7 per cent respectively). This is obviously attributable to the *competition of the beech underwood impeding the growth of the pine*, which accordingly must be estimated at a minimum of 10 per cent of the potential production of pure S. pine. The increased production of pure S. pine on plot IV in comparison to I (8·67 − 7·96 = 0·71 fm = 9 per cent) can be considered as the result of *increased decomposition* of the *litter and roots* which have remained after the removal of the beech under storey.

If, therefore, on the one hand, *the beech under storey* apparently *impedes the production of the pine top storey*, on the other hand *the dry matter production of the mixed pine–beech crop is greater by 45–50 per cent than that of the pure S. pine stand.*

The strikingly high increased production of the mixed pine–beech stand on this site with a sub-soil layer of loam can partly be explained with the help of the results of fairly recent root investigations by Hausdörfer (1959), Kilias (1957), Lemke (1956) and Wagenknecht (1959), about which the last mentioned author has given a summarised report. *It was found that the rooting of beech in the loamy layers below the surface layers of sand, is considerably more intensive than that of the pine*, whose fine root development decreases with increasing depth, so that on sites of this kind "the loam layers are opened up mainly by beech". The competitive effect of beech, which manifests itself in this, can also be explained by the larger number of fine roots (< 1 mm) per dm² of rooted soil, found in the course of these investigations.

The investigation of a mixed pine–beech stand in Waldau forest, near Kassel, Dept 77 and 78, is located on a typical site of the Hessisches Bergland (Hessian uplands).

Site. 370 m above sea level. Medium bunter-sandstone under a surface layer of loessic loam: deep-grounded sandy loam.

Climate. Average annual temperature = 8°C; temperature from May–September = = 14°C; annual precipitation = 654 mm, May–September = 329 mm.

Experimental layout. Two plots (77 I, 78 I) established in 1915, two plots (77 II, 78 II) in 1930 in a 69- and an 83-year-old mixed pine–beech stand which has originated from sowing of S. pine after clear cutting of the old "Hutewald" (shelterwood). The beech has grown mainly from coppice shoots, the S. pine is very branchy with large knots and has little heartwood. 78 I contains a few larch and Norway spruce trees. Thinning on plot 1 was light, on 2 moderate, on 3 heavy and on plot 4 the S. pine underwent open-stand thinning.

Height quality class of S. pine according to Wiedemann = I.0.

Based on results, published by Bonnemann (1939) and an excursion guide, set up by Schober in 1953, the following values shown in Table 115 have been compiled.

According to Wiedemann's yield table, which Schober used for comparison in the construction of his excursion guide, the *increment* in a pure S. pine stand with G = 33·7 m² (= 80 per cent of the basal area of S. pine on plot 1) would have amounted to only *6·7 fm*, corresponding to 2·81 t dry matter, *as compared to the actual amount of 8·5 fm.* Once again this shows how unsuitable this table is for West German sites.

Based on careful crown measurements by Bonnemann (1939), an approximate calculation of the areas under S. pine cover has been made (second but last line in Table 115). As indicated by the derived percentages, *the increment of S. pine is to a striking extent closely proportional to the area under canopy as also to the basal area.* The positive

TABLE 115

EXPERIMENTAL SERIES WALDAU 77/78

ACCORDING TO FIGURES BY BONNEMANN (1939) AND SCHOBER (1953)

Experimental plot Species		1/78 II			2/77 I			3/78 I			4/77 II		
		Pine	Beech	Total	Pine	Beech	Total	Pine	Beech	Total	Pine	Beech	Total
State at the age of 105 years								(La, Sp.)					
Mean *height*	m	28·8	24·0		28·7	24·8		29·1	24·7		27·9	24·5	
M. *diam.*	cm	38·9	20·3		41·0	23·4		43·6	23·8		46·4	22·6	
Basal area	m²	*42·1*	12·5	54·6	*28·5*	13·8	42·3	*26·6*	13·8	40·4	*22·0*	17·1	39·1
		100%			*68%*			*63%*			*52%*		
Ann. increment at the age of 83–105 years													
In *volume*	fm	*8·5*	4·8	13·3	*6·2*	5·5	11·7	*6·6*	5·7	12·3	*5·1*	7·2	12·3
In *dry matter*	t	*3·56*	*2·69*	*6·26*	*2·61*	*3·08*	*5·69*	*2·77*	*3·19*	*5·96*	*2·14*	*4·19*	*6·33*
As % of pl. 1		*100*		100	73		91	*78*		95	*60*		101
With a total canopy area of S. pine, ha		*0·53*			*0·39*			*0·36*			*0·31*		
		100%			*74%*			*68%*			*59%*		

deviation in plot 3 can easily be explained by the proportions of larch and Norway spruce mixture there. If the S. pine cover extended over 0·70 ha, which in this case would correspond to a maximum basal area of S. pine amounting to approximately 55 m², the *potential production of pure S. pine* to be expected on this site within the same period would be 10 to 11 fm, corresponding to 4·0–4·5 t dry matter. *But as against this relatively enhanced value, the dry matter production in a mixed stand would be yet further increased by the considerable amount of approximately 40 per cent!* The high total production of plot 4 might be explained by the fact, that the large proportion of beech there is in a phase of high increment production.

As the height quality class of free-growing beech is unknown, the potential dry matter production of a pure shade-tolerant stand of C. beech unfortunately cannot be estimated. The site being located in a natural beech region with good rainfall it is possible that the production of a pure shade-tolerant stand cannot be surpassed there.

Bonnemann's (1939) *yield table for mixed S. pine–C. beech stands* is based on twenty-two plots with mixed crops, partly in the East German diluvium and partly in the Hessian uplands (Hessiches Bergland). The growth and production of the S. pine fraction in this table are matched with the Scots pine yield table of Schwappach (1908).[1] Large proportions of the basal area and total crop volume are ascribed to beech. The basal area of the remaining stand at different ages amounts to:

	40 years	120 years	180 years
S. pine	29·0	20·0	18·0 m²
C. beech	5·2	15·7	20·2 m²

The m.a.i. assumed at the age of 180 in S. pine = 5·0 fm
in beech = 2·9 fm

[1] The height development assumed for the pine top storey is exactly the same as the one in the yield table by Schwappach (1908) and Wiedemann (1949) for height Quality Class I.

FIG. 126. Mixed pine–beech stand at Waldbrunn forest. Ninety-year-old beech and oak stems growing under approximately 150-year-old pine stems.

which in comparison with pure S. pine of height Quality Class I would correspond to an *increase in dry matter production of 68 per cent.*

The programme of treatments in this particular yield table is based on an even-aged mixture. However, the majority of plots in mixed stands used in the construction of this table have been created by subsequent underplanting with beech. All three of the analysed experimental series with mixed stands show a common reduction of volume yield after heavy thinning in the upper storey of S. pine, which, however, has not induced an equivalent increased production of the beech under storey. The programme of treatments of this table appears silviculturally acceptable, provided the S. pine is of moderate quality, with a small proportion of high-grade timber, and the site permits the production of well-shaped beech with an acceptable proportion of stem-wood.

The value production of the Common beech fraction

In such stands this is—especially with present-day prices—very little owing to the small yield of stemwood and the frequently indifferent stem quality. Therefore a lower and middle storey of beech to provide necessary soil protection, beneath a no more than lightly thinned upper-storey of well-shaped S. pine, seems silviculturally the best and most feasible solution.

The prospects of greater value production improve if in addition to, or instead of, beech we underplant with high-grade shade-bearers and half-shade bearing species such as Silver fir, Norway spruce and Douglas fir.

(iii) *Mixed stands of Scots pine–Norway spruce (Silver fir, Douglas fir)*

Information about the production of such stands is given in a recently published work by Zundel (1960). This author examined, with the aid of sample plots, the growth conditions of mixed stands of two ages, created by underplanting in open pine stands (due to snow breakage); most of these are situated in the dry and warm wine-growing region of the lowlands of Württemberg. Comparable pure stands of S. pine were not available; no increments were measured in the four assessed pure shade-tolerant stands (Norway spruce, Silver fir).

The canopy values measured in the *pine top storey* are strikingly small, lying between 14 and 57 per cent.[1] The following *values per ha of the pine top storey* were measured in the sample plot series Güglingen (age = 90 years):

TABLE 116

Sample plot	Basal area		Crown canopy		Volume inc. (wood over 7 cm diam.)		Basal area of the under storey	Difference in height: upper minus under storey
	(m²)	(%)	(m²)	(%)	(m³)	(%)	(m²)	(m)
II	32·3	100	4600	100	5·5	100	14·6 (S. fi) 1·7 (Hornb.)	7·4
III	22·2	69	3600	78	3·2	58	18·4 (S. fi) 2·4 (Oak, C. be.)	5·2 5·2
I	19·6	61	2800	61	2·7	49	21·9 (*Dougl. f*, C. be.)	−1·2*

* The Douglas fir has penetrated into the crown space of the S. pine and has largely overtaken it.

[1] Sample plot Güglingen IV, with $G = 39·2$ m², which according to Zimmerle (1933) corresponds to a degree of stocking of 1·10 has *a cover percentage of* only *37 per cent*. In addition, there is a beech under storey of 11·2 m². Either the crown radii have systematically been underestimated or the stand has, after a long period of closure (present age 90 years) been heavily thinned. The maximum basal area can be estimated as 50 m²; but even this would be equal only to a canopy of 47 per cent. In Zundel's opinion the crowns have damaged each other by whipping.

The volume increment of the upper storey according to these values reduces at a steeper rate than the figures of basal area and percentage of crown cover. Zundel assumed this to have been caused by increasing competition by the under storey, especially root competition. After open-stand thinning, *the height increment of the upper storey drops to very small values* (for example, in 30–40 years only 6 cm annually or for 50 years even an average of 4 cm annually) yet surprisingly enough, it picks up again when the under storey has grown up into the crown space of the upper storey (cf. p. 395, Mang, 1955).

The reduction of *volume production of the under storey due to the pressure of the upper storey canopy* is greater than was expected by currently held optimistic views. This is impressively displayed in Fig. 127. According to Zundel, *an increase in stem numbers in the upper storey by fifty pine trees per hectare results in an average reduction of the basal area increment in the under storey of 0·15 to 0·20 m²*. This effect of canopy pressure is due probably not so much to the interception of photosynthetically effective regions of the spectrum as to the *heavy reduction in total radiation* to be expected according to results by Baumgartner (cf. p. 118). With the structure of the stand in question, the highest radiation levels occur either in the crown space of the upper storey or *certainly fairly high above the ground so that the amount of energy conducted into the under storey is insufficient for the endothermic transpiration process.* Moreover, according to investigations by Neuwirth (1962, 1966) *the productivity of transpiration*, i.e. the ratio of transpired water to assimilated CO_2, *also changes unfavourably under a canopy.*

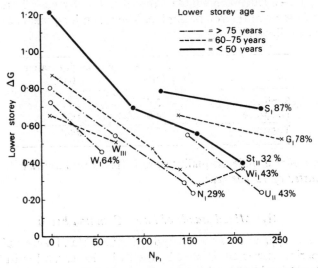

FIG. 127. The basal area increment of the lower storey decreases while the number of stems in the upper storey increases *(Zundel)*.

Even though the "additive increment" according to Krenn therefore cannot exceed a certain amount, *the total volume production of the upper and under storeys is* nevertheless considerably *higher than that of an even-aged pure light-demanding stand.* In the existing climatic and local site conditions, however, it is to be reckoned *that severe opening of the S. pine upper storey would cause it to lose increment, which cannot be fully made up by the under storey.* This applies also to types of stands where both the under and upper storeys are harvested in one regeneration operation. Stands which are felled in two operations will be discussed separately (p. 369). Zundel considered probable that the volume production of an even-aged *shade-tolerant stand* of Silver fir or Norway spruce, as far as this is practicable on this site, may be *higher* than that of the stand of mixed light-demanding and shade-tolerant species.

In *value production* this type of mixed stand with two ages is *considerably superior* to the even-aged S. pine stand, especially if the pine in the upper storey is of *high-grade timber quality*. Because of the increased width of the annual rings (in the first two decades after open-stand thinning on average 1·5 mm = 160 per cent of the width of annual rings in a closed stand) high-grade timber dimensions are reached within acceptable rotations. To the value of the upper storey is added the produce of the under storey of Silver fir, Norway spruce and Douglas fir, which even with small dimensions is capable of earning favourable prices, so that the potential production of a pure S. pine stand within the same rotation is definitely exceeded. On the other hand, Zundel considered it probable that the value production of a pure Silver fir (Norway spruce, Douglas fir) stand is *not* exceeded. But we must remember that, on these sites, such a stand is not practicable without considerable risks and losses.

The growth processes and productions of this type of mixed stand can, as also stressed by Zundel, be revealed only by long-term experiments, in which especially the early yields from both storeys are recorded; these cannot be assessed by measurements of temporary sample plots.

In the *yield table for the mixed S. pine–Norway spruce stand*, constructed by Christmann in 1939, Schwappach–Wiedemann's table values for quality class I are assumed for the growth process of the upper storey of S. pine. The mean increments achieved by the age of 160 years are as follows:

	Volume (m³)	Woody dry matter (t)
S. pine	3·6	1·51
N. spruce	4·0	1·56
Together	7·6	3·07

As compared to pure S. pine of quality class I, this would amount to an *increased production in dry matter of 15 per cent.*

(iv) *Mixed stands of larch–Common beech*

The results of an experiment with this type of mixed stand were published by Burger (1941b). This experiment was established by the Swiss Research Institute on the *Rehalpe* near Zurich. The *total volume production up to the age of 90 years* was compared for (a) pure beech, (b) larch with beech of the same age, (c) larch with subsequently underplanted beech. It amounted to:

	Volume (m³)		Woody dry matter (t)	
(a) Pure beech		655		377
(b) Larch with	401		182 ⎫	
beech	451	852	261 ⎬	443
(c) Larch with	755		342 ⎫	
underplanted beech	175	930	101 ⎬	443

In this case, the dry matter production of the mixed stand is superior even to that of the *pure shade-tolerant stand by 18 per cent.*

Burger discovered further that *Common beech* in admixture with larch, at given diameters upwards from 30 cm, grows to greater heights than in a pure crop. While the *mean height of larch* in case (b) amounts to *38 m*, in case (c) it is *41 m*. The subsequently underplanted stand therefore was more favourable to the growth development of the larch than the beech of the same age, which, as we know, conveys little benefit to the former unless energetic early tending operations are applied. Moreover, the form of the larch stems in case (c) is better, whilst, according to Burger's observations, *the form of the beech stems in both types of mixed stand is considerably poorer* than in a pure stand. Thus the *value production* in case (c) is incomparably higher than in case (b).

On the basis of numerous temporary sample plots and permanent experimental plots, Schober (1949) declared that the increment production of the mixed larch stand with larch in the upper storey and a broad-leaved species in the under storey *considerably exceeds that of a pure larch stand.* He assumed that a broad-leaved under storey fraction of 0·3 in the total crop is capable of producing approximately 1–2 fm additional hardwood over 7 cm in diameter per annum. The much more vigorous growth of beech after the larch has reached a considerable age permits of rotations for large-diameter timber of approximately 140 years whilst the total crop volume of such mixed larch stands continues to be satisfactory.

This superiority of mixtures with *European larch* in the top canopy layer applies similarly for such stands with *Japanese larch* which, according to Schober's monograph (1953), itself produces higher yields than European larch. After analyses of a fairly large number of mixed stands of Japanese larch both in even-aged mixture and with underplanted shade- and semi-shade tolerant species (among others beech, Norway spruce, D. fir, *Thuja plicata*) Schober (1953) arrived at the following conclusion: "A satisfactory assimilation and growth of the shade-tolerant species in the under-storey appears to be possible without reducing the Japanese larch in the upper canopy layer much below the volume table level for heavy thinning." Thus mixed stands with an upper storey of Japanese larch have a *considerably increased production*, especially as this species in the same height quality class produces long stems with larger diameters than European larch. Especially high levels of production can be expected from combinations with a high-yielding exotic shade-tolerant species such as *Thuja plicata* or *Tsuga heterophylla*; examples of such combinations are already in existence.

(v) *Mixed stands of Common beech and high-grade hardwoods*

This type of mixed stand is of special importance on hilly and submontane sites with soils which are sufficiently moist and rich in bases. The development of beech in such mixed stands ought to be controlled early enough to favour the valuable light-demanding species, e.g. ash, elm, maple and others, in the upper storey. As such treatment was practised only in a few of the existing older experiments, we generally have only small proportions of the above-mentioned high-quality hardwoods and an unsatisfactory diameter development.

According to a recently published work by Erteld (1959), who evaluated the results of long-term experiments in the Muschelkalk (shell limestone) region of North Thuringia, the necessary treatment of high-quality hardwoods is accompanied (owing to their slightly inferior volume production) by a moderate loss of volume increment in comparison to pure beech stands. A calculation by Erteld based on prices fixed by economic planning in East Germany, showed the *superiority in value production of this type of mixed stand*, where the added species occupies barely 15 per cent of the final stand, *of as much as 26 per cent in comparison to a pure beech stand*. The high prices realized in late years in the free market of West Germany for high-quality hardwoods of large diameters (over 40 cm if possible) make it seem probable that their production would be equally profitable there also. In particular, the price for maple (and even more so for the now rare species of elm and cherry) can today be expected to be twice as high as that for beech of the same dimensions. As the demand for woods of these species, combining pleasing colour and texture, is likely to increase, the enrichment of our beech stands with such quality hardwoods by suitable cultivation and tending seems the most effective measure for increasing the future value of broad-leaved crops, and perhaps even for making them competitive again alongside the now depressing preponderance of coniferous timbers.

(b) COMBINATIONS OF SHADE-TOLERANT AND SEMI-SHADE-TOLERANT SPECIES

The natural processes which govern these mixtures are much more difficult to assess than the growth conditions in mixed stands with a natural predominance of the light-demanding species in the upper storey.

(i) *Mixtures of beech and spruce*

A crucial aspect concerning this type of mixed stand is *the production ratio Norway spruce : Common beech* which, as we learned in Section C, III, p. 188, *can fluctuate within wide limits, depending on the site.* Wiedemann (1942), for example, found it necessary to construct two tables for mixed stands, namely one for "spruce sites with nearly equal growth of the beech" and the other for "weak growth of the beech". The results of the fourteen experimental series on which Wiedemann's tables are based, supply the following conclusions: If *the dry matter production of a pure Norway spruce stand is used as a basis for comparison, then mixed stands* of Norway spruce–Common beech are *inferior*:

(a) on acid sites,
(b) if the beech is too much favoured, i.e. the spruce is cut back.

Mixed stands are superior

(a) on alkaline sites for which beech has a particular partiality,
(b) if the spruce is not cut back to favour the beech and the beech remains in an accessory role.

In this comparison of performances, it is to be remembered that Norway spruce in a mixed stand is nutritionally favoured by the more easily decomposed mixed litter, the more favourable climate of the stand, and the more varied ground fauna. This applies also to pure spruce following in succession upon a beech crop. The larger root volume and deeper rooting of the preceding beech stand offers advantages to the subsequent spruce stand which in the acidic, spent and densely-packed soils of a second-rotation spruce crop are not available. When these favourable conditions have ceased to exist, the productive superiority of spruce might also be reduced. The fact, however, that this superiority is bound to continue, even after these particularly advantageous conditions have disappeared, has already been shown (on p. 188) to be due to the "tracheid wood structure" of Norway spruce which is bound up with its evolutionary development.

The figures already given for *the production ratio Norway spruce:Common beech* show that the proportions of both species are *dependent on the site. The higher the lime content of the soil, the more favourable this is to Common beech; the higher the acidity, the greater becomes the superiority of Norway spruce.* According to observations so far, *the production ratio spruce to beech*, measured in the total production up to the age of 100 years, *can fluctuate between the following extremely wide limits:*

The *volume*   1·6 up to 3·0 : 1·0
Dry matter   1·1 up to 2·0 : 1·0.

It is fairly safe to say that the volume production of Norway spruce is overwhelmingly superior even in cases where the conditions for beech are most favourable.

This production ratio, which applies to pure stands lying adjacent on the same site, may *vary* to a marked degree in mixed crops, depending on the mode of establishment, the proportions of the species, the type of mixture and particularly upon the thinning technique. For example, where we have a proportion of 20 per cent of beech measured by basal area, the crucial question is whether these trees are distributed over the whole area of the stand as subordinate under-, or intermediate storeys, or whether they are present in groups and small clumps, uniform in growth with the Norway spruce. Both for yield-study analyses of such mixed stands and for subsequent diagnoses of growth and predictions of yield, based possibly on already existing yield study information, it is essential to make a careful assessment of the structure of the stands, by comparing storeys and canopy ratios of the two species within the storeys. On the other hand, all *estimates* of production from mixed stands by comparison with *yield table values* of pure stands, carried out by means of corresponding proportions of pure stands belonging to the same height quality class, are more or less doubtful, even if these comparisons are supported by complicated calculations (in this connection see especially Baader, 1942, p. 69). The kind of reckoning employed which, among other aspects, was discussed in a literary debate between Wiedemann (1943) and Baader (1942, 1943) is in this case less important than the unnatural character of the limits (for basal area and volume of the standing crop) of some yield tables and the manner in which the proportions of the mixed species have been assessed. As regards this aspect, the reader is reminded of the yield table comparisons in the experiments with mixed stands of Scots pine and Common beech.

As repeatedly stressed, a safe calculation of the proportions of mixed species is possible only by means of the respective canopy area projections. Incidentally, *the shares of basal area occupied respectively* by spruce and beech in mixed stands can be converted for practical purposes into a rough apportionment of the growing-space between the species *by employing a ratio of specific gravities* thus: Spr.:Be = 390:560 = 1:1·44 ≅ 0·7:1·0. *To the share of basal area belonging to Norway spruce is applied the factor 0·7,* the result giving approximately correctly the proportions of the mixed species in terms of the growing space.

Whilst this book was being printed a partial result of some current investigations of mixed stands by Kennel[1] became available. Figure 128 gives a photograph and Fig. 129 a crown map of a group of beech, entirely surrounded by spruce, in the experimental plot Wieda 58. The approximately 74-year-old (68–88) beech trees of this group, occupying approximately 3 ar, have well-shaped stems, thanks to the intensive treatment of this

[1] Kennel, R. (1965), *A.F.J.Z.*, **136**, Nos. 7/8.

FIG. 128. Experimental area 58 at Wieda, a mixed stand. A beech group surrounded by spruce. Details in the text.

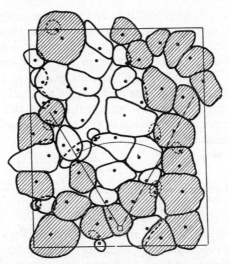

Fig. 129. Experimental area 58 at Wieda, a mixed stand. Crown map of a section of the stand occupying 500 m². Hatching = spruce. The position of the camera and the sectional angle of the picture in Fig. 128 are marked.

stand. They merge smoothly into the adjoining 56-year-old (51–58) spruce which is more than 3 m higher. The most important data for the section, shown in the two mentioned figures, which covers 500 m² are:

| Species | Canopy area | | Remaining stand | | | | Annual increment 1954–60 | |
| | | N | d_m | h_m | G | V | | per m² canopy area |
	(m²)		(cm)	(m)	(m²)	(m³)	(m³)	(dm³)
C. beech								
Tree cl. 1–4	3432	360	16·7	19·8	7·85	88	3·64	1·06
Tree cl. 5	488	240	8·5	13·3	1·37	11	0·03	0·06
N. spruce								
Tree cl. 1–4	5734	480	27·1	23·3	27·76	309	11·41	1·99
Total	9654	1080			36·98	408	15·08	

Volume data for C. beech = total treewood; for N. spruce = stem-wood.

Transforming the increments of the two species, as limited to tree classes 1–4, into terms of production per hectare of a pure crop, by means of their relative proportions in the total canopy area we obtain the following results:

	Volume (m³)	Dry matter (t)
C. beech	9·7	5·4
N. spruce	18·2	7·1

This corresponds to a volume production ratio for Norway spruce : C. beech of 1·88 : 1·00 and for dry matter of 1·31 : 1·00. The production on this particular site (transition from "Kulmkieselschiefer" (siliceous slate to calcareous schist) is considerable. The height quality classes according to Wiedemann are for Norway spruce = I.0, for C. beech = II.7. The total area contains all possible grades and types of mixtures. Silviculturally the most promising in this case seems to be an admixture of Norway spruce by clumps and groups in a matrix of beech, which, following the removal of the spruce by the age of about 100 years, is then capable of producing a considerable subsequent value increment.

Financial production of mixed Common beech–Norway spruce stands; mixed stands or pure stands?

Since the present average net *value per cubic metre of Norway spruce timber*, free of harvesting costs is about *double that of Common beech, the value production of the spruce*, assuming the above ratios of out-turn, is almost *overwhelmingly superior*. Provided production is undisturbed, its value out-turn is three to six times that of beech. It is therefore understandable that Wiedemann's (1942) chief concern regarding mixed beech–spruce stands was a somewhat narrow preoccupation with the loss in value among the better spruce trees resulting from increasing proportions of beech. Baader (1943), on the other hand, stressed that our question ought to be: which would be the more advantageous for the national economy, to produce the needed quantities of both species of timber separately, i.e. in pure stands, or together in mixed stands? In view of the principles governing conservation of the site and lasting security of management, remembering also the more efficient water-retaining economy of beech (Eidmann, 1959) and the steadily increasing importance of forests for recreational purposes, we must today decide in *favour of mixed stands* on many sites where hitherto, without much thought, we have allowed extensive areas to be stocked with pure Norway spruce.

Most crucial for the potential yields of mixed stands are the *proportions of the several species and the type of mixture*. These aspects, together with the *exercise of cutting techniques*, determine the timber, volume and financial yield. For example, in the lower Alps there are many places where the introduction of beech to serve an ancillary role would not prejudice the high yields of spruce in the upper storey, and by merely keeping in check the development of grass and weeds in the older spruce stands, would be of even greater utility than any timber thus produced, which in most cases we may consider to be quite *accessory*. Conversely, the yield of a beech (or some other broad-leaved) crop on a well-chosen site can be increased by *imparting an admixture* of spruce for a *part of the beech rotation*. In this case, the different growth cycles of the two species (early culmination of increment with spruce, later in beech) can be used to promote yield. After the removal of the spruce, which soon reaches useful dimensions, the remaining broadleaved stand can, because of its ability to continue growing, yet supply valuable yields.

Should the beech be intended to participate decisively in the dominant crown space, the *type* of mixture gains in importance. In this case it is necessary to remember that, owing to its strong capacity for lateral crown projection, beech is inclined to develop coarse branches in the areas of contact between the two species, causing trees in the neighbouring spruce thicket to die off, and only firewood will be produced on a considerable area of the stand. This can be avoided by timely treatment[1] and may be restricted by cultivating in fairly large groups.

The importance of the size of the groups becomes clear by the following reflection: assuming that the shape of the beech groups were square, and the beech trees had developed coarse branches, the following ratios of the rough knotty outer *"shell" and the valuable, more knot-free "core" would ensue.*

| Size of group | Area of | | Proportion of |
| | "shell" | "core" | "shell" |
(m)	(m²)	(m²)	(%)
5× 5	16	9	64
10×10	36	64	36
30×30	116	784	13

The size of the beech groups therefore ought not to be too small, in fact the top limit ought to be chosen (with diameter equal to one mature tree-length, cf. p. 208) so that the area stocked with broad-leaved trees can also produce high quality timber.

Especially in all regeneration and tending measures, the future requirements in growing space of the two species should be kept well in mind: for example, an area of approximately 50 m² which would be required to accommodate twenty-five spruce trees when introduced at 1·5 m square spacing into a beech regeneration provides adequate growing space for only one large spruce when the stand is mature. Planning which takes these natural conditions into account also permits of some reduction in the *unavoidable increased expense of tending* of such mixed stocks. A few paltry beech groups later introduced into an ocean of spruce can hardly be expected to have a perceptible effect on the soil biology or to afford any added protective features. That will demand stronger measures, for example by laying down *wide* strips of broad-leaved trees (which could perhaps be "improved" in value by a mixture of larch) orientated perpendicularly to the direction of the main source of danger and by other methods.

The abandonment of pure spruce stands, which admittedly earn larger incomes, but at the same time entail correspondingly greater risks, is rewarded by the improved resistance to hazards and greater diversity of produce resulting from mixed crops. By skilled handling of the type of mixture so as to adjust it to the given local conditions of site we can utilize the growth potential of mixed stands in such a way that unavoidable reductions in the financial returns are minimized.

(ii) *Mixed stands of Silver fir–Norway spruce–Common beech*

In this highly productive type of mixed stand, which fortunately still exists on fairly large areas in the region of the natural mixed forests of Silver fir and beech, Silver fir plays an important part.

---

[1] The areas of contact of the beech should initially be held back (by lopping, topping, etc.) and later, when the spruce has reached utilizable dimensions, thinning should favour the beech.

Characteristics of the species Silver fir (Abies alba Miller)

In Section C, III (p. 132) we have already set down a few facts concerning the crown morphology and the production of Silver fir in selection forests and natural mixed stands. This is a markedly *shade-tolerant species*, distinguished by a great tolerance to shade, a long life span and persistently high increment. Whereas in artificially raised pure stands without the shade of an upper canopy, we can expect a relatively early culmination of the current and mean annual volume increments per unit area (nearly as early as that of Norway spruce), under a crown canopy, especially in selection forests, this may be delayed to a considerable age. According to Gehrhardt's (1922) yield table, compiled from tables by Eichhorn (1902) and Dieterich (1922), the culmination of the increments on unshaded Q. Cl. I sites are to be expected as follows:

height increment	at the age of 40 years of 0·45 m per annum
c.a.i. of volume	
(over 7 cm in	
diameter)	at the age of 55 years of 23·3 fm per annum
m.a.i. of volume	at the age of 100 years of 14·9 fm per annum

In the new table by Hausser (1956), the c.a.i. and m.a.i. culminate approximately 10 years later at lower values.

The stems of Silver fir having a less pronounced ratio $h/d_{1·3}$ are noticeably more full-boled than those of Norway spruce. This *thick-set form of stem* provides a *high resistance to snow breakage*. Its green heartwood gives fir a greater resistance to fungal attacks than spruce. Owing to a powerful root system its ability to open up compact and multi-layered soils is also superior to that of spruce. Because of its greater demand on the water economy, fir also requires greater warmth than spruce. The liability to disease of Silver fir on suitable sites and with correct silvicultural treatment is small. Optimum growth is achieved in selection forests. Among fungal parasites we should mention Silver fir canker *(Aecidium elatinum)* and among parasitic animals especially *Dreyfusia nüsslini.*

Growth production of Silver fir stands and mixed stands of Silver fir–Norway spruce–Common beech

Among the results of yield experiments in Württemberg in Table 117 below, which were published by Zimmerle (1936), the *production of the pure Silver fir stands* No. 54 and 55 (Oberndorf) is particularly striking. The basal area of 91·2 m² and timber production of 1470 fm in experimental plot 55 are impressive figures. This plot still had a c.a.i. of 16·8 fm between the ages 147 to 157 years and even after heavy thinning during the following period (157 to 178 years) the increment still amounted to 12·4 fm. Still higher production may be expected on these sites from mixed stands of S. fir–N. spruce and S. fir–N. spruce–C. beech, but for these, with the exception of No. 79, Zimmerle has as yet been unable to estimate the increments.

For the production per unit area of Silver fir and the other species accompanying it in this type of mixed stand there are so far only a few results relating to selection forests (Badoux, 1949) and natural mixed stands (Magin, 1959) which we have already partly dwelt upon (p. 132). For more or less even-aged mixed stands of this kind, we have as

TABLE 117

RESULTS OF YIELD RESEARCH IN S. FIR STANDS AND MIXED S. FIR–N. SPRUCE–C. BEECH STANDS IN WÜRTTEMBERG AFTER THE DATA BY ZIMMERLE (1936), PARTLY ALTERED OR SUPPLEMENTED ON THE BASIS OF MORE RECENT RESULTS

No.	Description	Age	Timber species	Main crop					Annual increment of wood over 7 cm diam.
				N	G (m²)	d (cm)	h (m)	V_D (fm)	incr. per. fm
5a	Steinwald forest, upper and med. bunter-sandstone; 830 m, E. slope 6% A.r. 1520 mm A.t. = 6·5°C	43 62	N.spr. S. fir Be	864 300 76	23·5 10·2 1·5	18·6 20·9 15·8	17·3 16·1 16·5	198 85 10	
			Total	1240	35·2			293	
8a	As before, upper bunter-sandstone; 830 m, level. A.r. 1400 mm A.t. = 6·5°C	142	S. fir N. spr. Be	212 62 30	38·8 11·8 0·8	48·3 49·2 18·4	31·5 35·0	568 178 7	142–158 10·2
			Total	304	51·4			753	
54	Oberndorf, diluvium over shell lime, 665 m, level. A.r. 1100 mm A.t. = 6·75°C	143 153	S. fir S. fir	512 364	71·8 65·5	42·3 47·9	34·2 35·5	1172 1085	143–153 15·6
55	As before, 670 m, level otherwise as before	147 157 178	S. fir S. fir S. fir	356 284 128	91·2 87·4 48·8	57·1 62·6 69·7	37·2 39·7 42·5	1470 1454 846	147–157 16·8 157–178 12·4
79	As before, 670 m, S. slope 5% otherwise as before	75 85 106	S. fir+ N. spr. S. fir+ N. spr. S. fir N. spr.	1256 948 468 72	55·6 54·5 48·6 7·3	23·7 27·0 36·4 36·0	23·9 26·4 30·6 32·0	672 745 729 109	75–85 22·6 85–106 18·7
			Total	540	55·9			838	
80	As before, 670 m, NNE. slope, 7% otherwise as before	72 82 103	S. fir S. fir S. fir	1160 884 476	53·7 54·5 56·0	24·3 28·0 38·7	24·1 27·2 31·5	655 751 862	72–82 22·7 82–103 20·3

A.r. = mean annual rainfall.
A.t. = mean annual temperature.
V_D = Volume in "Derbholz" (wood over 7 cm dia.).

Yields *before* the establishment of the experiment being unknown, the values for total increment and m.a.i. cannot be stated.

yet no observations which would allow us to draw safe conclusions about the utilization of growing space and the relative production of fir and spruce. Hitherto it has been generally assumed that when fir and spruce occur on the same site, the former is superior in production per unit area. This, however, does not always seem to be the case. For example, in Section C, III we discovered that the canopy area of Silver fir in the experimental selection forest area Dürsrüti is larger than that of Norway spruce. In the experimental selection forest area Biglenwald, on the other hand, it is equally large for both species; in the alpine natural stand near Partenkirchen the spruce is superior.

Among other species used in the planting experiment in Baden on the Köcherhof (Vanselow, 1937), Black Forest, on former agricultural soils at approximately 450 m above sea level, Silver fir and Norway spruce were planted in three- and five-row mixtures (three or five rows of 6–8 year-old fir respectively alternating with an equal number of rows of 5–6-year-old spruce. Because of strong competition by grass, it took a long time until the plantations closed canopy. In the mixture of three rows each, fir at first lagged well behind the spruce. By the age of 60 years informative ratios of production had emerged, according to Table 118.

TABLE 118

PRODUCTION OF S. FIR AND N. SPRUCE IN THE CULTIVATION EXPERIMENT KÖCHERHOF UP TO THE AGE OF 60 YEARS, AFTER VANSELOW (1937)

Mixture	m.a.i.			Dry matter production	
	Norway spruce (fm)	Silver fir (fm)	Together (fm)	annual (t)	% standard error
Pure Norway spruce			10·5	4·1	100 ± 0%
Pure Silver fir			11·1	4·1	
Three-row mixture	9·4	2·0	11·4	4·4	
ditto	8·5	3·2	11·7	4·5	115 ± 5·3%
ditto	12·5	0·9	13·4	5·2	
Five-row mixture	8·9	5·3	14·2	5·4	
ditto	10·5	4·3	14·8	5·7	137 ± 1·6%
ditto	10·9	3·5	14·4	5·6	

The mixed Silver fir–Norway spruce stand in this experiment *surpasses both the pure spruce stand and the pure fir stand in the* average annual total *production of volume as well as of dry matter*; the mixture of five rows each has a *very safe superiority of 37 per cent*. As both the pure spruce and the pure fir stand have produced equal quantities of dry matter and nearly equal volumes, it is obvious that the *mixture* must *actually increase increment*. This is probably due to a satisfactory provision for the different light requirements of the two species in the mixture and to the complementary use of soil space by the two species.

Financial production of mixed stands of Silver fir–Norway spruce–Common beech

The mutually beneficial association of Silver fir and Norway spruce permits of some supplementation by beech, but the proportion of that adaptable species should undoubtedly be kept within bounds in view of the soil protective role already exercised by the

Silver fir. *The probable higher out-turn*[1] *of mixed fir–spruce–beech stands should render a yield hardly less profitable than that of pure spruce stands*, notwithstanding that the average price obtained for fir lies some 10–15 per cent below that of spruce timber. Those foresters whose duties still comprise extensive areas of mixed forests, at once so highly productive and immune to dangers, are much to be envied. Endeavours to rehabilitate Silver fir on sites where it formerly grew naturally (v. Hornstein, 1951; Nosek, 1955; Holzapfel, 1960) ought in the long run to prove amply rewarding. As to whether it is politic to promote a greater incidence of that species by a general change-over to selection forests (among other authors, Dannecker) can remain for the time being undecided. For large forest estates, Schlagwald types with long-term regeneration under shelterwood offer many advantages, provided this has been well planned ahead.

VII. INCREMENT AND YIELD IN OPEN-STAND SYSTEMS AND STANDS WHICH ARE FELLED IN SEVERAL CUTTING OPERATIONS ("MEHRHIEBIG")

In common speech we talk about *single-storey* ("einhiebig") stands when timber production in a more-or-less even-aged crop is brought to a close in the course of one discrete operation by securing its *regeneration within one continuous and limited period of time*. In a two-storeyed or twice-felled ("zweihiebig") stand, on the other hand, timber production takes place *in two layers, separated by height and age, which are independently harvested and regenerated at different times*. Therefore, under-planting of a light-demanding crop with shade-tolerant species results in a two-storeyed stand, provided the under-planted shade-tolerant crop is harvested and regenerated at a later stage, subsequent to the conversion of the light-demanding crop. On the other hand, we should still talk of a single-storeyed (einhiebig) stand, if the harvesting and regeneration of both storeys took place simultaneously, or immediately one after the other. Although there are many transition stages, which are difficult to differentiate between, a *fundamental* separation is none the less advisable, because in a *planned* two-tiered system one has to take into account the particular silvicultural and economic conditions. It is especially these transitions which make it unavoidable that, in the following chapter, single-storeyed and two-storeyed open-stand systems are discussed simultaneously.

1. Open-stand and High Forest with Reserves System in Common Beech

A special form of open-stand system with the same species, though of different ages, in both storeys is

v. Seebach's classic open-stand system,

also known as "modified beech high forest". Chr. v. Seebach (1845) developed this under special historical and political conditions (timber shortage in despoliated hardwood forests of the Solling, which were encumbered by firewood, litter and pasture rights), and after detailed yield study investigations he took systematic steps to meet these special conditions. *His extremely heavy interventions*, which removed 50–60 per cent of the growing stock in 70–80-year-old beech stands, *were calculated to allow complete crown closure*

---

[1] Assuming a proportion of beech in the total basal area of no more than 10–15 per cent.

to be re-established after three to four decades. The natural *regeneration which had mean-time established itself was intended to serve only as soil protection* and to die out after crown contact had been re-established, or otherwise it had to be artificially removed before the appearance of a subsequent young crop from the re-opened stand. *The original historic Seebach system therefore is a single-storeyed system.*

A few practical foresters, who after the decease of v. Seebach experimented with the proved and attractive "Seebach system", and in particular the forest research institutes, were not satisfied with one or two heavy thinning operations but repeatedly *rethinned* heavily so that the soil-protecting regeneration which had established itself was enabled to form a closed under storey. It was assumed that this oncoming pole-wood could be regarded as a future *succeeding stand,* and the resulting form of crop by this system was called a "double-storeyed beech high forest". These *later modifications of the original Seebach system* were then considered as almost identical with it, which is evident in the synonymous use of the two expressions. This we shall have to remember when, in the following passages, we discuss the performance of "Seebach systems" on the basis of experiments undertaken by the Forest Research Institute.

(a) Performance of the "Seebach System", based on Experimental "Seebach" Series

A *typical experimental series* established in the historical region of v. Seebach's activities, is *Uslar 97.*

Position. Solling, 250–300 m above sea level, NW. slope.

Climate. Temperature: annual mean 7·0°C, May–August 13·7°C; precipitation: annual mean 850 mm, May–August 300 mm; damp and cool.

Soil. Shaley clay-loam of bunter-sandstone; impoverished by previous removals of litter.

Layout. Established in 1881 in an 88-year-old stand of height Quality Class IV (quality class since increased to nearly III).

Plot I. Heavy low thinning.

Plot II. Initial basal area of 32 m² gradually reduced to 11·9 m² in two cutting operations; later increment thinnings to open-stand; thus, a *"gradual open-stand thinning".*

Plot III. Opened up and reduced to 9·2 m² by one cutting operation; later severely rethinned for increment: *"Sudden open-stand thinning."*

Table 119 below, containing the principal experimental results according to data by Wiedemann (1943), clearly shows the repeated thinning out of plots II and III as well as the increased severity of interventions from the age of 105 years on the comparative plot I. The volume increments unfortunately have been calculated only as from the age of 100 years. Nevertheless, the great growth-plasticity of beech is once again displayed by the relative percentages of the mean periodic basal area and increment at the foot of Part 1 of the table. According to these, the *average annual volume increment by gradual liberation fellings* during this 41-year increment period, *amounts to barely 6 per cent less than that by heavy low thinnings* although with sudden open-stand thinning it is 28 per cent less. But the *loss of volume increment* in comparison to a *light* low thinning would be *greater still,* because the mean natural degree of stocking of plot I with a probable maximum basal area of nearly 40 m², amounts to barely 0·7. Accordingly the mean *natural* degree of stocking for plot II would amount to only 0·47 and for III only 0·40. Therefore the

TABLE 119

EXPERIMENTAL SEEBACH SERIES USLAR 97 AFTER DATA BY WIEDEMANN (1943)

1. Periodic basal area and increment

(a) at start   (b) at the end of the age period

Age period	I. Heavy low thinning				II. Seebach "gradual"				III. Seebach "sudden"			
	N	G (m²) (a) (b)	p.m.a.i. of G (m²)	p.m.a.i. of timber > 7 cm diam. (fm)	N	G (m²) (a) (b)	p.m.a.i. of G (m²)	p.m.a.i. of timber > 7 cm diam. (fm)	N	G (m²) (a) (b)	p.m.a.i. of G (m²)	p.m.a.i. of timber > 7 cm diam. (fm)
88–100	874	31·8 / 36·5	0·40		277	11·9 / 18·0	0·51		194	9·2 / 13·5	0·36	
100–105	664	32·1 / 33·8			274	17·8 / 20·0			157	11·7 / 13·5		
105–111	470	25·7 / 27·9	0·36	6·1	253	17·7 / 20·3	0·44	5·1	156	13·4 / 15·3	0·33	4·3
111–117	411	25·8 / 28·7			176	15·7 / 18·6			153	15·0 / 17·4		
117–131	307	23·7 / 29·8	0·45	7·4	136	15·6 / 21·1	0·42	7·2	116	14·3 / 18·3	0·32	5·1
131–136	234	24·3 / 26·1			103	16·2 / 17·9			97	15·5 / 16·7		
136–141	231	25·6 / 27·9	0·40	6·8	100	17·7 / 19·5	0·36	6·2	94	16·4 / 17·9	0·28	5·4
100–141 Means:		27·4	0·41	6·9		18·3	0·41	6·5		15·6	0·31	5·0

2. State at the age of 150 years

(Timber in "Derbholz" = >7 cm dia.)

N	G	d (cm)	Timber vol.	N	G	d (cm)	Timber vol.	N	G	d (cm)	Timber vol.
183	26·5	43·0	363	99	21·9	53·1	321	94	20·2	52·2	275
Add underwood:					3·4		2		8·3		5·1

3. Value reduction of the volume of stemwood over 7 cm in diameter in the stand of 1941 by epicormic shoots

	Heavy low thng. (fm)	(%)	"Gradual opening" (fm)	(%)	"Sudden opening" (fm)	(%)
Without epicormic shoots	214	94	114	80	89	65
Thin epicormic shoots	5	2	5	4	6	4
Thick epicormic shoots	9	4	12	8	22	16
Very thick epicormic shoots	—	—	11	8	11	8
Dead and decayed shoots	—	—	—	—	9	7(!)
Total	228	100	142	100	137	100

short-fall of increment as compared with the achievable optimum on plot II lies approximately between 10 to 15 per cent.

Part 2 of Table 119 shows how much the under storey has developed after the top canopy has been heavily opened up and later rethinned severely (8·3 m² of b. area and 51 fm of timber on plot III). At the same time the values for d_m prove that diameter development on the severely thinned plot has been greatly augmented.

As regards *value production*, the information disclosed by Wiedemann in Part 3 of the table must assuredly provide food for thought. Epicormic shoots, which appeared in large numbers after the heavy thinning, have—not least because of the repeated rethinnings—developed into strong shoots and from these into thick green branches, some of which have died off and caused the intrusion of rot. Thus plot II has been reduced to C-quality by the considerable loss of 16 per cent of valuable stem-wood timber, and plot III has lost as much as 31 per cent.

Based on the prices of 1943, Wiedemann calculated the following total gross value production:

Plot	Main crop	Total of thinnings	Total value production	
	(RM)	(RM)	(RM)	(%)
I	7226	3927	11,153	100
II	7871	4995	12,866	115
III	6422	4073	10,495	94

In view of the deterioration in stem quality due to epicormic branches and loose knots, the high level of production of plot II seems open to question.

In the *experimental "Seebach" series Dalheim 98*, on a site similar to that of the crown-thinning series Dalheim 116 (cf. p. 271), the "Seebach system" (plot I) is compared with a C/D grade plot (later called "gradual open-stand thinning", plot II) and since 1928 also with moderate thinning (plot III). Calculations by Assmann (1950) resulted in the following production ratios for the period 77–109 years:

Plot	Mean period bas. area		Mean periodic increment in wood > 7 cm diam.	
	(m²)	(%)	(m³)	(%)
I. "Seebach"	21·7	85	9·0	90
II. C/D grade	25·4	100	10·0	100

Thus as compared to heavy thinning, and with a probable average natural stocking density of approximately 0·65, the production is already reduced by 10 per cent. In the further course of the experiment, the basal area of plot I has been allowed to increase, whilst on plot II it was further reduced slightly and on plot III it was kept at approximately 0·85 of the natural stocking density. An excursion guide, published by the Lower

Saxony Forest Research Institute (Prof. Dr. Schober), shows the following data for the age of 137 years (1953):

TABLE 120

Exp. pl.	Definition	N	G (m²)	h_m (m)	d_m (cm)	Mean diam. of the 96 trees with the largest diameter (cm)	V (fm)	Mean ann. increment during the age per. 113 to 137 years in		
								G (m²)	V (fm)	%
I	"Seebach"	144	34·3	31·3*	55·0	58·0	567	0·47	10·4	74
II	C/D, and									
	open-stand	96	24·3	32·3	56·8	56·8	413	0·47	10·7	76
III	Mod. thng.	188	35·0	33·1*	48·7	57·0	608	0·56	14·1	100

* The differences in mean height between I and III, amounting to no less than 1·8 in favour of moderate thinning, were caused by the strong lateral crown projection, with simultaneous reduction of height growth following open-stand thinning.

If *diameter production* is to be compared *by reference to* the *mean diameter of the ninety-six largest trees* (total stem number of the thinned stand) as Schober has done in this particular case, the *Seebach system*, despite a temporary reduction to a basal area of 16·3 m², *is not superior even to moderate thinning* And that must be taken along with a *poorer volume increment over the last 24 years, amounting to 26 per cent!*

The reason for this unsatisfactory result lies in the fact that in this "Seebach system", *unnecessarily heavy interventions to let in light* were practised *over fairly long periods without favouring any definite category of trees*. A timely start to favouring those trees with the best stems can, as already demonstrated (among other examples cf. p. 275), achieve still higher diameter increments without such a *selective increment thinning* having to encroach below the critical degree of stocking.

Confirmation can also be found in the "Seebach experiment" of the Forest Research Institute of Württemberg, the results of which were reported, among other authors, by Zimmerle (1944). There indeed the initial opening-up operation was not so heavy, and subsequent thinnings were likewise less frequent. The true mean annual diameter increments in these experiments after separating them from the "statistical shift" (Zimmerle, 1944) were only 3·1–4·3 mm (and in the extreme case of Ravensburg 4·7 mm), so that Zimmerle himself felt rather inclined to take a pessimistic view regarding the diameter production likely to be achieved in increment-felling systems for beech ("Buchen-lichtwuchsbetrieb").

The fact that much better diameter growth is attainable by different procedures is proved by the results of the *experimental increment-felling plots in Ravensburg forest*, which were established in 1935, but had, several decades earlier, already received *free-crown thinning* "of the Danish type" by the great Forstmeister v. Falckenstein, Württemberg.

According to the excerpts from a working plan, published by Zimmerle (1944), v. Falckenstein began treatment of this stand before it had reached the age of 60 years.[1]

[1] On nine occasions of cutting within 20 years a total of 352 fm/ha were removed. The condition at the age of 79 years is described by v. Falckenstein as follows: "Beech in open-stand felling. *Crown isolation of the best stems carried out*, though not with sufficient thoroughness."

The relevant figures per hectare for this "Lichtwuchs" plot *at the age of 112* were: $N = 130$, $G = 31\cdot2$, $d_m = 55\cdot3$, $h_m = 36\cdot0$, $V = 550$ fm. One hundred and twelve trees had b.h. diameters above 46 cm, *eighty-four trees above 51 cm* and two trees over 81 cm! The fact that, in this case, it is not the excellent site (recent moraine) which was the decisive factor is proved by a comparison with the poor diameter development of "normally" treated experimental beech plots of the Württemberg Research Institute on a similar site in the neighbouring forest of Wolfegg. It was undoubtedly the result of the treatment, which in Zimmerle's opinion amounted "more to an increment-felling ('Lichtwuchs') system, or at least a considerably modified Seebach cutting".

(b) Modern Increment-felling Procedure ("Lichtwuchsbetrieb")
in Common Beech

The increment-felling system received new and strong impetus from a situation of economic emergency. During the Second World War, large quantities of timber had to be produced in Germany within a short time, without causing artificial restocking of the areas. This was to be achieved mainly by a transition to the Lichtwuchs system (especially in beech stands and in Scots pine stands with an under storey), and the then Reichsforstamt (State Forest Department) appointed suitable experts to make effective preparations accordingly in all forest regions. Numerous demonstration plots of the Lichtwuchs system in beech, which were established, among others, by v. Rechtern (1942, 1944), Olberg, Pflaum, W. Freist and Assmann (1943, 1949), today offer welcome opportunities *for an examination of the productivity of the modern Lichtwuchs system*. This has been done in a work by H. Freist.

Models in the forests of Brunswick (Mahler, 1937) and personal experience induced Assmann (1943) to stress the advantages of a "purposeful opening-up of the stand", which favours the trees with the best stems, and to warn against any unnecessary increase in the opening-up of the stand. Reflection concerning the incurred increment losses led him to the *concept of the "critical basal area"* (1949a, 1950a). The attempt made in Table 121 at dividing the "felling systems for beech stands" into the individual types in practice allows the "Lichtwuchs system" to be defined with sufficient accuracy. The criterion for the difference between ordinary *thinning* ("Durchforstung") and *open-stand felling* ("Lichtung") in this case is the *cutting to below the critical basal area* in the latter system which causes *increment losses of more than 5 per cent in a decade*. In comparison with these, the *"Lichtwuchs system" appears as an intermediate form*, somewhere *at the margin between thinning and open-stand thinning*, with concessions to temporary increment losses up to 10 per cent.

The *classic Seebach system is a single-storeyed form of open-stand system*, clearly set apart from the two-storeyed types with which the Seebach system has hitherto mistakenly been identified. In the (modern) Lichtwuchs system we distinguish between two forms. The first one, characterized as "intensive heavy crown thinning with a limited number of final stems", is identical with the ideal thinning method for beech with which we have already become acquainted (p. 283) except that, in this case, the *extreme permissible degree of heavy thinning* is consciously sought. The second type, being a modification of the classic Seebach system, is defined as "moderate Seebach system". It is used in older stands of beech which are devoid of a sufficient under storey. As a rule, the advance regeneration which has become established is intended to serve as soil cover to prevent

TABLE 121

FELLING SYSTEM IN BEECH STANDS (AFTER ASSMANN)

I. *Thinning system*

("Durchforstungsbetrieb")

Characteristics:

As a rule, interventions repeated at short intervals, *but avoiding cutting to below the critical level of basal area.*

II. *Open-stand system*

("Lichtungsbetrieb")

Characteristics:

As a rule, few but heavy thinnings *cutting to below the critical basal area,* so that the opened stand suffers increment losses of more than 5 per cent per decade relative to its original state.

1. *Single-storeyed form*

The emphasis of the system lies upon the opened stand; any possible undergrowth has merely silvicultural functions (soil protection, safety of the main regeneration): *"Classic Seebach system".*

2. *Double-storeyed forms*

The underwood is considered to be the succeeding stand.

(a) The emphasis of the system is shared almost evenly between the opened stand and the undergrowth: *"Two-storeyed high forest".*

(b) The emphasis of the system lies in the underwood as succeeding stand: upper storey limited to 25–40 stems (up to approximately 6 m^2):*"System of Reserves".*

III. *Increment-felling ("Lichtwuchs") system*

Characteristics:

Whilst cautiously approaching the critical basal area—temporary increment losses up to 10 per cent can be allowed—the aim is to achieve the fastest possible diameter increment of the best-shaped trees of the stand with a minimum of silvicultural disadvantages.

Form 1:

Without soil protecting regeneration:

Soil protection is provided by the existing under storey: *"Intensive, heavy crown thinning, retaining a limited number of final stems".* Modifications in accordance with the degree of tending already given.

Form 2:

With soil protecting regeneration:

Soil protection is provided by the intermediate regeneration which has to give way to the main regeneration: *"Moderate Seebach system".*

weed growth; owing, however, to its poor shape, which is to be expected after having been overcast for some decades by the dense crowns of a Lichtwuchs stand with 22–25 m^2 basal area, it should not be considered suitable to take the place of the present main crop. This is much more suitably formed from a second, or principal regeneration.[1] Of course,

---

[1] Examples of a very successful second regeneration, in which the "soil protecting regeneration" was cleverly used to form a combined canopy, were shown by Forstmeister Metelmann in a section of Leinefelde forest (Eichsfeld).

it is also possible, following the originally introduced "moderate Seebach system", to rethin severely in the upper storey before the soil-protecting young crop becomes mis-shapen, and thus to transform to a two-storeyed "reserves system". The form chosen will have to depend on the site, the structure of the stand, the number of trees per hectare with good stems worth favouring (unfortunately there are frequently only thirty or forty of these) and the requirements of the system.

The Lichtwuchs indicator plots of Common beech in Fabrikschleichach forest

A particularly good opportunity to examine the production of a modern Lichtwuchs system and to compare it with the results of long-observed experimental beech series is given in Fabrikschleichach forest where such an indicator plot exists directly adjacent to the experimental beech series Fabrikschleichach (cf. p. 256) in the same stand and on the same site. As at Ravensburg, this Lichtwuchs plot has been systematically crown-thinned for almost two decades by a first-class practical forester, Oberforstmeister Pflaum. The analyses of increment, made by Freist (1960) showed the results (Table 122) in comparison to the B-plot.

TABLE 122

REMAINING STAND AT THE AGE OF 135 YEARS

Plot	Percentage of ground cover	N	G (m²)	d_m (cm)	Wood over 7 cm diam.		
					Total (fm)	Quality A (fm)	% of stock
B	85	376	43·9	38·9	756	57	8
Lichtwuchs	71	134	24·6	48·0	405	71	18

Annual increment during the period 120–135 years

	i_d without statistical shift (mm)	I_V (fm)	%	with a mean per. basal area of (m²)	(%)
B	2·5	11·5	100	41·1	100
Lichtwuchs	5·1	8·8	77	22·9	56

Not with standing that a loss in volume increment was incurred amounting to 23 per cent in comparison to the B-plot (which has nearly optimum increment), the true mean annual diameter growth of the mean stem on the Lichtwuchs plot (after deduction of the statistical shift) amounted to 5·1 mm, being twice that on the B-plot, whilst at the same time the quantity of stem-wood of quality A was noticeably increased. As shown in Fig. 130, which is based on the development of the mean diameter of the 100 largest trees per hectare, the Lichtwuchs plot overtook all three neighbouring plots, including the C-plot; after rising sharply in 1932 (crown thinning by Oberforstmeister Pflaum) the rate of diameter increase became steeper still from 1943 onwards.

The mean stems of two other plots in Fabrikschleichach forest, with mean periodic basal areas of 19–20 m², achieved annual diameter increments (without statistical adjustment) of 4·5 and 5·0 mm respectively.

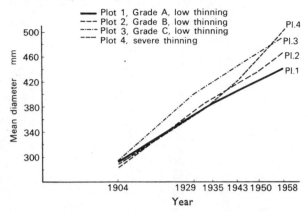

FIG. 130. Beech trial series at Fabrikschleichach. Diameter development of the 100 largest stems per hectare.

Results of Lichtwuchs experiments in the Taunus, Solling and Harz

Similarly favourable production figures were obtained from *five Lichtwuchs plots in the Taunus*, which were *established by* Rechtern. With mean periodic basal areas between 14 and 28 m², usually between 20 and 22 m², the mean annual *diameter increments fluctuate between 4·3 and 5·5 mm*. With mean periodic basal areas between 20 and 22 m², 80–100 per cent of the volume increment production shown in Wiedemann's yield table for moderate thinning were achieved, which suggests that there are volume increment losses of from 5–25 per cent below the potential local optimum production.

Assmann established an indicator plot in Uslar forest (medium bunter-sandstone under a thick surface layer of loessic loam) which at the age of 95 years, after 17 years under Lichtwuchs treatment, had a ground cover of 89 per cent (with a current annual increment of 117 per cent of Wiedemann's yield table), the mean stem of the remaining 259 trees of Kraft classes 1–4 on this area achieved a mean annual diameter increment of 5·2 mm; *in the remaining 165 trees of tree class 1 this is even 5·6 mm*. The stock of A-quality timber on this plot at the age of 95 years amounted to no less than 113 fm = 45 per cent of stem-wood and 24 per cent of the wood (Derbholz) over 7 cm in diameter. Of the original eighty-five (per ha) specially favoured high-grade trees, the seventy-seven which remain have a mean diameter of almost 45 cm (largest measured value 55 cm). The mean periodic basal area amounted to 25·4 m², the under storey with 1·9 m² not being included.

Two plots established by Assmann in 1943 in beech stands more than a century old in Wieda forest are also notable for having large quantities of A-quality timber (see Figs. 131-2), namely 95 fm in each contributing respectively 46 and 35 per cent of the total stem-wood and 26 and 21 per cent of the total wood of timber dimensions ("Derbholz"). The mean diameter increments of the existing 109 and 120 trees per hectare of Kraft classes 1 and 2 amount to 4·1 and 4·6 mm respectively. In connection with the production figures set forth in the discussion upon crown thinning experiments (p. 281), these results prove *the superiority of a Lichtwuchs system which systematically promotes the growth of those trees with the best stems as contrasted with the unspecified and excessively*

FIG. 131. Open stand trial 59 at Wieda. Beech. Inventory, 1960. Felling age = 130; $N = 158$ including eighty high grade trees; $G = 23 \cdot 4$ m², of this $13 \cdot 7$ m² were high grade trees with a mean diameter of 47 cm. Stemwood Cl. A = 95 fm/ha.

liberal admission *of light such as has frequently been practised in outdated imitations and rather unwise modifications of the classic Seebach system.*[1]

[1] A great practical forester in the Solling, Forstmeister Bräuer, who during the establishment of a new Seebach experiment reduced the basal area of the stand in question over a period of 13 years by several well-proportioned felling operations from 32 to 20 m², and considered further open-stand thinning as unnecessary, was forced by the inspecting authority to reduce the basal area to 16 m² by a further severe thinning operation!

FIG. 132. Open stand area 61 at Wieda. Beech. Inventory 1948. Felling age $= 104$; $N = 240$, including eighty-eight high grade trees; $G = 22\cdot5$ m², of this $11\cdot8$ m² were high grade trees with a mean diameter of 41 cm.

The effect of the Lichtwuchs system on the stem taper, specific gravity and quality of timber

Whilst Zimmerle (1936, 1944), by observation of the diameter development at $5\cdot0$ m height and with the help of the form quotient $q_5 = d_{5\cdot0} : d_{1\cdot3}$, observed a considerable increase in the taper of the valuable butt-log, recent measurements by Freist (1960) proved that, on the observed fourteen Lichtwuchs plots, no such lowering of the form could be attributed to the fellings. "In the examined material there is no evidence that crown isolation has affected the form of stem shaft up to the base of the crown. The cause may well lie in the strength and solidity of the beech timber."

Freist also examined the *influence of the widening of annual rings* by the Lichtwuchs system *on the specific gravity* of the wood. For this purpose he used a new method, developed by Kennel (1965, *A.F.J.Z.*, No. 7), which allowed him to determine the specific gravity from increment cores obtained with the help of ordinary borers. From 3653 individual samples, he found a *mean specific gravity of 564 kg/m³* ($\pm 3 \cdot 86$ per cent), which meant that the *specific gravity had dropped slightly (by 1–2 per cent)* during the 15 to 20 years since the beginning of open-stand treatment. But this corresponds to the normal systematic decrease in specific gravity with increasing distance from the pith. *According to this observation, open-stand treatment has no effect on the specific gravity, nor*—as proved by Pechmann's related investigations (1953)—*on the strength characteristics of beech timber*.

On the other hand, Lichtwuchs stands were found to carry a *typical zone of thick green branches and thickened epicormic shoots* which reduce the timber quality from grade B to C. Depending on the severity and suddenness of thinning, the volume ratio of the correspondingly less valuable timber amounts to 8–26 per cent of the total stem-wood. In agreement with statements by Wiedemann for the experimental series Uslar, Freist estimated that *an average of 20 per cent* of the stem-wood ratio in the final yield is thus reduced in quality and that *30 per cent of the stem-wood may be reduced to C-quality by extremely heavy open-stand thinning* (compared to 10 per cent by moderate thinning).

On the other hand, an average 40 per cent of stem-wood sizes in the final growing-crop capable of qualifying in the higher price-bracket (class 3b and larger sizes) do yield A-quality timber. "The proportion of assortments which can command a higher price range is a function of the mean diameter, so that given the equivalent combination of conditions governing quality at the outset, those stands which have been well opened up are superior in their A-quality production according to the respective diameter categories than more lightly-thinned stands. The proportion of cordwood timber (cf. p. 268) expressed as a function of the mean diameter of the stand remains unaffected by the severity of thinning, and only after further isolation of the crowns (so that they become standards) does it increase by some 5–10 per cent."

TABLE 123

COMPARISON BETWEEN WIEDEMANN'S YIELD TABLE (W) FOR OPEN-STAND THINNING IN BEECH (1943) AND FREIST'S YIELD TABLE (F) FOR A LICHTWUCHS TREATMENT OF BEECH (1960)

Age	Stem number		Main crop Basal area		d_m		Total crop volume		Thinnings percentage	
	W	F	W (m²)	F (m²)	W (cm)	F (cm)	W (fm)	F (fm)	W (%)	F (%)
40	2605	2215	24·6	23·0	11·0	11·5	153	154	5·4	7
60	1205	770	30·0	23·0	17·8	19·5	383	348	19·4	32
80	369	360	20·8	24·0	26·8	29·1	614	570	53·1	41
100	144	205	15·9	25·0	37·5	39·4	799	784	69·8	48
120	99	128	17·4	26·0	47·4	50·8	971	975	69·4	52
140	80	86	20·7	27·0	57·3	63·2	1146	1149	66·1	55

Freist's (1960) new yield table for the Lichtwuchs treatment of Common beech

Freist summarized the inter-relationships between stem number, basal area and dia-meter increment of the mean stem *in a regression function,* derivable from his collected data. This serves as a basis for a new yield table for the Lichtwuchs treatment. This is characterized as *"heavy crown thinning with a restricted final number of stems"* in the sense used by Assmann and corresponds to form 1 in Table 121. The mean height devel-opment is based on Wiedemann's yield table for open-stand thinning, 1943 and the total crop volume yield of that table is exceeded by only a very trifling amount. On the other hand, the new table avoids those heavy reductions of basal area after the age of 70 years, as can be seen by comparing the data columns in Table 123.[1] These reductions were probably provided by Wiedemann, not only in order to have a close link with the average results of the Seebach experiments (as stressed by Assmann, 1953, in his criticism) but in order to meet the then (1943) acute need for large yields of billetwood (fuel for generators) Nowadays such treatment would be quite mistaken because it would cause an unneces-sary loss of increment and supply material of such low value that the income would hardly cover the harvesting costs. The values in the new table are restricted to Kraft's tree classes 1–4. In addition, this table provides for an *under storey for soil-cover and stem-cleaning* with an ultimate basal area of 2 m² and timber amounting to 20 fm; the yields of this can be disregarded.

The total production of timber ("Derbholz") at different final ages thus amounts to:

Yield tables	120 (fm)	140 (fm)	160 (fm)
Wiedemann, qual. cl. I, mod. thng.	1042	1243	
Wiedemann, qual. cl. I, heavy thng.	1018	1193	
Wiedemann, qual. cl. I, open-stand	971	1146	1314
Freist (1960), Lichtwuchs treatment	975*	1149*	—

* Without under storey.

At the same time, the following mean diameters with thinning volume percentages are arrived at in the final stand:

Final age	120 d_m (cm)	Thinning (%)	140 d_m (cm)	Thinning (%)	160 (d_m) (cm)	Thinning (%)
Wiedemann, qual. cl. I						
moderate thinning	40·1	44	47·9	49	—	—
heavy thinning	43·6	58	53·6	62	—	—
Wiedemann, open-stand	47·4	69	57·3	66	67·1	64
Freist, Lichtwuchs treatment	50·8	52	63·2	55		

[1] The new table assumes heavier interventions at the pole-wood stage—the phase when the form and shape are most easily influenced and the elasticity of the increment is most pronounced—than does Wiede-mann's table, in which the basal area at the age of 60 years corresponds to a natural degree of stocking of 0·80–0·85. It thus gains a lead in diameter development which is retained with an approximately con-stant degree of stocking of 0·60.

As a result of consequent tending and encouragement of the best-formed trees, the new table achieves *higher mean diameters with lower percentages of intermediate yields.* As the main proportion of the value production lies in the final stand, this of course means *lower cordwood produce and at the same time higher money yields.*

Financial production in the Lichtwuchs treatment of beech

Freist's calculation of the financial production is again based on extremely cautious assumptions. For example, he used the average incomes of the Hesse territory in 1959, and obtained only a small price-range for stem-wood with diameters larger than those of class 4 and only a *19 per cent increase in the price for A-quality* in comparison to B-quality. In addition to harvesting costs, there are 55 per cent taxes and 10 per cent surcharge for local difficulties. The "value curves per solid cu. m" (cf. Fig. 133) obtained by Freist for the two methods of treatment with the following assumed percentages:

	C-quality ratio in stemwood	A-quality ratio in stemwood
Moderate thinning	10%	7%
Lichtwuchs	20%	40%

are distinctly different only in the upper part, i.e. from b.h.d. = 50 cm, but the differences in favour of the Lichtwuchs treatment are disappointingly small owing to the small price differentials and other connected circumstances. Despite this, the Lichtwuchs method does fairly well in a *comparison of the average value increments* (av. val. inc.), the values for the different rotations being as follows:

	$R = 120$ av. val. inc.		$R = 140$ av. val. inc.		$R = 160$ av. val. inc.	
	(DM)	(%)	(DM)	(%)	(DM)	(%)
Wiedemann, mod. thng.	254	100	312	100	—	—
Wiedemann, heavy thng.	254	100	299	96	—	—
Wiedemann, open-stand	250	99	290	93	315	—
Freist, Lichtwuchs	288	*113*	320	103	—	—

Owing to the small yield of billetwood and the large production of A-quality timber, the Lichtwuchs treatment at R = 120 is considerably superior to all other compared methods and at R = 140 also to open-stand thinning. The fact that the production by moderate thinning undergoes a strong increase from $R = 120$ to $R = 140$ is not surprising and corresponds to the fundamental conclusions and views of Mitscherlich (1954) and Olberg (1951).

Unfortunately there is a strong probability, in agreement with an assumption by Zycha (1948), that with increasing age the *proportion of dark heartwood increases.* This was proved by Freist with the help of the results of carefully collected statistics in Walkenried forest; according to Fig. 134 their total result makes it probable that the *proportion*

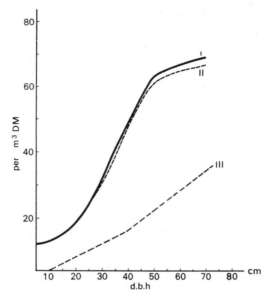

FIG. 133. Value curves d.b.h. (per festmetre) for beech. Prices less harvesting costs for Hesse territory, 1959. Curve I: open stand system; II: moderate thinning, without tending of the young growth; III: curve by Wiedemann, 1931 and 1943 *(Freist)*.

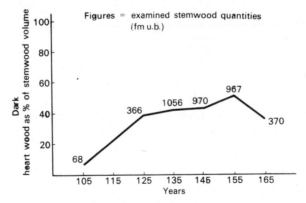

FIG. 134. Proportion of stem-wood containing dark heartwood plotted over the stand age. Figures = examined quantities of stem-wood in festmetres *(Freist)*.

of dark heartwood undergoes a considerable *increase with age*, especially from the age of 105–155. Seen in this light it is a decisive advantage that the optimum saleable stem-wood dimensions in the Lichtwuchs method are reached 20 years earlier than with moderate thinning.

Taking into consideration the currently expected general costs (data of the economic results of the Hesse territory), Freist calculated also *the net forest yield* per annum for the same methods of treatment. Owing to the high proportion of fixed costs the Lichtwuchs system in this case does even better. It should be remembered that, assuming a total initial cost (including tending of the young growth and first cleaning) of 2000 DM per hectare of an established young stand, these with $R = 120$, amount to 17 DM annually per hectare of a working section area, with $R = 140$ to only 14 DM and with $R = 160$ to 12 DM.

Freist arrived at the following values for *forest net yield* for the different rotations:

	$R = 120$		$R = 140$		$R = 160$	
	(DM)	(%)	(DM)	(%)	(DM)	(%)
Wiedemann, mod. thinning	27	100	88	100	—	—
Wiedemann, heavy thinning	27	100	75	85	—	—
Wiedemann, open-stand	23	85	66	75	95	—
Freist, Lichtwuchs	61	226	96	109	—	—

These figures display, amongst other facts, that for existing rich stocks of beech timber and complete felling series there is *no necessity to provide for lower rotations*, and especially not in the present economic situation. A compelling reason, however, might arise where there is an increase of dark heartwood, if this starts early owing to local conditions.

(c) TWO-STOREYED HIGH FOREST AND HIGH FOREST WITH RESERVES SYSTEM

The suggested scheme in Table 121 (p. 375) distinguishes between two special forms of the two-storeyed system, the "two-storeyed high forest" and the "high forest with reserves system". Between these, obviously, there can be many intermediate forms. However, with reserves, it is of crucial importance to limit the amount of shade permitted to be cast by the trees in the upper canopy, or to restrict the basal area of those trees accordingly. It is only by keeping within bounds the intense shade thrown by the wide crowns of the old beech trees that it will be possible to safeguard the quality of the trees in the under storey so that the succeeding crop is not imperilled. This situation is convincingly demonstrated in a stand which was closely examined by Freist, viz.

The beech crop under Lichtwuchs treatment in the locality of "Kleinengelein",
in Hundelshausen forest

This beech stand, which at the 1958 assessment was 178 years old, has remained at the espacement to which it was opened up 44 years age for regeneration. The remaining crop of approximately 100 trees per hectare have reached impressive diameters and again formed a completely closed canopy. At the same time, the quality of the under storey which now consists of slender poles, is decisively reduced after 44 years under top spade. The most important data for the *upper storey* are as follows: $N = 104$, $G = 31 \cdot 6$ m², $d_m = 62 \cdot 3$ cm, $h_m = 37 \cdot 5$ m; $V = 623$ fm; annual increments during the last 15 years: $I_G = 0 \cdot 247$, $I_V = 5 \cdot 8$ fm. Ground cover percentage $= 81$.

The dimensions and quality of the *under-storey* are best judged by comparing it with a neighbouring pole crop of the same age originating from a parent crop which was systematically cleared and removed 40 years ago. In both cases the age is *53 years*.

TABLE 124

COMPARISON BETWEEN TWO 53-YEAR-OLD BEECH POLEWOOD STANDS IN HUNDELSHAUSEN FOREST
(KLEINENGELEIN)

Definition	Still under cover	Uncovered 40 years ago
Height qual. cl.	V.0	II.0
Stem number	2420	2744
Of these dominant	933	
Well-formed	182	
Basal area m²	3·24	29·49
d_m cm	4·1	11·7
h_m m	6·1	16·4
V_D fm	2·9	223·1
Removed in thinnings, fm (u.b.)	—	34

Clearance of the overwood today, even by the most cautious felling and previous lopping of the crowns, would leave hardly any useful trees in the under storey.[1] As a succeeding stand it would be completely useless. This would have to be created anew, which imposes great difficulties. The overwood contains no less than 215 fm which is 35 per cent A-quality timber and represents a value, free of harvesting costs, of 40,140 DM/ha, compared with 38,130 DM of the B-plot of Fabrikschleichach on a comparable site. The current value increment,[2] on the other hand, has already dropped to 310 DM/ha, compared to 797 DM/ha of the B-plot of Fabrikschleichach. Unfortunately it is to be feared that this value increment, which has been estimated from external characteristics, will be further diminished by a possible increase in dark heartwood development and the beginnings of heart-rot. Although the Lichtwuchs stand "Kleinengelein" is very valuable as an example and, so to speak, as a living monument, in practice this system is hardly to be recommended.

Two-storeyed beech high-forest system in Walkenried forest

Another instructive example is that of Walkenried forest in the Southern Harz. The 1885 working plan for this area provided 127 hectares to be treated by this system, and clear prescriptions, based on the doctrines of v. Seebach and Kraft, were formulated for bringing it into effect.

According to these, the *ground cover* at the end of the second rotation was *not to exceed 0·3*, which according to Kraft corresponds approximately to 0·2 of the basal area

[1] That this kind of inferior shape of tree in the under storey may be expected even under a less extreme canopy, is shown by the experimental plot in *Koppenbrügge* forest, *Compt. 50*, which Wiedemann (1953, *Z.f.F.u.J.*, p. 230) described as follows: 117-year-old, Q. Cl. I, seventy-seven mature beech trees per hectare, 17 m² basal area and 250 fm timber volume. "Ideal example of a two-storeyed high forest on lime soil consisting of the best quality beech, the old trees showing excellent stem and crown shape *but with heavily suppressed undergrowth despite their permanent isolation*" (italics by the author). The author was able to obtain confirmation of this during an inspection of the locality in 1950. This is, as widely known, unfortunately a common phenomenon; it is, however, willingly overlooked by foresters who like to have selection or at least group selection treatment even in broad-leaved crops.

[2] The average value of 66 DM per solid m³ has remained unchanged during the last 15 years, based on the price graduation adopted in the average-income statements of the Forest Administration of Hesse in 1958.

of the full stand. From the age of 70 years, fifty to sixty trees per hectare were to be selected and marked with oil paint and then to be prepared as reserves by releasing the crowns. With an expected number of only thirty reserves at the age of 100 years some forty to fifty stems were initially to be retained in groups, in order to provide against possible casualties.

The anticipated losses, however, did not eventuate, and forty to sixty reserves were counted per hectare in the 110-year-old overwood at the 1929 working plan; under their canopy a 45-year-old pole crop, grown from natural regeneration, was badly suppressed. The extraction of the reserves was gradually and successfully carried out without much damage to the under storey, thanks to an unproved crown-lopping pro-cedure, which was organized by Forstmeister Freist. Thus from an initial growing-stock of 13,635 *fm (over bark)* ($=$ 107 fm o.b. per ha.) in 1929, 13,655 *fm u.b. of timber* had been extracted by 1960.

This supplied   36 per cent billet wood over 7 cm diameter,
and   64 per cent stem-wood,

divided into   30 per cent A
                            40 per cent B
                             4 per cent C
                            26 per cent sleepers

The present growing-stock (1959) amounts to 4720 fm timber volume (o.b.). Refrain-ing from realizing approximately 2570 fm (o.b.) in the year 1885 has been rewarded by a *production of about 18,500 fm* o. b. in the shape of *large-diameter beech*, which on average have yielded 19 per cent of cl. 3, 41 per cent of cl. 4, 31 per cent of cl. 5 and 9 per cent of cl. 6 so far; the additional harvesting costs due to topping the crowns amounted to 5 DM per fm.

The *quality of the succeeding stand* which at present has an average age of 75 years is satisfactory as proved by an inventory of a representative sample plot (see Table 125).

TABLE 125

Tree class	N	G (m²)	d_m (cm)	h_m (m)	V_D (fm)
1	158	6·71	23·3	21·1	
2	192	4·15	16·6	19·0	
3	95	1·46	14·0	17·3	
4	236	2·28	11·1	14·2	
5	1368	3·61	5·8	7·2	
1–3	445	12·32			
1–5	2049	18·22			170·4

The stem quality of approximately 70 per cent of the 445 dominant and co-dominant trees is good to fair. Owing to the shade cast by the upper canopy, the number of stems is small and the height quality class of approximately II.5 is a half-class lower than for a stand which had not been so covered. The periodic mean annual increments over the last 10 years amounted to:

basal area	0·71 m²
timber (over 7 cm diameter)	6·8 fm
At the same time, increment of the reserves[1]	1·6 fm
Therefore present total volume growth	8·4 fm

As against this we can expect from a 75-year-old stand of II quality about 10·5 fm.

How considerably the *canopy pressure of the reserves reduces the production of a covered beech polewood*, has been shown by increment measurements on a circular sample plot with a radius of 5 m around one of the surviving standards. Freist found the following *ground cover values*:

For the reserve	0·75 dm³/m² ground cover
For the covered polewood	0·32 dm³/m² ground cover

From these can be calculated the following yields per hectare:

	Degree of disengagement	Production per hectare (fm)
Reserve	8·3 (= 12% total ground cover)	*0·9*
Covered polewood	1·18 (= 85% total ground cover)	*2·7*

It is difficult to estimate the percentage of total ground cover occupied by reserves which would cause a general increment reduction of such gross extent in the under storey. Assuming 65 per cent, corresponding to a degree of disengagement of 1·54 with a production of 4·9 fm by the reserves, there would be an additional 2·7 fm from the second storey. Bearing in mind the considerable amount of side light which the shaded polewood receives with only 12 per cent cover (eleven reserves per ha), it becomes obvious, what *small productions of increment we can count upon getting from the under storey if the cover were made any heavier.*

On the basis of assessments of other opened stands with an under storey, Freist calculated *critical limits for the density of cover in the two-storeyed system*, beyond which a lower quality of stem and stunted form of growth of the under storey is to be anticipated. For this calculation he assumed a mean annual diameter increment of the reserves of 4–6 mm and a crown projection ratio of 10–20 (corresponding to a canopy area factor of 350–400).

State of development of the under storey	Largest acceptable upper storey	
	G (m²)	Ground cover (%)
Thicket	16–20	50%
Saplings	12	40%
Small pole-wood	8	30%
Medium pole-wood	4	15%

[1] The number of remaining reserves is eleven per hectare with 3·1 m² basal area and 12 per cent ground cover.

FIG. 135. A 160-year-old beech standard among 60-year-old polewood at Wieda forest. Inventory, spring 1948. $d = 97$ cm. Stemwood Cl. A = 4·5 fm.

This is assuming that it is possible progressively, to *reduce the over storey*, without causing too much felling damage. This has been shown possible by means of the excellent silvicultural technique employed in Walkenried forest, but ought not to be taken as applying in general. For average practice, therefore, it is advisable *to limit the number of standards to thirty at the start of a two-storeyed system*, as provided in the far-seeing plan of 1885, and to concentrate the reserves in strips along paths, etc., in order to facilitate extraction. With a mean b.h.d. of 45 cm in the reserves 4 m² of basal area would amount to twenty-five reserves and 6 m² to thirty-eight, equal to a total ground cover already at the start of the system of 14 and 21 per cent respectively. This definitive type of

System of reserves

This corresponds to the two-storeyed type II, 2, b, of the scheme by Assmann (Table 121). *It is to be preferred to the "two-storeyed high forest"*, described under (a), *because it enables large target diameters to be achieved in trees of selected quality, without endangering the quality of the succeeding stand or prejudicing too severely its development and productivity.*

An example of the potential capabilities of individual reserves or standards is to be found in the locality of Knicking, Wieda forest (close by Walkenried), where it grows at the end of a water-collecting trough on weathered diabase. In 1959, at the age of 171 years, this tree had achieved a b.h. diameter of 105 cm (cf. data by Assmann, 1949, in *Fw. Cbl.*, p. 149); about 70 years ago it was isolated, and since that time it has produced a mean *annual i_d of 7 mm* (!) with still no signs of slackening. Unfortunately, increment drillings of this tree show evidence of heart unsoundness and the beginnings of white rot, so that the value of the butt-log although outwardly of A-quality, is imperilled for at least 5 m³ of its contents. Once again, this illustrates the marvellous capacity for increment production of beech, even in old age. In this connection see Fig. 135.

Proportionality limit in beech; degree of disengagement and production per unit area

A considerable body of relevant data led Freist to pose the question: *"Below what basal area per hectare will liberation cuttings in beechwoods of 100 or more years in age lead to a proportionate falling-off in the increment per unit area?"*

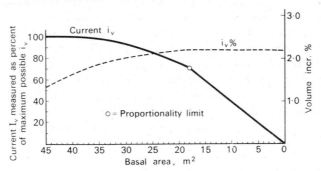

FIG. 136. Schematic representation of the relationship between basal area, volume increment and increment percentage in over 100-year-old beech stands on sites to Quality Classes I and II *(Freist)*.

Research upon this problem in an experimental Lichtwuchs plot in Fabrikschleichach produced a *basal area value of 18·5 m²* with a *total ground cover of 67 per cent*[1], corresponding to an average *degree of disengagement of 1·5.* Further calculations produced basal area values for the proportionality limit between 18 and 22 m² mean periodic basal area, which ought to be equal to *natural degrees of stocking maintained between 0·40–0·50.* Figure 136 shows the probable average relationships between the periodic basal area, current volume increment and increment percentage. A maximum basal area of 45 m²

[1] Measured not immediately after open-stand thinning, but at least 5 years later.

in a 100–130-year-old stand is assumed with height Q. Classes I and II. Accordingly the increment at the proportionality limit of approximately 18 m² basal area would still be approximately *70 per cent of the attainable optimum increment of timber*. Although the curve gives only approximate expression of the relationship and an exact experimental determination on given sites would show somewhat different trends, the one shown is probably *fundamentally correct*. It leads to noteworthy conclusions. Whereas the increment-reducing consequences of thinning in the region between the maximum and the critical basal areas are almost entirely balanced by the increasing open-stand increment of the individual trees, this balance is no longer quite so likely in the region between the critical basal area and the point where proportionality begins. Below this limit the open-stand increment of the individual trees does not increase; the increment percent remains constant. Thus it follows that the removal of every 1 m² of basal area from the crop leads to *increasing losses to the possible optimum increment*. Assuming for the maximum basal area of 45 m² a current annual increment of 10 fm, we would obtain the following results:

Basal area	Increment	Therefore in the region of	Average increment losses per m², of reduced basal area
(m²)	(fm)	(m²)	(fm)
45	10·0		
31	9·5	45–31	0·04
18	7·0	31–18	0·19
0	0·0	18–0	0·39

This means that the absolute figures of increment loss for every square metre reduction of basal area go on increasing to a maximum value of 0·39 fm per square metre, at which they reach the proportionality limit and from then on they stay at that value. Progressive open-stand thinning thus causes grave increment losses. Despite the excellent elasticity of increment in beech, these losses are *heavier than* Wiedemann's range of basal areas for nearly full increment *had hitherto led us to suppose*.

The lower limit given by Wiedemann, namely 20 m² basal area, is already near the proportionality limit, certainly for older stands on good-quality sites. Wiedemann's mistake is understandable if one bears in mind the extreme variability of the volume increment values at his disposal, which scarcely allowed him to detect possible differences of production within the region of 40–20 m² where the falling-off of increment is both moderate and gradual. But for those basal areas below 20 m² such steeper losses were involved that Wiedemann was driven to assess them only by cruder methods of reckoning. Furthermore, all the comparative plots in the experimental open-stand series of the former Prussian Research Institute were "heavy thinning" plots, in many cases with a natural stocking density of 0·6 and less.

Investigations in the *covered under-storey* have further made it clear that *drastic increment losses* will be suffered there. Even with a ground cover of 20 to 60 per cent, these must none the less be considerable. According to investigations by Baumgartner (cf. p. 118) a cover of that order already cuts off so much of the incoming *total radiation* that the effect on the increment of the under storey is more detrimental than the simultaneous deprivation of photosynthetically effective rays. Again, this consideration speaks clearly against the "two-storeyed high forest" as commonly conceived and in favour of a definite "system of reserves".

With reference to the scheme of felling systems for beech in Table 121, the following points are summarily stressed:

1. Lichtwuchs system, Type 1: "Intensive, heavy thinning with a limited number of final stems" represents the *ideal solution*, which within relatively short production periods supplies a maximum of valuable large diameter timber and ensures systematic regeneration.

2. Lichtwuchs system, Type 2: "The moderate Seebach system" is a *make-shift solution* for our beech forests with large stocks of old trees but inadequate diameter development. It should be suitable, where there are sufficient trees with good stems (at least eighty per hectare) as future "producers of A-quality timber".

3. For stands possessing but few trees of A-quality potential, *deferred clearance and conversion to the reserves system* seems advisable. This demands closed natural regeneration of good shape on a sufficiently large area of the stand (strip, or shelter-wood felling), so that high quality is ensured for the succeeding stand. Even if gaps in the regeneration have to be filled with fast-growing coniferous trees, for example Japanese larch or Douglas fir, it seems a mistake to endanger the quality of the future broad-leaved crop by a regeneration method of the selection type.[1]

2. The Scots Pine Standards (or Reserves) System

In this two-storeyed form of felling system, which is widespread in the German Scots pine regions (Görlitzer Heide, Lüneburger Heide, Upper Hesse and Rhine-Main plain, Pfälzerwald, Upper and Central Franconia, Lake Constance region), we can distinguish between two forms:

(a) with almost pure Scots pine in the under storey,
(b) with a rich proportion of shade-tolerant species in the under storey.

(a) SCOTS PINE STANDARDS SYSTEM WITH PURE SCOTS PINE IN THE UNDER STOREY

Baader (1941) discussed this type in an excellent and exhaustive manner in his well-known paper: "Der Kiefernüberhaltsbetrieb". The investigated systems have a combination of rotations, as a rule 80 to 100 years in the under storey and 160 to 200 years in the upper storey. The number of reserves as a rule *drops initially from approximately 50 to approximately 20; thus the ground cover percentage*, with crown diameters of, on average, 6 m (at the start) to 9 m (at the finish), amounts to *12–15 per cent*.

Baader compared the volume production of the standards system with the potential yield of a normal single-storeyed system on a rotation of 80–100 years. Obviously the canopy shade of the reserves must severely reduce the growth of the light-demanding pine trees in the under storey. This canopy pressure is clearly demonstrated in the shape of the so-called *"plates"*. These are areas around the base of the stems of standards,

---

[1] Arnswaldt's (1958) comparison of the production of a "normal age class forest" and an "irregular shelter-wood system" *(femelschlag)* in beech forests favours the latter system, because it contains opinionated basic assumptions as to the advantages of that system; but, in the three methods of treatment of the "normal age class forest", which are sketched here, such advantages may be realized at least equally as effectively.

completely bare or stocked with dying individuals of the under storey. As illustrated in Fig. 137, they are not round but elliptic, and their widest distance across is perpendicular to the prevailing direction of the wind. Oddly, there are no definite relationships between the site and the size of the "plates". Baader found especially small plates in Isenburg forest, where natural regeneration is practised, in Fulda South forest and in Görlitz forest (on alluvial sand); very large plates occurred in Ütze forest (Lüneburger Heide) and in Gartow forest (south-east of Hamburg), i.e. in regions with strong winds. Wölfle (1937) explained the plate formation as a *phenomenon of extreme impoverishment* and, apart from the withdrawal of soil moisture by the roots of the old pine trees, the effects,

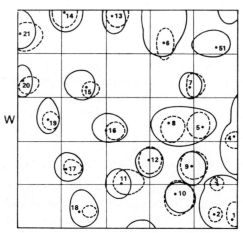

FIG. 137. "Plate" diagram for a system of pine standards with underwood at Ütze forest. Dotted lines = = crown projections; continuous lines = "plates" (affected areas). Main direction of wind from left (W) (*Baader*).

of drip and lack of sunlight, a major part is played by *the increased speed of the wind as it rushes past the stems*. This is highest *along the sides* of the stems (at 1 m distance away it amounts to 60 per cent) which provides a nice explanation of the already-mentioned elliptic shape of the plates.

Baader examined the expected *increment loss in the under storey* on circular sample plots which were pegged off concentrically around the stems of standards, using radii of 5·0, 7·5, 10, 15 and 20 m.

A comparison between the basal area (expressed as a value per hectare) of the innermost circle ($r_1 = 5$ m) and the basal areas of the rings around this towards the outside, showed that the basal area of the ring on the extreme outside ($r_5 - r_4$) was in all cases uninfluenced, and that the basal area reductions were generally not apparent beyond the 7·5 m radius. As shown in Fig. 138, which is based on extensive surveys in Eberstadt forest, Hesse, the reductions on the innermost sample plot and the nearest ring area increase markedly with age whilst the ring area 10–7·5 m suffered no further reductions beyond the age of 60 years. The simultaneous reduction of height increment was determined by a comparison of the mean heights on special sample areas in the non-covered stand. By further surveys Baader succeeded in deducting the total crop volume of wood over 7 cm in diameter in a covered as well as an uncovered stand.

Thus, with twenty final reserves, height quality class I/II, corresponding to a basal area of 4–6 m²/ha and a *ground cover of 12 to 14 per cent*, he found that *by the age of*

80 years, production of the covered under storey had been reduced by approximately 19 per cent of total timber crop volume. This reduced yield of the under storey has to be *compensated by the increased increment of the reserves.* Whether or not this takes place depends, according to Baader's investigations, not only on local site conditions, but *also on the varying and strikingly different productions of the individual reserves.* In the example of

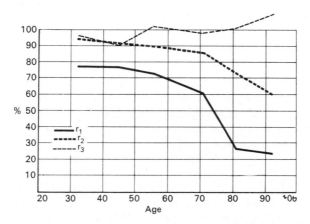

FIG. 138. Relative basal areas of the lower storey crop beneath old pine standards in the circular plots r_1 (radius 5 m), r_2 (radii 5·0–7·5 m), r_3 (7·5–10·0 m) (*Baader*).

Table 126, there are five reserves on a good-quality site (Quality Class I.5 and better) whose production varies so strongly that their *increment, reckoned per hectare,* during the age period 80–160 would *fluctuate between 53 and 179 fm.* As the number of final reserves is small, their individual productive capacity understandably plays a decisive part. This therefore depends on the correct selection of reserves and their timely preparation for isolation.

As a rough average Baader found a *2–4 per cent lower total volume yield under the standards system* as compared to that of non-shaded (uniform) crops (with $R = 80$–100). With Q. Cl. I and a favourable choice of reserves it is indeed possible that the yield may be greater; with Q. Cl. III, on the other hand, yield is always smaller.

The *value production of the system depends on the dimensions and quality of the large-diameter timber* of the standards. In this connection, the possible risk of deterioration from fungal attack (e.g. by *Trametes pini*) must be kept to the fore. On the basis of 1941 prices Baader found that the value of the average converted festmetre increases particularly steeply between breast-height diameters of 40 and 50 cm. Therefore a b.h.d. of at least 45 cm should be aimed at. Thus the financial production also depends on the individual increment production of the standards. The value production per hectare of the five above-mentioned standards of Q. Cl. I thus fluctuates between 2000 and 8500 RM, as shown in Table 126. As the average short-fall of income from the covered primary crop on these sites amounts to 1800 RM per hectare, Baader calculated a *possible appreciation in value production of between 200 and 6700 RM.* The result depends substantially on the final diameter of the standards, which ought to amount to at least 45–50 cm b.h.d. On sites with height Q. Cl. I and II this is achievable within acceptable periods of time, but not on sites with height quality class III and less, because the liability to disease at the much older final ages are too great.

The mean annual diameter increments of the examined standards were as follows:

Height qual. cl.	Age periods		
	80–130	131–150	151–160
I	3·0	1·8	1·7 mm
II	2·4	2·0	1·6 mm
III	1·7	2·1	1·1 mm

It seems that it is possible *to improve the production of the standards by starting early to prepare these trees for their future position*, even at the polewood age. A large sustained growth production is to be expected only from healthy individuals with well-shaped crowns fully covered with needles. The possibilities for improving the yield by fertilizer treatment are discussed on p. 424.

TABLE 126

COMPARISON OF THE INCREMENT PRODUCTION OF FIVE S. PINE
STANDARDS DURING THE PERIOD 80–160 YEARS, RECKONED IN VALUES
PER HECTARE (TWENTY STANDARDS PER HECTARE), ACCORDING TO
ANALYSES OF STEMS BY BAADER (1941)

Standard no.	Increment production per hectare			
	volume		financial	
	(fm)	(%)	(RM)	(%)
1	99	97	3500	81
2	73	72	2840	66
3	53	52!	1990	46!
4	179	175!	8530	198!
5	105	103	4760	110
Mean values	102 =	100	4320 =	100

(b) SCOTS PINE STANDARDS SYSTEM WITH A LARGE PROPORTION OF SHADE-TOLERANT SPECIES IN THE UNDER STOREY

This type has long been in practice in the forest at Lindau, Lake Constance. In addition to the excellent soil conditions of this young morainic landscape there are ample supplies of water (app. 1300 mm annual rainfall, 600 mm in May–August) and a high degree of warmth (8·1°C annual temperature, 15·4°C May–August). On this site, which offers an optimum growth potential to all tree species, the S. pine standards, at 180–200 years, reach top dimensions of 40 m height and 80 cm b.h.d. The under storey is constituted of approximately 20 per cent S. pine, and about 80 per cent of Silver fir and Norway spruce from natural regeneration. "Plate"-formations are non-existent on this site.

Lowered production in the under storey

Investigations by Mang showed unexpectedly large reductions of increment in the under storey. Among other facts, he determined the canopy areas, volumes and volume increments of all individual trees on fourteen sample plots each of 0·0314 hectare (radius 10 m), always in adjacent pairs, with and without standards. In this connection see Figs. 139 and 140. Calculations resulted in the following percentages of lowered production in the under storey, in relation to the non-shaded circular sample plot:

	Average of all seven plots	Mean error ±
Volumes	−10%	5·0
Volume increments of the last 10 years	−13%	4·7

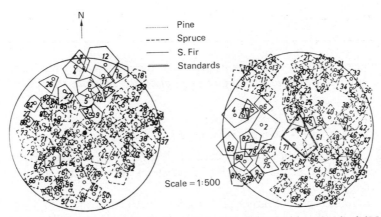

FIG. 139. Comparative sample circles 1a and 1, without and with a standard (*Mang*).

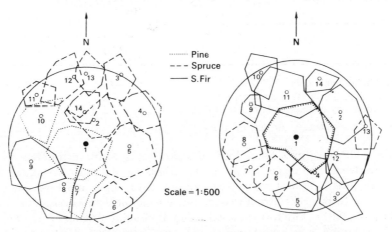

FIG. 140. Comparative sample circles 6a and 6. As Fig. 139.

Because of the unavoidable large fluctuations (mixed stocks, differences in the type of stocking) the calculated means are unreliable. Remembering that with this size of circular sample plot (one standard per 3·14 ar) the estimated number of standards per hectare amounts to thirty-two and therefore with moderately wide crowns the extent of ground coverage amounts to only 5–13 per cent (cf. Fig. 69, p. 127), so that the average loss of yield is considerable, especially considering that extreme cases of −26 per cent and −35 per cent (in increment) have been found to occur.

Mang calculated the production per hectare of the under storey for the following plots:

p_1: directly below the top shade of the standards,
p_2: within a radius of 5·0 m around the standards,
p_3: ring area between the radii 7·0 and 5·0,
p_4: ring area between the radii 10·0 and 7·0.

The reductions in comparison with the non-shaded adjacent plots amounted to:

	p_1	p_2	p_3	p_4
Volume	− 61·2	− 34·6	− 5·7	− 8·7%
Volume increment	− 47·7	− 22·0	− 4·6	− 7·6%

If the average production *of all the p_2-plots* (i.e. the innermost 5-m circles around the standard) is compared *with the mean of all p_3+p_4-plots*, the *reduction in yield* of the p_2-plots amounts to

(a) in volume   −29·5 per cent;
(b) in increment   −30·6 per cent, i.e. *an average* of −30 per cent!

This 30 per cent reduction on every area of 78·5 m², with one standard representing forty-five *standards/ha* (i.e. the number of final stems provided in Lindau) results in a *reduction of 10·6 per cent*.

In another examined pair of larger plots each of 0·1017 ha, one with a group of standards (seven stems) and one without standards, Mang found the following *reductions in yield on the plot with standards* (ground cover = 25 per cent):

	Volume (%)	Volume increment (%)
On the whole sample area	− 14	− 16
On a 4-m circle around the standards (352 m²)	− 22	− 20
Under the canopy of the standards (249 m²)	− 33	− 30

On the basis of these and other local measurements Mang estimated *the expected increment-reduction of the under storey for the whole period under standards*, beginning with sixty standards/ha (= 12 per cent ground cover) and finishing with forty-five standards/ha (= 16 per cent ground cover), *as amounting to an average of 10 per cent*, which ought to be fairly close to the actual value. It should however be remembered that the *increment reduction in covered S. pine is extraordinarily large*, as already seen in Table

40, p. 129. According to specific measurements by Mang, directly below the canopy of the standards, these reductions amounted to 80 per cent. Also, the impediment to growth increases with the height of the under storey and is at a maximum when the crown edges of the standards come into contact. The large demand for light and the *sensitivity of S. pine to canopy pressure* become obvious in Fig. 141. This diagram illustrates how close to the stems of the standards S. pine, Norway spruce and Silver fir of certain heights have been found surviving. Whereas pines move far beyond the outside circle of the crown, fir trees grow directly into the crowns of the standards. Spruce adopts an intermediate position. As a S. pine standards system requires a sufficient number of pines to be raised in the under storey, this is *a clear warning against having standards too close together.*

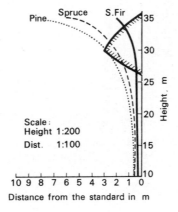

FIG. 141. Distance of tree species in the lower storey from the stem of the standard (*Mang*).

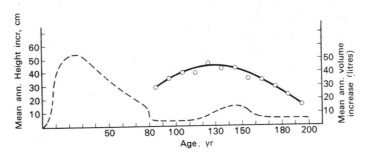

FIG. 142. Height increment of the pine standards and volume increment during the reservation period.

The growth of standards

The *height increment curve* in Fig. 142 represents the average height growth of sixteen analysed standards. The culmination with 54 cm per annum is rapidly reached at the age of 25 years; the height increment then tapers off evenly and, after the trees have been isolated at the age of approximately 80 years it undergoes a sudden sharp fall to a value of only 4 cm. Between the ages 120–130 a renewed rise to approximately 14 cm sets in, when the crowns of the standards are hemmed about by the rising under storey. This could be regarded as something akin to "anxiety reaction".

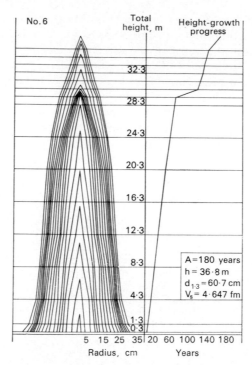

FIG. 143. Stem analysis and height growth progress of a typical standard (*Mang*).

The canopied areas of the fairly slender crowns of the standards grow from an average of 20 m² ($b = 5$ m) at the age of 80–100 to an average of 37 m² ($b = 7$ m) at the age of 150, the crowns become immersed in the rising under storey and by the age of 180 they have *decreased* again to approximately 31 m² ($b = 6.3$ m).

The *diameter increment* under bark between the ages of

90   110   130   150   170   190

achieves average values of

3·7   4·0   2·8   1·8   1·3 mm

These values are considerable for S. pine at these ages.

The *current* annual *volume increment* u.b., also represented in Fig. 142, culminates at 45 dm³ (litres) per year shortly before the age of 130 years and then at first decreases slowly, but, beginning at the age of 150, more sharply, apparently owing to the lateral crown pressures which then occur.

The growth pattern of a particularly vigorous standard with a good crown and large persistent production is illustrated in Table 127 and Fig. 143. Over four decades, the height increment stays at very small values of 2 or 4 cm respectively per annum, and then during the age period 140–150 years climbs back once more to the value of 20 cm.

TABLE 127

GROWTH PATTERN OF A S. PINE STANDARD (LINDAU FOREST) DURING ITS PERIOD
AS STANDARD

Age: 180 years; b.h.d. = 66·4 cm (o.b.); h = 36·8 m; isolated at the age of
75 years; v_s = 5·06 fm o.b. or 4·65 fm u.b.
Crown measurements: l = 10·5 m; b = 7·2 m; $c = 41\ m^2$.
$l : h$ = 0·39; $b : h$ = 0·20; $b : l$ = 0·68; $b : d$ = 10·8.

Age	v_s u.b. (m³)	i_v (m³)	Mean $i_v\%$ (ann.)	h (m)	i_h (ann.) (cm)
80	1·100			29·4	
		0·259	2·11		2
90	1·359			29·6	
		0·361	2·34		4
100	1·720			29·8	
		0·359	1·89		2
110	2·079			30·0	
		0·305	1·37		2
120	2·384			30·2	
		0·372	1·45		8
130	2·756			31·0	
		0·286	0·99		15
140	3·042			32·5	
		0·283	0·89		20
150	3·325			34·5	
		0·342	0·98		11
160	3·667			35·6	
		0·485	1·24		6
170	4·152			36·2	
		0·495	1·12		6
180	4·647			36·8	

Total volume production and financial production

With such very good production of the standards in Lindau it is no surprise that the reductions in increment by the under storey are often not only compensated but even overcompensated. This is the case particularly during the early decades after the standards have been isolated, while the height of the under storey is still inconsiderable.

For a more exact comparison of the production, the volume increments of six pairs of sample circular plots (ground cover conditions and produce of the standards may be seen in Fig. 69, p. 127) were converted by means of the specific gravities of the participating mixed species, into "cubic metres of S. pine". Because of the higher specific gravity of pine timber in comparison to fir and spruce timbers, this results in certain alterations to the production relationships found by Mang when using the timber volumes. The result is given in Table 128. The total increment in sample plot 1, combining a particularly vigorous standard and a low under storey, is superior to the comparative sample plot 1a (without standard) by 10 per cent. The averages of the sample plot pairs 2+3, where the under storey has just reached the base of the crowns of the standards, show identical growth. In contrast, the averages of the last three pairs of sample plots, where the crowns

TABLE 128

VOLUME PRODUCTION IN THE STANDARDS SYSTEM AT LINDAU, BASED ON SIX PAIRS OF CIRCULAR SAMPLE PLOTS. THE YIELDS OF THE PARTICIPATING MIXED SPECIES HAVE BEEN CONVERTED BY MEANS OF THEIR RESPECTIVE SPECIFIC GRAVITIES INTO "CUBIC METRES (FM) OF S. PINE"

Sample plot pairs	Under storey with standards		Increments per ann. and per ha.				Reduction of yield in the under storey	More (+) or less (−) yield with standards
	age	mean height	without standards	with standards				
				under storey	stand-ards	total		
		m	fm	fm	fm	fm	%	%
1		12·1		13·1	1·9	*15·0*	−4%	+10%
1a	22		*13·6*					
2+3		24·1		14·2	1·1	*15·3*	−7%	±0%
2a+3a	65		*15·3*					
(Mean)								
4+5+6		30·4		10·6	1·1	*11·7*	−21%	−14%
4a+5a+6a	88		*13·6*					

of the standards are already surrounded by the under storey, show a decisive decrease of yield with standards.[1]

In the systematically organized system at Lindau, Mang expected a reduction of 10 per cent in the final yield of the covered stand (68 fm out of 686 fm u.b.) and neglected a possible loss in earlier thinning yields. If we estimate this latter at 5 per cent (35 per cent thinning yield = 50 per cent of the volume of the final stand), the reduction in the covered stand increases to 15 per cent = 102 fm u.b. A cautiously calculated total increment of 155 fm u.b. produced by the standards during their period of reservation (90 years) thus would result in *a net increase of the volume production of the standards system of 50 to 60 fm u.b.* in comparison to Mang's 87 fm u.b.

For the standards system in Lindau, where the proportions in the mixed under storey amounted to 0·2 for S. pine, 0·4 for Norway spruce, 0·3 for Silver fir and 0·1 for beech, Mang calculated the following *total gross value production per hectare* (Table 129).

At the start of such a new standards system, therefore, one has to sacrifice an amount of 6000 DM in order *to obtain*, within 90 years, *the increased financial production of the standard system of 24,000 DM*. The increased production for the first standards period of 90 years thus amounts to only 18,000 DM.

Assuming today's prices, such a large increased financial production can be safely anticipated in a standards system, provided the standards have been carefully selected and preparations made for their later isolation. As well as good crowns, we must, however, expect the *ground cover to increase to 22–23 per cent* at the end of the standards period. The number of forty-five standards thus appears as the *highest acceptable number* not to be exceeded, even if the pine regeneration can be intentionally concentrated on those parts which are free of standards.

---

[1] The *proportion of S. pine* in the pair of sample plots 7 + 7a amounts to *68 and 81 per cent respectively*. At the same time, there is beech present to the extent of 16 and 19 per cent respectively, which in the other sample plots is *absent*. The decreased production of the sample plot with standards in this case, after transformation of the increments to dry matter, amounts to 36 per cent.

TABLE 129

90-year-old stand without standards	56,000 DM
90-year-old stand with standards	51,000 DM
Therefore decrease in production by canopy shade	5,000 DM
Value of 45 S. pine trees at the beginning of their period as standards	6,000 DM
Value of 45 S. pine trees at the end of their period as standards	35,000 DM

Comparative age	Yields at the end of 90 years in a standards system		in a normal system	Increased yield by the standards system, every 90 years
	Value of the stand when the standards system was introduced	= 56,000 DM		
	S. pine retained as standards	6,000 DM		
90		50,000 DM	56,000 DM	− 6,000 DM
	Final value of the standards	35,000 DM		
	Covered stand	51,000 DM		
	Total stand	86,000 DM		
	S. pine to be retained for standards	6,000 DM		
180		80,000 DM	56,000 DM	+ 24,000 DM
270	As before	80,000 DM	56,000 DM	+ 24,000 DM
360	As before	80,000 DM	56,000 DM	+ 24,000 DM
	And so forth!			

3. The "Perpetual Forest" System of Bärenthoren

This particular system, which has made Bärenthoren forest the home of the "perpetual forest" concept (Möller, 1920) and the origin of the "perpetual forest" movement, owes its existence to a situation of economic emergency. An area of about 900 ha of private forest (up to 1945) is located near Dessau directly to the West of the river Elbe, in a region with a warm and dry climate (mean ann. temperature = 8·7°C; ann. precipitation = 550 mm). The specific soil characteristics of the predominantly diluvial high plateau sand favour a soil vegetation which offers to the natural Scots pine regeneration —and incidentally also to the neighbouring forests—specially favourable conditions (Wiedemann, 1925; Wittich, 1931–51). At the beginning of the 1870's, when Chamberlain Friedrich v. Kalitsch took charge of this forest, it had been completely run down by excessive cutting and litter utilization. After the establishment of the forest in 1873 (Möller, 1920, 1921), the distribution of the age classes in the main part of the forest was then as follows:

Age class	Area (ha)
1–20	317
21–40	222
41–60	160
61–80	24
Total	723 ha

Despite this very bad start, Friedrich v. Kalitsch succeeded, in the following decades, in achieving from his forest increasing yields by abolishing litter utilization, by leaving all slash and fallen branchwood on the forest floor and by intensive, almost annually-repeated heavy thinning of all stands. In the almost mature stands he was able to change over from practice of the "Lichtwuchs" system, favouring the best trees, to "Lichtungs", or open-stand increment-felling, because a wealth of natural regeneration which had become established and which he was far-seeing enough to utilize, relieved him of the need for underplanting and costly establishment operations.

In 1911 Alfred Möller, silviculturist at the Forest Academy of Eberswalde, discovered by chance this system in which there is no clear-felling, and which consequently led him to conceive the idea of the "perpetual forest". Lack of knowledge about natural laws of forest yield led him to regard the considerable increase in yields in Bärenthoren as being solely, or at least mainly, due to the omission of clear-felling and to maintaining essential forest conditions. And yet, with the help of the tested yield table of Schwappach (1908), he could easily have calculated that, with the abnormal age class conditions of Bärenthoren, even normal treatment would have caused an increase of 38 per cent of the current annual increment within the two decades from 1873 to 1893, simply because the stands were advancing into age-classes with a high increment! *Despite this error, Möller's basic ideas are valuable for our understanding of the life processes in the forest and for the purposeful direction of these* (Lemmel, 1939). By contrast, the unsustainable claims of loud-voiced prophets, who praised this system as the ideal method of treatment for all East German pine forests and promised increases of 100 per cent yield, did little to bring about a fruitful application of Möller's concept of the perpetual forest. Dengler, Wiedemann and Wittich deserve deep and lasting recognition of their subsequent endeavours to obtain factual elucidation.

Commissioned by the Saxony Forest Administration's office, Krutzsch examined the conditions relating to growing crops and increments and described them in his well-known works (1924, 1934), one of which, *Bärenthoren 1934, Der naturgemässe Wirtschaftswald*, by Krutzsch and Weck, published in 1934, is particularly important. Details of the investigations of the two authors cannot be discussed here; but a study of the thorough and pertinent critique of Wiedemann (1925, 1926, 1936) is suggested. Based on surveys of the stocks of 1924 and 1934 and on recorded harvests, Krutzsch and Weck calculated *the mean annual increment* of the 10-year period 1924–34 for a 548 ha section of the forest ("excluding frass areas and Compt 47") as *amounting to*

$$6.14 \pm 0.19 \, fm \, (Derbholz) \, o.b.$$

and subsequently estimated the mean annual increment *for the whole forest* as

$$5.83 \pm 0.16 \, fm \, (Derbholz) \, o.b.$$

They compared this to the increment of a fully closed S. pine working section, taken from Schwappach's yield table of 1908, with annual production in a 100-year rotation of

$$3.8 \, fm \, (Derbholz) \, o.b. \, in \, Q. \, Cl. \, IV \, and \, 5.2 \, fm \, (o.b.) \, in \, Q. \, Cl. \, III.$$

Upon the assumption that before the introduction of the "perpetual forest system", the quality class was IV and that today (1934) it corresponds to III, they drew the following conclusions: "It can be maintained, that *by careful treatment of the forest, especially as a result of the abolition of litter removal and leaving the fallen branchwood on the forest floor, a sustained increase in the timber yield of approximately 37 per cent has been achieved and that this has been raised to 53 per cent by the special extraction methods used to minimize damage to the standing crop.* Even then the very considerable appreciation in value of growing stock and converted produce has still not been taken into account, nor yet the fact that Friedrich v. Kalitzsch's management has quite incidentally created the conditions which enabled the natural regeneration of the forest to be brought to profitable account" (italics by the author).

These conclusions, other than those expressed in the last sentence, are not correct, because they were based partly on arbitrary assumptions about the mean quality class of the forest and partly on a faulty identification of the height quality classes, which had been determined from the tables of Schwappach (1889 and 1908) and Gehrhardt (1921). Wiedemann (1936), who had an opportunity to examine the files at the forest establishments office of Saxony, proved that:

1. the *mean quality class* of the forest in 1934 was not III.0, but, as a weighted mean of all compartments, II.4 according to Schwappach (1908);
2. the height quality-class between 1884 and 1934 increased not by one whole quality-class, but by no more than half a quality-class interval;
3. therefore the initial quality class in 1884 was not IV but was already III according to Schwappach.

By simple averaging (weighted means could not be calculated owing to the lack of data per unit area) of the quality-class data in Appendix I of Krutzsch and Weck's book (p. 68 and following pages)[1] for the above-mentioned 548-hectare portion of the forest, the author found an *arithmetic mean of the height quality-classes* according to Schwappach 1908, *of II.33.*

Thus, by adopting a by no means excessive estimate of the *mean quality class* of the whole forest of 1934 *at II.5*, the *corresponding m.a.i. is 5·8 fm (o.b.) of timber*; in other words, exactly the amount found by Krutzsch and Weck for the increment of the whole forest! Of course it is somewhat risky to compare the current increment of a working section which is abnormally constituted with the m.a.i. of a normal working section. And furthermore, the increment period in question, 1924–34, was climatically a favourable one. If we accept the values found by Krutzsch and Weck, for the whole forest, we obtain the following picture:

	Bärenthoren	Normal working section, $R = 100$ according to Schwappach (1908), Quality Class II.5
Growing stock of 1934	143	
Growing stock of 1924	130	
Growing stock at mid-period	137	176
Annual *yield* (1924–34)	4·52	5·8
Annual *increment*	5·83	5·8
Increment per cent	4·25	3·3
Yield per cent	3·3	3·3

[1] The data used for the upper storey included all quality classes, but for the under storey only those for the young regenerated class IV and for the standards, because these latter can be assumed to have had an almost undisturbed development of the young growth. Thus, altogether 275 individual values became usable.

This comparison with yield table values, which correspond to the *actual mean height quality classes of the forest* in 1934, furnishes clear but *sober evidence of a structure that is still understocked; and incidentally the figures of attained increment are well within the average range of normally treated high-forest systems.*

The data furnished in the above-mentioned Appendix I further provide useful information upon the general handling of the crops during the last decades. *The treatment is reflected by the data for age, mean height and basal area of the upper and under storeys* of the regenerated classes (stands in which the regeneration is at approximately the same stage) as well as of the high forest crops with reserves, given in Table 130.

The differences between the average ages of the upper and lower storeys enable us to determine *the average age at which the parent crops had reached a degree of opening which enabled regeneration to start developing.* We find that, in the case of the crops with reserves, this, on average, occurred *at the age of 52 years* and with the other parent crops, at average ages of *72 to 84 years.* Thus we can judge the intensity of thinning in young stands which Friedrich v. Kalitsch was forced to practise because of the shortage of mature harvestable timber. For this purpose, he apparently sought out the crops of poorest quality in order to be able to tend the high-grade stands and to raise them to acceptable dimensions, always retaining the trees with the best shape in the progressively opened upper storey. One is reminded of a capable contractor, who from lowly beginnings and short of working capital slowly but purposefully makes good.

Bärenthoren represents a two-storeyed S. pine high forest system with (natural) *shelter wood regeneration.* The density of the upper storey fluctuates and, in the stands which are intended to produce standards, approaches a typical standards spacing.

TABLE 130

CHARACTERISTIC DATA FOR THE UPPER AND LOWER STOREYS OF STANDS AT BÄRENTHOREN
ACCORDING TO DATA BY KRUTZSCH AND WECK (1934)

Definition	Number of stands	Age			Mean height		Basal area		
		U	L	Difference	U (m)	L (m)	U (m²)	L (m²)	Total (m²)
Regeneration class									
II	31	97	13	*84*	21·8	2·0	19·9	—	—
III together	42	106	22	*84*	22·0	5·4	14·6	(8·7)	—
simultaneously*	17	111	33	*78*	22·4	9·2	13·9	8·7	22·6
IV	13	96	24	*72*	20·6	7·2	9·1	8·1	17·2
Standards	17	83	31	*52*	19·6	11·7	4·6	15·7	20·3

* Stands in which the *basal areas* of *both the upper and the lower storeys* have been measured and recorded simultaneously.

After all that we have learned, such heavy incursions[1] must lead us to expect *considerable reductions in volume increment.* Wiedemann (1936) characterized the "Bärenthoren régime" as "heavy low thinning, in some cases intensified to the degree of open-stand felling". His optimistic opinion (1936) that "if the crowns are thus systematically developed, a comparatively small number of stems is sufficient to secure the full production

[1] The mean natural degree of stocking of the thirty-one stands of regeneration class II in Table 129, for example, amounts to approximately 0·55–0·60.

of a closed stand" is no longer sustainable, especially since Erteld (1960) reported the new results of the former Prussian S. pine thinning experiment (cf. p. 327). *Furthermore, in two-storeyed S. pine crops where the basal areas of the upper-storey trees,* have remained for several decades within the order *of 10 to 15 m² a considerable loss in total volume production must be anticipated. However, to determine the actual amount of the loss in increment, systematic experiments are indispensable.* Comparison with a yield table does not afford sufficiently conclusive demonstration.

FIG. 144. Two-storeyed mixed oak–beech stand in Lohr-West forest, Block "Gaul". Average age of oak = 350 years, average age of beech = 150 years. $N = 68+180$; $G = 22\cdot2+15\cdot5\,\text{m}^2$; $V_D = 371+248$ fm, total 619 fm. High proportion of veneer timber.

In the system at Bärenthoren, these losses are partially compensated by the natural regeneration, which ensures an *uninterrupted transition of the production process from the old to the new generation* and avoids the increment losses of the clear-felling system, which are not to be underestimated. The increments may even be slightly higher, because the average harvesting age so far has always been low. After all, the m.a.i. of S. pine reaches its culmination at low rotations.

The *value production* can be judged as being more favourable than the volume production. But, in this case, the importance lies not only in the production of the present upper storey, but also in the future value production of the present under storey, for which the number of stems is relatively small. Krutzsch and Weck were of the opinion that in quality of stems and fineness of branches, the rising "half-shade-tolerant high-grade S. pine trees" are superior to pines grown from self-sown regeneration which has been uncovered at a very early stage. That may be so, but final judgment cannot be passed until that generation has developed utilizable dimensions over fairly large areas. *The threat of damage by felling and extraction*, in this case, *must not be underestimated*. This and the special sensitivity of young trees of 5–10 m height have rightly been stressed by Wiedemann, who gives actual examples. The author incidentally has heard that the under storey has, in the meantime, suffered heavy damage by *snow breakage* and that large areas have unfortunately been destroyed by repeated fires.

The rise in quality class since 1884 by one half-class interval can be explained simply as a result of the abolition of litter removal and the well-known favourable effect of a cover of small branchwood.

Most remarkable about the perpetual forest system of Bärenthoren is the performance of the owner Friedrich von Kalitsch, who managed to transform an impoverished forest into a highly productive one by using new methods and demolishing old routines. Although the accompanying expressions of the perpetual forest movement were in some degree disturbing and not entirely flattering to the state of forestry knowledge they have had a stimulating influence. Despite the fact that doctrinaire and misplaced activities have caused some losses to ensue, these may well be less harmful than schematism and bureaucracy, by which practical forestry nowadays is threatened with paralysis.

Besides those systems discussed, numerous other many-storeyed forms are conceivable in unlimited variety (cf. Fig. 144), but we do not yet know very much about their structure and productive relationships. One multiple-storeyed, all-aged mixture is the selection forest, but we cannot discuss this in detail until we have explained working sections and their problems.

VIII. YIELD CHANGES CONSEQUENT ON DETERIORATION OR IMPROVEMENT OF THE LOCAL SITE CONDITIONS

1. Deterioration of Yield

Everywhere in the world we meet alarming evidences of the devastation of forests by man. Among the examples familiar to us are the karstic limestone mountains of the Mediterranean region, where soil and humus have been irretrievably washed off from the disafforested steep slopes and lost in the sea. In the Alpine region we come upon the sore consequences of improvident forest exploitation, amounting to the unskilled and misdirected felling of whole protective forests. Not only have the yields of subsequent forest produce been reduced to negligible proportions but re-afforestation would require funds almost impossible to raise, and the extent of the damage by avalanches, landslips and flood water is almost beyond estimation. Where slope gradients are moderate and the climatic conditions are equable and temperate, the consequences of clear-felling are generally not so serious, although the unfavourable effects on gley soils and soils which tend to become compacted must not be overlooked. Our discussion, however, will be limited to such instances of impairment the extent of which can be quantitatively assessed.

Degradation by the cultivation of pure crops

There are many inhospitable soil conditions, e.g. deep surface humus layer, a high degree of acidity, low porosity, shallow rooting, which are found in susceptible soils under pure coniferous stocks, especially spruce. Prior suspicion of the presence of such conditions (*inter alia* Krauss 1936, 1939) has been strengthened by a *falling off of height quality class*, which has been observed on many sites, especially when spruce is grown outside its natural habitat (Wiedemann, 1923). However, we have to make a distinction here, because in many cases this represents a *misinterpretation of irregular growth processes in Norway spruce*, which on relatively warm sites and with limited moisture supplies, at first grows vigorously and subsequently slows up markedly. Thus, from the age of 30 up to 100 years, the quality may easily drop by one whole class when compared with the yield table (cf. p. 186). *Such phenomena are apt to be repetitive.* In one example on the rubble plain (Schotterflur) of Schwaben, south-east of Ulm, the author discovered that the height–age curves of two crops of 1st and 2nd generations on the same site showed exactly the same conformation, which differed from that in Wiedemann's yield table. A comparison between the mean heights of numerous 1st and 2nd generation pure spruce stands (1st generation, seventy stands; 2nd generation forty-seven stands) in the well-known forest of Laugna (Krüdener, 1943) growing on a topsoil of loessic loam showed no falling off in attainment by the 2nd generation. *"A lowered quality class" which is a mere expression of growth phenomena peculiar to the site and which repeats itself in the same way in the next generation, therefore must not be considered as site "degradation".* That a rapidly progressing degradation on extreme sites is possible must not, on the other hand, be overlooked, although spruce is often unjustly blamed for the consequences of extreme impoverishment due to litter removals, pasturage, forestry combined with (or alternating with) field crops and silvicultural mistakes, such as clear-felling and grass-wrack utilization (with impoverishment of the phosphoric acid content). But much more serious than the consequences of genuine soil degradation, the extent and progress of which have still to be accurately assessed, are *hazards to management and the loss of sustention in pure spruce plantations covering large areas, induced by noxious animal and plant pests and by injuries from climatic causes.* Let us envisage what would happen if some day our Norway spruce stands were attacked by a fungal disease or a pest with the fatal effect of, say, *Graphium ulmi* or as hard to combat as *Phylloxera vastatrix*. Such reflections should be sufficient to prevent us from cultivating pure Norway spruce on excessively large areas.

Lowering of the ground water level

Sustained damage causing considerable loss of increment occurs when the level of the ground-water drops, as for example after the building of canals and the regulation of river beds. Thus, when the Mittellandkanal (Middle Land Canal) was built in North Germany the oak tree-tops on extensive areas withered and some of the trees died. The weakened crops are attacked by secondary agents, such as the oak roller-moth and mildew.

The approximate extent of such reductions in yield was calculated by Feierabend (1951) for a low-lying grassy woodland of about 400 ha between Basle and Breisach. There, following upon a correction in the course of the Rhine carried out between 1840 and 1864, the ground-water level at low water has dropped by about 4 m in the last 100 years. The resulting loss of growth was the greater in proportion to the lowering of the water level. Detailed investigations in this communal forest showed that the increment there had decreased from an initial 9 fm to 2 fm in 1950. The loss of increment in this instance was particularly heavy because the forest is located in a particularly dry region with only 550 mm annual rainfall. Even if the present crop were to be entirely replaced by a new one consisting of the more suitable Scots pine giving an improved performance, it will never again attain to the level of production of the original meadow forest. Similar effects caused by a drainage canal between Karlsruhe and Heidelberg were reported by Jordan (1951).

Edge effects

Wherever forest stands are exposed towards the south or west, by the clearing of sections for motorways, power lines, etc., or for other special purposes, the trees on the exposed edges respond by a slowing down of their subsequent height growth, transferring increment to the basal section of the stem, developing pressure-wood on the sheltered side (in coniferous trees) and giving a *lowered volume increment*. On p. 61 we have already dealt with some typical changes in shape and increment. Investigations by two collaborators of the author, Siostrzonek and Zahn, resulted in the discovery of much retarded height increment in spruce as a result of cutting to give S. and SW. exposure, coupled with considerable reductions of volume. These latter reductions occurred, despite the fact that the basal area increments at breast-height were sometimes increased, simply because of the almost entire transfer of increment to the stem cross-sectional area near the ground. Figure 145 shows the average growth changes in four or five analysed sample stems.

Typical and important is *the more favourable behaviour of edge trees on the NNE. edge*, where the reductions of i_h, i_g and i_v are only temporary. As seen in Fig. 146, *the lowering of increment per unit area on the SSW. edge* in the example of Jettingen amounts to *almost 25 per cent*. By contrast, *at the NNE. edge* it amounts *to not quite 10 per cent*. In another case (Krumbach), the *increment* of spruce along a *N. edge* was even *increased*.

Scots pine on various sample edge-plots reacted with a similar transfer of increment (cf. Fig. 33, p. 62) but with smaller setbacks to i_h and i_v.

Evidently the origins of growth losses along the marginal zone are of a composite character. Perhaps of even greater consequence than the mechanical effects of wind-action in retarding height growth is the increased rate of transpiration which causes the stomata to close repeatedly, thereby reducing assimilation. One cannot ignore also the drying-out of the lower parts of the stand wherever the sun's rays penetrate into the already impoverished wind-swept margins, causing a lowering of the soil population (and a reduced nitrogen supply) with loss of moisture-availability to the edge-trees. Precise soil studies conducted alongside experiments in plant physiology would be desirable in this connection.

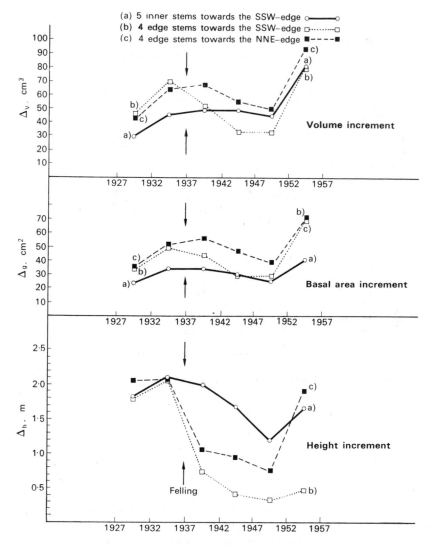

(a) 5 inner stems towards the SSW–edge ○——○
(b) 4 edge stems towards the SSW–edge □·······□
(c) 4 edge stems towards the NNE–edge ■– – –■

Fig. 145. Edge effect trial plots at Jettingen. Mean increment of the analysed sample trees for 5-year periods.

Further evidence that the influences most detrimental to growth on exposed S. and W. edges are to be traced to increased buffeting by winds and to sunlight striking in upon the lower parts of the stand was provided by Zimmerle (1937, 1938, 1939), who investigated the edges of the favoured marginal system, evolved by Wagner. He compared the height increment and the annual ring widths at different stem heights of "outside stems" (zone III of the inside border, adjoining the outside border) with those of "inside stems" in the closed interior of the stand. In the forests at Giengen, Härtsfeldhausen, and in the well-known "marginal-system" forest of Gaildorf, he found the following uniform conditions: a relatively small reduction of the height-increment (i_h) of the outside stems, but *considerably increased diameter increment, even to some height up the stems* of these trees (contrary to Haufe, 1927). Not so clear are Zimmerle's results for Pfalzgrafenweiler forest (1942) where, on a site with ample water supplies, the open-stand increment reactions are smaller and the differences between outside and inside stems have become blurred by heavy thinning in the past decade.

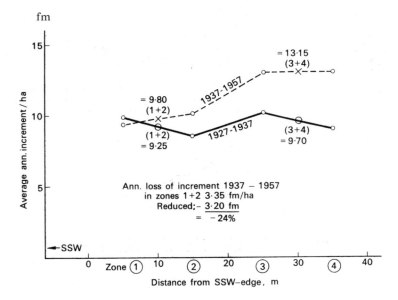

FIG. 146. Jettingen. Volume increments in four zones of the SSW.-edge sample plot before and after exposure.

These results show the decisive *influence of the direction* towards which a stand is exposed as well as the fundamental correctness of Christoph Wagner's (1923) reflections from the point of view of production technique. Zimmerle's work provides *no conclusions about changes in increment performance per unit area*, but in connection with the above-mentioned investigations upon increment on N. edges, it is to be expected that within the immediate range of a moderately wide (10–15 m) strip *at an edge facing N. or NE., increment losses will not occur at all, or only in moderation*, depending on the degree of opening of the stand. This is understandable, because after all, the immediate edge-trees enjoy complete isolation on at least one side.

The results of Baader's (1952) paper do not contradict this. According to his published figures, *the average reductions in the annual height increment at the edge* ("strip 1") in comparison to the undisturbed interior of the stand ("strip 7") amount to the following values:

Tree species	Number of years exposed	Number of examples	Exposed towards	%
S. pine	5	4	ENE. to NNW.	− 19
	11	8	NW. to E. (via S.)	− 31
Norway spruce	13	3	ENE. to NNW.	± 0
	14	18	NW.–S.–E.	− 52

The average increase of the annual diameter increment at the same time was:

S. pine	17	2	ENE. to NNW.	+ 7
	15	3	NW.–S.–E.	+ 9
Norway spruce	12	1	ENE. to NNW.	+45
	14	16	NW.–S.–E.	+ 4

Even making allowance for the great uncertainty of some of the means, the slight reaction of pine by comparison with spruce which was commented upon by Baader, as well as the *distinct tendency for smaller reductions to occur at the N. and NE. are clearly evident.* Baader's suggestion that the probable increment losses may be calculated by way of lower quality classes corresponding to the reduction of heights, is problematic because the actual increment reductions are not proportional to the height reductions.

The greatest significance must be attached to the *technical damage* which was found by Baader at the S. and SW. margins of *beech and spruce* stands. The damage caused by fungal attacks (Polyporus spp.) on beech with bark-scorch is much worse on basaltic soils than on bunter-sandstone or Greywacke. Beech soon dies and collapses after succumbing to fungal attack and the advance of the disease *can not* be halted. On the basis of his examples of stands on bunter-sandstone and Greywacke, Baader calculated that the average pace at which mortality advances in the trees of the diseased edge-zone amounts to about 1 m per annum, and on basalt and lower Permian sandstone on average as 2·5 m per annum! This loss of trees is accompanied by considerable *increment reductions in the edge-zone due to the dispersal by wind of fallen leaf-litter and to general soil impoverishment.*

The technical damage caused by bark-scorch in spruce is not quite so serious. Accord, ing to investigations of the author and his collaborators, this occurs mainly in the pole-wood and early mature stages while bark is still thin. But wind-throw and wind-break at the edges of opened, unprotected spruce stands have a much more devastating effect.

The *loss of increment along stand margins due to rills and water-channels* where they border on agricultural fields or meadows is, according to prevailing opinion, unimportant when adequate cover is maintained, but on the other hand the quality of the timber may be reduced by heavy branch development. However, this question requires further inves-tigation. Reference to it in the work by Kramer (1958) is limited to a comparison of the volumes of the timber stocks. But this is not sufficient and one would need to compare also the *increments* of the marginal strips with those of the inner parts of the stands. Considering the loss of height which is very evident from the profile of windswept edges, we must suspect that increments are reduced, unless the contrary is shown.

Litter utilization

Litter utilization leads to a steady deterioration of soil conditions and, if continued, to heavy reductions of the yield. Older experiments of research institutes, as well as certain special investigations, have furnished no clear results. Even methodical and reliable litter removal experiments in pine stands have provided no significant differences between the increment of experimental plots from which the litter has been removed and those whence it has not been removed, although the observations may have lasted over a period of 20 to 30 years. Soil study investigations (Ramann, 1883) provided a contradictory result in showing an increased nitrogen content in soils where litter removal had been practised. This has only been clarified by the more recent researches in soil biology, especially those by Wittich (1938, 1951, 1954) which proved that by litter removal the so-called *genuine humus substances*, which are the most important permanent source of nitrogen nutrients for our forest trees, are largely exhausted. The remaining nitrogen occurs in such ways that it is difficult or even impossible for the trees to utilize. *Long periods of time are required after the cessation of litter removal to compensate for the damage on inactive soils*, in some cases up to 80–100 years when the *genuine humus substances have slowly been restored.* It takes a long time until normal increments are reached again, and it is therefore easy to understand that litter utilization experiments in stands where it has been removed over long periods, cannot provide clear results.

More recent experiments by Wiedemann (1950) in spruce and beech stands, where up to that time the litter had not been removed, showed that even after comparatively cautious annual litter removals the increment was subsequently reduced by one-third to one-half. According to Wiedemann's experimental results, even the (in his opinion) less sensitive *Scots pine* suffers so much damage by annually or biannually repeated litter removals that, even on good soils, *increment losses of up to 50 per cent* are possible.

According to a memorandum of the Bayerischer Forstverein (Bavarian Forest Association) of 1952, the amount of litter removed annually in Bavarian forests between 1945 and 1950 was estimated as 2 million Ster (cubic metres). The loss of increment thereby is cautiously estimated as 1 million festmetres. Fortunately, by the initiative of the forest administration, almost complete abolition of litter utilization has now been secured in Bavarian state forests by relief payments and compensation in kind. In many private and common forests, however, the raking up of litter continues. The author examined a small farm forest in the Fränkischer Jura, where the litter had been utilized for centuries; there, on a surface layer of Alb over white Jura, he found a miserable crop of pine of Q. Cl. IV–V, with an estimated m.a.i.$_{100}$ of approximately 3 fm. The potential mean annual yield of pine, however, amounts to at least 6 fm and in spruce to at least 8 fm (m.a.i.$_{100}$).

More recent investigations by Wittich (1954) in pine stands in the Oberpfalz reveal the catastrophic damage to the soil fauna and flora from litter utilization while on the other hand they demonstrate the possibilities for achieving increases in increment by the cultivation of legumes. Thus we can, to some degree, estimate the extent of an existing loss of yield by the rapid reversal of the destructive processes; results in this respect, however, will be discussed later under the heading "amelioration".

2. Yield Improvements by Amelioration and Fertilizer Treatments

According to Laatsch (1957), amelioration is a term combining "all measures which increase the productivity of the soil over long periods". *Fertilizer treatment*, i.e. the artificial supply of nutritive elements, may be one *specific part of such action*. Isolated fertilizer treatment, which causes a temporary increase in increment (for example, a single application of 40 kg of nitrogen fertilizer per hectare), does not, under this definition, represent amelioration. By amelioration the original productivity of devastated soils (as, for instance, after litter utilization) can be restored and indeed, the natural productivity of a given forest site may be lastingly raised.

Within the scope of this book, the problems of amelioration and fertilizer treatment in the forest can only be broadly sketched in by way of some illustrative examples. The proper field for a thorough treatment lies with forest soil research, from which we may in the near future expect a "Waldernährungslehre" (textbook of forest nutrition).

Amelioration and fertilizer experiments and their consequences

Despite the commendable initiative of some forest scientists who established forest fertilizer experiments as long as 60 years ago, there were until recently only a *small number of experiments which provided clear and positive results*. Many experiments have been established by practical foresters without expert knowledge and without reliable controls. Fertilizer experiments for soil-study purposes have been restricted in many cases to the assessment of soil changes and the changes in increment have either not been recorded at all or only inadequately.

The methodically consistent *fertilizer experiments in Saxony* reported on by Vater and Sachsse (1927), concerned mainly pine and spruce stands on poor soils, mostly belonging to Q. Cl. IV and poorer, with low exchange capacity and very scanty supplies of moisture.

As almost all the yield-controlling factors in these experiments exist at minimum levels, especially that of water supply which is decisive and cannot be artificially increased, it is not astonishing that, in some cases, even complete fertilizer treatment with N, P and K provided no measurable success. Besides, *Scots pine* shows relatively little reaction to mineral fertilizers, with the exception of N. Definite successes were achieved in one experiment with pine by complete fertilizer treatment plus lupin cultivation and in two experiments with Norway spruce by supplies of Thomasmeal and complete fertilizer treatment.

Wiedemann (1927) and Wittich (1942) have informed us of the great success achieved by *the application of lime along with the cultivation of legumes* (lupin and broom) in *Ebnath* in the Fichtelgebirge and on the shaley soils of the Vogtland in Saxony which had become impoverished by litter utilization. After the breaking down and activation of heavy surface layers of raw humus by dressings of lime and soil working plus initial fertilizer supplies of phosphoric acid and potash, the lupins thrived in profusion. By enrichment of the soil with organic substances rich in nitrogen, favourable humus forms are produced and growth becomes rapid. Thus, according to Wiedemann, treatment with 45 dz (dz = 2 cwt) of lime nearly doubled the height increment of a young spruce plantation within 17 years, while the simultaneous introduction of lupin and broom after treatment with lime, along with spruce planting, trebled the mean height of the treated plantation in comparison to the untreated control within 13 years.

Unusual successes were achieved by the supply of *lime* to the poor, cretaceous sandy soils of the Egge mountains in the forests of Neuenheerse and Altenbeken. Wiedemann reported that, in the experimental series in Compt. 140, *Neuenheerse* forest, where in 1927, 30 and 60 dz of burnt lime per hectare (24 cwt and 48 cwt/acre) had been harrowed into the soil of a 90-year-old spruce stand, the treated plots achieved within the 17-year period 1931–47, a relative superiority in timber production (Derbholz) of 22 and 32 per cent, corresponding to an annual increase in increment of 2·3 and 3·8 fm/ha respectively. The basis of this success was the existence of a thick surface accumulation of organic material.

A process widely known as the *"rehabilitation of forest soils"* ("Waldbodensanierung") was developed by Forstdirektor O. Lidl in his private forest of *Sauerlach* on the low-, and high-terrace sites south of Munich. Litter utilization and three generations of nearly pure spruce crops had allowed the soils to become acid and compacted so that, under the oldest stands, layers of raw humus material over 10 cm in thickness had collected. In order to promote the speedy break-down of these heavy layers into more favourable humus forms, Lidl in the course of three decades, *gradually increased the supplies of lime* (100–150 dz $CaCO_3$, corresponding to 50–75 dz CaO), and towards the end the lime was superficially spread, without soil working, or blown out by machines. At the same time, *blue lupin was sown.* Whereas his first experiments were made on an open plot during the establishment stage, he later started his "soil-restorative measures" in the old stands, some 10–15 years before their regeneration in order to get the soil into optimum biological condition to receive the new crop. In this he was completely successful, as shown by Wittich's (1952) investigations, wherein the soil of an ameliorated plot was found to contain, *inter alia,* "a living mass of earthworms of 960 kg/ha". The author, whilst accompanying him on some of his stimulating forest inspections, was able to satisfy himself of the successes achieved before his lamentably early death in 1958. For example, under the thin canopy of some black alders, on a soil reminding one of the mildest of good garden loam, some vigorous young spruce were eagerly aspiring to pierce this canopy. Owing to the absence altogether of control plots or else to the insufficient size of those few that were available and the lack of permanent identifying markings a collaborator of the author, Dr. R. Mayer, could succeed only in one case in demonstrating a considerable improvement in growth of a lime-treated crop in the thicket stage. The condition of the soils which had been restored by Lidl would enable the most demanding broad-leaved trees to thrive. On the other hand, he himself anticipated that spruce, being adapted to more acid soils, would be susceptible to a certain risk from red rot and honey-fungus attack. This was mentioned by Rauchenberger (1959) in an acknowledgement of Lidl's work and person.

Worthy too of remark are the results of an *amelioration method* developed by Hassenkamp (1941) on the decalcified "Flottlehm" soils (of high silt content) in the forests of Erdmannshausen and *Syke*, which allows pine stands of but moderate quality (III), with thick surface layers of raw humus and matted bilberry cover, to be succeeded by mixed crops wherein highly demanding species (such as Douglas fir, Silver fir, larch) can achieve heights such as may be expected only on the best sites. In order to cover costs, Hassenkamp included in his method 2 years of field crops (winter rye, oats). This, however, is not essential to the method whereby the surface organic material is partially mineralized, but for the major part is converted into valuable permanent humus.

The fertilizer experiment at Owingen

A classic older fertilizer experiment which can furnish more detailed information is that in *Owingen forest* established by Lent (1928) in 1906, on the NW. slopes of the Swabian Alps, south of Haigerloch.

Site. 570–590 m above m.s.l., NW. slope, 10 per cent gradient, annual precipitation 900 mm; "Keuper" with remnants of "Lias"; sandy loam with nodular sandstone. The twenty-one parcels, 7×72 m = 5 ar each in area, lie side-by-side as narrow downhill strips, not entirely comparable as regards site conditions. Two out of the five control parcels inserted between the other parcels had been cultivated with clover. The volumes of thinnings unfortunately are not recorded, but have been reconstructed by approximation, as the whole experiment has received very uniform treatment and thinnings were only moderate.

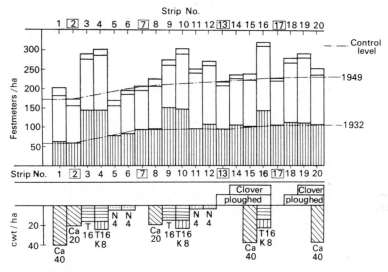

FIG. 147. Fertilizer experiment at Owingen. Above: total growth performance of parcels 1–20: hatched, up to the age of 30 years; unhatched, up to the age of 47 years. The broken line connects the values for the four unfertilized controls. Below: fertilizer quantities in hundredweights (50 kg) per ha *(Hausser)*.

In the work by Hausser (1950), the most important experimental results are presented in the form of highly instructive graphic representations, two of which are shown in Figs. 147–8. These diagrams reflect the *significant and sustained effect of Thomasmeal* which was only slightly increased by the addition of Kainit. The effects on production of the other fertilizers were also insignificant.

Assuming only the average yield increase of 90 fm which was achieved in parcels 3 and 9 by the application of 8 dz of Thomasmeal, the increase in financial yield of nearly 3000 DM at present-day prices would require an outlay of barely 110 DM.

The clear result of this experiment is due to the extraordinary growth response of the spruce stand to the supply of phosphoric acid. The deficiencies which have become manifest prove how necessary it is to make *preliminary reconnaissance of the site, including soil studies under adequate supervision along with a precise check on yields* before the start of forest fertilizer experiments. This was done in the following highly instructive experiment.

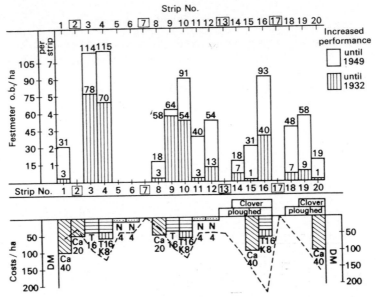

FIG. 148. Improved performances of the fertilized fields (top) and fertilizer costs (bottom) *(Hausser)*.

The fertilizer experiment in the municipal forest of Speyer

In this experiment, which was established at the suggestion of Forstmeister Weinkauff (municipal forest administration, Speyer) in 1928 by Dr. Römer of the agricultural research station Limburgerhof of the Badische Anilin and Sodafabrik A.G., the experience and principles of agricultural fertilizer trials have been sensibly applied to the forest experiments. Owing to the large number of stems in the young Scots pine stand, a plot size of 12·5 ar was sufficient. Each treatment has three replications. Unfortunately, the shape of twelve of the eighteen plots is a narrow rectangle (15×83·35 m), which for forestry purposes is a disadvantage because of the large number of edge-trees. In 1932 the experiment came under yield study supervision by the Bavarian Forest Research Institute, i.e. Geheimrat Prof. Dr. Fabricius.

Site. 105 m above m.s.l., flat, gently undulating. Mean ann. temp. = 9·8°C; ann. precipitation = 560 mm.

Soil. Diluvial fine sand with dune formation; from 50 cm depth veins of clay; between 40–75 cm depth evidence of lime. pH values (in KCl) to 30 cm depth = 3·7; at 30–40 cm = 4·1. Mean height quality class according to Wiedemann, 1943, (moderate) at the age of 62 years (1957) = I.5.

Fertilizer treatment plan 1928–34. While plot group IV received *no soil working or fertilizer at all*, the "moss litter" on all other parcels was raked up in 1928 and sold. The three plots in group II were *lightly hoed but received no fertilizer*. The plots of groups I, III, V and VI were treated with fertilizers and after the first dressing of lime, the soil of those plots was loosened by hoeing as in group II. *Groups I and III* then received the following amounts of fertilizer:

Date	Leuna lime (dz/ha)*	P_2O_5 (kg/ha)	K_2O (kg/ha)	N (kg/ha)
12. 10. 1928	35			
8. 11. 1928		100	60	
10. 4. 1929				40
20. 5. 1931		100	60	40
21. 11. 1933	35			
	70	200	120	80

* Doppelzentner = 100 kilogrammes. 1 Doppelzentner (dz) per ha = 0·8 cwt. per acre.

The types of fertilizer used were: Thomasmeal, a 40 per cent potassium salt, Leuna-nitre in group I and urea in group III.

Group V received on the	Leuna lime (dz/ha)	P_2O_5 (kg/ha)	Nitrophoska K_2O (kg/ha)	N (kg/ha)
12. 10. 1928	35			
10. 4. 1929		40	52·3	40
20. 5. 1931		40	52·3	40
21. 11. 1933	35			
	70	80	104·6	80

Group VI received the same treatment as groups I and III, but *without nitrogen.*

The results of 1929–34 were reported by Fabricius (1940). They will be statistically examined below. The density of stocking and the stage of development of the stands being nearly equal on all plots we can use *basal area increment* as a criterion.

TABLE 131

FERTILIZER EXPERIMENT SPEYER

(a) *Mean basal area of the plot groups in 1929 and their basal area increment, 1929_s–1934_s*

Group	G $(1929)_s$ (m^2/ha)	i_g (1928–34) (m^2/ha)	Production increase in comparison with Group II (%)	Group IV (%)
II no fertilizer, soil worked	23·17	4·77	—	−10·3
IV no fertilizer, soil unworked	24·51	5·32	+11·5	—
VI, PK, lime, soil worked	23·64	4·98	+4·4	− 6·4
III, NPK, lime, soil worked (urea)	23·81	5·84	+22·6	+10·0
I, NPK, lime, soil worked (Leuna-nitre)	23·39	6·10	+27·9	+14·7
V, NPK, lime, soil worked (nitroph.)	22·77	6·24	+30·9	+17·3

(continued)

TABLE 131 *(cont.)*

(b) *Significant minimum production increase, 1929–34*

The minimum production increase is considered to be the *difference* between the group mean compared in each case, *less three times the standard error of the difference.*

Group	Significant minimum production increase		
	in basal area		in volume
	(m²/ha)	(%)	(m³/ha)
In comparison with group II (= without fertilizer, *soil worked*)			
IV without fertilizer, *soil unworked*	0·19	4·0	2
VI PK	—	—	—
III NPK (urea)	0·60	12·5	7
I NPK (Leuna-nitre)	1·03	21·6	12
V NPK (nitrophoska)	1·17	24·6	14
in comparison with group IV (= without fertilizer, *soil unworked*)			
VI PK	—	—	—
III NPK (urea)	—	—	—
I NPK (Leuna-nitre)	0·33	6·2	4
V NPK (nitrophoska)	0·47	8·8	5

c) *Analysis of variance*

Basal area increment, 1929–34.

Group	IV no fert., untrtd.	VI PK	III NPK (urea)	I NPK (L.nitre)	V NPK (nitroph.)
II no fertilizer, soil worked	+	—	+ +	+ +	+ +
IV no fertilizer, unworked		—	+	+ +	+ +
VI PK			+ +	+ +	+ +
III NPK (urea)				—	—
I NPK (Leuna-nitre)					—

$$+ + = \text{highly significant}; \quad P < 0·01.$$
$$+ = \text{significant} \quad\quad P < 0·05.$$
$$- = \text{not significant} \quad P > 0·05.$$

The analysis of variance shows that the plots which were given complete fertilizer treatment, including nitrophoska and Leuna-nitre, *show a very significantly increased production* as compared with those which were given no fertilizer and those which received only phosphoric acid and potassium. The last-named show no significant growth-increase over the plots without fertilizer treatment. Within the plots given no fertilizer, the significantly better performance of the unworked plots over that of the worked plots indicates, furthermore, that *soil working* (moss-removal plus hoeing) actually *resulted in a lowered increment.*

Comparison with group VI points unequivocally to a rapid and highly significant effect of nitrogen additions. We can confidently accept the possibility of a superior perform-ance by those plots over group II (no fertilizer, but with soil-working) because the comparison shows that disturbance of the soil is not necessary to implement the use of nitrogen fertilizer media such as Leuna-nitre or nitrophoska.

If one accepts that with Scots pine an enhanced production of 12 fm over 5 years is a feasible result of two applications of 2 dz Leuna-nitre (or other nitrogenous fertilizer of equal value) in accordance with Table 131(b), then there will be an increased monetary yield of 350 DM for an additional outlay of 120 DM.

As we have learned from more recent experience, *the effect of the two applications of 40 kg pure nitrogen per hectare is ephemeral, passing off comparatively soon.* This gradual weakening of the effect is already apparent during the increment period 1929–39, but it becomes more noticeable in the increment put on between the years 1929 and 1952; during the latter period, however, certain disturbances to the experiment which occurred in the post-war years must be taken into consideration. If the plot groups which received nitrogen treatment are combined and compared with group VI (only P and K) and with groups II and IV combined (no fertilizer), the result for the period 1934–52 is, peculiarly enough, a quite significantly better production by group VI as compared to groups II + IV and a significant improvement over groups III + I + IV. Possibly the effect of the treatment with phosphoric acid + potassium is a *retarded* one.

When the experiment was continued after 1953, groups I and V received every year in spring, from 1953 until 1958, 40 kg N per ha each, i.e. a total of 240 kg N per ha, group III the same, plus 80 kg P_2O_5 per ha and a total of 120 kg of K_2O. Group VI received the same quantities of phosphoric acid and potash but no N, whilst II and IV had again no fertilizer treatment. Surprisingly, these *repeated applications of nitrogen no longer caused any definite reactions,* just as the analysis of variance shows no significant differences in increment. A partial explanation is obtained from chemical analyses of the needles made in autumn 1957 by the Institute for Soil Studies of the Forest Research Establishment in Munich[1] (Table 132). According to these the nutrient content of the needles is high on all plots, including those without fertilizer treatment. In particular, the *percentage content of nitrogen* is, with slight fluctuations, *in all cases near the optimum.*

TABLE 132

FERTILIZER EXPERIMENT, SPEYER. NUTRIENT CONTENT OF NEEDLES IN AUTUMN 1957

Group	Fertilizer treatment 1952–8	N (%)	P (%)	K (%)	Ca (%)
I	N	1·85	0·183	0·687	0·343
II	no fertilizer	1·91	0·184	0·747	0·317
III	NPK	2·01	0·194	0·717	0·330
IV	no fertilizer	1·85	0·185	0·693	0·315
V	N	1·81	0·168	0·660	0·315
VI	PK	1·90	0·204	0·700	0·333

On the one hand, it is possible that the pines on all plots have meanwhile been able to tap underlying layers of rich loam. On the other hand, it is conceivable that the wind has blown fallen needles with an ample nitrogen content from plots under fertilizer treatment

[1] My cordial thanks to Prof. Dr. Laatsch are recorded here for his kindness in allowing me to use the analytical data.

into the unfertilized plots thereby causing an improvement of the litter break-down and to an increase of the soil population.

A striking phenomenon was the *profusion of raspberry plants* which came in underneath the relatively thin top-canopy of pine after the last fertilizer application. A careful determination of the relative areas occupied by the ground-flora on the plot groups, carried out by the agricultural department of the B.A.S.F., afforded a clue as to where the applied quantities of fertilizer had come to reside. In this connection see Table 133.

TABLE 133

FERTILIZER EXPERIMENT, SPEYER. RELATIVE AREAS OF GROUND FLORA

Group	Fertilizer treatment	Area proportions in per cent				
		Raspberry	Grasses	Mosses	Heather	Others
I	N	43	11	22	—	24
II	no fertilizer	1	18	57	4	20
III	NPK	33	48	5	—	14
IV	no fertilizer	2	27	63	3	5
V	N	21	33	35	—	11
VI	PK	37	18	33	—	12

The agricultural department of the B.A.S.F. further discovered that according to the mean of ten samples, an additional 11,200 kg/ha of dry matter were produced on the areas of pure raspberry. At the same time, an average of 1·93 per cent N-content was found in the dry matter, which is equivalent to a withdrawal of 216 kg N per ha; this in the case of group I, which carries a proportion of 43 per cent of raspberries, works out to a *withdrawal of approximately 90 kg N per ha* on these plots. The experiment therefore is continued in a form whereby the research area after fencing is underplanted with broadleaved trees in order to observe any possible further effects of the fertilizers upon these.[1]

The detailed rendering of the results so far obtained in this experiment will have shown the complicated relationships to be expected in fertilizer experiments and the absolute necessity for careful specialized investigations in soil research and particularly in soil biology. Yield research for its part might well develop methods which are capable of detecting even small differences in increment, which may, after all, be of high diagnostic value.

Another outstanding consideration is *that nitrogen-deficiency is* obviously *a factor of the first order*, second only to water availabilities. This is also proved by numerous other fertilizer experiments in forestry (among others by Hesselmann and Malmström). But for the moment we shall take a quick look at the results of the forest fertilizer experiments up to 1953.

Summary of the results of forest fertilizer experiments prior to 1953

A satisfactory survey is provided by Hausser (1953) from whose work Table 134 has been obtained. From the higher percentages of successes of the experiments after 1932 we may conclude some improvement in the experimental methods. The general results are as follows:

---

[1] Sincere thanks are once more expressed here to gentlemen of the B.A.S.F., Direktor Dr. Huppert, Dr. Buchner and Dr. Jung for their generous promotion of this experiment and for allowing me to use the soil research surveys.

1. Norway spruce responds more readily to fertilizer treatment than Scots pine. Reasons: the root-system of spruce, as a rule, is shallow, that of pine on the other hand, deep. Pine is not so demanding and in most cases grows on rather poor sites, where many yield factors exist at a minimum.
2. Spruce responds particularly strongly to treatment with phosphoric acid.
3. Both species react readily to supplies of nitrogen, the effect of which, however, is only temporary.

The successes achieved by a cover of brushwood are remarkable. This refers especially to the Weckenhardt experiment in Württemberg, the results of which have been published by Zimmerle (1949). Similar favourable results from a soil cover of vegetable refuse were achieved by Fabricius (1956).

Results of more recent fertilizer experiments

Accounts of recent forest fertilizer experiments have become so numerous and extensive that it is impossible to discuss them here in great detail. It must suffice for us to draw a few inferences from some recent exerimental results regarding possibilities of improving yield and suitable types of fertilizer treatment.

According to van Goor (1956) die-back, yellow needles and defective growth of shoots of *pine* on some poor, podsolized sandy soils in Holland are due to a *deficiency in potassium* and may successfully be overcome by treatment with potash (potassium sulphate). Vascular experiments by van Goor (1953) with young *Japanese larch* as well as numerous fertilizer experiments in J. larch plantations (1956) established *that maximum yields are only attainable if the supply of N is accompanied by sufficient quantities of P*, unless the soil already contains sufficient P. If, for example, in consequence of unbalanced applications of N, the optimum ratio of N : P in the needles, i.e. of 5 : 1, is exceeded to the extent of 8 : 1 or 10 : 1, the larch reacts with *a lowered yield*.

Laatsch (1957, etc.), who repeatedly stressed the *necessity of "balanced fertilizer treatment"*, in this connection commented on "overfeeding with nitrogen". On this problem he stated: "In order to maintain the capacity for resistance of our trees we must endeavour to achieve a healthy ratio of carbohydrates to proteins... A surplus of carbohydrates must always be available to produce strong cell walls of adequate thickness and to develop a vigorous root system. The more that carbon assimilation is restricted by other factors such as lack of water or potash, the sooner will the addition of balanced quantities of nitrogen and phosphates serve to restore optimal conditions for vigorous and healthy growth."

Conclusions of a similar nature arise from a *fertilizer trial* (deficiency experiment) by Wittich (1958b) in Scots pine, Japanese larch, red oak and spruce *on a typical podsolized sandy soil in the Lüneburg Heath*. The pine, planted in 1950 on a burnt-over area, had barely reached a height of 1 metre in 1954 at the beginning of the experiment. The height growth of the pine, which progressively improved from 1954 to 1957, was much superior on the plots which had received N to that on the plots which had received only P, K and Ca. The dry weight of pine needles on the plots which had received full fertilizer treatment of NPKCa amounted to 9·1 mg on the average, as against only 5·6 mg on the control plots. The increment of diameter and thus also *of volume* of the young pine trees increased at even faster rates than the height increment; by 1957 the pine trees on plots which—regardless of the combination of other fertilizers—had received N, had produced

TABLE 134

SUMMARY OF RESULTS OF FERTILIZER TRIALS IN FORESTRY ACCORDING TO HAUSSER (1953)

Type of fertilizer	N. spruce			S. pine		
	Total number of series	Of these significantly successful number	%	Total number of series	Of these significantly successful number	%
Fertilizer experiments until 1932						
Lime (caustic lime, carbonated lime, calcareous marl, magnesia lime)	10	4	40	18	6	33
Thomasmeal	10	8	80	26	5	19
Superphosphate+lime	3	—	0	—	—	—
Thomasmeal+Kainit	6	3	50	23	8	35
Thomasmeal+lime+potash	2	2	100	2	—	0
Thomasmeal, Kainit, lime, sodium nitrate	3	2	67	2	—	0
Kainit	4	—	0	28	3	11
Sodium nitrate	3	1	33	8	3	38
Ammonium sulphate	2	—	0	8	—	0
Total of 1–9:	43	20	46	115	25	22
Perennial lupin only	1	1	100	—	—	—
Perennial lupin with art. fertilizer	4	4	100	1	1	100
Brushwood cover	3	2	67	11	4	36
Fertilizer experiments 1932–53						
Lime (caustic lime, carbonated lime)	11	9	83	2	—	0
Thomasmeal	4	3	75	—	—	—
Thomasmeal+lime	3	3	100	—	—	—
Thomasmeal+potash	2	1	50	—	—	—
Thomasmeal+lime+potash	2	2	100	—	—	—
Thomasmeal+lime+potash+ nitrogen	5	5	100	2	1	50
Calcium nitrate, calcium-ammonium nitrate, lime+nitro-chalk	3	3	100	1	1	100
Ammonium nitrate (Sweden)	1	1	100	—	—	—
NPK (Norway)	—	—	—	2	2	100
Total of 1–9:	31	27	87	7	4	57
Perennial lupin with art. fertilizer	6	—	0	—	—	—
Brushwood cover	3	3	100	—	—	—

of which 1 is Silver fir

2–3 times the volume of the pine on the control plots. At the end of the eighth vegetative period since the beginning of the experiment, the *volume production of pine trees on the plots* which had received NPKCa *amounted to approximately 2·6 times that of the trees on the control plots!* The positive response to N-additions by larch and red oak was even stronger; on the comparative plots without fertilizer treatment most of these trees died.

The progressive increase in production of organic substances on the deficient plots was accompanied by *progressive "dilution"* (Lundegårdh) *of the particular scarce nutrient which had been omitted in the fertilizer treatment.* This has been proved, *especially regarding P and K,* by foliage analyses.

Following the extraordinary success of this fertilizer experiment in raising young crops, Wittich concluded that "there can be no doubt about the profitableness of expert mineral fertilizer treatment in pine forests... Not only is it possible thereby to achieve large increases in yield but also to provide the conditions requisite for the cultivation of mixed stands with greater reliability in management."

C. Mar: Møller and M. Schaffalitzky de Muckadell (1957) reported about an extensively laid-out *fertilizer experiment in the raising of Norway spruce* which ran concurrently *on different sites in Denmark.* There, the effect of "full" and "half" doses of calcium cyanamide, potash, and superphosphate was measured *by the height increment* of the cultures, the height increment of 1952 having been set equal to 100. The following results were obtained:

In nine experiments on best-quality sites

   significant response to NPK in *six* experiments.

In four experiments on medium-quality sites

   in 40 per cent of the cases response to NPK,
   in 10 per cent of the cases response to N,
   doubtful response to P,
   no response to K,

In twelve experiments on poor-quality sites

   in 50 per cent of the cases a significant response to NPK,
   in 30–40 per cent of the cases significant response to N.

The experiments are to be continued for another 10 years in order to obtain clearer results. The results obtained so far have disclosed wide differences in response, depending on the particular soil conditions, which are to be expected in fertilizer experiments.

A paper by Mayer-Krapoll (1954) provides information concerning the appropriate use of fertilizers in forestry and on successes achieved thereby.

Among *new fertilizer experiments of the Forest Research Institute of Württemberg established by* Hausser, the two discussed in the following passages, about which Hausser reported in 1958 and 1960, have provided particularly informative results:

Fertilizer experiment No. 58 in *Dornstetten* forest, in the foreland on the east side of the Black forest, at 600 m above sea level, annual precipitation 950 mm, mean annual temperature 7·0°C. High flat plateau, gently sloping towards N, on upper bunter sandstone (Plattensandstein). Slightly podsolized loamy sand, becoming more compact with increasing depth, some surface loess. 3–6-cm surface layer of humus, pH (in H_2O) = = 4·1, in A_1 horizon = 4·5. Stand: pure *Norway spruce*, plantation; age in 1955, 66–71 years; Q. Cl. according to Wiedemann = I.6.

Fertilizer experiments with: $CaCO_3$ and "Hüttenkalk" (basic slag), Thomas-phosphate and nitro-chalk. Additionally, on small sample plots (2 ar), dosages of 200, 400 and 800 kg N per hectare.

The following *increases in increment* resulted as a rough average within 5 increment years (1952–1957) in comparison to the control plots:

Basal area increment	of approximately	corresponding to an ann. increase in incr. of approximately
by Ca+Thomasphosphate	9%	1·5 fm
by Ca+P₂O₅+N	40%	4·0 fm

This remarkable success in a stand which was approaching maturity proves that the prospects of forest fertilizer treatment are particularly favourable on medium or even superior quality sites, because even moderate percentage increases in this case are equivalent to considerable absolute yield increases. Moreover, in pole- and middle-aged stands these can *soon be realized* in the shape of increased yield from thinnings. As the total cost for treatment with Ca, P₂O₅ and N, according to Hausser, must be estimated as approximately 600 DM/ha, in the case of Dornstetten this would be returned already within 3 years in the form of increased increment.

FIG. 149. Fertilizer experiment at Hofstett. On right, pine standards with nitrogen effect. On left, without nitrogen *(Hausser)*.

Fertilizer experiment in *Hofstett* forest, Black Forest, 710 m above sea level; annual precipitation = 1170 mm, annual temperature = 6·5°C. Upper reaches of a valley, 15 per cent gradient towards NW.; middle bunter-sandstone, upper conglomerate. Below a surface layer of 10–15 cm raw humus, strongly podsolized, very stoney, medium-grain sand. Stand: 20–30-*year old natural pine regeneration*, fairly open and unevenly distributed, with very slow growth. Upper storey partly consisting of *pine standards*, approximately 190 *years old.*

The intention in this experiment was to give a boost to the slow-growing young pine trees by a basic supply of 36 dz Ca and 9 dz Thomasphosphate per hectare (i.e. *c.* 29 cwt and 7 cwt per acre respectively) after the removal of heather and bilberry and subsequent supplies of 5 dz nitro-chalk per hectare (4 cwt per acre) repeated every 3 years.

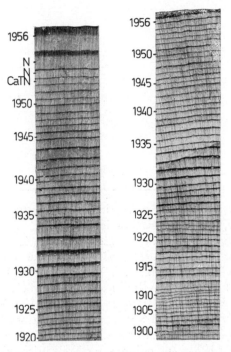

FIG. 150. Increased widths of the annual rings of 190-year-old pine standards as a result of nitrogen fertilizer application. *Left:* fertilized. *Right:* unfertilized *(Hausser).*

If we disregard the complications which were caused by the simultaneous trial of several types of nitrogen, the nitrogen in this case again manifested itself in increasing promotion of height growth, despite the negative effect of the removal of bilberry cover. At the same time an unexpected side-effect became apparent in the 190-year-old pine standards on experimental plot 1; within 3 years the scant needle foliage had become denser and the colour of the needles turned to dark green. In Fig. 149 this is apparent in the contrast between the standards with fertilizer treatment and those without. The favourable outward impression is matched by the unexpectedly large *increase in width of the annual rings* on stem sections of these old pines which were examined by Hausser. As a result of the supply of nitrogen the width of the annual rings, which before the age of 100 years had already dropped to below 1 mm, *increased to 1·5 mm, i.e. to approximately twice the former width.* This widening of the rings is illustrated in Fig. 150.

V. Pechmann (1960), who investigated the timber structure, found that this widening of the annual rings does *not reduce the density and quality of the wood,* a discovery which he had also made on samples of wood of the above-discussed Speyer fertilizer experiment and on samples from spruce nutrition experiments. *There are therefore good prospects for securing an effective improvement to the slackening growth of pine standards by means of fertilizer treatment and thereby for the production of valuable large-diameter timber.*

Mitscherlich and Wittich (1958) reported some *new fertilizer experiments in old forest stands in Baden.* In order to get information about growth changes, Mitscherlich made use of increment cores to supplement the more usual calipering which as we know, fails to provide significant differences in basal area increment over short intervals of time.[1] As average of all fourteen experimental series Mitscherlich calculated the following increases of the current volume increment:

TABLE 135

Fertilizer supplied	Ca	Ca + P	Ca + N	Ca + P + N
Ann. increase in incr. corresponding to an app. increase in revenue within	0·8–1·1	2·2–2·4	3·0–3·4	3·2–4·7 fm
6 years =	354–528	1056–1152	1440–1362	1536–2256 DM
Cost of fertilizers	176	250	315	363 DM
Net gain due to fertilizers	208–352	806–902	1125–1317	1173–1893 DM

If one remembers that a large part of the increased production becomes harvestable within a fairly short time, this is a considerable success.

The most interesting special case in these experiments is the experiment 3/I–VI in *Badenweiler forest*, in a cold and exposed position near the western slopes of the Black Forest mountains at 1200 m above m. s. l. Very stoney and gritty (skeletal fraction 50–75 per cent), sandy loam. Weakly developed base-deficient earth. Norway spruce stand, 1st generation following beech, 105 years old, Q. Cl. IV/V according to Wiedemann. The parent rock is a *hybrid granite* of abnormal composition, having *a high content of potash*, the ratio K : Ca is 23 times that in normal granite, so that a *toxic effect is produced by the absorption of excess potash*, as pointed out by Wittich. *Treatment with lime alone* produced an excellent effect here by rectifying the cation relationship. The increase of the mean annual ring width in comparison to the control plot in this case amounted to approximately 20 per cent, corresponding to an *increase* of the basal area and *volume increment of approximately 40 per cent.* The addition of P and N, or N alone, caused an increase in volume increment of 60–70 per cent.

The recently published book by Brüning (1959) records that young crops of Scots pine, red oak, and robinia on diluvial sand of low nutrient content and deprived especially of potash experienced *an unexpectedly vigorous renewed impetus to growth* which continued into the pole-wood stage, *after additions of potassium and magnesium.* In an experiment, started in 1954 (Brüning, 1959) with the objective of discovering the effect of fertilizers on young under-planted red oaks, the 100-year-old pine in the upper storey simultaneously experienced a considerable improvement in growth. The complete fertilizer treatment caused an increase of the mean annual ring width of these trees by approximately 24 per cent; when N was omitted, the increase was only about 11 per cent, with the omission of K it was only 10 per cent and with lime alone the increase was 7 per cent.

---

[1] It is for this reason that the author has for the last 7 years used girth measurement tapes made of steel to measure increments in fertilizer experiments.

The economic aspect of fertilizer treatment in the forest

The fact that fertilizer treatment of forest soils is today an economic proposition has been proved, by Hausser (1958) and others; the same may also be gathered from the above comparison between the cost of fertilizer treatment and the increase in yield. It must be stipulated, however, that fertilizers should not be applied "blindly", but only after a preliminary exhaustive examination of the soils, to which a foliage analysis can provide a serviceable guide.

Baule (1960) estimated the cost and financial result of a full fertilizer treatment based on the reasonable expectation of a 20 per cent yield increase from two spruce felling series (Wiedemann, moderate thinnings) on 100 years rotation, yielding an assumed average of 50 DM per fm (o.b.) and calculated the following result:

	Q. Cl. II	Q. Cl. III
Increased income	9500	7500
Cost of fertilizer treatment	2000–3000	2000–3000 DM per ha
Gain	6500–7500	4500–5500

The difficult question of interest charges on the costs of fertilizer treatment partially solves itself if the treatment takes place at the pole-wood stage, because then a large part of the increased increment can be harvested soon after the treatment. In this connection Assmann (1958) made the following estimate: if a full fertilizer treatment (say with 50 dz calcium carbonate, 6 dz calcium-ammonium nitrate, 8–10 dz Thomasphosphate or a similar material) at an estimated cost of approximately 500 DM causes the increment of a 50-year-old spruce pole-wood within 20 years to increase by 30 per cent = 66 fm (u.b.), this corresponds to a cash increase of the increment of approximately 2500 DM, At least two-thirds, or approximately 1600 DM, of this can be harvested without difficulty in this 20-year period.

The currently unfavourable financial returns from many forests of the Federal Republic of Germany are caused by relatively low timber prices as well as the *disproportionally heavy burden of fixed costs* (in this connection see Speer, 1959). Strehlke (1958) drew attention to the fact that the yield situation for forestry might be substantially improved, if the productivity of the respective areas under working could be put on a better financial footing. In many places this can be achieved by rational manuring of the forest soil. The *relative* extent of such gains is greater on poor-quality sites than on medium and better sites, whereas the *absolute quantitative increases are higher on medium and better sites*. Thus, for example, an increase of the m.a.i. at 100 years on a pine crop of Q. Cl. V by 20 per cent, i.e. from 2·3 to 2·8 fm, would mean an absolute increase in production of only 0·5 fm, whilst an increase of the m.a.i.$_{100}$ of spruce, Q. Cl. II by 20 per cent, i.e. from 9·6 to 11·5 fm, would produce an increase of the increment by 1·9 fm. At relatively low cost it should be possible to achieve the greatest successes:

1. on soils with a satisfactory cation-exchange capacity but abnormal or disturbed ion-relationships,
2. on sites with medium to good yield potentialities, which have been severely impoverished by litter withdrawal.

Improvement of soils after litter exploitation

Examples of forest soils which have been impoverished by litter-removals of several centuries are found in the extensive forest areas of the Oberpfalz. For decades past, foresters there have made strenuous endeavours[1] to restore productivity, mainly by the cultivation of lupins. Wittich (1954), after thorough soil-analyses, achieved notable successes in certain typical instances, particularly by soil enrichment through the introduction of humic substances of favourable constitution. These helpful discoveries have been supplemented by yield research investigations made by the author in the *forest of Pfreimd.*

There, in 1935, a plot of the then 69-year-old Scots pine stand was under-planted with perennial lupin, which then spread unaided over large parts of the stand.

Soil conditions (according to Wittich) 40 cm thickness of sandy loam over very compact, stiff loam; weakly podsolized brown earth, sub-soil slightly gley-ized. For details, cf. contribution by Wittich.

In autumn 1954, two permanent sample plots were established, one in the part of the stand under-planted with lupin and one in the part not yet colonized by lupins; two borings were obtained from each of the sixty-five sample stems of each plot. The observed data are given in Table 136.

TABLE 136

LUPIN EXPERIMENT PFREIMD. STAND-DATA AND 10-YEAR INCREMENT OF THE TWO SAMPLE PLOTS (FIGURES PER HECTARE)

		Sample plot with lupin	Control plot without lupin
Basal area over bark	m²	23·311	20·514
Stem number		745	975
Mean diameter	cm	19·96	16·37
Mean height	m	16·85	14·75
Volume of stemwood	fm	178·3	140·7
Probable increment o.b.			
spring 1945 to autumn 1954	fm	*56·1*	*40·6*

The superiority in growth of the "lupin plot" therefore amounts to *15·5 fm = 38* per cent.

The mean error of the volume increment thus found amounts to approximately ± 12 per cent. Assuming the "significant difference in yield" to be that part of the difference in production which exceeds the standard error of this difference multiplied by 2 ($2 \mu_D$), then this for the lupin plot amounts to approximately *15* per cent.

In the further course of this experiment, twenty-five *dominant sample trees* were felled on, and in the surround of, each of the two sample plots; the height increment of the last 30 years and the basal area increment (on stem cross-sections) for the same period and for 5-year intervals were determined. The striking elongation of the leading shoots observed on the pine trees in the part under lupin influence showed itself also, although in a much less marked degree, on the pines in the part of the stand not yet under lupin influence, and the dominant trees chosen for felling in both parts of the stand therefore had to display this phenomenon.

---

[1] Great credit in this respect has been earned by Oberregierungsrat Dr. Schödel who died in 1959.

TABLE 137

LUPIN EXPERIMENT PFREIMD. DEVELOPMENT OF THE MEAN HEIGHTS OF TWENTY-FIVE
SAMPLE STEMS IN EACH CASE

Year	Age (years)	Mean height and 5-year height increments			
		with lupin		without lupin	
		(m)	(m)	(m)	(m)
1954 (autumn)	89	18·22		17·47	
1950 (spring)	84	16·50	1·72	16·45	1·02
1945	79	14·74	1·76	15·36	1·09
1940	74	13·60	1·14	14·10	1·26
1935	69	12·94	0·66	13·11	0·99
1930	64	12·36	0·58	12·16	0·95
1925	59	11·86	0·50	11·49	0·67

Supposing that the basal area increments of the sample trees can be regarded as representative of the corresponding parts of the stand, the result for the crop under lupin influence shows a *"significantly greater growth"* of basal area of approximately *25 per cent*. The figures in Table 137 give the results of height analyses. These results are also displayed in Fig. 151.

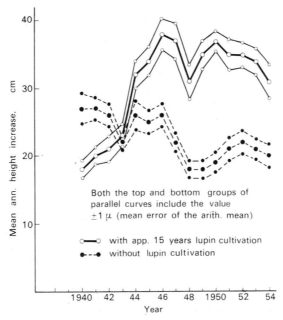

FIG. 151. Pfreimd forest. Mean annual height increments of twenty-five sample stems with and without the influence of lupin cultivation.

It emerges from this experiment that *the current height-growth of the sample stems subject to lupin influence has over the last 10 years, shown a markedly superior performance; in terms of greater volume increment, it amounts to nearly 60 per cent*. Over the same period, the height analysis shows a distinct improvement in the growth of trees constituting that part of the stand which, up to the present, has been free of lupins; the somewhat lower figures of height-growth in 1925 and 1930 indicate a slight inferiority in quality-class of the area not yet under lupin influence.

Two representative individuals of the felled sample stems were fully analysed. Their higher rates of growth during the last 10 years makes the responses even more distinct, as shown in Table 138A and Fig. 152.

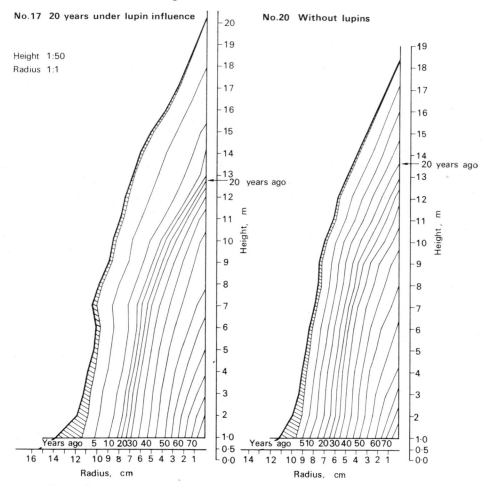

FIG. 152. Pfreimd forest. Stem analyses of two typical sample stems with and without lupin effect.

There are several main factors participating in these different increment responses:

1. the beneficial effects of lupins,
2. the abolition of litter utilization,
3. the severe opening up of the stand.

Owing to the loss of records at the end of the war the local forest administration (Ober-forstmeister Kürzdörfer) was unable to furnish exact dates of the last removal of litter or of fellings and it is therefore impossible to assess how far these factors participated in the strong stimulation of growth. However, according to the results of Wittich (cf. *Fw. Cbl.*, 1954, p. 193) there can be no doubt that *lupins played the largest part*. The *rise*

TABLE 138A

RESULT OF THE COMPLETE ANALYSIS OF TWO REPRESENTATIVE SAMPLE STEMS

Point of time	Height and height incr.				Volume and volume increment			
	with lupins (m)	(m)	without lupins (m)	(m)	with lupins (fm)	(fm)	without lupins (fm)	(fm)
At the time of felling	20·15		18·30		0·402		0·263	
		2·40		1·10		0·118		0·053
5 years ago	17·75		17·20		0·284		0·210	
		2·40		1·20		0·095		0·041
10 years ago	15·35		16·00		0·189		0·169	
		1·35		1·25		0·042		0·033
15 years ago	14·00		14·75		0·147		0·136	
		1·00		1·10		0·017		0·025
20 years ago	13·00		13·65		0·130		0·111	
		0·25		0·75		0·016		0·019
25 years ago	12·75		12·90		0·114		0·092	
		0·35		0·50		0·015		0·014
30 years ago	12·40		12·40		0·099		0·078	
		0·40		0·65		0·023		0·016
35 years ago	12·00		11·75		0·076		0·062	

in height quality class in the part under lupin influence after 1940 amounted to no less than *0·7 quality-class intervals* according to Wiedemann's yield table (1943) for Scots pine, and the current increment over the preceding 10 years exceded the values in the table by 33 per cent, despite a stocking density of only 0·8. The improvement in quality class accordingly is likely to continue and reach at least one full interval.

From this experiment we can assess *how effective are lupins, as liberators of nitrogen, in raising the productivity of soils after litter-exploitation.* But at the same time we can also judge *the extent of the loss in production due to litter utilization,* even on medium-quality sites.

In view of such highly satisfactory results from a lupin under-crop there arises the question *whether or not lupins are generally to be preferred to a mineral nitrogen fertilizer.* In this connection it is to be noted, that good lupin growth on poorer sites depends directly on heavy *initial manuring* (Zimmerle, 1936a; Wehrmann, 1956) and that the upper storey must as a rule be *opened up,* which demands a *sacrifice of timber increment.* This is further *increased by soil working,* which has been shown to lead to increment reductions because of the damage caused to roots (cf. p. 418). If one further remembers that, on poor soils, the unbalanced additions of nitrogen reduces the other, already insufficient, nutrients to a minimum and that these therefore need to be supplemented artificially, then the scales tip in favour of direct mineral fertilizer treatment for pine in the pole-wood and mature stages, although in the establishment stage the introduction of lupins appears especially to be recommended.

Wehrmann (1956) rightly warned against the dangers of unbalanced fertilizer treatment and excessive additions of nitrogen to soils wherein the exchange-capacity of cations is low and where therefore "only small quantities of the artificially supplied nutritive elements can enter into combination by way of exchange".

However, on the whole, the results of new experiments with mineral fertilizers on poor soils, which have in the meantime been established by the Bodenkundliches Institut (Institute for soil research) of the Forestry Research Institute, Munich (among others Zöttl, 1958; Wehrmann, 1959) are quite favourable and promising.[1] In particular it has been discovered that it is possible thus to produce a favourable influence on the soil fauna.

[1] In these experiments the Institute for Yield Research in Munich observes the increment effects. The measurements and evaluations are not yet concluded but it is probable there will be increases in increment corresponding to the favourable soil study diagnoses.

Fertilizer treatment of forest soils, soil biology and the living community

How favourable is this influence on the soil fauna has been proved by the investigations by Franz (1956a, b) and Ronde (1957, 1960) on experimental plots with mineral fertilizer treatment. For an example see Fig. 153. According to Ronde, "the biological structure of the forest soil is profoundly influenced" by fertilizer treatment. "The ameliorative effects of nitrogen application in combination with lime and phosphates in medium climatic conditions are quick-acting.... Complete fertilizer treatment has a specially stimulating effect on the reproduction and activity of the small animals in the soil—the most strongly favoured members of the fauna are earthworms, mites and myriapods."

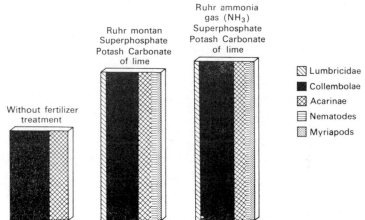

FIG. 153. Changes in the ground fauna as a result of fertilizer treatment in a pine stand of low vigour. Schwabach forest *(Ronde)*.

As the biological changes in the cases examined by Ronde were not yet completed, the total effect on the soil fauna, in her opinion, cannot yet be assessed. Of great importance *is her assertion that* on the examined coniferous sites in Ebersberger forest, in Nuremberg State forest and in the municipal forest of Schrobenhausen, which are well recognized as foci for repeated mass infestations of forest pests *the soil micro-fauna have become impoverished and have undergone* some *change of species* which may be considered *typical of forest sites predisposed to infestation by noxious insects.* This impoverishment and change of species is *favourably transformed* by fertilizer treatment of the forest soil.

Zwölfer (1953, 1957) saw that the well-known liability of mass outbreaks of destructive insects to occur on forest sites with poor soils and in connection with mono-cultures of pure coniferous species is associated with the physiological condition of the trees. That the mortality of noxious insects is correlated with the mineral supply of trees has been proved by Büttner (1956) and Merker (1958), and according to Nessenius (1956), Merker (1958) and Thalenhorst (1958) the water supply also plays a part. Oldiges (1958, 1959) subsequently proved by feeding experiments, carried out in the field, at Schwabach and Bodenwöhr forest, *that the mortality of caterpillars of the pine looper, pine moth, pine beauty and nun moth is considerably increased by feeding on needles of Scots pine which had received mineral fertilizers.* Figure 154 demonstrates this considerable increase in mortality of caterpillars of the pine looper during the 2 years of the experiment (L_1, L_2, etc. = different caterpillar stages).[1]

[1] In contrast, an increase of the nitrogen concentration in parts of the plants apparently has a favourable effect on the health of the *sucking* insects.

By means of mineral fertilizer additions to forest soils we can:

1. on sites so endangered create mixed stands with a richer diversity and greater innate resistance against mass-outbreaks of a single species;
2. cause favourable changes in the soil fauna population;
3. by better nutrition, improve the capacity of trees to ward off such attacks and intensify the mortality of insect pests by changing their mineral intake.

The automatic aversion of many foresters even today to the use of fertilizers in the forest because of its "artificiality" is understandable on the grounds that it goes contrary to much experience in the annals of forestry; but in view of these new aspects it is no

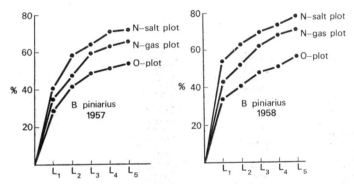

FIG. 154. Mortality of pine looper caterpillar on forest soil areas with and without fertilizer treatment
(Oldiges).

longer justified. Indeed, those felling methods which as a result of long usage are regarded as "natural", cannot be acknowledged as being that either. Timber harvesting continually deprives the forest soil of such quantities of nutrients that on poorer sites this must necessarily lead to reductions in yield without some restitution be made in the shape of fertilizers. According to calculations by Rennie (1955) the felling of Scots pine even of only moderate quality in the course of a 100-year rotation causes an average loss of 80 kg P_2O_5, 180 kg K_2O, and 530 kg $CaCO_3$ (quoted according to Wehrmann, 1956). The harvesting of 1st quality Norway spruce in the course of a 120-year rotation is equivalent to the withdrawal of approximately 1500 kg N, 320 kg P_2O_5, 800 kg K_2O, 1900 kg CaO and 370 kg MgO (quoted after Baule, 1960). Obviously an untouched virgin forest may accumulate over the centuries considerable quantities of nutritive elements in the humus, even on poor soils, because in this case they were never reduced by timber removals.

The normal methods for the regulation of growing space in forestry (Assmann, 1957), as we have already learned, can only in exceptional cases produce an increase in timber volume and in present-day practice as a rule they even result in a loss of increment; on the other hand, soil amelioration and manuring now for the first time offer prospects of considerable increases in organic production by the forest. If these possibilities are put to effect on correct scientific principles and with the right objectives, the profitability of our forests will be enhanced along with the general health of our managed forests and their resistance to hazards.

FOREST ORGANIZATION AND YIELD

I. GROWTH AND YIELD RELATIONSHIPS IN WORKING SECTIONS OF THE NORMAL HIGH FOREST

In order fully to apprehend the structure, growth relationships and yield of an entire forest we must use simplified models which enable us to gain an insight into the laws governing these complicated structures.

1. Model of the Normal Working Section

Those forest stands which have been collectively arranged in order to secure sustained management form a "working section" (or "felling series"). For an outline of definitions a study of Abetz (1935) is suggested. In contrast to such a "realistic" working section, the model of a "normal" working section is based on simplified conditions, which are never in practice realized; for that reason it is also referred to as an "ideal" working section.

It is assumed that an uninterrupted sequence of age gradations exists on ground which is uniform throughout, and that all age gradations consist of a single species and occupy equal areas. A continuous policy of management is furthermore assumed. The oldest age-class must be felled in the autumn of every year and restocked the following spring.[1] By an extreme simplification, namely by the further assumption that equal increments are produced in all age gradations, we arrive at *the primitive model*, illustrated in Fig. 155.

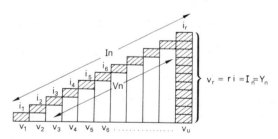

$$v_r = r\,i = I_n = Y_n$$

FIG. 155. Highly simplified model of a normal working section.

In the autumn, before a felling, there are present all age gradations from 1 to r years covering areas of equal size. Each area of 1 hectare annually produces the normal increment of i. The total of these increments i_1, i_2, ..., i_r on the total area of the working section then obviously amounts to $r \times i$. If the timber growing-stocks by volume on each

---

[1] The clear-felling here implied is merely in order to facilitate later steps in the argument; with appropriate modifications, these will be found applicable to a system employing natural regeneration.

of the age-class areas are known as $v_1, v_2, \ldots, v_r$ these must grow proportionally to their age and, in the oldest age class, reach the value $v_r = r \times i$. Each year this class is harvested and represents the *annual normal increment* of the working section $= I_n$ which is also *the sustained normal possible yield* $= Y_n$. The total of growing-stocks of all age-classes then gives the *normal growing stock of the working section* $= V_n$. This forms an *arithmetic progression* with the *first* member $v_1 = i$ and the last member $v_r = r \times i$. Therefore

$$V_n = \frac{r}{2}(i + r \times i) = \frac{r \times r \times i}{2} + \frac{ri}{2} \quad (autumn\ stock).$$

After felling *in spring*, the first member $= 0$ and the last member $= (r-1)i$; consequently the

$$stock\ in\ spring = \frac{r \times ri}{2} - \frac{ri}{2}; \quad \text{for the middle of the summer } V_n = \frac{r \times ri}{2}.$$

This normal stock at mid-summer can otherwise be calculated as the area of a triangle of base r (r age-classes) and height $r \times i$ (growing-stock in the last age class), i.e. $= r/2 \times ri = \frac{1}{2} r \times ri$. As $r \times i$ is harvested each year, the *total yield within a rotation* $= r \times ri = 2V_n$. The *total yield* within the rotation r is assessed as *double the amount of the normal stock*.

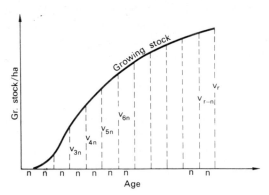

FIG. 156. Calculation of the normal growing stock in one working section *(Pressler)*.

Now, even if the site remains the same and the climate does not change, the increment changes with age. *The curve representing the growing stock of a working section is not a straight line.* Instead it corresponds to the development of a crop upon a given site in the way represented by the successive yield table volumes for the standing crop in each particular instance. This crop-volume curve must now be integrated by an approximation, for which purpose we will use the familiar formula by Pressler. This gives the normal growing stock as the total of an arithmetic progression, equal conditions applying for autumn and spring stocks as in the above primitive model: in this connection see Fig. 156.

If n = the number of age gradations per age class (5 or 10).

v_n = the volume of timber at the age n,

v_{2n} = the volume of timber stock at the age $2n$, etc., then the following formula applies:

$$V_n = n\left(v_n + v_{2n} + \ldots v_{r-n} + \frac{v_r}{2}\right) \pm \frac{v_r}{2}.$$

TABLE 138B

CALCULATION OF THE NORMAL GROWING-STOCK OF A WORKING SECTION, BASED ON A YIELD TABLE EXCERPT FROM THE SCOTS PINE YIELD TABLE OF GEHRHARDT (1921) FOR MODERATE THINNING, HEIGHT QUALITY CLASS II (VOLUMES IN FESTMETRES OVER BARK OF WOOD OVER 7 CM IN DIAMETER PER HECTARE)

Age	Standing crop volume (m³)	Removals Per decade volume (m³)	Removals Total volume (m³)	Total crop volume (m³)	Annual increment current (m³)	Annual increment mean (m³)
10	3	—	—	3	—	0·3
		7			5·1	
20	47		7	54		2·7
		19			9·9	
30	127		26	153		5·1
		34			*10·0*	
40	193		60	253		6·3
		39			9·0	
50	244		99	343		6·9
		39			8·2	
60	287		138	425		7·1
		35			7·2	
70	324		173	497		*7·1*
		34			6·3	
80	353		207	560		7·0
		30			5·5	
90	378		237	615		6·8
		26			4·6	
100	398		263	661		6·6
		23			4·0	
110	415		286	701		6·4
		20			3·3	
120	428		306	734		6·1

The last term is added in the case of the autumn stock, whereas for the spring stock it is deducted. In the yield table, growing stocks are always given per hectare. The above formula thus supplies the normal stock for an area of r hectares. For a complete working section of area F(ha), therefore, the result of the calculation has to be multiplied by the factor F/r. Table 138B gives the growing-stocks of a Scots pine working section for three rotation periods, calculated on the basis of a yield table for Scots pine by Gehrhardt (1921).

Normal growing stocks according to the formula by Pressler, for a 100-hectare working section (spring stocks, without thinnings).

Rotation	Total stock v_n to v_{r-n} (fm o.b.)	$\dfrac{v_r}{2}$ (fm o.b.)	Col. 2 + col. 3 ×10	for r ha (fm o.b.)	Factor $\dfrac{F}{r}$	Spring stock for 100 ha (fm o.b.)	for 1 ha (fm o.b.)
80	1225	176	14,010	13,834	1·25	17,292	173
100	1956	199	21,550	21,351	1·00	21,351	214
120	2769	214	29,830	29,616	0·833	24,670	247

Only the growing-stocks representing crops after thinning appear in Pressler's formula. But a considerable proportion of the total growth is from time to time removed ("skimmed off") by thinnings. If these thinnings are not done annually but at 5-yearly or 10-yearly intervals, growing-stocks representing the unharvested annual thinning yields must accumulate. Although the out-turn from intermediate fellings may amount to 40–60 per cent of the total out-turn of a working section, the growing-stock which accrues from such unharvested thinnings is nevertheless quite small. It can be easily shown that with a thinning cycle of t years, this must amount to

$$\frac{t}{2} \text{ (sum of the thinning yields)} \pm \frac{1}{2} \text{ (sum of the thinning yields)}$$

depending upon whether the growing-stock is calculated for the autumn or spring of the year. Thus, for $t = 5$ and a crop calculated in spring, 5 fm attributable to thinnings would be added to the calculated normal growing-stock volumes of the main crop given in Table 138.

The relationships between stock and yield are better expressed in an improved model of a working section by Assmann (1956b) than in the hitherto customary models which are restricted to the standing crop; Fig. 157 shows this improved model, based on the yield table of Wiedemann for spruce.

The growing-stock representing unharvested annual thinning yields of 930 fm, distributed over a working section area of 70 ha of crops which are suitable for thinning, forms a strip of on average only 13 fm height on the ordinate. It is hatched. This narrow band could be compared to a "cambial layer" which continually produces increment. Part of this goes into the upper section as early yield, whilst the other part goes down into the normal stock.

The course of the increment is represented in the bottom left-hand diagram, from which it is easy to see that a growing proportion, on average 38 per cent, of the increment of the age-classes which are ready for thinning is constantly being realized, whilst the remaining 62 per cent is incorporated into the growing-stock, and at the age r it is harvested as final yield. The different proportions in which the individual age-classes participate in the increment of the working section are aptly demonstrated. The broken line at 12·2 fm height on the ordinate defines the mean annual increment of the working section, the familiar "m.a.i."; it is equal to the arithmetic mean of the (current) increments of all age classes.

The large rectangle at top right represents the total yield of the working section during a 100-year rotation. These 100 annual yields with a total of 121,800 fm are produced by a growing stock of only 39,160 fm, which therefore *within 100 years produces 3·1 times its own volume*. If the annual yield of 1218 fm is related to the growing-stock, the result (after multiplication by 100) is the familiar *yield percentage*, which in a normal working section is *identical with the* (average) *increment percentage* (of all age classes). In this case it is = 3·1 per cent.

This could be compared with a capital C invested at an interest rate of p per cent which produces an annual rental $AR = C \times 0·0p$. Thus C corresponds to the normal stock and AR to the annual yield of the working section. C in that case is also $= AR \times 100/p$. The factor $100/p$, which is the familiar factor of capitalisation, shows *how many annual incomes are contained in the capital*. The normal stock in the above example consequently contains 32 annual yields.

The analogy, however, is not complete, because, as demonstrated in Fig. 157, there are 100 "little stands" or parcels of capital, all working at different increment rates. Our "*p*" represents an *average* percentage of increment or interest respectively, which, if the rotation is curtailed or prolonged and the proportions of the age-classes vary, changes in a

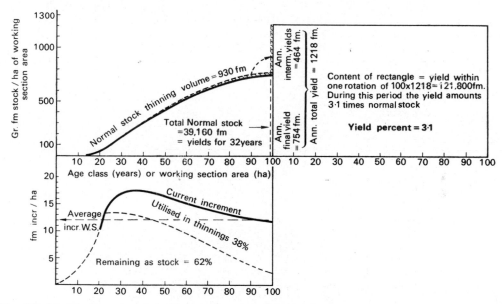

FIG. 157. Model of a normal working section according to Wiedemann's spruce yield table; Quality Class I, moderate thinning; $r = 100$.

complicated and not easily calculable manner. But if we know "*p*", we can estimate the effects of certain manipulations, such as excessive exploitation or an amplification of the growing-stock.

2. Changes in the Characteristic Values of Working Sections due to Different Grades of Thinning and Different Rotations

The above-discussed characteristic values of working sections vary in a definable manner according to the thinning grade and the rotation, as shown in Table 139. The values shown for spruce, Q. Cl. I, with $r = 100$ years, are for both moderate and heavy thinnings. Heavy thinning in this case considerably reduces the normal growing-stock (by 14 per cent). Although according to Wiedemann's—incorrect—assumption, the increment is only reduced by a quite insignificant amount, the yield percentage increases from 3·1 to 3·6 per cent. The factor $100:p$ drops from 32 to 28, i.e. the normal growing-stock now contains four annual increments less.

To a woodland owner who feels constrained to increase his returns, this suggests the remarkable opportunity for liquidating these four annual coupes, possibly by conducting fellings 50 per cent in excess of normal over a period of 8 years, without further reducing the overall increment. In fact, for a woodland owner who is intent on profit, obviously the interest rate should increase along with the yield per cent. The problem of increasing the exploitable yield is discussed mainly in the works by Baader (1944), Crocoll (1940) and Künanz (1950) which are recommended reading. Herein we are going to examine, on the basis of concrete long-observed experimental stands, the *actual* effect of intensified thinning on a spruce working section.

TABLE 139

CHARACTERISTIC VALUES OF NORMAL WORKING SECTIONS ACCORDING TO YIELD TABLES; FESTMETRES OVER BARK PER HECTARE; SPRING STOCK; $t = 5$ YEARS

Yield table	Timber species and degree of thinning	Qual-ity class	r	Normal stock in Main crop (fm)	Thngs. (fm)	Total (fm)	Total yield during rotn. (fm)	m.a.i. (fm)	Thinning yield (%)	Yield (%) (p)	100:p
Schwappach (1893)	*Beech*										
	mod.	I	140	384	6	390	1225	8·7	32	2·2	45
	heavy	I	140	349	8	357	1225	8·7	44	2·4	41
Wiedemann (1931)	*Beech*										
	mod.	I	140	326	9	335	1243	8·9	49	2·6	38
	heavy	I	140	254	10	264	1193	8·5	62	3·2	31
	mod.	I	100	225	6	231	835	8·3	38	3·6	28
	heavy	I	100	185	9	194	826	8·3	53	4·3	23
	mod.	II	100	175	5	180	677	6·8	36	3·8	26
	heavy	II	100	148	8	156	707	7·1	53	4·6	22
Wiedemann (1943)	*Pine*										
	mod.	I	140	297	7	304	982	7·0	53	2·3	43
	heavy	I	140	249	8	257	966	6·9	62	2·7	37
	open-std.	I	140	207	9	216	915	6·5	65	3·0	33
	mod.	I	100	237	7	244	779	7·8	45	3·2	31
	heavy	I	100	204	9	213	776	7·8	56	3·6	28
	open-std.	I	100	171	9	180	735	7·4	63	4·1	24
Wiedemann (1936)	*Spruce*										
	mod.	I	100	383	9	392	1218	12·2	38	3·1	32
	heavy	I	100	325	12	337	1206	12·1	50	3·6	28
	mod.	I	80	298	7	305	974	12·2	30	4·0	25
Gehrhardt (1921)	*Silver fir*										
	mod.	I	150	635	10	645	2007	13·4	38	2·1	48
	heavy	I	100	391	10	401	1487	14·9	35	3·7	27

Just as a yield table can represent the *growth and yield of a single stand at successive stages, or equally well the state of all other age-classes of a normal working section existing contemporaneously alongside each other, so can we at any time construct models of working sections from measurements of individual crops taken over a sufficiently lengthy period.* For this purpose we shall use the results of the B- and C-grade plots of the experimental spruce series of Denklingen. With moderate thinning, according to Fig. 158, the normal growing-stock of 51,200 fm, with $p = 2.9$ per cent, supplies an annual yield of 1505 fm; with heavy thinning, according to Fig. 159, the growing-stock which has been reduced

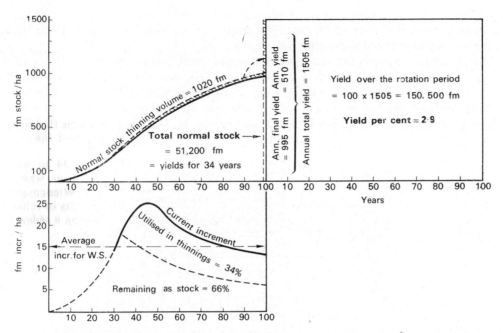

FIG. 158. Model of a working section, based on the treatment of plot II of the spruce trial series 5 at Denklingen (moderate thinning).

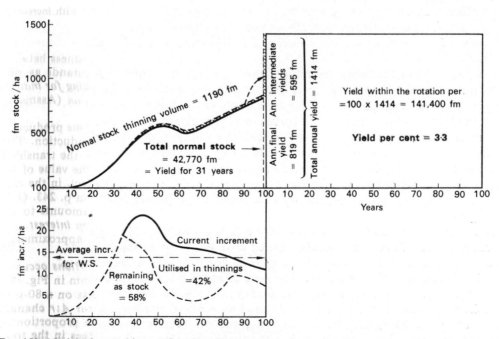

FIG. 159. Model of a working section, based on plot III of the trial series at Denklingen (heavy thinning).

to 42,770 fm, at $p = 3.3$ per cent supplies annually 1414 fm yield. We recognize that heavy thinning in the age classes 40–80 years has caused an obvious indentation of the curve of the stock and reduced the current increment.

The comparatively small increase of the thinning yield percentage from 34 to 42 in this case, already causes a *reduction in the possible sustained yield by 5 per cent*, whereas the reduction caused by the transition from 38 to 50 per cent in both of Wiedemann's yield tables is assumed to be even less than 1 per cent. According to the results of reliable thinning experiments (cf. Section D, IV, 2) we must in this instance count on a *reduction*

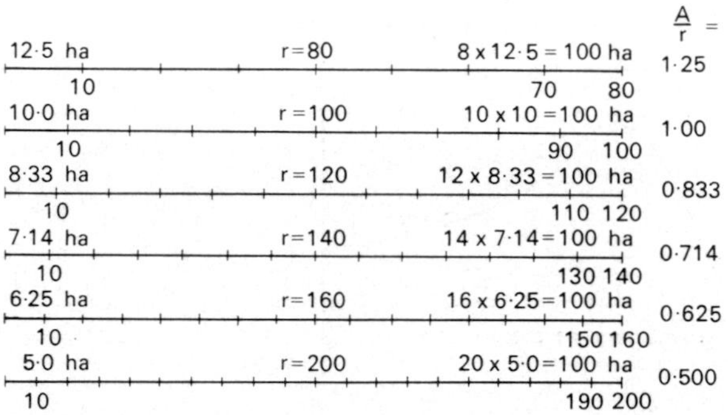

$$\frac{A}{r} =$$

12·5 ha	r=80	8 x 12·5 = 100 ha	1·25
10		70 80	
10·0 ha	r=100	10 x 10 =100 ha	1·00
10		90 100	
8·33 ha	r=120	12 x 8·33 = 100 ha	0·833
10		110 120	
7·14 ha	r=140	14 x 7·14 = 100 ha	0·714
10		130 140	
6·25 ha	r=160	16 x 6·25=100 ha	0·625
10		150 160	
5·0 ha	r=200	20 x 5·0=100 ha	0·500
10		190 200	

FIG. 160. The area fractions for the several age classes become progressively smaller with increasing rotation.

of the total yield by at least 5 per cent, because the established inter-relatedness between the natural degree of stocking and the increment is valid for individual stands as well as for correspondingly treated working sections. *The critical degree of stocking for individual stands is matched by a critical level of the stock for the working section* (Assmann, 1956a, d).

Cutting to below the critical level of the growing-stock in relation to *volume* production does not necessarily imply that there will be a lessening of the *value* production. This may be seen, for example, in the Lichtwuchs system for beech. However, the transition from moderate to heavy thinning in spruce does not, as a rule, increase the value of the average converted festmetre, at least not within the usual rotations. In fact, in the case of Denklingen with $r = 104$ years it is reduced by 2 per cent as shown on p. 243. Only if incomes from thinnings are *computed at compound interest* or, what amounts to the same thing, if the timber stock of the working section is intended to *earn interest*, will heavy thinning result in a superiority of the net value production by approximately 10 per cent.

A change of the rotation simultaneously affects a *change of the proportions occupied by each age-class in the total working section area*. As shown in the diagram in Fig. 160, in a working area of 100 hectare, the area occupied by a 10-year age-class on a 80-year rotation is 12·5 ha which drops to 5·0 ha on a 200-year rotation; the factor $A:r$ changes correspondingly. Hence the longer the rotation, the smaller becomes the proportion of juvenile crops and of young stands with large numbers of small-sized trees in the total content of the working section. The stem number per hectare must obviously fall with longer rotations whilst at the same time the timber growing-stock per hectare becomes considerably larger.

The influence of the rotation on the characteristic values of the working section is shown in Table 139. If the rotation for beech is reduced from 140 to 100 years the annual yield per hectare, assuming the same grade of thinning, becomes smaller, because the m.a.i.$_r$ decreases. In pine, the reverse happens, because—owing to the early culmination of the m.a.i.—the m.a.i.$_r$ increases. In both cases, the normal growing-stock per hectare as well as the factor $100:p$ decreases, whilst the yield percentage increases. The average timber prices per fm of beech and pine at breast-height diameters over 40 cm increase considerably, especially if the stems are clean-boled; therefore short rotations are as a rule financially unrewarding. Of course, the use of short rotations releases considerable timber stocks and large values, but it is easy to see that *it would require long periods of time to replenish the reduced stocks.* Therefore in cases of emergency, especially in a species like beech, where the increment is particularly elastic, an intensification of thinning is the more advantageous. For example, the transition to heavier thinning and an open-stand system in a normally stocked beech working section, which up to that time had been thinned moderately, enabled a growing stock of 330 fm o.b. per hectare to be reduced in the course of 10 to 15 years by approximately 80 to 90 fm without danger of incurring any large increment losses. In fact, the value of the future yield might even be increased by selective crown-isolation of the trees with the best form, as proved by the results of the open-stand system in beech (p. 384).

On the whole, however, the data in the table prove that the ratio of yield/growing-stock, i.e. the exploitation percentage, cannot be varied to any great extent, and that, *if the exploitation percentage is over-strained, the reserves of all growing-stocks dwindle to a dangerous extent. Working sections with longer rotations and ample timber stocks are in all cases less subject to crises than those with low stocks and short rotations.*

From the above figures, as from those offered by Wiedemann (1950, pp. 288 ff.) we can deduce the parallel between the yield percentages of working sections and the corresponding interest percentages. This is demonstrated here in a comparison between two spruce working sections according to the yield table of Zimmerle, Quality Class II (prices = 180 per cent of the M.I.).

r	Normal stock fm o.b. (felled)	Yield fm (felled)	Exploita-tion (%)	Value of normal stock (DM)	Value of yield (DM)	Gross interest (%)	Value per fm stock (DM)	yield (DM)
80	249	11·6	*4·66*	11,950	719	*6·02*	48·–	62·–
120	410	11·7	*2·85*	22,550	830	*3·68*	55·–	71·–
		r 120 : *r* 80						
			0·61			*0·61*		

We find that when yield and growing-stock are rated at equal assortment prices, *the gross interest percentages change proportionately with the exploitation percentages.* But it must be remembered that the values assumed for the growing-stock are values after conversion, because other values carry too many uncertainties.

Thus, the following sentences by Lemmel (1922, 1925) are confirmed: "The interest rate follows essentially upon the natural rate of timber volume accrual" and "Profitability can never rise much above the natural interest percentage". This also explains the manipulations of the soil rental theory; these had to be employed in order to achieve harmony between the one-sided concepts of interest and revenue-yielding capacity on the one hand and the natural relationship between timber growth and productive timber stock on the other. Here we meet a basic problem affecting all "primary production" which is based on natural life processes. Unlike industrial production, the capacity to produce cannot be increased beyond certain fairly confined limits. To demand customary rates of interest from the productive timber crop or to calculate for the whole forest productive enterprise starting from the bare soil upon the same premisses as for an industrial project leads either to unnaturally low rotations and open-stand types of thinning or to a liquidation of the contemplated "enterprise" (inter alia Dieterich, Köstler). Such a method of calculation might still be acceptable for small forests which are not required to provide sustained yields, or for outright afforestation projects, but in extensive management within the frame of forestry for a whole region, country or even the entire world, this leads to incompatible contrasts between productivity and profitability. The end is forest annihilation.

The place of thinning yields in the concept of rotation

The hitherto commonly accepted idea of the rotation in forestry is focused wholly on the average final age at which even-aged high forest stands are felled. This comes more into question as the proportion of the intermediate yield to the total yield gets larger and as natural regeneration is prolonged. Such reflections are the basis of Assmann's (1954b) proposal to introduce a *mean harvesting age* as a generally applicable measure in place of the rotation, e.g. a *harvesting age which is weighted by volume*. The formula corresponds to the familiar one for the mean "volume age" of Block and is expressed as follows:

$$\text{Mean harvesting age (m.h.a.)} = \frac{a_1 \times v_1 + a_2 \times v_2 \ldots + a_n \times v_n}{v_1 + v_2 \ldots + v_n}$$

where a represents the age of the individual harvested trees or the mean age of trees felled in one thinning operation, and v the volume. The mean harvesting age can be calculated for any form of forest, including selection forests.

Below, this is calculated for three beech working sections of Table 139.

The calculation with $r = 140$ and height Q. Cl. I produces the following result:

Yield table	Early yield percentage	Mean harvesting age
Schwappach (1893), moderate	32·2	124·2
Wiedemann (1931), moderate	48·7	119·7
Wiedemann (1931), heavy	61·8	111·6

As was to have been expected, heavier thinning has reduced the mean harvesting age from 124 to 112, i.e. by a full 12 years. These figures furthermore, demonstrate how much the same "thinning grade" has changed quantitatively in the course of 40 years.

3. Age Divisions and Increment of Working Sections with an Irregular Structure

With the help of yield tables we are able to construct models of working sections which approximate more or less closely the conditions of actual, or "realistic", working sections. If, to begin with, we change the simple hypothesis of an uninterrupted regular sequence of the age classes so as to admit irregular age-class distributions, we can examine the effects of arbitrary combinations of age classes on the increment and potential yield.

The two typical cases (b) and (c) in Table 140 have been calculated on the basis of the Scots pine yield table of Gehrhardt (1921) and compared with a normal working section (a). The growing-stocks per hectare of the abnormal working sections are defined as V_w, those of the normal as V_n and the increments likewise as I_w and I_n. In case (b), where the middle age-classes predominate, the growing-stock, by comparison with the normal working section in case (a), is smaller ($V_w < V_n$) and the increment larger ($I_w > I_n$). In case (c), where the old stands predominate, these conditions are reversed, so that $V_w > V_n$ and $I_w < I_n$. The effect caused thereby on the possible or the available *felling quantity* can be theoretically calculated with the help of the familiar formula by Gehrhardt (1923):

$$Y = \frac{I_w + I_n}{2} + \frac{V_w - V_n}{a} \quad \text{in which } a = \text{the adjusting time-interval.}$$

Case		Felling quantity per ha	Yield (%)	Increment (%)
(a)		6·05	2·4	2·4
(b)	$\dfrac{7 \cdot 3 + 6 \cdot 05}{2} + \dfrac{217 - 249}{40} = 6 \cdot 67 - 0 \cdot 80 =$	5·87	2·7	3·4
(c)	$\dfrac{4 \cdot 50 + 6 \cdot 05}{2} + \dfrac{320 - 249}{40} = 5 \cdot 27 + 1 \cdot 78 =$	7·05	2·2	1·4

In the "normal" working section (a) I_w and I_n as well as V_w and V_n are equal; thus Y becomes equal to I_n. In case (b) Y becomes less than I_n, and the exploitation percentage is smaller than the increment percentage; in case (c), Y is greater than I_n and the yield per cent is larger than the increment per cent which owing to the predominance of older stands with decreasing increments, is low.

If in addition to the age, we know also the quality class, we can construct models of arbitrary combinations and, what is important, *calculate in advance the changes of the characteristic values for fairly long periods of time, possibly for an entire rotation.* The same applies to realistic working sections, where the stocking is definable by age and area and distributed accordingly. This elucidates the inestimable value of properly constructed and locally suitable yield tables for the calculation of present and future yields, i.e. for the regulation of sustained yield (cf. Section C, p. 181). With the help of the rationally designed yield tables and normal working sections, we can penetrate the extremely complex relationships existing between site, growing-stock and timber production of a given forest and control these in a manner which complies with our human objectives. But we must beware of violating unnecessarily the biological facts. Besides, the normal working section is not a stationary structure because it is a collection of living organisms. As in a living being, which, according to Bertalanffy (1932, 1942) can be physically defined as an open system in a state of balance with its environment, the old cells are continually discarded and replaced by younger ones; or again, as in a nation, while the old people die children are born and move in as the new generation. The organic structure as such remains, although the individuals of which it is composed continually change.

TABLE 140

GROWING STOCK AND INCREMENT RELATIONSHIPS OF SCOTS PINE WORKING SECTIONS WITH DIFFERENT AGE-CLASS COMBINATIONS (CALCULATION OF NORMAL STOCK, SCHEMATIC, BY 20-YEAR AGE CLASS; $r = 120$; HEIGHT Q. CL. II)

Age classes	Y. table values for gr. stock per ha (fm o.b.)	c.a.i. per ha (fm o.b.)	(a) Normal age. cl. distr.			(b) Predominance of medium-aged stds.			(c) Predominance of old stds.		
			area (ha)	stock (fm o.b.)	incr. (fm o.b.)	area (ha)	stock (fm o.b.)	incr. (fm o.b.)	area (ha)	stock (fm o.b.)	incr. (fm o.b.)
1–20	3	7·5	17	51	127	9	27	67	9	27	67
21–40	127	9·5	16	2032	152	32	4064	304	8	1016	76
41–60	244	7·7	17	4148	131	34	8296	262	9	2196	69
61–80	324	5·9	16	5184	94	8	2592	47	8	2592	47
81–100	378	4·3	17	6426	73	8	3024	34	32	12,096	138
101–120	415	3·3	17	7055	28	9	3735	15	34	14,110	56
					($\frac{1}{2}$ I.)			($\frac{1}{2}$ I.)			($\frac{1}{2}$ I.)
Total working section per ha			100	24,896	605	100	21,738	729	100	32,037	453
				249	6·05		217	7·3		320	4·5
				$= V_n$	$= I_n$		$= V_w$	$= I_w$		$= V_w$	$= I_w$
				$= V_w$	$= I_w$						

II. GROWTH AND OUTPUT OF SELECTION FORESTS

When dealing with crops containing trees of widely differing ages, as in the case of selection forests, we are faced with considerable difficulties, because it is nearly impossible, or at least very difficult to assess the actual, apart from the physiological age and thereby the growth prospects of the variously mingled age-classes. Nevertheless, the same relationships apply to stands so constituted: the selection forest simply represents a special case of a working section.

1. The Selection Forest as a Special Case of a Working Section

The selection forest is a particular kind of felling series. Like the working section of an even-aged high forest, it contains trees of all ages and sizes which in the normal constitution are distributed in an orderly fashion according to their dimensions. But while the age-classes in a forest felled by compartments are segregated by area, in the classic selection forest, trees of different ages are disposed in an intimate stem-by-stem mixture both horizontally and vertically, even upon the smallest areas. Fundamental differences in the stand structure occur accordingly with respect to the forms of stem and crown, growth phases and tree performance in relation to area occupied. These have been already discussed in Section C, II.

(a) DIAMETER DISTRIBUTION CURVES AND HEIGHT CURVES FOR A WORKING SECTION OF AN EVEN-AGED HIGH FOREST AND FOR A SELECTION FOREST

Zimmerle (1941) pointed out the similarity between the decrease in stem numbers of high forest stands in the course of a rotation, i.e. the decrease in stem numbers of a yield table, when the numbers of stems are plotted against the respective diameters of the mean

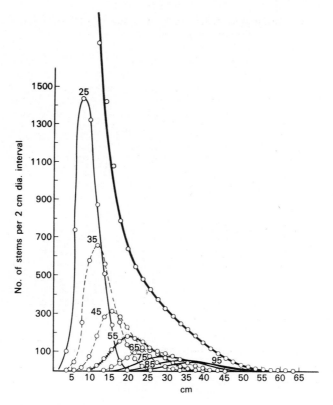

FIG. 161. Diameter distribution for a spruce working section, deduced by adding the diameter distributions of 10-year age classes.

stem, and the diameter distribution $N = f(d)$ of selection forests. Zimmerle's comparison (p. 117 in his work), however, is reliable only when the diameter distribution of the high forest working section is obtained by another method. We are indebted to Zimmerle (1949a) for publishing smoothed diameter distributions for 10-year age classes in Norway spruce, according to three separate quality classes. Summating the numbers of stems in the age-classes according to their diameter classes provides the diameter distribution of a working section. Figure 161 illustrates *how the diameter distribution of a Norway spruce compartment*, height quality class I (Zimmerle), with a rotation of 100 years *arises from the distribution curves of the age classes* 20–30 (25) to 90–100 (95). How perfectly the distribution curve of a normal even-aged high forest felling series corresponds to the typically falling curve of diameter distribution in the selection forest is shown when the distribution curve of a spruce felling series of Q. Cl. II (Zimmerle)[1] is compared with that of the experimental selection forest area No. 7 (Schomberg) in Württemberg, the figures of which were published by Zimmerle (1941).[2]

Table 141 gives the original distributions alongside the distributions obtained by graphical fitting on semi-logarithmic paper according to H. A. Meyer (1933) for high-forest working sections with $r = 80$ and $r = 120$, as well as for the selection forest plot. Figure 162 illustrates the striking similarity between the diameter distributions.

TABLE 141

ACTUAL AND FITTED DIAMETER DISTRIBUTIONS FOR TWO EVEN-AGED HIGH FOREST WORKING SECTIONS
AND ONE SELECTION FOREST STAND

Diameter class (d) (cm)	Spruce working section				Selection forest plot m.h.a. ≅ 190*	
	$r = 80$		$r = 120$			
	Stem number		Stem number		Stem number	
	true	fitted	true	fitted	true	fitted
12	449	450	258	258	204	189
16	221	247	151	176	132	141
20	144	135	108	120	95	103
24	89	73	83	83	71	75
28	46	40	61	58	50	55
32	22	21	46	39	45	40
36	10	11	34	27	29	29
40	4	6	24	19	19	21
44	1	3	16	13	14	15
48	1	2	9	9	14	11
52		1	5	6	10	8
56			2	4	8	6
60			1	3	5	4
64			1	2	2	3
68				1	1	2
72					1	1
Total	987	989	799	818	700	703
Parameter	$\alpha = 0{\cdot}1523$ $k = 743{\cdot}3$		$0{\cdot}0938$ $207{\cdot}1$		$0{\cdot}0776$ $124{\cdot}1$	

* m.h.a. = "mean harvesting age" (see p. 444).

F. de Liocourt (1898) showed that the normal diameter distribution curve of a selection forest corresponds to a decreasing geometric progression

$$A; \quad Aq^{-1}; \quad Aq^{-2}; \quad \ldots Aq^{n-1}.$$

[1] Landforstmeister Hausser kindly provided some fitted *d*-distributions for 5-year age classes from the data collected by the Research Institute of Württemberg.

[2] The values which were given by 5-cm classes have been recalculated for 4-cm classes.

where A represents the number of stems of the lowest measured diameter class,
    q the quotient which determines the shape of the curve,
    n the number of diameter classes.

H. A. Meyer (1933) showed that this kind of distribution curve can be described by the exponential function
$N = ke^{-\alpha d}$, which expressed in logarithms reads as follows:

$$\log N = \log k - M\alpha d \quad (N = \text{the number of stems per 1-cm class},$$

$$d = \text{the diameter class},$$

$$M = \log e = 0{\cdot}4343)$$

and that this function is identical with de Liocourt's "law". A quick calculation of the parameters is possible by an elegant graphical method wherein the logarithms of the stem-numbers plotted over the corresponding diameters (on semi-logarithmic graph

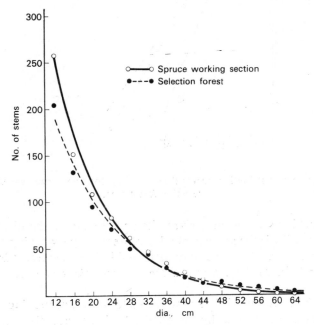

FIG. 162. Diameter distribution curves for a spruce working section (quality class II; $r = 120$) and for a selection forest *(Schömberg)*.

paper) can be fitted by a straight line. The slope of the line is determined by the constant α, its position (intercept with the vertical axis) indicating thereby the density of the stand, by the constant k. Both constants are correlated, i.e. they increase, or decrease, in the same sense. Figure 163 shows the three distribution curves on semi-logarithmic paper as straight lines. As we can see, the slope of the line decreases in the transition from $r = 80$ to $r = 120$, and the α-value also decreases. At the same time, the total number of stems decreases. When the rotation is lengthened, the relative proportions of young age-classes (with large numbers of stems per hectare) become smaller, as shown on p. 442, Fig. 160, whilst at the same time, those age-classes with small numbers of stems per hectare, but larger diameters, increase. The diameters at the extreme upper limit then reach higher values, as shown in Table 141. The shift of the regression of the numbers of stems in the way shown here is apparently causal. This can be expressed as follows: the longer the

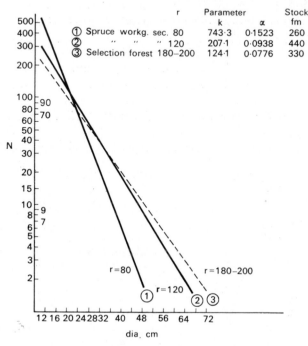

		r	Parameter		Stock
			k	α	fm
①	Spruce workg. sec. 80		743·3	0·1523	260
②	" " " 120		207·1	0·0938	440
③	Selection forest 180–200		124·1	0·0776	330

FIG. 163. Fitted diameter distribution curves (log $N = f(d)$) for two spruce working sections and one selection forest area.

rotation of a working section on a given site and the larger the diameters of the trees so obtained, the smaller is the average number of stems of the working section per hectare, and the smaller are the values of the constants α and k. These represent *important indicators by which we can judge the structure and the age conditions of selection stands on given sites.*

The fact that the constant α is linked to the factor q of a decreasing geometric progression can easily be demonstrated by the fitted selection forest distribution in Table 141. The constant $\alpha = 0.0776$ corresponds to a *constant decrease in the percentage of the number of stems of 7.76 per cent per 1-cm diameter increase:*

Diameter	Stem number		
$d = 24$	$N =$		75
25	$75-7·76\% = 75 - 6 =$		69
26	$69-7·76\% = 69 - 5 =$		64
27	$64-7·76\% = 64 - 5 =$		59
28	$59-7·76\% = 59 - 4 =$		55

A "rotation" for this selection stand cannot be exactly stated. The mean age of six trees felled in 1949, according to careful counts of the annual rings, is 181 (140–214) years, their *mean harvesting age* is *191*. Based on the actual ages of the felled trees with the largest diameters, we might estimate the "rotation" of this selection stand as nearly 200 years. The position of the straight line representing the numbers of stems of the selection stand relative to that of the even-aged working section with $r = 120$ would conform to that expectation, if in addition allowance is made for the probability that the site of the selection area belongs to a lower quality class for spruce than II, according to Zimmerle.

Because of the far-reaching similarities between the curves of diameter distribution for even-aged normal high forest working sections and selection stands, their employment as indicators of a possible selection structure must be taken with some reserve. This is shown by the comparison of three constructed distribution curves of a spruce working section according to Zimmerle, height Q. Cl. I, in Table 142.

TABLE 142

DIAMETER DISTRIBUTIONS OF FOUR HYPOTHETICAL SPRUCE WORKING SECTIONS (ZIMMERLE, QUALITY CLASS I) N PER HECTARE

Diam. (cm)	Case (a)	(b)	(c)	(d)	
12	316	325	488	487	(a) Age-classes 25, 35, 45, etc., to 95;
16	186	190	285	261	(b) Age-classes 35, 65, 95;
20	118	97	146	80	(c) Age-classes 35, 65;
24	91	73	103	21	(d) Age-classes 35, 95.
28	70	65	80	19	
32	54	54	53	28	
36	40	44	30	35	
40	27	30	11	34	
44	16	19	2	27	
48	8	11		16	
52	4	5		8	
56	2	3		4	
60	1	2		3	
64		1		1	
Total	933	919	1198	1024	

By adding together the distribution curves of the three age-classes 35, 65 and 95 a typical selection forest distribution curve is obtained. In fact, even adding together the distribution curves of the two age classes 35 and 65 provides a selection forest distribution curve. If these age-classes were located in small plots each of 0·25 ha in a total area of 0·75 ha, these three even-aged high forest stands would together provide a nearly ideal selection forest distribution curve. Only in case (d), where the two age-classes are 60 years apart, a repetition of the frequencies from the 32-cm class onwards makes us aware that this represents a combination of just two populations each with one peak frequency. In such a series of spruce stands, a mere inspection of the forest would immediately reveal the actual conditions. But with shade-tolerant species, as for example in beech stands, there are under-storey trees of the same age as the upper-storey trees, although the former are only half the height and less than one-fifth of the diameter of the upper-storey trees, so that the impression of a selection structure is easily obtained. This is possibly the case in the well-known beech selection forest Keula, in Thuringia.

On small experimental selection areas there occur, in consequence of the few stem numbers, irregular fluctuations of the class frequencies (at 4–5-cm class widths) which make it difficult to reveal characteristic trends in distribution. These can be the more readily expected on small areas, because an ideal selection structure is attainable on a small area only after a long period of time. Thus, Mitscherlich (1952) in decades of observations discovered, on the relatively small experimental selection plots in Baden, an undulating trend of striking frequency culminations of the stem-number and growing-stock distributions. Probably a regular distribution can soonest be achieved and recorded on large areas. But at the same time, there is the greater danger of creating an illusion. Therefore probably an additional condition to be demanded for a selection structure is a suitable range and mixture of ages, e.g. at least three age-classes and corresponding size classes within a circular ambit of one large tree-length radius. Without consideration of age the difficult problems of structure and increment of the selection forest cannot in any case be solved.

The mean height curves of working sections

These can be constructed in a manner similar to the construction of the mean diameter distribution curves. As shown by Assmann (1953b), these height curves undergo a shift when lengthening the rotation in a manner analogous to that of the selection forest height curves, if the stock of tall trees with large diameters in the selection forest increases.

TABLE 143

MEAN HEIGHT CURVES OF N. SPRUCE COMPARTMENTS WITH ROTATIONS OF 80–110 YEARS

Diameter classes (cm)	8	12	16	20	24	28	32	36	40	44	48	52	56	60
Rotation	Mean heights of the classes in metres													
80 years	9·2	13·2	17·6	21·1	23·7	25·6	27·1	28·3	29·1	29·8	30·1			
90 years	9·2	13·2	17·6	21·4	24·1	26·3	28·1	29·3	30·1	30·9	31·3	37·8	32·0	
100 years	9·2	13·2	17·6	21·5	24·5	26·9	28·8	30·2	31·3	32·1	32·6	33·1	33·4	
110 years	9·2	13·2	17·6	21·6	24·6	27·3	29·3	31·0	32·1	32·9	33·6	34·1	34·9	35·8

Table 143 shows mean heights of the diameter classes of spruce working sections (Zimmerle, Q. Cl. II) for the rotations of 80–110 years. As may be seen, the average heights of trees in the larger size categories are systematically and quite considerably increased by prolonging the rotation; for example, in the 48-cm class, this increase amounts to 1·0–1·3 m for a 10-year increase of rotation. Figure 164a also shows the peculiar form of the compartment height curve with one point of inflection. How completely this agrees with a selection forest height curve is shown in Fig. 164b. Based on height curves of the Swiss experimental selection forest area in the Toppwald, this shows from data provided by Flury (1933) how these have grown in the period from 1905 to 1929, i.e. within 24 years.[1] During the same space of time, the proportion of trees in the diameter classes over

---

[1] Shifts in the same sense, though not so impressive, occur also in other Swiss selection forest areas; thus, in the Hasliwald selection research plots during the period 1908–32 the shifts in the 52–70-cm classes for Silver fir amounted to +1·6 m and to +2·4 m with Norway spruce.

38 cm has increased from 59 to 70 per cent while the total growing stock remained nearly unchanged. A similar reaction is likely in a compartment-felled high forest series, if the thinning is intensified whilst extraction of the oldest stands is postponed and the rotation thus prolonged.

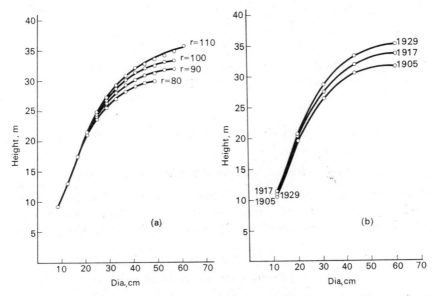

FIG. 164. The height curve for a spruce working section shifts as a result of increased rotation (a) and that for the selection forest area at Toppwald also as a result of the increase of big diameter stems (b).

That a shift of the height curve of a selection forest is by no means rare is stressed by Mitscherlich (1961) in his new and recently published work on the selection forest. In this he gives the following values for the height curves of Silver fir on the experimental selection plot Wolfach 3/II:

Height	Diameter classes	
	50	60
1950	25·0	25·6 m
1956	27·3	28·5
1960	28·2	28·6

In selection forests, as in compartments of a high forest felled by compartments, the mean height as well as the mean harvesting age of the trees of given diameter classes are increased by such a procedure. This ultimately constitutes an *age effect*. Leibundgut (1945) stated aptly: "Although some theoretical and some practical workers consistently deny that 'age' is a factor relevant to the selection forest, it is incorrect when investigating the increment and growth phenomena of the selection forest completely to disregard the age." And further: "... the problem of individual ageing also plays a part in the selection forest, in that the life functions in that case follow an optimum curve whose course and culmination depend not only on the total effect of the living conditions, but also on the age."

The mean height curves and the tariff curves of selection forests which are derived from these can remain stationary only if the *balance of selection* for a given level of growing-stock is maintained, which may be achieved by aiming at and *retaining a "normal" diameter distribution*. The "constancy of class heights" stipulates a *"constancy of the diameter distribution"*. The conclusions upon the accuracy of increment calculations by means of tariff methods (Knuchel, 1950) are obvious, because systematic changes of the tariff curve are accompanied by systematic increment errors. Still more important, however, is the established shift of selection forest height curves for a possible *quality classification of the selection forest* according to the mean heights of certain diameter classes, such as have been suggested by Flury (1929, 1933).

(b) THE QUALITY CLASSIFICATION OF SELECTION STANDS

Flury's selection forest qualification by class heights

Based on numerous surveys of the Swiss experimental selection areas, Flury designed the following *quality classification frame for the* selection forest, which is founded on the mean heights of the diameter classes 38–50 and 52–70 (Table 144).

TABLE 144

QUALITY CLASSIFICATION ARRANGEMENT BY FLURY

Diameter class	38–50 cm (mean = 44·5 cm)					52–70 cm (mean = 61·5 cm)				
Quality class Class heights in metres for	I	II	III	IV	V	I	II	III	IV	V
Silver fir	36	32	28	24	20	40	36	32	28	24
Norway spruce	38	34	30	26	22	42	38	34	30	26

As the class height of spruce in the Toppwald during the period from 1905 to 1929 in diameter class 52–70 increased from 31·3 to 35·1, its "quality class" ought to have improved from III.7 to II.7. That this in fact represents the same age-effect as in a spruce working section, becomes clear by the observation that the mean height of the diameter class 56 is increased by 2·9 m when the rotation is prolonged from 90 to 110 years, which amounts to a quality class stage of 0·65 according to Zimmerle.

A selection forest quality classification according to Flury's *class heights without regard to age therefore is not clear and therefore cannot be accepted*. Flury, when first publishing this suggestion (1929) also cited the following *"free-growing ages"* of Silver fir and Norway spruce for the diameter classes in question:

	Hasliwald		Toppwald	
	Cl. 38–50	52–70	Cl. 38–50	52–70
Fir	101	122	162	190
Spruce	122	140	168	200

By "free-growing-age" he means the *age of the butt-section, after excluding the "dense core"* whose extremely narrow annual rings indicate the period of suppression or the *period under heavy top-shade*. This, according to Flury can occasionally last 80 to 100 years and even longer. As it is "purely coincidental" and "without importance to the yield", the stem should not be "encumbered" with it, Flury thought. Although in comparisons with yields of other types of forests the period spent under the shade of overhead canopy is by no means unimportant, the quality classification by height classes none the less can be based on the *age of free growth* according to Flury, provided the limits of the "dense core" can be clearly defined. As an alternative, a *cross-sectional age* (= number of annual rings on the cross-section) would have to be used, either at breast-height or at 5 or 10 metres height depending on the proportion of the variable period of suppressed growth under shade which is to be eliminated and as provided in the customary timber register. The quality classification limits of Flury must then be supplemented by a *statement of the free-growing or cross-sectional age* and by adding the heights at younger and later ages. The required basic material can fairly easily be produced in experimental selection plots by age-counts on felled trees.

Both Zimmerle (1936, 1941) and Prodan (1949) consider that the quality classification limits of Flury are too high, which was confirmed by Leibundgut (1945) on the basis of his very accurate height measurements on all Swiss experimental selection plots. Taking into consideration the aspects which have been worked out here, the height limits of Prodan (1949) are probably more suitable for South German conditions.

The range of ages within diameter classes of the selection forest

How much the actual ages of selection forest trees of the same breast height diameter vary is proved by the results of age-determinations carried out at Mitscherlich's[1] request on the occasion of recent selection forest studies upon more than 200 trees of the selection research plot Wolfach 3/II, by means of borings at stump height. The following means and standard errors of the age were calculated on this basis:

Diameter classes	7·5–10	10–20	20–30	30–40	40–50	50–70 cm
Means	82	116	137	150	151	170 years
(Number of ind. val.)	(45)	(59)	(45)	(27)	(27)	(12)
Standard error ±	23	30	26	19	21	24 years

The correlation ratio η for the relation age/diameter is calculated as $0·756 \pm 0·029$. This ratio has not been calculated for the relation age/height because the correlation table suggests a much looser relationship. The graphically fitted regression of age on diameter in Fig. 165 further illuminates this relationship.

Although the standard errors of age within the diameter classes are fairly large the most important class 50–70 cm for example, for which twelve ages have been determined would have a calculated standard error $s_{\bar{x}}$ of the mean age of ± 7 years $= \pm 4$ per cent.

---

[1] Prof. Dr. Mitscherlich not only furnished informative experimental results but also the manuscripts of his new work on selection forests, for which kindness cordial thanks are expressed here.

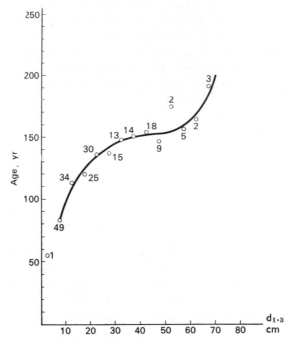

FIG. 165. Selection trial area 3/II at Wolfach. Mean age for the individual diameter classes given according to figures by *Mitscherlich*. (Figures = number of age values.)

In order to determine the mean of the ages in this "quality classification class" with a precision of ± 5 per cent, corresponding to 8·5 years ($t = 2$, probability coefficient = 5 per cent) thirty-two age-determinations would be necessary. As the range of the free-growing age or a conventional cross-sectional age is probably smaller, there are thus favourable prospects for an age/height quality classification in the selection forest.

Mitscherlich's quality classification by the diameter increment

In connection with Prodan's (1949) statement that the average diameter increment of the higher diameter classes (over 50 cm) largely depends on the quality class, Mitscherlich (1952) suggested the use of the diameter increment of the trees over 50 cm b.h.d. as a quality classification scale. His quality classification table, arranged in five classes, gives the required diameter increment for increasing numbers of trees over 50 cm and thus takes into consideration the influence of greater or smaller density of stocking on the diameter increment. Owing to the fact that diameter growth is more susceptible to differences of treatment and climatic influences than the tree height at given ages, the selection forest quality classification by height would probably give more reliable results. But if the structure and diameter distribution are known, the diameter increment, especially within the frame of Mitscherlich's quality classification table, is at least a valuable additional indicator of the site quality.

The taper and form of trees in a high forest cut by compartments and in a selection forest

The characteristic differences in the taper and form of the trees in high forests cut by compartments and selection forests require special attention in a quality classification by height, diameter and age. Zimmerle (1951) succeeded in deducing from measurements of a great number of sample stems (app. 11,600) of Silver fir and spruce from even-aged compartments of high forest and selection forest stands, *the mean stem curves for height classes of 3 m intervals.* These show the great superiority of the trees of normal even-aged high forests of both species in taper and shape. For example, trees of height class 33 m have the following diameters:

	Silver fir	Norway spruce
In the selection forest	61·7	49·1 cm b.h.d.
In the compartment-felled high forest	43·0	35·7
Difference	18·7	13·4

Trees raised in compartment-felled high forests and having only 70 to 72 per cent of the diameter of the selection forest trees have the same height of 33 m.

Another conclusive comparison is given in Table 145.

TABLE 145

COMPARISON OF SILVER FIR AND NORWAY SPRUCE FROM A SELECTION FOREST AND A COMPARTMENT-FELLED HIGH FOREST (AFTER VALUES BY ZIMMERLE)

Tree species and origin	Height (m)	$d_{1\cdot3}$ (cm)	$d_{0\cdot9}$ (cm)	$h : d_{1\cdot3}$	$h : d_{0\cdot9}$	$\lambda_{1\cdot3}$ (0·)	$\lambda_{0\cdot9}$ (0·)	α (cm/per m)
Silver fir								
High forest	29·9	36·3	33·8	82	88	504	582	0·64
Selection forest	*30·1*	*51·1*	*46·7*	*59*	*64*	*474*	*567*	*0·91*
High forest	36·0	49·7	44·5	72	81	463	577	0·72
Norway spruce								
High forest	29·9	30·7	27·9	97	107	463	560	0·56
Selection forest	*30·0*	*43·2*	*38·6*	*69*	*78*	*440*	*551*	*0·82*
High forest	35·8	42·6	37·4	84	96	438	568	0·64

Remarks:

$d_{0\cdot9}$ = diameter at 0·9 of the tree length, measured from the tip;

$h : d_{0\cdot9}$ = "true slenderness ratio" corresponding to $\lambda_{0\cdot9}$ = "true form factor";

α = "true" taper according to Krenn = diameter reduction in cm per metre run within the range from $d_{0\cdot9}$ to $d_{0\cdot5}$.

The existent typical differences stand out particularly clearly in Fig. 166. The figures in the table reveal among other facts, that Silver fir and Norway spruce trees are about 6 m taller in high forests felled by compartments than their counterparts of the same

diameter in selection forests. The differences in Zimmerle's sample stem figures are however especially marked because the high forest trees in most cases originate from older
stands on good sites (we think of the superlative stands in Oberndorf, for example, and
compare them to Table 117), whilst the selection forest trees have been obtained from
experimental selection areas with relatively low average felling ages. From Table 145
and Fig. 166 it is easy to see that trees of a specified diameter in both types of forest
must have increasing "slenderness ratios" (form factors) with greater harvesting age. Better
sites and higher density of stocking have similar effects. Thus for example, in Table 42,
p. 131, both Silver fir and spruce trees of 70 cm diameter in Dürsrüti, which is a superior
site and well stocked, have a bigger height: d.b.h. ratio than in the Biglenwald, where
the largest diameters of Silver fir are approximately 82 cm whilst in Dürsrüti they are 140
cm and more. The trees of 70 cm d.b.h. in each case belong to different social strata.

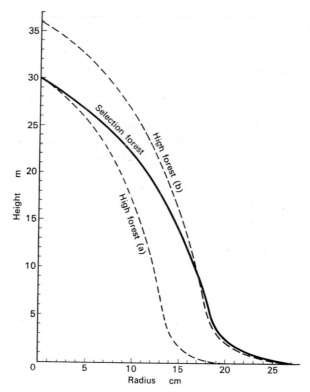

FIG. 166. Comparison between stem profile of a selection forest spruce and of a high forest spruce of
equal height (a) and equal diameter (b). Figures by *Zimmerle*.

Again this illustrates how indispensable a knowledge of the age is to enable a reliable
height quality classification to be made in the selection forest; and even more so, if an
attempt is to be made at height quality class comparisons for example, between even-aged
high forest and selection forest stands. Comparisons of performance between the two
types of forests are possible in the first instance only by comparing actual stands of
similar combinations of tree species on the same site.

Size classes, the lower limit of measurement, and recruitment

It is nowadays customary to define the size classification of growing-stock and exploitable yield by Flury's grouping of diameter classes. This author combined an increasing number of diameter classes according to the following unequal intervals:

Diameter class	Lower limit (cm)	Mean (cm)	Upper limit (cm)	
8–14	7·5	11·5	15·5	
16–24	15·5	20·5	25·5	= small timber
26–36	25·5	31·5	37·5	
38–50	37·5	44·5	51·5	= medium timber
52–70	51·5	61·5	71·5	= large timber
over 70				

The distribution by small, medium and large timber is sufficient for a rough characterization. Mitscherlich (1952) rightly protests against the unequal class widths of this classification, which is not suitable for an accurate description, and himself uses 10-cm stages. Specially suitable for testing and comparing diameter distributions are 4-cm classes as adopted by H. A. Meyer, provided the surveyed area and stem numbers are large enough. If the stem numbers are small, it would probably be an advantage to test the classification by 10-cm classes in a semi-logarithmic graph as recently used by Hildebrandt (1960).

The lower the threshold of measurable diameter the smaller is the amount of recruitment; the latter represents on the one hand a transition by the younger stands of a compartmented high forest to timber sizes (Derbholz) and to that extent it is a fictional increment; but on the other hand, it is also associated with the sequential character of selection forest crops which causes a continual entry of young trees from the current regeneration. The in-growth at the lower diameter limit of 7 cm is insignificant; yet in a comparison of increment with normal high forest working sections or with the mean annual production of even-aged high forest stands, it has to be included as genuine increment.

The control method. Growing-stock, yield, increment and optimum stocking

In *Méthode du Contrôle* Gurnaud and Biolley (1920) developed an elegant procedure[1] which enables the increment, volume and structure of the growing-stock of a complex forest formation to be assessed and kept under review in the process of making precise measurement of all extractions. By scribing the trees at the points of application of the calipers at the time of the first enumeration, the identity of the "inventory" which is to be controlled is totally assured and the check is made conclusive by calipering all extracted trees before they are felled. Thus any possible absence of trees

---

[1] For comprehensive reviews of the related topics we are indebted to, amongst others: Knuchel (1950), Popescu-Zeletin (1936), Prodan (1949, 1951), Schaeffer, Gazin and d'Alverny (1930).

will be noticed. The minimum diameter measurement can be high, because the recruitment is clearly taken into account. Tariffs facilitate the increment calculation, which, if the control compartments are large enough, can achieve considerable accuracy. In fact, under the assumption that the sequence or ranking order of the trees in the diameter classification does not change, it is possible by the aid of the "Tariff Difference Method" (Prodan, 1949) to determine the increment of the individual size-classes and thereby roughly that of the social strata. The enthusiasm of foresters thus able for the first time directly to control the effects of their treatment of the forest and, so to speak, to feel the pulse of the increment, is understandable. On the other hand, their hopes of recognizing in such a manner also the most favourable ratio between growing-stock and increment, the "optimum growing-stock", and thereby also the most suitable type of forest treatment, were disappointed.

As in selection forests the age-proportions and type of age admixture, as also the distribution upon areas of different site qualities, are, as a rule, unknown, the increment at any given level of the growing stock does not permit reliable conclusions to be drawn about the correctness of the particular method of handling the crop, based for example on the amount and type of produce extracted.

The following hypothetical example explains how, without knowing the age proportions in the crop and their distribution on sites of different qualities, one cannot possibly draw conclusions from the ratio of growing stock to increment.

According to the yield table of Gehrhardt (1921), the following values can be calculated for a spruce working section of 120 ha, in which age classes 30, 70 and 110 have different proportions by area and their distribution to quality classes I and III fluctuates according to six arbitrary combinations:

Combination	Growing-stock	Increment
1	501	12·3 fm (o.b.)
2	450	10·6
3	453	12·0
4	551	13·9
5	585	11·7
6	538	10·3

For a working section consisting of 40 ha of each of the above-named age-classes, one half always being of Q. Cl. I and the other half of Q. Cl. III, the growing-stock amounts to 475 fm and the increment to 11·4 fm over bark. Whilst the stock thus fluctuates between 95 and 123 per cent and the increment between 90 and 122 per cent of these "normal values", there is apparently *no recognizable connection between the growing-stock and the increment*.

The control method can ensure sufficient accuracy in the measurement of increments only if the control areas are at least 10 to 15 ha. in area. Areas of such a size however have unavoidable local differences which may often be as extensive as in the above example (two quality-class stages). Moreover, if the increment is calculated in the familiar manner as the difference between the final crop volume plus exploitation minus the initial crop volume, and accordingly the annual increment for a working plan interval of T years, by the formula

$$I = \frac{V_f + N - V_i}{T}.$$

T must not be too long, because if N is assessed, *not at the end* of, but *during* the prescribed interval, the calculated increment values are, as we know, incorrect and the ratios of growing-stock to increment misleading. In this connection, see among other authors, Gascard (1936). If, however, the prescribed periods are short, i.e. 5 to 7 years, *climatic influences* become important, since on certain sites they can quite easily decrease the increment for the said period by one-third, as instanced by the familiar example of Boveresse and Couvet (Favre 1928, 1931; Knuchel, 1933).

The concept of an optimum growing-stock is meaningful only in terms of a given site and a definite objective described around the requisite tree dimensions. The optimum growing-stock for a given combination of the two quantities can be determined only by way of experiment. A lastingly effective utilization of the desired combination is then obviously achievable only if the diameter distribution and age mixture are approximately normal. As Mitscherlich (1952) found and rightly stressed, there are *any number of ways in which selection can be in equilibrium with the site and the aim of management* (large-diameter timber, construction timber). Furthermore, it is important to decide whether certain diameter classes have been recruited from older trees of even-aged stock—possibly by conversion from compartment-felling to a selection forest system—or from physiologically young selection forest trees perhaps in the course of reconstituting a selection forest after it had been exhausted by over-exploitation. Seen in this light, Biolley and Flury's data for an "optimum" structure of the growing stock appear as provisional guiding figures for the production of large-sized timber where there exist medium-sized crops and assured regeneration.

The generalized relationships which are hereupon arrived at must be investigated in *long-term experiments* with *numbered*—and therefore always identifiable—*trees* because only then can the increment responses by given dimensions of stems and crowns and certain growth patterns be observed. In this connection, the importance of the works by Burger and E. Badoux can be seen in their proper light. The production of selection forest trees per unit area and their growing space economy has already been discussed in Section C, II, and it therefore only remains to examine critically the long-term production of selection forest research areas and to compare it with that of the normal even-aged high forest series.

2. Production of Selection Stands and Comparison with the Production of Normal Evenaged High Forest Stands

Results from long-term selection experiments

Reliable production figures, especially increment values, are obtainable only from long-observed experimental selection plots of a sufficient minimum size (0·5–1·0 ha). Results from fairly large selection compartments of 10–15 ha are, owing to the reasons stated overleaf, problematic. Table 146 gives production figures of experimental selection plots in Switzerland and Baden. The observation periods cover 21 to 39 years, av. 29 years (Switzerland), and 21 to 68 years, on the average 45 years (Baden).

The well-known experimental selection forest area of *Dürsrüti*, with 84 per cent of its crop in large timber sizes, is according to Leibundgut (1945) "typical of an over-stocked managed selection forest". The mean height of diameter class 52–70 cm (hereafter called the "site-index class") is still rising at the rate of 1·3 m together with an increasing standing

TABLE 146

LONG-TERM INCREMENT PRODUCTION OF EXPERIMENTAL SELECTION AREAS IN SWITZERLAND AND BADEN
(AFTER BADOUX, FLURY, AND MITSCHERLICH)

Exp. area, altitude and slope gradient	Percentage of mixed species			Obs. period	Standing volume of "timber" in the rem. std.			Average annual	
	Fir (%)	Spr. (%)	Be. (%)		at start (fm)	at finish (fm)	average (fm)	yield (fm)	incr. (fm)
Dürsrüti 900 m, NW. 13°	89	11	—	1914–1947	668	818	—	9·4	13·9
Schallenberg-Rauchgrat 1060 m, SSW. 27°	73	8	19	1931–1946	464	476	—	12·4	13·2
Hasliwald 570 m, level	79	21	—	1908–1947	445	444	—	12·2	12·1
Bois de Pays 980 m, N. 28°	54	35	11	1913–1947	296	483	—	8·1	12·9
Toppwald 970 m W., N.,	81	19	—	1905–1929	444	421	—	9·9	8·8
E., 15–25°	34	66	—	1928–1947	486	474	—	11·9	11·2
Guffre 1120 m, N. 11°	40	60	—	1918–1945	488	415	—	12·3	9·7
Biglenwald 930 m, W. 23°	70	28	2	1882–1950	562	284	348	12·7	8·6
Wolfach 4/II 740 m, E. steep do. 5/II as before, SE., leaning to steep	69	29	2	1887–1950	479	310	315	13 5	10·8
do. 6 750 m, ESE. gentle	78	20	2	1897–1950	585	316	371	16·4	11·3
do. 7/I 780 m level	67	31	2	1897–1950	464	331	397	13·1	10·6
do. 8/II 760 m, NE., leaning	75	22	3	1903–1950	411	206	251	11·7	7·4
do. 9 800 m, S., gentle	52	44	4	1910–1949	455	485	464	7·2	8·0
Todtmoos 1/III 1000 m, level	43	48	9	1926–1947	278	403	344	4·0	10·0
do. 2/II 930 m NW., gentle	37	49	14	1926–1947	230	315	274	4·0	8·0
Kandern 910 m SE. steep	98	1	1	1904–1947	181	255	213	10·0	11·7

volume. It has achieved the highest hitherto recorded *long-term* annual increment of any experimental selection area, amounting to 13·9 fm. Closely on this, with an increment of 13·2 fm follows the experimental area of *Schallenberg-Rauchgrat* having 53 per cent of its crop in large timber sizes, which Leibundgut described as being "of exemplary structure". The experimental area at *Hasliwald* with a 52 per cent proportion of large timber has a stationary standing volume, which according to Leibundgut is yet too high to secure adequate regeneration; this has achieved 12·1 fm and the age of the site-index class is only 122–140 years. The *Bois de Pays* in the Val de Travers of the Jura region has done better with an increment of 12·9 fm. On the other hand, the *Toppwald* on a moderate site is much inferior with 8·8 fm but there, the standing volume and the mean height of the site-index class, which according to Flury's estimation has a free-growing age of 190–200 years, have considerably increased during the observation period. The experimental selection area of *Guffre*, estimated by Flury as belonging to selection quality II, has an increment of 11·2 fm, which at an altitude of 1200 m is considerable. The experimental area of *Biglenwald*, with a 48 per cent proportion of large timber and reduced standing volume, reached 9·7 fm.

If the free-growing ages of all experimental selection areas were known it should be possible to achieve a definite grouping into height quality classes and with consideration of the level of the standing volume also a fixed correlation between quality-class and long-term increment. A reliable comparison with the production of even-aged high forest stands is not possible, because there are no long-observed comparative stands. Compared with the m.a.i. production of long-observed even-aged high forest stands on sites of the Lower Alps, the increments of these selection stands, some of which are on excellent sites, must be considered as modest.

The growth performance of the *experimental selection areas in Baden* in the same table is also of a moderate order. In some cases, the large initial standing volumes of the five experimental plots at Wolfach, shown first in the table, have been reduced to varying degrees in the course of the observation period, whilst, in the remaining four plots, the initial standing volume in some cases was considerably increased. The history of origin, specific treatment and changes in the structure of the standing crop will be found in the paper by Mitscherlich (1952). Figure 167 gives an impression of the experimental selection plot Todtmoos 1/III.

In 1882 three high forest plots were laid out for comparison with the *experimental selection plots* at Wolfach, not very far from these, but unfortunately at *100 m higher altitude;* this has enabled comparisons of the volume production to be made, as here presented in Table 147, based on Mitscherlich's (1952) results and on information from the Forest Experimental and Research Institute of Baden–Württemberg. Despite the comparatively disadvantageous conditions of the high forest plots, their m.a.i. at the final age, which nearly corresponds to the maximum m.a.i., is clearly superior to the selection plots. The maximum m.a.i. would be equal to the increment of a correspondingly constituted "normal" working section and therefore may be compared alongside with the long-term increment of the selection plots. Thus compartment-felled plot No. 2, which in view of its proportions of fir and spruce can most easily be compared, is superior in increment (m.a.i.) to the selection plot 4/II by about 42 per cent and to the experimental selection plot 5/II by 13 per cent. According to information from Prof. Dr. Mitscherlich, the compartment-felled high forest plots 1 and 2 definitely originate from natural regeneration, probably from shelterwood fellings. Their actual age may, having regard to the regeneration period estimated by Prof. Mitscherlich at 30–50 years, be older than the age stated by the Research Institute; the mean harvesting ages calculated from that age are 109 and 105 years respectively. Even if their actual harvesting ages were higher, they are nevertheless considerably younger than those of the selection plots, which are certainly older than 160 years.

For a comparison of the respective performances of selection forests and high forests, we can now draw upon plots 5/II and 2, because they are alike as regards the relative proportions in admixture and in having the highest increment production.

FIG. 167. Selection trial area at Todtmoos.

TABLE 147

COMPARISON OF THE PRODUCTION OF EXPERIMENTAL SELECTION FOREST PLOTS WITH EXPERIMENTAL HIGH FOREST PLOTS, AFTER DATA BY MITSCHERLICH

Def.	Size (ha)	Forest, altitude slope grdt.	Percentage proportions			Standing volume of "timber" in the rem. std.			Average annual	
			Fir (%)	Spr. (%)	Be. (%)	at start (fm)	at finish (fm)	average (fm)	yield (fm)	incr. (fm)
Sel.	0·5	Wolfach 4/II 740 m, E., steep	70	28	2	562	284	348	12·7	*8·6*
Sel.	0·5	Wolfach 5/II 740 m, SE., leaning to steep	69	29	2	479	310	315	13·5	*10·8*
H. For.	0·25	Wolfach 1 Schierenbühl 840 m, SW., gentle	40	60	–	248	810	561	8·4	16·6
H. For.	0·25	as before, 2 845 m, SW., gentle	80	20	–	314	543	550	14·6	16·0

(continued)

TABLE 147 *(cont.)*

Additional data for the high forest plots:

Observation per. and age			Height qual. cl. for Fir	Height qual. cl. for Spr.	Early yield (%)	Estimated norm. stock for $r=120$	Estimated norm. stock for $r=140$	Actual m.a.i.	Curved values of the max. c.a.i. fm at age		Curved values of the max. m.a.i. fm at age	
1882 to 1949 Pl.												
54	*121*	1	II. 5	II. 7	41	350	415	*11·4*	19·5	80	11·4	121
1882 to 1949												
50	*117*	2	II. 2	II. 5	61	340	390	*12·0*	19·8	78	12·2	117

The height quality classes have been determined for Silver fir after Hausser (1956), for spruce after Gehrhardt (1921).

From the two yield tables, the following total crop volumes of "timber" have been calculated for the final age of the two high forest plots, the species proportions being according to their respective basal areas.

		Silver fir	Norway spruce	Total
Plot 1	acc. to Y.T.	484	611	1095 fm
	true	578	796	1374
	Excess	94	185	279 fm = *25%*
Plot 2	acc. to Y.T.	986	213	1199
	true	1127	276	1403
	Extra	141	63	204 fm = *17%*

The following values apply for the 63-year period 1887–1950 for the selection plot 5/II:

850 fm *removed in fellings*
of which   681 fm represented *increment*
and   169 fm *reduction in standing volume.*

The 67-year observation period upon plot 2 from 1882 to 1949 runs almost *synchronously but is* 4 years longer. A completed normal working section of 117 ha, corresponding to the development of the stand on plot 2, would have supplied annually a yield of the amount of the total crop volume of that plot, namely 1402 fm, distributed over the diameter classes of that plot. This total crop volume, divided by 117, gives us an annual production per hectare of 12·0 fm, which, when multiplied by 67, results in *the possible sustained yield per hectare* for the observation period, namely 12·0×67 = 804 fm. This must be compared with a sustained yield of the selection forest plot *for the same period*. Here the true increment of 681 fm, obtained after subtracting the 169 fm by which the growing-stock was reduced, must be enlarged in the ratio 67/63 = 1·063, i.e. to *724 fm.* The actual total exploited *produce* on plot 5/II, split according to diameter classes, must be reduced in the ratio of sustained/actual total produce, i.e. by approximately 15 per cent, in order to make it comparable to the total production of plot 2. The total crop volume of that plot, in its constituent diameter classes, must itself be reduced in the ratio 67/117 (observation period/rotation).

Thus, in Table 148, the possible effective extractions in stem numbers according to diameter classes have been calculated for the two plots over the same observation period of 67 years and set alongside for comparison one with the other.

TABLE 148

PRODUCE EXTRACTED OVER A PERIOD OF 67 YEARS, AND DISTRIBUTION OF STEM NUMBERS TO DIAMETER CLASSES IN THE NORMAL GROWING-STOCK OF A SELECTION FOREST STAND AND A COMPARTMENT-FELLED HIGH FOREST WORKING SECTION RESPECTIVELY (FIGURES PER HECTARE)

Limits of the diameter classes	Exploitation over 67 years		Growing crop (fitted)	
	Sel. stand 5/II	Norm. high for. std. 2	Selection std. $r=180$	Norm. high for. working section $r=120$
(cm)	Stem nos.	Stem nos.	Stem nos.	Stem nos.
7				
10	375	852	–	–
20	411	848	205	460
30	84	300	105	208
40	39	160	54	75
50	29	92	28	26
60	53	23	14	9
70	34	2	7	2
80	14		4	–
90	1		1	–
Total	1046	2277	418	780

As expected, the selection stand is considerably superior in the yield of stems with large diameters over 50 cm (102 compared to 25); this is partly due to the reduction of the growing-stock. In contrast, the yield of stems with medium diameters of 30–50 cm is inferior (68 compared to 252). The diameter increment of the high forest trees in the 40–60-cm classes can be estimated as approximately 10 cm in 20 years; therefore if these trees were advanced through one diameter class by a lengthening of the rotation to 140 years the superiority of the selection forest would be almost eliminated.

Despite the local site disadvantage of the compartment-felled high forest plot, its value production with $r = 140$, corresponding to a mean harvesting age of approximately 125, will be equal to that of the selection forest, especially under the assumption of present-day timber prices and revenues free of harvesting costs. Besides, the high forest trees are superior in quality owing to their better form, smaller taper and lower crown proportions.

A comparison of the value production of the selection forest plots in Baden with the same high forest plots as above led Mitscherlich (1952) to the conclusion that, in the southern part of the Black Forest "the selection forest has a great superiority in comparison with the high forest". However, this is only the case if the final age of the high forest plots used in the comparison is considerably lower than the average maximum ages in the selection forest plots. None the less, such a comparison obviously is no more admissible than the comparison between working sections with correspondingly different rotations.

As Table 147 shows, the normal standing crops computed for a 140-year rotation are considerably higher than the average standing volumes or even the present final standing volumes of the selection plots; in fact, these have already been overtaken by the normal standing crops on a 120-year rotation. *The usual growing-stocks of normal high forest working sections for equal mean harvesting ages are very considerably higher than those of selection stands maintained at a level of standing volume in keeping with the regeneration.* The perception gained in Section C, II in connection with the crown dimensions of selection forest trees makes it clear that this is to be expected as a natural consequence, because in the normal high forest, the trees which are separated into age classes of almost equal height, and possessing slender crowns in nearly complete contact with each other can be accommodated on a given area in much higher numbers than is possible in the selection forest where the upper-storey trees are vertically staged, with wide crowns over-shadowing intermediate-storey trees and diffusely distributed under-storey trees with plagiotropic shade-bearing crowns.

Based on new assessments of the *experimental selection plots in Württemberg*, the author has in Table 149 compiled increments of these plots for a simultaneous 16-year observation period from 1936 to 1952. These fluctuate between limits of 7·0 to 13·2 fm annually. In order to characterize the periodic standing volume he calculated, in a similar fashion as for the mean periodic basal area, a *"mean periodic volume"*. Note the strong positive deviation of this from the usual volume in the remaining stand. It has further been possible, by means of counts of annual rings on sample stems which had kindly been made available, to calculate *mean harvesting ages* for three plots (including corrections for the varying stump heights).

Plot 1, Oberndorf, has been laid out in an old selection forest and observed since 1908. Based on seventeen sample stems (sixteen of them Silver fir) a mean harvesting age (1949) of 149 has been calculated. The *height of the site-index class* for Silver fir, read on the height curve above the diameter 61, is *31·3* m. This therefore is a selection forest with fairly *low mean harvesting ages* on a site of the best quality, which also carries the well-known superior stands of the compartment-felled high forest (Table 117). The large increment production seems credible.

Plots 2 and 3 in the Teuchelwald at Freudenstadt have been converted *from a high forest to a selection forest:* increment performance is good.

Plot 4, again Oberndorf, formerly under a "group-selection type" ("femelschlagartig") system has been observed since 1908 but is too small as a selection plot: a high increment, approaching that of plot 1. Plot 5 in the Steinwald ("Kaspersloch") was bought in 1925, after having been completely worked out by the previous owner. According to Mitscherlich (1961), no ages over 160 were measured, therefore a relatively "young" selection forest with slightly increasing standing volume, which on a poor site (according to Zimmerle) has a relatively large increment. Plot 6 was laid out in 1936 in an existing "model" selection forest. It has a decreasing, medium-large standing volume and small increment in accordance with the site.

Plot 7, also laid out in 1936 in an old selection forest, has "an ideal selection structure". Mean harvesting age (1947) according to four fir and two spruce sample stems = *191*. Class height = *32·5*. With a late felling age, tight, slowly increasing growing crop and a moderate increment.

Plot 8, also laid out in 1936 in an old selection forest, has acceptable selection structure; there is a deficiency in small timber sizes. Mean felling age according to eight fir sample stems = *201*, class height = *36·0*. Slightly rising increment, owing to a reduction of the

TABLE 149

STANDING VOLUMES, ANNUAL EXTRACTIONS AND INCREMENT OF THE EXPERIMENTAL SELECTION PLOTS
IN WÜRTTEMBERG DURING THE PERIOD 1936–52
FROM DATA OF THE FOREST RESEARCH AND EXPERIMENTAL INSTITUTE OF BADEN-WÜRTTEMBERG, FIELD
STATION, HECHINGEN

No.	Size (ha)	Forest, altitude and slope gradient in %	Percentage of mixed species			Standing volume of timber in the rem. std.		Mean per. gr.-stock	Average annual	
			Fir (%)	Spr. (%)	Be. (%)	at start (fm)	at finish (fm)	(fm)	yield (fm)	incr. (fm)
1	0·5	Oberndorf 665 m, WNW., 10%	86	14	–	471	482	*519*	10·8	*13·2*
2	1·0	Freudenstadt 800 m, NE., 2–4%	34	63	3	487	467	*523*	11·6	*10·8*
3	2·5	Freudenstadt 815 m, NE., 4–5%	52	48	–	502	504	*550*	12·3	*12·3*
4	0·25	Oberndorf 665 m, WNW., 5%	92	8	–	589	443	*608*	21·9	*12·9*
5	1·0	Steinwald 830 m, level	66	34	–	381	400	*438*	8·3	*9·5*
6	1·0	Schömberg 760 m, SE., 10%	68	30	2	453	417	*509*	9·3	*7·0*
7	1·0	Schömberg 760 m, SSW., 6%	63	37	–	324	339	*378*	6·9	*7·9*
8	1·0	Schömberg 800 m, S., 2%	73	26	1	628	482	*660*	17·8	*8·7*

growing crop by the previous removal of mainly old trees. Comparative high-forest plot 8a is situated immediately adjacent.

The mean periodic standing volume has been calculated from the crop volume *in the middle* of the interval between each of two felling incursions, the individual values having been weighted against the length of the cutting period. On the other hand, the timber (Derbholz) volumes at the beginning and end of the generally 16-year observation period (exception No. 5 with 15 years) were stated in each case after a felling incursion (V_i).

The increments contain the recruitment (annual average 0·2 fm, maximum 0·5 fm in No. 3).

The noticeably high increment in plots 1 and 2 of Oberndorf with approximately 13 fm has to be considered against the background of the high production of the high-forest plots at Oberndorf, especially *Silver firs plot 55*, which, according to Table 117, during the age-period 147–157 still had a current increment of 16·8 fm but, during the age-period 157–178 this was reduced by heavy interventions to 12·4 fm. According to careful calculation by Zimmerle (1936) the *m.a.i.* for the age of 147 years, with only 33 per cent taken out in early yields, would amount to *15·3* fm. After reckoning in the later increments, the m.a.i. for the age of 178 then amounts to 14·8 fm.

Under the local site conditions of Oberndorf, therefore, *pure Silver fir stands with high densities can at final ages corresponding to those in selection forests achieve a performance of 15 fm m.a.i.* The m.a.i. of plot 55 for a mean felling age of 150 years, such as is to be assumed for selection plot 1, certainly reaches higher than 15 fm!

A further *comparison between selection and normal high forests* is possible on the basis of the two immediately adjacent plots 8 (selection forest) and 8a (normal high forest comparison) in the Stiftungswald (institutional forest) at Schömberg, on upper bunter-sandstone, at 800 m altitude (ann. precipitation = 1400 mm, precipitation in vegetative period = 520 mm). This comparison is possible because interim growth-data are available for both plots. Owing to the hitherto short period of observation for plot 8a, however, it is not possible to construct an analogous working section.

As shown in Table 150, the high forest stand which in 1952 was approximately 158 years old, having originated from long-term shelterwood felling regeneration (Zimmerle 1936), has almost exactly the same proportions of mixed species as the selection forest.

The peak frequencies of the diameter distribution occurring in classes 10–20 (beech and fir under-storey) as well as in the 50–60 class, along with four big fir trees in classes 90–110 indicate that this was formerly a shelterwood stand with a selection type of structure, which has achieved high-forest closure.

In contrast, the *selection plot*, with passable selection structure, has a striking deficiency in small sizes. The *ages* measured at varying stump heights on eight sample stems (without corrections), suggest an average figure of 181 ± 25 years (limits 148–208) for b.h. diameters of 43–85 cm.

The mean harvesting ages of the two stands may not be very different. If it were possible to construct a working section diameter distribution for the high-forest plot, this would deviate very little from that of the selection stand.

For a comparison of the production, it is necessary to determine the probable m.a.i. of the high forest stand. If one calculates the total crop volume performance without consideration of age, from the curves of total crop volume over mean height, like those constructed by the author according to Gehrhardt's yield tables for Silver fir and spruce, the total crop volume values for the mean heights at the reference age of 158 years are as follows:

Species	Proportion of mixture	h_m (m)	Total crop volume (timber) fm
Silver fir	0·72	35·0	1307
Norway spruce	0·28	37·2	466
		Total	1773

providing a m.a.i.$_{158}$ of *11·2 fm*.

According to experiences gained in the mixed fir–spruce stand at Wolfach, the yield level must be assumed to be at least 10 per cent higher, so that the m.a.i. of plot 8a, even assuming a higher age, ought to be *over 11 fm*.

The high forest stand, therefore, is not only *superior in current increment* over the last 16 years, and that *by as much as 19 per cent*, but assuredly *also in m.a.i. for the same harvesting age. Contrary to current widely prevailing views, the pronounced vertical layering of selection forests has an efficiency-reducing effect which puts it at a disadvantage as regards increment in comparison to closed stands of compartment-felled high forest character.* The above comparison merely confirms expectations on the basis of investigations about crown dimensions and production of selection forests (Section C, II).

TABLE 150

COMPARISON BETWEEN A SELECTION STAND (8) AND A 158-YEAR-OLD HIGH FOREST STAND (8a) OF A SIMILAR SPECIES MIXTURE

Definition	Plot	Silver fir		Norway spruce		C. beech		Total stand	
		N	V (fm)	N	V (fm)	N	V (fm)	N	V (fm)
Remaining	8	343	328	64	147	7	7	414	482
Gr.-stock 1952	8a	134	494	56	189	26	12	216	695
Exploitation	8	178	246	19	38	2	1	199	285
1936–52	8a	78	209	6	12	4	1	88	222
Annual incr.	8		6·6		2·0		0·1		8·7
1936–52	8a		8·4		1·5		0·4		10·3

(Volumes in timber, over 7 cm diameter.)

Heights of some diameters and "degrees of slenderness" according to the height curves of 1952

b.h.d. cm	Plot	Silver fir		Norway spruce	
		h m	h : b.h.d.	h m	h : b.h.d.
38	8	26·5	70	29·7	78
	8a	31·6	83	31·6	83
58	8	32·6	56	33·4	58
	8a	35·4	61	38·1	66
78	8	35·8	46	36·0	46
	8a	36·6	47	41·9	54

Comparison of the diameter distributions

Limits of the diameter classes	Removals 1946–52		Gr-stock 1952 after thinning	
	Plot 8	8a	Plot 8	8a
7				
10	1	—	77	—
20	6	2	131	24
30	1	2	54	16
40	1	4	43	28
50	7	14	33	42
60	10	6	44	46
70	7	—	27	36
80	3	8	3	20
90	3	—	2	—
100	—	—	—	2
110	—	—	—	2
Total	39	36	414	216

Results of temporary (once-measured) selection-forest sample plots

Moderate growth performance of selection stands is also demonstrated by increment measurements carried out by Köstler (1956, 1958) and Saukel (1959) in the Allgäu, in Bregenz forest, and in the Bavarian Forest in the course of extensive selection forest investigations.

The forty-four enumerated plots in the Allgäu are in Landkreis Lindau, at 600–1000 m above sea level, mostly on fresh-water sediments and clayey marl which are sparsely covered by young moraine. Annual precipitation = 1600–2000 mm, annual temperature ~6°C.

Köstler (1956) divided the stands from a silvicultural aspect into three main groups: (I) "genuine selection structure", (II) "selection structure imperilled", (III) "selection structure lost" which in each case are further subdivided by the level of the growing-stock ("richly stocked", "well stocked", "poorly stocked"), the specific kind of treatment (for example "Hortungswald" (protective forest), "Plünderwald" (exploitation forest)) or manner of their formation (for example "Fichtenhallenbestand"), vaulted spruce stand.

Increment borings have established the increments for 9 stands with genuine selection structure. *The increments of wood of timber dimensions* lie *between 5·6 and 9·8 fm*, with levels of growing-stock between 241 to 777 fm and increment percentages between 0·6 and 3·4 per cent.

The production potentials in this growth region are illuminated by the following production figures from long-observed experimental plots in the forest of Betzigau, east of Kempten, at 780–800 m altitude, with 1400 mm annual precipitation, in level to gently sloping position on young moraine. The area is afforested former pasture land.

The sown spruce plots, 36/II, 37/II and 43/II, thinned at grade B, have, at the *age of 83* years, achieved the following *m.a.i. production in stemwood: 21·1; 21·5; 20·1 fm*. The planted C-grade plot 43/III at the same age achieved *19·7* fm and the planted C-grade plot 65/III at the age of 88 years *21·1* fm. The experimental spruce–fir series Ottobeuren 7 which lies approximately 10 km further north, at approximately 860 m altitude, on a similar though not so good site as Ottobeuren 8 (Table 93), achieved up to the age of 116 the following stemwood increments:

Degree of thinning	Proportions of mixed species		m.a.i.	Average ann. increment from 45 to 116 years
	Spruce	Fir	(fm)	(fm)
A	0·74	0·26	15·7	18·4
B	0·53	0·47	15·3	19·2
C	0·26	0·74	13·6	17·3

The m.a.i. of the C-plot is reduced by unassessed early yields prior to the start of the experiment. When made equal to the initial production of plot A it increases to 14·5 fm. The values are based on actual ages.

The yields of the *selection stands in Bregenz* forest (Köstler 1958) are in all cases higher than in the Allgäu. They arise from well-favoured sites, both ecologically and climatically, at altitudes between 565 to 1290 m above m.s.l. with a precipitation between 1200 to 2500 mm. The increment values for sixteen "selection stands, rich in fir", lie between 6·3 and 14·7 fm with growing stocks between 354 to 706 fm. The maximum values for growing-stock and increment are achieved by the top quality stand, No. 16, which at an altitude between 580–600 m grows on older deposits on a mild north slope, with a trough across the slope, so that the site is greatly favoured by its relief. The increments recorded for the "selection stands rich in C. beech" amounted to between 5·0 and 12·0 fm with growing-stocks between 457 to 721 fm, whilst the increments achieved in the "selection stands rich in spruce" were apparently due to the high altitude only between 4·2 and 7·9 fm.

FIG. 168. Selection stand at Zwiesel-West forest, sub-compt. "Quarzbruch". "Fliesserde" (structureless soil of high silt content that gets muddy when wetted), at the lower end of the slope, at the foot of gr. Falkenstein. S. fir = 420 fm, N. spruce = 250 fm, beech = 60 fm, together 730 fm/ha.

The increments of eighteen *selection stands in the Bavarian Forest*, which were analysed by Saukel (1959), achieved values between *2·0 and 10·4 fm* with standing volumes between 60 to 726 fm. In group 1a ("moderately well-stocked—good site") the average increment of six stands, with an average standing volume of 337 fm, amounts to 7·7 fm, within the range of 6·5–8·3. In group 2a ("heavily stocked—good site") the corresponding figures for standing volume are 516 fm and for increment 8·1 fm (6·5–10·4). The stands which are thus constituted into characteristic groups clearly show similar production trends. The inter-relations which doubtless exist between site, growing stock, treatment and increment can only be clarified when a sufficient number of *ages have been determined* which, will enable well-founded statements to be made about the all-important *age* factor in the particular selection stands.

Comparisons of production and tree age

The two comparisons of production as between selection stands and mixed stands from regeneration of high forest by compartment fellings have left open the question as to what length of time must be taken as a basis for arriving at the yields from working sections comprising such naturally regenerated mixed crops, if these are to be derived from long-term observations upon growth-data of individual stands. In the model of the ideal working section for pure crops this question was avoided by the simple assumption that the area containing the oldest crops, after having been felled in the autumn, is completely resown next spring, and in the following autumn will be fully restocked with 1-year-old seedlings. In this case the rotation is equal to the age of the oldest stand; it can be defined as *final age*. If, on the other hand, a mixed fir–spruce stand is regenerated over a long period, possibly extending to 40 years, then when the last trees of the parent crop are felled at (say) the age of 150 years, the oldest individuals of the new generation which follows on will already have reached 40 years of age. *The production processes of the preceding and the succeeding stands overlap in each case over a period of 40 years.* This introduces the complicated question, as to what is the amount of increment put on by the parent crop which is under gradual clearance, how much accrues to the new crop which is coming along under shade and what is the total production of the two crops together. Suitable experimentation is urgently needed to clarify this point. When one bears in mind, for example, how severely the growth of the young beech in the "Kleinengelein" Lichtwuchs stand (p. 384) was checked by the initial very severe opening up of top canopy, one is sceptical that with a shade-bearing species the joint increment of the opened-out parent crop along with that of the young crop will be equally as large as the increment of the original stand if the canopy had remained unbroken and the under storey were allowed to grow up through it.

Figure 169 gives a schematic representation of the probable progress of the current increment of three succeeding generations of a mixed fir–spruce stand for regeneration periods of 40 years, the actual increment values of the compared high forest plot Wolfach 2 having been used as a basis. *The periods of low increment in that case overlap*

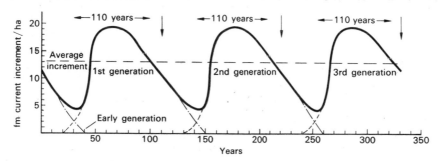

FIG. 169. Possible progress of the current increment for three generations of a mixed fir–spruce–beech stand with long-term natural regeneration.

in such a way that the same periods repeat themselves at an interval of 110 years (150—40). The increment of the period of overlapping has been assumed at such a level that the total crop yield in a 150-year period becomes equal to the uncurtailed total increment of plot 2, Wolfach, which is likely to be achieved on the basis of age-data obtained from the research institute and assuming the same kind of treatment as practised hitherto. As this plot at 117 years had achieved a total crop yield of 1402 fm (= 12·0 fm m.a.i.), it is likely to reach a m.a.i. of 11·4 fm at 150 years, i.e. a total crop yield of 1720 fm. As demonstrated in Fig. 169, the total crop yield for 150 years (= 1720 fm) contains not only the increments of a full phase-interval of 110 years, but also the increments of a period of 40 years which at the same time constitutes the next phase of diminished increment. The total increments of a full phase-interval amount to a total crop vol. of 1457 fm, which would be equal to a *m.a.i. of 13·2 fm of a correspondingly constructed working section.* As demonstrated in Fig. 169, 13·2 fm is equal to the ordinate of the arithmetic mean of all increments within the difference of a complete phase. The m.a.i. of the normal high forest working section in the working section model in Fig. 157 is also equal to the arithmetic mean of the current annual increments of all stands of which the working section is composed.

Accordingly, a calculation of the m.a.i. of a working section of mixed stands with long-term natural regeneration must not be based on a period which corresponds to the highest occurring final age, but *only the period of a full phase-interval.* At the same time, however, the increment of the overlapping phase must be correctly determined and the succeeding generation must always be treated in the same way. The potential production of a comparable working section of mixed crops therefore in the case of Wolfach 2 is probably higher than that assumed in our comparison with the selection plot 5/II.

The growth processes of all trees in a real selection forest overlap in an unpredictable manner. If, however, an equilibrium is maintained and the values of extractions and growing stock are kept at a constant level over a sufficiently long period, i.e. if the stock is constant, then the mean age of the harvested trees must also be approximately constant. Just as the annual increment of a normal working section is composed of the increments of all trees which constitute the working section in an orderly distribution by diameter and age, so does this apply equally for the observed annual increment of a balanced ("normalized") selection stand. Apart from climatic fluctuations, it is likely to remain unchanged if a balance in selection is preserved by removal of certain stem-number quotas from all diameter classes. This, after a sufficiently long period of time, will moreover result in a regular age-distribution and constant average harvesting age of the annual yield. Certainly, the sustained potential production for a given level of growing-stock and treatment in a selection forest can be discovered even without knowledge of the mean harvesting age, but as soon as these values are altered, the average harvesting age of the selection forest trees must also change. The latter not only represents an important indicator for the estimation of production in selection forests, but it is also indispensable for possible comparisons of production of normal high forest stands. The *oldest* harvesting age, i.e. the "final age", is not suitable for such comparisons. Therefore it is necessary to choose a *serviceable age definition.*

The simple arithmetic mean of the ages of all harvested trees would give too much weight to the numerically preponderating small-sized trees which, however, contribute little to the volume production. Therefore, a *weighting by volume,* as provided for the *"mean harvesting age"* (mha), ought to be suitable. In transitions from one type of forest to another, which cannot be carried out without sharp alterations of the harvesting ages the *actual age* has to be used as a basis for age determinations. For comparisons between the production of such types of forests, as are basically operated under more or less long-term natural regeneration, it may be advantageous to use the *breast height age* (i.e. number of annual rings at breast height) or an age even higher up on the stem, as possibly on a cross-section at 5 or 10 m height. It will prove difficult to determine the age of the stump from borings because of difficulty in hitting the pith. Breast height is certainly more suitable.

Comparison of production according to Flury. Selection or normal high forest?

In his classic comparison between selection and high forest, Flury (1929) compared the ideal stocking of a selection forest according to his quality classification scale with that of working sections of an even-aged high forest, using as a basis his yield table for Norway spruce (mountain region) of the same quality classes (selection forest I against high forest I) with $r = 120$. Obviously, such a comparison is unacceptable, owing to the arbitrary identification of incompatible quality classes, the enormous differences in mean harvesting age and the fact that the comparison is made between the yields of mixed stands and those of pure spruce. However, it is comprehensible when seen in the light of the situation at that time, because then the science of forestry in Central Europe was still dominated by the concept of the maximum expectation value of the soil, the consequences of which were that management was largely persuaded in favour of the *clear-felling* of spruce forests. The enormous superiority of selection forests in respect of the proportion of large-diameter timber (over 52 cm)—in quality class I, 67 per cent in comparison to 8 per cent!—was further demonstrated by Flury in comparing the yield of the selection forest of Couvet with the municipal forest of Winterthur: 50 per cent large-sized timber as against only 7 per cent! Dannecker (1936) also attempted the comparison which was even less convincing, quoting amongst others the average growing-stock of the State Forest of Württemberg. But from the above detailed comparisons there can be no possible doubt that a normal high-forest working section with long-term natural regeneration and species admixtures similar to those in the selection forest is the superior of the two systems in volume production at nearly the same mean harvesting ages and at least the equal in value production.

For localities which are at all suitable for selection working e.g. in a natural fir–beech–spruce forest or in montane or high-montane forests of spruce, the alternative ought not to be as between selection forest and spruce even-aged forest, but between selection forest with individual or group-selection and even-aged high forest with systematic regeneration. None the less, let us in addition examine what production may be achieved in an even-aged high forest of pure spruce on an optimum site. Table 151 shows the actual total crop volumes up to the age of 101 years and the probable volumes up to the age of 150 years for the B-plot of the experimental series Sachsenried 2, divided into Flury-classes. According to these figures, the total production by the age of 101 years already consists of as much as 15 per cent "large timber"; this proportion, if $r = 150$, would increase to 48 per cent. And since the stand is very healthy (no red-rot) and wind-firm owing to its deep rooting, it is quite capable of reaching that age. At that age, the proportion of Heilbronn class 6 would amount to as much as 37 per cent. At the same time, the small value increase per festmetre and the fall in average annual value increment prove that with present-day price conditions the production of timber of such large dimensions is unprofitable.

Suitable selection sites have the following advantages and disadvantages for selection forests vis-à-vis high forest felled by compartments with natural regeneration:

Selection forests are very safe against hazards, especially snow breakage and gales. Sustained management is rendered possible on small forest areas, therefore the selection forest is particularly suitable for farm forests (Abetz, 1952, 1955). In small ownings of mixed stands, possible damage to neighbouring property is also avoided, whereas clearing by compartments of even-aged high forest stands, especially of pure spruce, can bring disaster upon neighbours (Abetz, 1952). The structure of the selection forest is particularly beneficial to the health and regeneration of Silver fir; the dangers to this species from *Dreyfusia nüsslini* under prolonged cover are less serious than when the young growth is suddenly exposed.[1] Once the selection forest is fully constituted, it permits the production of large timber sizes without the replacement of growing stock which is necessary in a clear-felling system.

TABLE 151

ACTUAL TOTAL PRODUCTION UP TO THE AGE OF 101 YEARS AND PROBABLE PRODUCTION UP TO THE AGE OF 150 YEARS IN THE EXPERIMENTAL PLOT SACHSENRIED 2, B-GRADE

(a) *Distribution of the stemwood volume to diameter classes according to Flury*

Class acc. to Flury	Final age 101 volume (fm)	(%)	Final age 150 volume (fm)	(%)
8–14	176	9	176	7
16–24	315	17	315	13
26–36	404	22	337	14
38–50	686	37	429	18
52–70	271	15	1035	42
over 70	—	—	153	6
	1852	100	2445	100

(b) *Distribution to Heilbronn classes and value of the total production*
(Prices = 200% of the m.i.)

	Firewood	Billetwood +stemwood class 1	Stemwood Class 2	3	4	5	6	Section	Bark and harv. lossess
$r = 101$	4	12	6	6	12	20	17	3	20%
$r = 150$	4	10	4	5	8	8	37	3	20%

	Value of total production (DM)	Value of average festmetre (DM)	Average ann. value incr. per ha (DM)
$r = 101$	116,680	62·7	1155
$r = 150$	161,690	65·8	1078

[1] Schneider-Orelli (1945) found the serious pest *Dreyfusia nüsslini* also in Emmenthal. In his opinion, the reason why it has not so far occurred in selection forest regions is that the danger of transmission by infested nursery stock is not so great there.

The sustained volume production of the selection forest is, however, less than that of high forest felled by compartments, even at the same felling ages. The timber so produced is more tapering and knotty. More particularly when stocking is of moderate or even low density, the trees exhibit relatively greater butt-swell, and branch development is more pronounced along with added depth of crown.

The comparison as regards self-pruning made by Flury (1933) is defective inasmuch as he considered only the diameter classes up to 36 cm, which in a selection forest, particularly one that is densely stocked and on a good site, do indeed possess cylindrical and relatively clean boles (Burger, 1942; Leibundgut, 1945). What is important is the amount of branching in the classes over 52 cm which after all are supposed to constitute the major part of a selection forest output on good sites.

Timber quality in the selection forest improves with greater density of the growing crop; however, in the case of single-tree selection the young crops are then endangered. It is questionable whether the lopping and careful felling, necessary to avoid damaging young growth, such as is standard practice in farm forests, can be feasible in extensive forests under present-day working and wage conditions.

The different opinions expressed in the literature about timber quality in selection and even-aged high forests are easily explained, if one remembers the importance of the structure and density of the growing crop. The selection system when applied to forests of high volume content, especially in more or less untouched natural forest, permits the expectation of a considerably better form and quality than when the volume of the growing stock is maintained at a low level to encourage young crops. The timber quality in the latter case would become particularly poor if in addition the object of management was altered from the production of large-diameter timber to construction material (Mitscherlich, 1952). Just as many present-day selection forests have originated from high forests and thus are sustained by the quality of the former high forest trees, there are also some high forest stands, which have originated from a former selection forest by closing up. Both are cases of "sailing under false colours".

The oncoming generation, which in a selection forest is distributed over the whole forest area, undergoes a *selective influence in favour of the more shade-tolerant individuals* whereas in the more or less closed young growth of high forest compartments a positive selection by inherent vigour of growth takes place at the same time. The regeneration and raising of young growth must necessarily suffer some shortcomings when individual selection is practised. It causes us to think when Leibundgut (1945), from his wealth of Swiss experience with both types of forest, talks of a development which, in certain selection forest regions, distinctly deviates from the individual stem selection forest to a more group-like type of structure. "Whether in this case we should more aptly refer to a selection forest ("Plenterwald") or a shelterwood forest ("Femelschlagwald") depends solely on the question, whether a separation in terms of time and place of the individual tending operations and of regeneration measures is demanded even on the smallest areas or whether the works of cleaning, thinning, opening up, regeneration and extraction are carried out in logical sequence, and according to regulation by area."

Thus, in large forest holdings transitional forms or outright high forest forms with long-term regeneration ought to be more suitable, because they allow closer crown contact with superior volume increment per unit area and better timber quality, whilst at the same time difficulties in safeguarding the young crops and avoiding felling damage are circumvented by systematic and spatially ordered regeneration. In this connection see Fig. 170. We must however, realize that with increasing uniformity of the crop, there

FIG. 170. Swiss Femelschlag in the Bürgerwald at Solothurn.

comes a diminished security, which at high elevations under extreme climatic conditions can have a decisive influence.

The great detail in which the selection forest has been discussed is not a measure of its present practical importance as regards those forest areas which are at all susceptible to management under this system, or even those which are actually stocked with selection forests (Zimmerle, 1941). Nevertheless, the selection forest has unmistakably served as a model for the perpetual forest movement and still does so for many disciples of "the forest economy in conformity with nature school". We have proved that the expected superiority exists neither in organic production nor in value production. The imposition of this ideal upon localities and growing crops which are unsuitable for selection working would bring economic losses and disappointments in its train.

III. STRUCTURE AND INCREMENT OF NATURAL FOREST STANDS

The particular condition of a forest characterized by the proportions of species, social strata and distribution by dimensions and age classes reflects the history of its development.

Catastrophes (Schenk, 1924) due to fires, gales and insect attacks which commonly recur at intervals in the coniferous virgin forests of the northern hemisphere and at times without human agency, as for example, fires started by lightning, are followed by regeneration which usually results in a nearly even-aged and uniform condition over large areas in succession to pioneer forest species. By contrast, the shade-bearing virgin forests of the European mountain regions[1] for the greater part build up into a form resembling *extremely richly stocked selection forests*, which are at the same time *deficient in young growth* (Rubner, 1925; Fröhlich, 1925, 1954). A densely stocked upper storey can indeed convey the illusion of an even-aged condition; but this is not real as may be proved by age determinations.

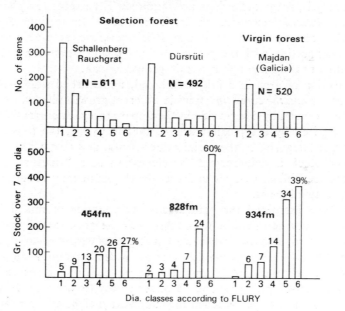

FIG. 171. Comparison between the structure of selection forest stands and the structure of a stand of shade-tolerant trees in a virgin forest (*Mauve*, 1931).

The close similarity between an overstocked selection forest and a primitive natural forest can be illustrated in the comparison of structures provided in Fig. 171. The stem numbers and standing timber volumes classified according to Flury's diameter classes are here displayed alongside: of the Swiss selection forest area Schallenberg-Rauchgrat, with an optimum selection structure; of Dürsrüti, with its extreme over-stocking in large diameter timber; and of the natural forest sample plot A surveyed by Mauve (1931) in the Galician Carpathians (Majdan domain) in a mixed virgin stand of fir, beech and

---

[1] In this connection see especially the expositions by Rubner in the 5th edition of his work *Pflanzengeographische Grundlagen des Waldbaus*.

spruce (720 m altitude, steep SSW. slope, app. 1000 mm ann. precipitation). Mauve's age determinations proved that an extremely intimate age mixture existed within the sample plot (which is only 0·2 ha extent) with maximum ages of over 300 years. It is obvious that with the undisturbed development of such a virgin stand, growing-stock and mean harvesting age (harvest to be understood as natural loss) must reach maximum values. The scarcity of young growth in shade-tolerant original forests, which has been stressed by many authors, is a necessary result not only of the structure but also of the long "natural rotation". We remember the general falling-off of the age-class proportions with increasing length of rotation (Fig. 160, p. 442). When comparing with the selection forest at Dürsrüti, we must further take into consideration that this grows on a better site and therefore is capable of producing large tree dimensions within given harvesting ages.

Stages of development in natural forests

In order to clarify the history of origins, structure and production of natural stands by yield research analysis, some definitions are required. The expression *phase* has already been used for the *natural growth-phases*, i.e. for characteristic sections of the smoothed curve of increment as a function of the age. It is, therefore, advisable to use the term "phase" only in connection with the progress of individual trees or a number of trees, which are just then passing through a certain growth epoch.

A delimited section of area in a fully developed, undisturbed shade-tolerant natural forest contains *at one and the same time* trees in different growth phases, the phases of full vigour and decline occurring side by side in the upper storey. A currently existing forest condition characterized by a typical structure, that is to say, the trees distributed by size-classes and age categories to the social height-strata, and therewith the concomitant levels of growing stock and increment, is referred to as a "stadium" or *stage*. In a natural forest region, different stages of forest development may occur side by side on large as well as on small areas.

Magin (1959) who examined the natural mountain stands of mixed species in the Bavarian Kalkalpen, distinguished between three social height strata. By setting the arithmetic mean of the 100 highest trees per hectare (all heights were measured) as 90 per cent, he divides the stands into three relative height strata with nearly equal enjoyment of light (Assmann, 1954), namely the upper storey (80–100 per cent of this indicator height), an intermediate storey (50–80 per cent) and an under storey (lower than 50 per cent). The young growth which has not yet reached the calipering height of 1·3 m is assessed separately. On Magin's nineteen sample plots averaging, 0·3 ha, the trees are assorted into three height layers each of approximately the same age, so that we may refer to *generations*. The age intervals between the generations, each of which is strongly represented, amount to between 80 and 100 years.[1] As a rule, Magin was able to distinguish between three generations, because they roughly coincided with the three social height strata and were distinguishable in the peak frequencies of their diameter distributions (cf. Fig. 75, p. 137).

On sample plot No. 18 in Kreuth forest, which, being situated in a deep trough across the slope, is protected against high winds, he found in the upper storey, not only an approximately 320-year-old generation, but also remnants of a generation of around 400 years

---

[1] According to Magin the age intervals found by Chenchine (1943) in virgin beech forests in Rumania and Turkey were 60 years for the most part.

FIG. 172. Remains of a virgin forest in a trough whence extraction is impossible. Kreuth forest. Photo by *Magin*.

with trees of up to 40 m height and up to 90 cm in diameter. The younger generations are approximately 230 and 150 years old. Under their dense shade, of which beech comprises a high proportion, only a few small nuclei of regeneration had been able to establish themselves despite some holes in the upper canopy resulting from the collapse of large trees. In this connection see Fig. 172. In such original shade-tolerant stands of fir, spruce and beech, a wealth of seedlings especially of fir, appear again and again under the close canopy, but a succeeding generation of young growth can develop only if the top canopy has been opened up sufficiently as a result of natural mortality amongst the very old trees, accelerated by windthrow and snowbreak. In a natural montane forest, situated at a high and exposed position, very damaging effects from gales and snowbreak must be expected to occur periodically, if at longish intervals, wherein the most exposed trees in the upper storey are the worst hit. When multiple losses of such trees, weakened by old age, occur in the upper storey, causing breaches in the intermediate and lower storeys in their fall, the conditions are provided for a mass of regeneration to appear in the gaps. Whilst the trees in the intermediate storey then grow to form a new upper storey and the former lower storey develops into an intermediate storey, the lower storey is replenished from the new surge of regeneration.

Thus Magin discovered in the Wettersteinwald on three sample plots, lying side by side in a surrounding area of a few hundred metres radius, three typical stages which he defined as "restocking", "full production" and "canopy change". In the *restocking* stage, which can also be referred to as the construction stage, as represented in plot 12 (Fig. 173), the upper, intermediate, and lower storeys contribute each one-third in the total ground cover of 7180 m² (per hectare of forest area). The upper storey, which gets the favoured advantage of full radiation, is not yet fully stocked. Whilst some trees from the intermediate storey are striving upwards towards a position in the upper storey, the intermediate and lower storeys are filling up. The stock so far is low, increment is moderate. The tendency

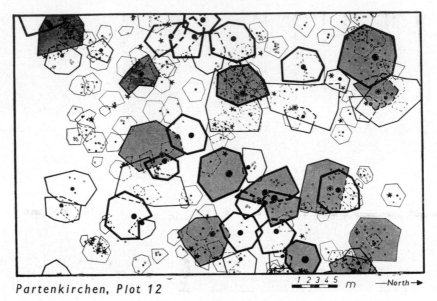

Partenkirchen, Plot 12   1 2 3 4 5   m   —North→

FIG. 173. "Restocking" stage. Crown canopy areas shown in shading: S. fir *(Magin)*. Stars = dead trees; small circles = young trees.

of both is towards an increase. In the stage of *full production* (plot 13, Fig. 174) the upper storey, occupying over 50 per cent of the total ground cover of 7103 m² per hectare, is nearly *fully stocked*. Stock and increment reach maximum values. In the stage of canopy change, which is reckoned as having been reached during the last phase of exhaustion (plot 4, Fig. 175), the major part of the upper storey and part of the intermediate storey have been lost, presumably as a result of some calamity. Only 4500 m² per hectare of the forest

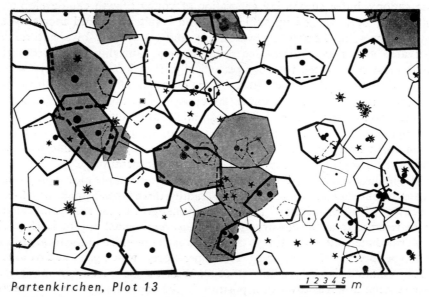

Partenkirchen, Plot 13   1 2 3 4 5   m

FIG. 174. "Full production" stage *(Magin)*.

area are still under cover, half of this being formed by the remainder of the upper storey and one-third by the intermediate storey. Favourable light conditions have enabled numerous centres of regeneration to develop. The present appearance of the forest is of markedly selection type. The growing crop is moderate, increment small; the increment percentage, owing to severe opening, is high. In a shade-tolerant virgin forest, this stage is unlikely to occur extensively, or so dramatically, except after calamitous losses in the upper and intermediate storeys; if the forest is left to the undisturbed processes of its own dynamic, following natural ageing, the stage of full production is likely to predominate. A section of the forest area when observed over a lengthy period, is seen to fall into a stage of decline, which is the prelude to a new building-up stage and a filling of the upper storey.

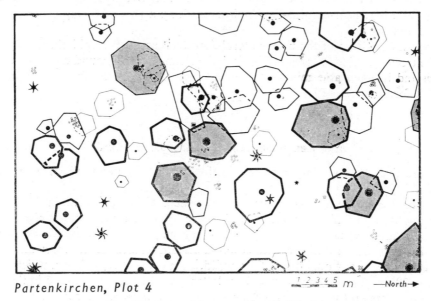

Partenkirchen, Plot 4

1 2 3 4 5 m   —North➤

FIG. 175. Stage of "canopy change" *(Magin)*.

The characteristics of succession following initial and reafforestation as described in Weck's (1944, 1947, 1956) "types of forest formations" ("Waldgefügetypen") are combined with the structural characteristics of the forest. In large virgin forest regions, these types of stand constitution can occur alongside, without the necessity of a repetition of the sequence: "pioneer forest, intermediate forest, prime forest, final forest". The climax stage of a shade-tolerant virgin forest, unbroken by areas of regeneration consequent upon some calamity, obviously is the "final forest". The highest increment in a shade-tolerant virgin forest area cannot be achieved until the upper storey has become fully stocked. If, however, this is predominantly occupied by very old trees, which are already at the end of their phase of decline and approaching their natural exodus, the increment per stocked forest area must be small; it starts increasing again when trees rising from the intermediate storey have occupied the vacated crown space in the upper storey. The increment of such a shade-bearing virgin forest could be kept at an even level by the current removal of those trees in the upper storey whose increment per unit of canopy area is decreasing, that is, by preventing the upper storey from becoming over-aged.

A conceivable alternative indeed would be to convert systematically to a selection-type structure, which apparently, according to Weck, typifies his "prime forest". This would be accompanied by a considerable reduction of the growing-stock and also, in consequence of a lowering of the age of extraction, a certain increase of increment, at least in comparison to the original increment with a large proportion of over-aged trees in the upper storey. If it were intended to practise regular exploitation of such an original stand, it would be important, with a minimum of "vertical layering" according to Weck, to achieve a steady replenishment of the upper storey by removing the oldest trees which show diminishing yield for the canopy area they occupy. The regularly recurring structure of an "overstocked selection forest" due to such a procedure might result, not only in optimum production, but at the same time necessitate the minimum of "unnatural" measures and associated forest conditions. This treatment appears to be a truly natural—or rather, near-natural—method of handling a shade-bearing original crop of fir, spruce and beech.

The exposed position of the three natural forest areas at Partenkirchen, only 200 m below the tree limit, finds expression in a relatively small total ground cover. It would be a serious and irremediable mistake to convert this natural forest into a compartment-felled high forest structure.[1]

Increment production of natural forest stands

Table 152 gives the most important production data of the stands which were analysed by Magin.

Nos. 5 to 9 of these are secondary stands, which, although remaining undisturbed after the abolition of felling for salt mines for over 100 years, have not yet regained their original structure. Apart from their position—the majority of the stands are, or have been until now, inaccessible for extraction—a certain guarantee of their inviolability is provided by the heavy quantities of dry wood, both standing and fallen, which amount to between 20 and 115 fm per hectare. This latter record quantity is found in the typical natural forest remnant of No. 18, Kreuth forest[2]. The *increment production* on average is *small*, whilst the growing-*stock* must be considered as being *large*, if one remembers that these stands possess the *characteristics of working section compartments* outwardly appearing more or less even-aged owing to their densely stocked upper storey. Thus, the resulting *increment percentage* is strikingly *small*, as a rule less than 1·0. The relatively large increment percentage (1·24 and 1·40) of the secondary stands Nos. 5 and 7 can be explained by their comparatively low age (151 and 115) years and the good site. These two stands at the same time have the largest absolute dry-weight increment, here best stated in forestry terms as "conifer festmetres". Obviously the potential yield of such mixed stands, with considerable proportions of *beech*, cannot simply be expressed by adding the total volume increments of the different tree species. Stand No. 8, like No. 9, has a large proportion of spruce in the upper storey; both stands are on a favourable site, No. 9 is sheltered against wind.

---

[1] The three plots, together with a fourth one, are under permanent observation. It is gratifying that by prohibiting all systematic exploitation within a sufficiently wide radius, the Bavarian Forestry Administration has enabled long-term observations to be kept upon the undisturbed development of this forest in its natural state.

[2] This also is to be preserved from all extractions.

TABLE 152

INCREMENT PRODUCTION OF NEAR-NATURAL MONTANE MIXED CROPS IN THE BAVARIAN ALPS, AFTER DATA BY MAGIN (PER HECTARE OF HORIZONTAL AREA)

No.	Forest, altitude and slope gradient	Proportions in the basal area of			Top height	Gr. Stock		Ann incr. of the last 10 years			Age weighted by volume of the storeys
						basal area	vol-ume	Incr.		Coni-fer	
		Spr.	Fir	Be.	(m)	(m²)	(fm)	(fm)	(%)	(fm)	
1	Partenkirchen 1200 m, NW. 20°	36	49	15	32·1	59·0	758	6·1	0·85	6·5	214
2	Ditto 1250 m, N. 9°	48	28	24	28·3	58·2	699	6·4	0·96	7·1	202
3	Ditto 1320 m, N. 22°	71	18	11	29·3	49·9	597	5·8	1·00	6·0	204
4	Ditto 1400 m, N. 22°	73	24	3	26·8	42·2	444	5·7	1·37	5·7	240
5	Reichenhall 950 m, NNW. 15°	20	29	51	29·8	44·9	549	6·4	1·24	9·3	151
6	Ditto 990 m, NNW. 14°	37	25	38	25·3	44·3	451	4·0	0·93	5·0	204
7	Ditto 790 m, N. 32°	60	4	36	33·0	45·9	575	7·5	1·40	10·0	115
8	Siegsdorf 1060 m, NNE. 29°	76	10	14	33·1	43·6	573	6·4	1·18	7·1	195
9	Ditto 1200 m, N. 15°	92	1	7	36·4	61·2	815	7·5	0·97	8·0	167
10	Tegernsee 1220, WNW. 30°	43	12	45	28·8	47·0	552	4·4	0·83	5·6	270
11	Ditto 1370 m, ENE. 19°	42	4	54	25·3	48·3	500	4·4	0·91	5·6	192
12	Partenkirchen 1390 m, N. 24°	58	48	4	23·3	42·1	384	4·9	1·37	5·0	142
13	Ditto 1380 m, N. 22°	79	19	2	27·2	55·2	599	7·1	1·26	7·2	227
14	Mittenwald 1440 m, NE. 24°	86	5	9	—	51·1	606	6·6	1·17	6·9	—
15	Ditto 1400 m, N. 22°	55	14	31	—	45·7	540	6·0	1·16	6·8	—
17	Kreuth 1210 m, N. 19°	31	41	28	—	49·6	602	5·9	1·03	6·7	—
18	Ditto 1260 m, trough on N. slope	28	26	36	—	41·5	542	4·2	0·81	5·4	—
19	Ditto 1030 m, NW. 24°	4	41	55	—	35·9	451	4·1	0·97	5·3	—

The proportions of maple, etc., have been included under beech. The top height stated is the (curved) mean height on basal area of the 100 largest trees per hectare. Under "conifer festmetres", the increments of leaf-trees have been converted by means of their specific gravities into corresponding fm-values of spruce and fir.

In the stands at Partenkirchen, clear relationships between growing-stock, increment, increment percentage and age are apparent. The latter has been calculated as the age weighted according to the volumes of the social height-layers and can thus be correlated with the *mean harvesting age*. The mortality, regarded as the *quota of deaths from natural causes*, ought not to differ greatly in the three storeys, so that by systematic removals which, however, only slightly forestall the course of nature, a m.h.a. approximately of the order shown in the last column of the table would result.

On that assumption, the measured growth performance can be reckoned to be approximately equal to the possibility of a normal working section. Where the mean harvesting age is of that order, this production is certainly quite considerable, especially if one remembers that all of these natural stands are situated above the elevation which is most favourable as regards precipitation and the number of vegetative days; this zone, according to climatic evaluations by Magin, lies between 700 and 1100 m.

When estimating the sustained yield, attention must be paid to the fact that an appreciable increment by natural mixed stands *depends on a high content of growing-stock*. If these stands are converted to a selection structure suitable for regeneration, with a slightly lower harvesting age, the increment percentage is likely to increase although the absolute increment is more likely to decrease. If they are converted to an even-aged high forest structure, a considerable proportion of the crop becomes temporarily available, but the even-canopied stands which would then ensue must at these altitudes be subject to heavy damage from snow-breakage and the young growth is liable to undergo a prolonged period in check, possibly from attacks by *Herpotrichia* on the young spruces and heavy snow pressure on steep slopes. Despite the opening up of roads, it remains doubtful under present conditions of labour and wages whether the large quantities of small-sized produce in these secondary stands will ever be susceptible to exploitation at the proper time. Thus it is possible that the enhanced increment of this succeeding crop in consequence of lower ages of conversion may after all be lost once again as "useless lop and top". Therefore, even with a predominantly economic orientation, consideration must be given to the decision whether or not such virgin high-elevation mixed stands which have been made accessible, should be left in their natural state and whether or not it would be wise to limit interference to the occasional extraction of part of their upper storey in carefully allotted fellings.

From Magin's investigations one can infer that the *protective forests in the Alps* fulfil their protective functions most effectively when they still retain their natural structure and implicit energies of growth and adaptation. Both can be most reliably preserved by the avoidance of any kind of systematic extraction.

It should be noted that these conclusions relate only to the special conditions investigated in this particular case; they do not apply generally to the conversion of natural stands in mountainous or sub-mountainous regions into economically managed forests. The economic conditions occasioned by the specifically different site and crop conditions in south-east Europe or in Turkey (where even now there are extensive inaccessible complexes of virgin forests) are completely different. Countries which lack capital are unlikely to be able to afford the resources for investment in opening up such areas, having largely to abandon the products of the region on account of unremunerative costs. Instead of rash expansion, it may nevertheless be possible here and there to introduce a carefully regulated form of conversion which makes use of the local conditions in order to exploit their economic potentialities. After all, the opportunities of benefitting from the usufruct of these precious natural resources without destroying their peculiar constitution are unique, and if missed may not recur.

IV. ORGANIZATION AND PRODUCTION OF INTENSIVELY MANAGED ECONOMIC FORESTS

Yield research upon the processes of forest production has afforded clear evidence that by far the largest timber producers on a given area and for a given length of time are even-aged stands of coniferous trees with conical-shaped crowns growing in close horizontal contact and without overhead shade. Severe vertical staging of the social storeys results in less effective utilization of light for assimilation, and also causes a shift of the phase of full vigour in individual trees to those of older ages with dimensions such as enable them to produce only moderate increment *per unit of ground area. Vertical layering, however, means increased safety, whilst horizontal closure means greater hazards.*

Most of the managed forests in densely populated Central Europe are so far removed from their original condition that, even with the appropriation of large sums it will not ever be possible to restore them to a quasi-natural condition. The site conditions and state of the growing-crops of the larger part of the present forested areas demand clear-felling and artificial regeneration as the most effective type of restocking from a financial aspect. Predominantly pure even-aged stands in close horizontal contact enable the highest possible financial yield to be obtained at low average felling ages and an ample production of medium-sized timber which is in great demand; but individual stands are then rendered susceptible to risks from climatic extremes and to attacks by pests. *This creates a measure of interdependence between adjacent stands* for the provision of protective cover, on the side from which the major danger can be expected whilst on the other hand selection stands for their part are "independent" and do not require such a protective cover. The great need for protection in the prevailing type of stand thus demands a carefully planned sequence of fellings, a most precise spatial order, whereby border protection and cover operate together. The negative effects of sun and wind on growth along unprotected margins render previous planning of the sequence of operations indispensable, even for the natural regeneration of mixed stands. Rigidly mechanical routine measures such as typically resulted from the official introduction in Württemberg of Wagner's Blendersaumschlagbetrieb are to be deplored. But the validity of Wagner's basic ideas (1923, 1928, 1935) remains unimpaired; fundamentally we must approve of a well-thought-out "system of working" (Baader 1931). A "confused patchwork" (Baader, 1931) devoid of any spatial order can have disastrous consequences, lasting into the distant future. Forest management is faced with important tasks in this respect (Baader, 1942; W. Mantel, 1959).

Well-thought-out regeneration methods have been developed in silviculture, and have been analysed in masterly fashion by Vanselow (1931). The judicious employment of these methods, however, is possible only within the framework of a complete long-term scheme, in which the tactics of procedure in individual stands are merely part of the superior strategy of systematic silviculture and forest organization (Klotz, 1959). The ideal of the "forest which is constructed in clumps, groups and strips of uneven-aged mixture" as visualized by Krutzsch (1950, 1952) is merely an adaptation of the selection forest ideal, which in this modified form can be realized even on sites which are not suitable for selection. It is unnecessary to discuss this further from the yield research angle. The basic idea of a quasi-natural handling of the forest, however, obviously must meet with our approval.

The large current yields of far-from-natural pure stands are bought at the expense of a reduced safety-margin and unstable health of our managed forests. Gales, snow-breakage and insect attacks disturb the systematic progress of planned management. Apart from the very grievous reductions in the cash proceeds from timber which must be realized after such disasters there is a loss of production over several years from the clear-felled areas and by increment reductions in the adjacent stands. The extent of these losses has yet to be ascertained in concrete instances alongside yield studies which will also have to provide urgently needed information upon the rates of growth in the regeneration stage.

Whilst planned felling and extraction procedures are intended to ensure an uninterrupted transition of the production process of the previous generation to the succeeding generation, we must do everything in our power to make individual stands more stable by means of mixtures and greater wind-firmness. The loss of production which is incurred by departing from a spruce monoculture can be made good by the cultivation of high-yielding exotic conifers in suitable admixture. The latest results of manurial experiments in forestry have provided the possibilities for creating mixed crops with a richer biotype, even on sites which hitherto have carried monotonously pure stocks of Scots pine which thereby created dangerous breeding places for recurring mass-infestations. The general object must be to build up *forest zones with the highest possible biological stability*. The growing importance of the forest for ensuring water supplies, air filtration and human recreation in an industrial landscape which is an increasing threat to natural life (Speer, 1960; Rupf, 1960) helps responsible foresters in their endeavour to create, not only highly productive, but also healthy and beautiful forests (Ruppert, 1960). Unique and universally applicable solutions are unlikely to be found in this respect; we shall have to be satisfied if, in the presence of so many opposing forces and contrasting demands, reasonable compromises can be achieved.

In view of the expected general population increase we cannot afford to neglect the raw-material function of the forest (Dieterich, 1953). Agriculture has, in the course of the last 100 years, been able to double or treble the harvest per unit area. And even forestry in Central Europe has increased the timber yields per hectare by 50 to 100 per cent, by going over from broad-leaved to coniferous crops, which, however, has at the same time enlarged the risks and dangers. The technique of regulating the growing space, which has been the principal tool of forest management up to now, is unlikely to effect any increase worth mentioning in organic production, but the financial yields can be considerably increased thereby.[1] *Only by means of soil-amelioration and fertilizer treatment can the organic production* on many forest sites be *stepped up* by amounts of the order of 10 to 50 per cent. Certain prospects are opened out also by way of systematic breeding, which however is not without its dangers, if it is likely to increase the "artificially created monotony of the living world" (Huber, 1953b). In contrast the general increase of the organic production of the forest area by balanced fertilizer treatment appears a better way. An advantage to forestry production arising from the industrial era may be seen in the ability to manage with a relatively small expenditure of manual labour. However, this advantage is diminished when disturbances to regular management occur which necessitate the taking of urgent and extraordinary measures with the help of a large number of workers. Seen from that angle, it is again advisable to make use of those crops and forest formations which provide the highest possible insurance against set-backs.

[1] The possibilities of increased timber production—primarily a concern of forest policy—by means of the afforestation of fallow tracts of land and marginal agricultural soils along with a desirable production increase in small private forests, can be neglected here. In this connection see, among others, K. Mantel (1956), Speer (1954), Weck (1955).

In conclusion, this account of our present state of knowledge in forest yield research should have indicated the extent to which we have been able to uncover the natural laws governing growth patterns in the forest and their potentialities when set in operation by sensible techniques. It has also become apparent how much is still left to discover and how little we know so far.

The employment of significant discoveries in forest science for the good of human society is the task of practical forestry and the following rule applies: *All techniques, including the biological technique of the forester, are good or bad to the extent by which they conform with natural laws, and as beneficial or harmful as the purpose they serve and the mentality of the human beings who employ them.*

Hohenadl's Method

THE argument and symbols employed are as follows.

Let $\qquad \eta_{0\cdot9} = \dfrac{d_{0\cdot9}}{d_{0\cdot9}} = 1\cdot0; \quad \eta_{0\cdot7} = \dfrac{d_{0\cdot7}}{d_{0\cdot9}}; \quad \eta_{0\cdot5} = \dfrac{d_{0\cdot5}}{d_{0\cdot9}}, \quad$ etc.;

$$q_H = \frac{d_{1\cdot3}}{d_{0\cdot9}} \quad \text{or} \quad \frac{\text{d.b.h.}}{d_{0\cdot9}} = \text{``the Hohenadl'', or ``butt-swell'' quotient.}$$

If L = total length of stem, which is divided into five equal sections, and
$\quad V$ = total volume of stem,

then $\qquad V = \dfrac{\pi}{4} \, 0\cdot2L \, (d_{0\cdot9}^2 + d_{0\cdot7}^2 + d_{0\cdot5}^2 + d_{0\cdot3}^2 + d_{0\cdot1}^2)$

$$= \frac{\pi}{4} \, 0\cdot2L \times d_{0\cdot9}^2 \left[1 + \left(\frac{d_{0\cdot7}}{d_{0\cdot9}}\right)^2 + \left(\frac{d_{0\cdot5}}{d_{0\cdot9}}\right)^2 + \left(\frac{d_{0\cdot3}}{d_{0\cdot9}}\right)^2 + \left(\frac{d_{0\cdot1}}{d_{0\cdot9}}\right)^2 \right]$$

$$= \frac{\pi}{4} \, d_{0\cdot9}^2 L \times 0\cdot2 \, (\eta_{0\cdot9}^2 + \eta_{0\cdot7}^2 + \eta_{0\cdot5}^2 + \eta_{0\cdot3}^2 + \eta_{0\cdot1}^2).$$

But $\dfrac{\pi}{4} \, d_{0\cdot9}^2 L$ = volume of a cylinder erected on $d_{0\cdot9} = W_{0\cdot9}$.

Hence the expression $0\cdot2 \, (\eta_{0\cdot9}^2 + \eta_{0\cdot7}^2 + \eta_{0\cdot5}^2 + \eta_{0\cdot3}^2 + \eta_{0\cdot1}^2)$ is a reduction factor applied to $W_{0\cdot9}$. By definition, this is the "natural" ("echte") form factor ($\lambda_{0\cdot9}$).

Also, since $\qquad q_H = \dfrac{d_{1\cdot3}}{d_{0\cdot9}}, \quad d_{0\cdot9} = \dfrac{d_{1\cdot3}}{q_H}.$

Hence, $\qquad V = \dfrac{\pi}{4} \, d_{0\cdot9}^2 \times L \times \lambda_{0\cdot9}$

$$= \frac{\pi}{4} \left(\frac{d_{1\cdot3}}{q_H}\right)^2 \times L \times \lambda_{0\cdot9} = W_{1\cdot3} \times \frac{\lambda_{0\cdot9}}{q_H^2},$$

where $W_{1\cdot3}$ = volume of cylinder erected on diameter at breast height; hence, breast-height form factor

$$\lambda_{1\cdot3} = \frac{\lambda_{0\cdot9}}{q_H^2} = \frac{\text{natural form factor}}{\text{square of butt-quotient}}.$$

Conversion Table of Metric into English Measurements

1. *Land area*

   1 hectare (ha) = 2·471 acres.

2. *Length*
   1 metre (m) = 3·28084 feet.

3. *Conversion of diameter into girth measurements*
   1 centimetre in diameter (cm d) = 1·2368 inches true girth,
   = 0·3092 inch quarter girth.

4. *Basal area*
   1 square metre (m²) = 8·45 square feet quarter girth.
   1 square metre *per ha* (m²/ha) = 3·42268 square feet quarter girth per acre.

5. *Volume*
   1 cubic metre (m³) = 27·7362 hoppus feet.
   1 cubic metre per ha (m³/ha) = 11·2294 hoppus feet per acre.

6. *Conversion of hoppus foot into cubic foot measurements, true measure*
   1 hoppus foot = 1·2732 cubic feet, true measure.
   1 cubic foot, tr.m. = 0·7854 hoppus foot.

Dimensions of German Assortments

Festmeter (fm) = solid metre (solid volume).
Vorratsfestmeter (Vfm) = stand volume.
Erntefestmeter (Efm) = volume of timber harvested.
1 Efm ≅ 0·8 Vfm.

Classification of Timber

"Heilbronn" assortment: defined by a minimum diameter at a minimum length.

Class	Minimum length m	Minimum top diameter under bark (u.b.) cm
1	6	8
2	10	12
3	14	14
4	16	17
5	18	22
6	18	30

Assortments of poles

Class	Minimum diameter 1 m above cut end cm	Minimum length m
1a	>7–9 outside bark (o.b.)	>6–9
b	7–9	9
2a	9–11	9–12
b	9–11	12
3a	11–14	9–12
b	11–14	12–15
c	11–14	15–18
d	11–14	18

REFERENCES

ABBREVIATED TITLES

AFF	Acta forestalia Fennica
AFJZ	Allgemeine Forst- und Jagdzeitung
AFZ	Allgemeine Forstzeitschrift
AfF	Archiv für Forstwesen
CfdgF	Centralblatt für das gesamte Forstwesen
DanskST	Dansk Skovforenings Tidskrift
DfFDanm	Det forstlige Forsøgsvaesen i Danmark
DDF	Der Deutsche Forstwirt
DFuH	Der Forst- und Holzwirt
FA	Forstarchiv
FuJ	Forst und Jagd
ForJourn	Forestry Journal
FwCbl	Forstwissenschaftliches Centralblatt
HoZbl	Holz-Zentralblatt
LJb	Landwirtschaftliches Jahrbuch
MeddfStSk	Meddelanden fran Statens Skogsforskningsinstitut (Stockholm)
MittADF	Mitteilungen der Akademie der Deutschen Forstwissenschaft
MittFuF	Mitteilungen aus Forstwirtschaft und Forstwissenschaft
MittFVOest	Mitteilungen aus dem Forstlichen Versuchswesen Österreichs
MittSchweizAFV	Mitteilungen der Schweizerischen Anstalt für das Forstliche Versuchswesen
MittStfBay	Mitteilungen aus der Staatsforstverwaltung Bayerns
MittWürttFA	Mitteilungen der Württembergischen Forstlichen Versuchsanstalt
MüFH	Mündener Forstliche Hefte
OestVF	Österreichische Vierteljahresschrift für Forstwesen
SchweizZF	Schweizerische Zeitschrift für Forstwesen
SvSkT	Svenska Skogsvardsföreningens Tidskrift
ThFJ	Tharandter Forstliches Jahrburch
ZfFJ	Zeitschrift für Forst- und Jagdwesen
ZfW	Zeitschrift für Weltforstwirtschaft

ABETZ, K. (1935) *FA* **11**, 209.
– – (1943) *DDF* **25**, 305.
– – (1952) *Ber. d. Bad. Würt. Forstvereins.*
– – (1955) *Bäuerliche Waldwirtschaft, dargestellt an den Verhältnissen in Baden* (Hamburg and Berlin).
ALTHERR, E. (1953) *FwCbl* **72**, 193.
– – (1960) *AFJZ* **131**, 226.
ANTEVS, E. (1925) Carnegie Inst. Wash. Publ. No. 352.
ARNSWALDT, H. J. v. (1953) *Forst und Holz*, No. 17.
– – (1958) *AFZ* **13**, 791.
ARTMANN, A. (1949) *Jahrringchronologische Unters. usw.* (Diss. Munich.)
ASSMANN, E. (1936) (a) *Silva* **24**, 385; (b) *MittFuF* **8**, 37.
– – (1938) *FA* **14**, 37.

– – (1943) *AFJZ* **119**, 7, 105, 133; **120**, 16.
– – (1944) *AFJZ* **120**, 69.
– – (1949) (a) *FwCbl* **68**, 129; (b) *ibid.* 414.
– – (1950) (a) *FwCbl* **69**, 256; (b) *ibid.* 373; (c) *AFZ* **5**, 315.
– – (1953) (a) *FwCbl* **72**, 69; (b) *AFJZ* **124**, 175.
– – (1954) (a) *AFJZ* **125**, 149; (b) *DFuH* **9**, 439; (c) *FwCbl* **73**, 257.
– – (1955) (a) *AFZ* **10**, 61; *FwCbl* **74**, 321.
– – (1956) (a) *FwCbl* **75**, 257; (b) *AFJZ* **126**, 85; (c) *DFuH* **11**, 364; (d) *Jahrb. d. Deutsch. Forstvereins*, 168.
– – (1957) (a) *Holzmeßlehre im Neudammer Forstlehrb.* 11th ed. (Neudamm); (b) *MittStfBay* No. **29**, 158; (c) *FA* **28**, 217; (d) *AFZ* **12**, Nos. 27/28, 29/30.
– – (1959) (a) *FwCbl* **78**, 1; (b) *AFJZ* **130**, 92.

ASSMANN, E. (1960) (a) *FwCbl* **79**, 65; (b) *MittStfBay* **71**, 16.
– – (1962) *AFZ* **17**, 817, 839.
– – (1964) *AFuJZ* **135**, 213.
– – (1966) *FwCbl* **85**, 355.
– – and FRANZ, F. (1963) *Vorläufige Fichten-Ertragstafel für Bayern.* Limited edition (Munich).
– – and FRANZ, F. (1965) *FwCbl* **84**, 13. (Authors' review.)

BAADER, G. (1931) *AFJZ* **107**, 246.
– – (1934) *AFJZ* **110**, 357, 393.
– – (1935) *AFJZ* **111**, 173.
– – (1937) *AFJZ* **113**, 201, 247.
– – (1939) *Geist und Natur am Beispiel d. Forstwirtschaft.* Göttingen Univ. lect. 1939/41.
– – (1941) *Der Kiefernüberhaltbetrieb* (Frankfurt).
– – (1942) *Forsteinrichtung* (Frankfurt).
– – (1943) *AFJZ* **119**, 151.
– – (1944) *MittADF* **4**, 74.
– – (1952) *Unters. über Randschäden* (Frankfurt).
BACKMAN, G. (1943) *Roux Archiv* **141**, 455 and *Bios* **15** (Leipzig).
BADOUX, E. (1939) *MittSchweizAFV* **21**, 59.
– – (1945) *ibid.* **24**, 405.
– – (1949/50) *ibid.* **26**, 9.
– – (1952) *ibid.* **28**.
BAUER, F. (1953) *Die Roteiche* (Frankfurt).
BAULE, B. (1917) *LJb* **51**, 373.
– – (1920) *LJb* **54**, 493.
– – (1924) *LJb* **59**, 341.
BAULE, H. (1960) *DFuH* **15**, 1.
BAUMGARTNER, A. (1956) *Ber. d. deutsch. Wetterdienstes* **5**, No. 28.
– – (1957) *MittStfBay* **29**, 23.
BAUR, F. v. (1881) *Das Forstl. Versuchswesen* I, 359.
BECKING, J. H. (1953) (a) *Netherl. Journ. of Agric. Science*, May issue; (b) *Ber. d. 11. Congr. d.* IUFFRO, Rome 1953.
BERTALANFFY, L. v. (1932) *Theoretische Biologie.* 1st Vol. (Berlin).
– – (1942) *ibid.* 2nd Vol.
BIOLLEY, H. (1920) *L'aménagement des forêts par ... la méthode du contrôle* (Neufchatel). German by EBERBACH (1922).
BITTERLICH, W. (1948) *Allg. Forst- u. Holzwirtschaftl. Zeitung.*
BONNEMANN, A. (1939) *MittFuF* **10**, No. 4.
– – (1956) *AFJZ* **127**, 33, 118.
BORGGREVE, B. (1891) *Die Holzzucht.* 2nd ed. (Berlin).
BORGMANN, W. (1915) *ThFJ* **66**, 129.
BORNEBUSCH, C. H. (1933) *DfFDanm* **13**, 117.
BOSIAN, G. (1960) Zum Cuvettenproblem usw. *Flora* **149**, 167.
BOYSEN-JENSEN, P. (1932) *Die Stoffproduktion d. Pflanzen* (Jena).

– – (1939) *Die Elemente d. Pflanzenphysiologie* (Jena).
BRADLEY, R. T., CHRISTIE, J. M., and JOHNSTON, D. R. (1966) *Forest Management Tables.* Forestry Commission Booklet No. 16 (London).
BREHME, K. (1951) *ZfW* **14**, 65.
BRÜNING, D. (1959) *Forstdüngung* (Radebeul).
BÜHLER, A. (1894) *MittSchweizAFV.* 3 Vol.
– – (1918) *Der Waldbau.* 1st Vol. (Stuttgart).
– – (1922) *ibid.* 2nd Vol.
BÜNNING, E. (1948) *Entwicklungs- u. Bewegungsphysiologie d. Pflanzen* (Berlin).
BURCHARD (1860) *AFZ* **15**, 81.
BURGER, H. (1925) *FwCbl* **47**, 281.
– – (1926) *MittSchweizAFV* **14**, 29.
– – (1928) *ZfFJ* **60**.
– – (1929) *MittSchweizAFV* **16**, 243.
– – (1935) *ibid.* **19**, 21.
– – (1936) *SchweizZF*, p. 152.
– – (1937) *MittSchweizAFV* **20**.
– – (1939) *ibid.* **21**, 3, 147.
– – (1940) *ibid.* **21**, 307.
– – (1941) (a) *ibid.* **22**, 10; (b) *ibid.* **22**, 164.
– – (1942) *ibid.* **22**, 377.
– – (1945) *ibid.* **24**, 7.
– – (1947/8) *ibid.* **25**, 211, 287, 435.
– – (1949) *SchweizZF*, No. 2.
– – (1950) *MittSchweizAFV* **26**, 419.
– – (1951) *ibid.* **27**, 247.
– – (1952) *ibid.* **28**, 109.
– – (1953) *ibid.* **29**, 38.
BÜSGEN, M. (1926) (and MÜNCH, E.) *Bau und Leben unserer Waldbäume.* 3rd ed. (Jena).
BUSSE, J. (1930) *FwCbl* **52**, 310.
– – (1925) (and JAEHN) *Mitt. d. Sächs. F. V. A.* II, No. 6.
– – (1931) (and WEISSKER, A.) *ThFJ* **82**, 309.
BÜTTNER, H. (1956) *Die Naturw.* **43**, 454.

CAJANUS, W. (1914) Über d. Entwicklung gleichaltriger Waldbestände *AFF* **3**.
CARBONNIER, CH. (1954) *MeddfStSk* **44**, No. 5.
– – (1957) *ibid.* No. 5.
– – (1959) *ibid.* **67**.
CHALK, L. (1926) *Oxford Forestry Mem.* **10**.
CHENCHINE, A. (1943) *Tabii ve saf kayin usw.* Orman ve Av. Türk. Translation by F. FIRAT.
CIESLAR, A. (1907) *CfdgF* **33**, 289.
CROCOLL, A. (1940) *Zwanzig Jahre Mehreinschlag i. Baden* (Berlin).
– – (1957) *Der Massenertrag v. Pappelbeständen usw.* Spec. ed. of *FwCbl* (Hamburg and Berlin).

DANNECKER, K. (1936) *AFJZ* **112**, 83.
DENGLER, A. (1930) *Waldbau auf ökologischer Grundlage.* 1st ed. (Berlin).
– – (1937) *ZfFJ* **69**, 321.
DIETERICH, V. (1922) *Silva*, 337.
– – (1923) *AFJZ* **99**, 152, 169.

DIETERICH, V. (1924) *AFJZ*. **100**, 566.
– – (1925) *ibid*. **101**, 16, 41.
– – (1928) *Unters. i. Mischwuchsbeständen* (Tübingen).
– – (1935) *Silva* **23**, 137.
– – (1939, 1940, 1941) *Forstl. Betriebswirtschaftslehre*. 1st ed. (Berlin).
– – (1953) *Forstwirtschaftspolitik* (Hamburg and Berlin).
DITTMAR, O. (1954) *AfF* **3**, 399.
– – (1958) (a) *Formzahluntersuchungen usw*. (Berlin); (b) *AfF* **7**, 1, 130.
– – (1959) *AfF* **8**, 923.
– – (1960) *ibid*. **9**, 266.
DOUGLASS, A. E. (1929) *Nation. Geograf. Mag*. **56**.

EBERMAYER, E. (1876) *Die ges. Lehre v. d. Waldstreu* (Berlin).
EICHHORN, F. (1902) *Ertragstafeln f.d. Weißtanne* (Berlin).
– – (1904) *AFJZ* **80**, 45.
EIDE, E. (1926) *Medd. Norske Skogsforsøksv*. **7**, 88.
EIDMANN, F. E. (1943) *Unters. üb. d. Wurzelatmung u. Transpiration unserer Hauptholzarten* (Frankfurt/M.).
– – (1959) *Die Interzeption i. Buchen- u. Fichtenbeständen usw*. Assoc. Internat. d'Hydrologie Scient., Publ. No. 48 (Gentbrugge).
ENGLER, A. (1924) (a) *MittSchweizAFV* **13**, 225; (b) *ibid*. p. 285.
ERTELD, W. (1953) *AfF* **2**, 97.
– – (1953/54) *Wiss. Z. d. Humboldt Univ*. **5**.
– – (1955) *AfF* **4**, 511.
– – (1956) *FwCbl* **75**, 160.
– – (1957) (a) *Grundflächenschluß u. Zuwachs bei Kiefer, Fichte u. Buche* (Akademie-Verl. Berlin); (b) *AfF* **6**, 361; (c) *FuJ* **7**, No. 11; (d) *Richtlinien f. d. Anlage u. Bearb. v. Versuchsflächen* (Eberswalde).
– – (1959) *AfF* **8**, 495.
– – (1960) *AfF* **9**, 326.
EULE, H. W. (1959) *AFJZ* **130**, 185.

FABRICIUS, L. (1930) *FwCbl* **52**, 201.
– – (1932) *ibid*. **54**, 753.
– – (1933) *ibid*. **55**, 415.
– – (1940) *ibid*. **62**, 76.
– – (1956) *ibid*. **75**, 1.
FAVRE, E. (1928) *Journ. for. Suisse*, **49**, 84.
– – (1931) *MittSchweizAFV* **17**, No. 1.
FEIERABEND, P. (1951) *FwCbl* **70**, 395.
FILZER, P. (1951) *Die natürl. Grundlagen d. Pflanzenertrages i. Mitteleuropa* (Stuttgart).
FLEMES, E. (1937) *ZfFJ* **69**, 369.
FLÖHR, W. (1956) *Unters. üb. d. Ertragsleistung usw. d. grünen Douglasie* (Diss. Eberswalde); also contr. to GÖHRE, K. *Die Douglasie* (Berlin, 1958).
– – (1954) (and DITTMAR, O.) *AfF* **3**, 385.

FLURY, PH. (1903) *MittSchweizAFV* **7**, 1.
– – (1926) *ibid*. **14**, 251.
– – (1927) *ibid*. **14**, 301.
– – (1929) *ibid*. **15**, 303.
– – (1932) *ibid*. **17**, 246.
– – (1933) *ibid*. **18**, 65.
FRANZ, F. (1965) *FwCbl* **84**, 357.
– – (1966) *ibid*. **85**, 134.
– – (1967) *ibid*. **86**, 98.
FRANZ, H. (1956) (a) *MittStfBay* **29**, 29; (b) *AFZ* **11**, 321.
FREIST, H. (1961) *Der Lichtungszuwachs d. Rotbuche u. seine Anwendung i. Forstbetrieb* (Diss. Munich, 1960).
FRICKE, K. (1904) *CfdgF* **30**, 315.
FRIEDRICH, J. (1897) *MittFVOest* No. **12**.
FRITZSCHE, K. (1919) *MittdVA Tharandt*, II, No. 2.
– – (1929) *Physiol. Windwirkung auf Bäume* (Neudamm).
– – (1933) *ThFJ* **84**, 1.
FRÖHLICH, J. (1925) *FwCbl* **47**, 199.
– – (1954) *Urwaldpraxis* (Radebeul).

GANGHOFER, A. (1881) *Das Forstliche Versuchswesen* (Augsburg).
GASCARD, F. (1936) *SchweizZF* **87**, 90.
GÄUMANN, E. (1935) *Ber. d. Schweiz. Bot. Ges*. **44**, 157.
GEHRHARDT, E. (1901) *Die theoret. u. prakt. Bedeutung d. arithm. Mittelst*. (Meiningen).
– – (1909) *AFJZ* **85**, 117.
– – (1921) *AFJZ* **97**, 241.
– – (1922) *Silva* **10**, 37.
– – (1923) *ZfFJ* **55**, 27.
– – (1925) *AFJZ* **101**, 276.
– – (1928) (a) *AFJZ* **104**, 241; (b) *ibid*. **104**, 377.
– – (1930) *Ertragstafeln*. 2nd ed. (Berlin).
– – (1932) *ZfFJ* **64**, 65.
– – (1933) *Deutsche Forstzeit*.
– – (1934) (a) *AFJZ* **110**, 89; (b) *ibid*. p. 325; (c) *ZfFJ* **66**, 609.
GÖHRE, K. (1958) *Die Douglasie und ihr Holz* (Berlin).
GOOR, C. P. VAN (1953) *Plant and Soil* **5**, 29.
– – (1956) *Die Phosphorsäure*. Vol. **16**, 81.
GRUNDNER, F. (1904) *Unters. i. Buchenhochwalde* (Berlin).
– – (1913) *Normalertragstaf. f. Fichtenbestände* (Berlin).
GÜNTHER, M. (1955) *Unters. üb. d. Ertragsvermögen usw*. (Diss. Munich), and *Mitt. d. Vereins f. Forstl. Standortskart*. No. 4.
GUTMANN, O. (1926) *MittStfBay* **17**, 1.
GUTTENBERG, A. v. (1885) (a) *OestFV* **3**, 209; (b) *Wachstumsgesetze des Waldes* (Vienna).
– – (1915) (a) *OestFV* **33**, 217; (b) *Wachstum u. Ertrag. d. Fichte i. Hochgebirge* (Vienna and Leipzig).

HARTIG, R. (1868) *Die Rentabilität d. Fichten-nutzholz- u. Buchenbrennholzwirtschaft usw.* (Stuttgart).
— — (1885) *ZfFJ* **3**, 66.
— — (1888) *AFJZ* **65**.
— — (1889) *ibid.* **66**, 65.
— — (1892) *Fortsl. naturwiss. Zeitschr.* **1**, 129.
— — (1896) *ibid.* **5**, 1, 33.
HASSENKAMP, W. (1941) *FA* **17**, 41.
HAUFE, H. (1927) *MittdVA Tharandt*, Vol. III, No. 1.
HAUG (1894) *AFJZ* **70**, 1.
— — (1897) *ibid.* Nos. 5, 7.
— — (1899) *ibid.* **75**, 9.
HAUSDÖRFER (1957) *AfF* **6**, 811.
HAUSRATH, H. (1926) *AFJZ* **102**, 430.
HAUSSER, K. (1950) *AFJZ* **121**, 23.
— — (1953) (and SCHAIRER, E.) Ergebnisse von Düngungs- und Meliorationsvers. *Mitt-WürttFA*, **10**, No. 1.
— — (1956) *Die Phosphorsäure*, **16**, 9.
— — (1958) *AFZ* **13**, 125.
— — (1960) *AFZ* **15**, 497.
HECK, C. R. (1898) *MüFH* **13**.
— — (1904) *Freie Durchforstung* (Berlin).
— — (1931) *Handbuch d. freien Durchf.* (Stuttgart).
HENGST, E. (1958) Contr. to GÖHRE, K. *Die Douglasie*, p. 21 (Berlin).
HENRIKSEN, H. A. (1951) *DfFDanm* **20**, 387.
— — (1952) *DanskST*, 488.
— — (1953) (a) *DfFDanm* **21**, No. 2, 139; (b) (and JØRGENSEN, E.) *ibid.* p. 215.
HESSELMAN, H. (1904) *SvSkT*.
HEYER, C. (1845) *Wedekinds Neue Jahrb.* No. 30, 127.
— — (1846) *Anleitung z. forstl. Untersuchungen* (Giessen).
HILDEBRANDT, G. (1954) *Unters. a. Fichtenbeständen über Zuwachs ... reiner Holzsubstanz* (Berlin).
— — (1960) *AFJZ* **131**, 169.
HOHENADL, W. (1923) *FwCbl* **45**, 186, 226, 261.
— — (1924) *ibid.* **46**, 460, 495.
HOLMSGAARD, E. (1955) *Tree-Ring-Analyses of Danish Forest Trees* (Copenhagen).
— — (1956) (a) *DanskST*, No. 3; (b) *AFZ* **11**, 306.
— — (1958) *Forest Science* Vol. **4**, No. 1.
HOLSTENER-JØRGENSEN, H. (1959) *DfFDanm* **25**, No. 3.
HOLZAPFEL, R. (1960) *FwCbl* **79**, 298.
HORNSTEIN, F. v. (1951) *Wald und Mensch* (Ravensburg).
HUBER, B. (1928) *Jahrb. f. wiss. Botanik* **67**, No. 5.
— — (1941) *MittADF* **1**.
— — (1947) *Sitz.-Ber. d. A. d. W. Wien*, I, 155.
— — (1949) *Pflanzenphysiologie* (Heidelberg).
— — (1950) *Ber. d. D. Bot. Ges.* **63**, 53.
— — (1952) *FwCbl* **71**, 372.
— — (1953) (a) (and JAZEWITSCH, W.) *ibid.* **72**, 234;

(b) *Das Prinzip d. Mannigfaltigkeit i. d. Natur.* Munich Univ. lecture, new series, No. 2.
— — (1956) *Die Saftströme d. Pflanzen* (Berlin, Göttingen, Heidelberg).
— — (1957) *MittStfBay* **29**, 81.
— — (1958) (and JAZEWITSCH, W. v.) *Flora* **146**, 445.
HUBER, F. (1824 and 1825) *ZfF u. Jw.* (Meyer and Behlen) Nos. 1, 2, 3; 1.
HUGERSHOFF, R. (1936) *Die mathem. Hilfsmittel des ... Biologen.* 2nd Part (Dresden, in manuscript form).
— — (1940) *Ausgleichrechnung, Kollektivmaßlehre u. Korrelationsrechnung* (Berlin-Grunewald).
HUMMEL, F. C. (1947) *For Journ*, p. 30.
— — (1953) (and CHRISTIE, J.) *Revised Conifer Yield Tables for Great Britain.*
HUNTINGTON, E. (1925) Carnegie Inst. Washington Publ. No. 352.

JACCARD, P. (1913) *Naturw. Z. f. Forst- u. Landwirtsch.* **11**.
JAHN, G. (1954) *Standörtl. Grundl. f. d. Anbau d. grünen Douglasie* (Frankfurt).
JAPING (1911) *ZfFJ* **43**, 663.
JAZEWITSCH, W. v. (1953) *FwCbl* **72**, 234.
JOHNSTON, D. R. (1963) and BRADLEY, R. T. *Commonwealth Forestry Rev.* **42**, (3) No. 113.
JONSON, TH. (1927) *MeddfStSk* **23**, No. 2.
JORDAN, H. (1951) *FwCbl* **70**, 747.

KELLER, TH. and KOCH, W. (1962) *MittSchweizAFV* **35**, No. 2.
KENNEL, R. (1959) *FwCbl* **78**, 243.
— — (1965) *AFJZ* **136**, 149, 173.
KILIAS (1957) (Diss. Eberswalde).
KLAUDITZ, W. (1948) *Holzforschung* **3**, 1.
KLOTZ, K. (1959) *Waldumbau* (Munich).
KNUCHEL, H. (1930) (and BRÜCKMANN, W.) *FwCbl* **52**, 380.
— — (1933) *SchweizZF* **84**, 261.
— — (1950) *Planung und Kontrolle im Forstbetrieb* (Aarau).
KOCH, W. (1957) *Planta* **48**, 418.
— — and WALZ, H. (1966) Neuer Wasserdampfabscheider mit Peltierkühlung usw. *Naturw. Rundschau* **19**, 163.
KÖHLER, CHR. (1919) *Stammzahlen* (Tübingen), No. X of the following: *Unsere Forstwirtschaft im 20. Jh.*
KÖSTLER, J. N. (1943) *Wirtschaftlehre d. Forstwesens* (Berlin).
— — (1950) *Waldbau* (Berlin and Hamburg).
— — (1952) *Ansprache u. Pflege v. Dickungen.* Spec. ed. of *FwCbl* No. 1.
— — (1953) (a) *Waldpflege* (Hamburg and Berlin); (b) *AFJZ* **125**, 69.
— — (1956) (a) *FwCbl* **75**, 65; (b) *ibid.* p. 422.
— — (1958) *CfdgF* **75**, 224.

KÖVESSI, F. (1929) *Mathem.-naturw. Ber. a. Ungarn* **26** and **27.**

KOPEZKY, R. (1899) *CfdgF* **25,** 471.

KRAFT, G. (1884) *Beiträge z. Lehre v. d. Durchforstungen usw.* (Hanover).

KRAMER, H. (1958) *FwCbl* **77,** 295; *AFJZ* **129,** 121.

KRAUSS, G. (1926) *MittStfBay* **17,** 93.

– – (1936) *ThFJ* **87,** 697.

– – (1939) (and GÄRTNER, G. *et al.*) *ThFJ* **90,** 517.

KRENN, K. (1941) *AFJZ* **117,** 213.

– – (1942) *ibid.* **118,** 41.

– – (1943) *ibid.* **119,** 53.

– – (1944) *Die Bestandesmassenermittlung usw.* (Frankfurt).

– – (1946) (a) *Ertragstafeln f. Fichte* (Freiburg, Publications of Bad. Forstl. Vers.-Anst.); (b) *Durchforstungskriterium f. Fichte, ibid.*

– – (1947) (and PRODAN, M.) *Durchforstungskriterien d. wichtigst. Holzarten, ibid.*

– – (1948) *Tarifez. Massenberechnung* (Freiburg, *ibid.*).

KREUTZER (1960) *Die Wurzelbildung junger Waldbäume auf Pseudogley.* (Diss. Munich.)

KRÜDENER, A. V. (1943) *Lößlehmböden u. Fichtenreinbestandswirtsch. usw.* (Frankfurt, Publications of A. d. D. F.).

KRUTZSCH, H. (1924) *Bärenthoren 1924* (Neudamm).

– – (1934) (and WECK, J.) *Bärenthoren 1934. Der naturgemäße Wirtschaftswald* (Neudamm).

– – (1942) *DDF* **24,** 137.

– – (1950) *AFZ* **5,** 85.

– – (1952) *Waldaufbau* (Berlin).

KÜNANZ, H. (1950) *Zwischen schwacher und starker Durchforstung* (Frankfurt).

KUNZ, R. (1953) *MittSchweizAFV* **29,** 335.

KUNZE, M. (1889) *ThFJ* **39,** 81.

– – (1895) *ibid.* **45,** 45.

– – (1902) *ibid.* **52,** 1.

– – (1907) *ibid.* **57,** 1.

– – (1918) *Mitt. d. Sächs. F. V. A.* I, No. 5.

KURTH, A. (1946) *MittSchweizAFV* **24,** 581.

LAATSCH, W. (1954) *Dynamik d. mitteleuropäischen Mineralböden.* 3rd ed. (Dresden and Leipzig).

– – (1957) *MittStfBay* **29,** 50.

– – (1963) *Bodenfruchtbarkeit und Nadelholzanbau.* (Munich, Basle, Vienna).

LADEFOGED, K. (1946) *DfFDanm* **16,** 365.

LEIBUNDGUT, H. (1945) *MittSchweizAFV* **24,** 219.

– – *Comptes rend. 11ème Congr.* IUFFRO, Section 23 (Rome).

– – (1956) *Rapports 12ème Congr.* IUFFRO, Vol. 2, Sections 23, 92, 95.

LEMKE (1956) *AfF* **5,** 161.

LEMMEL, H. (1922) *ZfFJ* **54,** 672.

– – (1925) *ibid.* **57,** 84.

– – (1939) *Die Organismusidee in Möllers Dauerwaldgedanken* (Berlin).

LEMMERMANN (1940) *Die Agrikulturchemie usw.* (Braunschweig).

LENT (1928) *ZfFJ* **60,** No. 11.

LIEBIG, J. V. (1855) *Nachtrag z.d. Grundsätzen d. Agrikulturchemie* (Brunswick).

LIEBSCHER, E. (1895) *Journ. f. Landwirtsch.* **43,** 49.

LIOCOURT, F. DE (1898) *De l'aménagement des sapinières* (Besançon).

LÖNNROTH, E. (1925) *Unters. über d. innere Struktur—naturnormaler Kiefernbestände* (Helsinki).

LOREY, T. V. (1878) *AFJZ* **54,** 149.

LUNDEGÅRDH, H. (1930 and 1949) *Klima u. Boden in ihre Wirkung a. d. Pflanzenleben.* 2nd and 3rd eds. (Jena).

MACKENZIE, A. M. (1962) *Forestry* **21,** 30.

MAGIN, R. (1952) *FwCbl* **71,** 225.

– – (1954) *ibid.* **73,** 103.

– – (1955) *AFZ* **10,** 117, 236.

– – (1957) (a) *MittStfBay* **29,** 176; (b) *AFZ* **12,** No. 46.

– – (1958) *AFJZ* **129,** 145.

– – (1959) (a) Struktur u. Leistung mehrschichtiger Mischwälder i.d. Bayer. Alpen, *MittStfBay* **30**; (b) *DFuH,* **14,** No. 15.

MAHLER (1937) *AFJZ* **113,** 69.

MANG, K. (1955) *Der Fohrenüberhaltbetrieb i. F.A. Lindau.* (Diss. Munich).

MANTEL, K. (1956) *DFuH* **11,** 391.

MANTEL, W. (1959) *Forsteinrichtung.* 2nd ed. (Frankf.).

MAR:MØLLER, C. (1945) *Unters. über Laubmenge, Stoffverlust u. Stoffproduktion d. Waldes* (Copenhagen).

– – (1954) (a) *DfFDanm* **21,** 253, 273, 327; (b) *Thinning Problems ... in Denmark.* Tech. Bull. 73, College of Forestry (Syracuse); (c) *FwCbl* **73,** 350.

– – (1957) (and SCHAFFALITZKY DE MUCKADELL, M.) *DanskST* No. 8.

MARTIN, H. (1894–99) *Die Folgerungen aus der Bodenreinertragstheorie.* 5 Vol. (Leipzig).

MASCHER, R. (1953) *Schriftenr. d. Forstl. Fak. Göttingen* **9,** 37.

MATERN, B. (1956) *MeddfStSk* **46,** No. 11.

MAUVE, K. (1931) *Über Bestandesaufbau usw., i. galizischen Karpathenurwald.* Diss. Eberswalde (Hanover).

MAYER, R. (1958) *AFJZ* **129,** 105, 151, 19. (Diss. Munich, 1957.)

– – (1959) *AFZ* **14,** 530.

– – (1960) *MittStfBay* **31,** 137.

MAYER-KRAPOLL, H. (1954) *Die Anwendung v. Handelsdüngemitteln ... i. d. Forstwirtschaft* (Bochum, Ruhr-Stickstoff A.G.)

MAYER-WEGELIN, H. (1936) *Ästung* (Hanover).

– – (1950) *AFJZ* **122,** 12.

– – (1952) *HoZbl* **78,** 1773.

– – (1955) (and TRENDELENBURG, R.) *Das Holz als Rohstoff.* 2nd ed. (Munich).

MERKER, E. (1958) *AFZ* **13**, 314.

METZGER, K. (1893) *MüFH* **3**, 35.

— — (1894) *ibid.* **5**, 61.

MEYER, H. A. (1933) *SchweizZF* **84**, Nos. 2, 3, 4.

— — (1934) *Die rechnerischen Grundlagen d. Kontrollmethoden* (Zürich).

MEYER, J. (1939) *ZfFJ* **71**, 369.

MEYER, R. (1929) *Z. f. Pflanzenernährung usw.* **A14**, 1.

MIKOLA, P. (1950) *Comm. Inst. for. Fenn.* **38**, 5.

MILLER, R. (1959) *FwCbl* **78**, 297.

— — and RÜSCH, J. (1960) *ibid.* **79**, 42.

MITSCHERLICH, E. A. (1910) *Landwirtsch. Jahrbuch* **38**, 537.

— — (1948) *Die Ertragsgesetze* (Berlin).

MITSCHERLICH, G. (1939) *MittFuF* **10**, No. 4.

— — (1949) *FwCbl* **68**.

— — (1950) *ibid.* **69**, 27.

— — (1951) *AFJZ* **122**.

— — (1952) *Der Tannen-Fichten-(Buchen)-Plenterwald* (Freiburg, publications of Bad. Forstl. V.A.).

— — (1953) (a) *Der Eichenbestand mit Buchen- u. Tannenunterstd* (Freiburg, publications of Bad. Forstl. V.A.; (b) *AFJZ* **124**, 125.

— — (1954) *FwCbl* **73**, 143, 362.

— — (1955) (a) *AF* **10**, No. 48; (b) *ibid.* p. 175.

— — (1956) (a) *AFJZ* **126**, 125, 193; **127**, 106. (b) *ibid.* **128**, 171, 219, 245. Also res. in publications of Bad. Forst. V.A. No. 14 (Freiburg).

— — (1957) (a) *AFJZ* **128**, 1.

— — (1958) (a) (and WITTICH, W.) *AFJZ* **129**, 169; (b) *DFuH* **13**, 1.

— — (1961) *Unters. i. Plenterwäldern d. Schwarzwaldes*, No. 17, publications of Bad.-Wurtt. Vers.-Anst. (Freiburg).

MÖLLER, A. (1920) *ZfFJ* **52**, No. 1.

— — (1921) *ibid.* **53**, No. 2.

— — (1922) *Der Dauerwaldgedanke* (Berlin).

MOOSMAYER, U. (1955) *Mitt. d. Ver. f. Forstl. Standortskart.* No. 4.

— — (1957) *ibid.* No. 7.

MORK, E. (1942) *Medd. f. d. norske skogforsöksv.* No. 29 (Oslo).

MÜLLER, D. (1954) *DfFDanm* **21**, 303.

— — (1954) (and NIELSEN *DfFDanm* **21**, 253.

MÜLLER, G. (1957) (a) *Über Gesetzmäßigkeiten im Wachstumsgang usw.* Diss. Freiburg; (b) *FwCbl* **76**, 34.

— — (1958) *ibid.* **77**, 41.

— — (1958) (and ZAHN, E.) *FwCbl* **77**, 129.

MÜLLER-STOLL, H. (1951) *Bibl. Botan.* No. 122.

NÄSLUND, M. (1929) *MeddFStSk* **25**, 93.

— — (1936) *ibid.* **29**.

— — (1942) *ibid.* **33**.

— — (1947) *ibid.* **36**, No. 3.

— — (1950) (and HAGBERG, N.) *Kubierungstabellen usw.* (Stockholm).

NESSENIUS, G. (1956) *FwCbl* **75**, 550.

NESTEROW, W. (1952) *Lesnoje Chosjaistwo* **11**, 28.

NEUWIRTH, G. (1962) *Tagungsber. d. Deutsch. Ak. d. Landw. Berlin* No. 53.

— — (1963) *AfF* **12**, 1224.

— — (1966) *AfF* **15**, 379.

NOSEK, K. (1955) *FwCbl* **74**, 330.

OLBERG, A. (1950) *Die Durchforstung d. Kiefer* (Hannover).

— — (1951) *FwCbl* **70**, 1.

— — (1953) *AFJZ* **124**, 221.

— — (1954) *FA* **25**, 1.

— — (1955) *AFJZ* **126**, 65.

— — (1956) *DFuH* **11**, No. 9.

OELKERS, J. (1932) *Waldbau*, Part III. *Durchforstung* (Hanover).

OLDIGES, H. (1958) *AFZ* **14**, 138.

— — (1959) *Z. f. angew. Ent.* **45**, 49 and *MittStfBay* **31**, 201.

PASSECKER, H. (1952) *Der Züchter* **22**, 26.

PATERSON, H. (1956) *The Forest Area of the World,* etc. (Göteborg Royal University).

PECHMANN, H. v. (1953) *Holz als Roh- u. Werkst.* **11**.

— — (1954) *FwCbl* **73**, 65.

— — (1955) (and SCHAILE, O.) *ibid.* **74**, 305.

— — (1957) *AFJZ* **128**, 13.

— — (1958) *SchweizZF*, S. 615.

— — (1959) *MittStfBay* **31**, 145.

— — (1960) (and WUTZ, A.) *FwCbl* **79**, 91.

PESCHEL, W. (1938) *ThFJ* **89**, 169.

PETRI, H. (1957) Zum ertragskundl. Verhalten d. Fichte usw. *Mitt. a. d. Forsteinrichtungsamt Koblenz,* No. 7.

PETTERSON, N. (1927) *MeddfStSk* **23**.

— — (1954) *Die Massenproduktion des Nadelwaldes, ibid.* **45**, No. 1.

PHILIPP, K. (1931) *Forstl. Hilfstabellen (Karlsruhe) und Hilfstabellen f. Forsttaxatoren* (Karlsruhe).

PISEK, A. and TRANQUILLINI, W. (1951) *Phys. Plant.* **4**, 1.

— — (1954) *Flora* **141**, 237.

— — and WINKLER, E. (1958) *Planta* **51**, 518 (Berlin–Göttingen–Heidelberg, Springer 1958).

— — and WINKLER, E. (1958) *Planta* **53**, 532 (Berlin–Göttingen–Heidelberg, Springer 1959).

POLSTER, H. (1950) *Die physiolog. Grundlagen d. Stoffproduktion i. Walde* (Munich).

— — (1955) *AfF* **4**, 689.

POPESCU-ZELETIN, J. (1936) *AFJZ* **112**, 135, 196, 233.

PRESSLER, M. (1865) *Das Gesetz der Stammbildung* (Leipzig).

PRODAN, M. (1944) *Zuwachs- u. Ertragsunters. i. Plenterwald* (Diss. Freiburg).
— — (1946) *Der Aufbau des Holzvorrates in Fichtenbest.* (Freiburg, publications of Bad. Forstl. V.A.).
— — (1949) *Normalisierung des Plenterwaldes* (Freiburg, publications of Bad. Forstl. V.A.).
— — (1951) *Messung der Waldbestände* (Frankfurt).

RAMANN, E. (1883) *ZfFJ* **15**, 577, 633.
RAUCHENBERGER, K. (1959) *Der Wald braucht Kalk.* 3rd ed. (Cologne) p. 50.
RECHTERN (1942) *DDF* Nos. 83/86.
— — (1944) *ibid.* Nos. 47/50.
REINEKE, L. H. (1933) *Journ. of Agricult. Res.* Vol. **46**.
REINHOLD, G. (1926) Die Bedeutung d. Gesamtwuchsleistung usw. *MittStfBay* **18**.
RENNIE, P. J. (1955) *Plant and Soil* **7**, 49.
RIPPEL, A. (1926) *Z. f. Pflanzenernährung usw.* **A8**, 72.
ROBERTSON, TH. BR. (1908) *Archiv f. Entwicklungsmechanik* **26**, 108.
ROHMEDER, E. (1935) *FwCbl* **57**, 205.
— — (1948) *ibid.* **67**, 32.
— — (1949) *ibid.* **68**, 680.
— — (1954) *AFZ* **9**, No. 48.
— — (1955) *AFZ* **10**, 201.
— — (1956) (a) *Z. f. Forstgenetik usw.* **5**, 142; (b) *MittStfBay* **29**, 186.
— — (1957) *Silvae Genetic.* **6**, 136.
— — (1960) *MittStfBay* **31**, 173.
ROMELL, L. G. (1932) *Soil Science* **34**, 161.
— — (1938) *Norrlands Skogsvardsförb.* **34**, 1–8.
RONDE, G. (1957) *FwCbl* **67**, 95.
— — (1959) *MittStfBay* **31**, 193.
— — (1960) *Z. f. ang. Entomologie* **1**, 52.
RUBNER, K. (1925) *FA* **2**, 145.
— — (1928) *Die pflanzengeograph. Grundlagen des Waldbaus*, 2nd ed. (Neudamm).
— — (1943) *ThFJ* **94**, No. 6.
RUPF, H. (1960) *Wald und Mensch im Geschehen den Gegenwart* (Lecture), *AFZ* **15**, 545.
RUPPERT, K. (1960) *Der Stadtwald als Wirtschafts- u. Erholungswald* (Munich).
RÜSCH, J. D. (1955) *Z. f. Pflanzenernährung usw.* **71**, 113.

SAUKEL, F. P. (1959) *FwCbl* **78**, 279.
SCAMONI (1951) *Waldgesellschaften und Waldstandorte*, (Berlin); 2nd ed. (1954).
SCHÄDELIN, W. (1926) *SchweizZF* **67**.
— — (1932) *FwCbl* **51**, 267.
— — (1942) *Die Auslesedurchforstung*, 3rd ed. (Berne and Leipzig).
SCHAEFFER, A., GAZIN, A. and D'ALVERNY (1930) *Sapinières etc.* (Paris).
SCHAFFALITZKY DE MUCKADELL, M. (1954) *Phys. Plant.* **7**, 782.

— — (1955) *ibid.* **8**, 370.
SCHENK, C. A. (1924) *AFJZ* **100**.
SCHIFFEL, A. (1904) *Wuchsgesetze normaler Fichtenbestände* (Vienna).
— — (1906) *CdfgF* **32**, 333, 405.
SCHLETTER, A. (1954) *AfF* **3**, 193.
SCHMIDT, H. (1952) *Z. f. Forstgenetik usw.* **1**, 81.
SCHMITT, R. (1959) (and SCHNEIDER, B). *Die Aufstellung von Massentafeln usw.* (Frankfurt).
SCHMITZ-LENDERS (1948) *Pappel-Ertrags- u. Massentafeln* (Hannover).
SCHNEIDER-ORELLI, O. (1950) *MittSchweizAFV* **26**, 837.
SCHOBER, R. (1937) *MittFuF* **8**, 293.
— — (1942) *ibid.* **13**, 89.
— — (1949) *Die Lärche* (Hanover).
— — (1950) *AFJZ* **121**.
— — (1951) (a) *AFJZ* **122**, 81; (b) *FwCbl* **70**, 204.
— — (1953) *Die japanische Lärche* (Frankfurt).
— — (1954) *AFJZ* **125**, 160.
— — (1955) *FwCbl* **74**, 36.
— — (1957) *AFZ* **12**, 321, 389.
SCHÖPF, J. (1954) *FwCbl* **73**, 275.
SCHOTTE, G. (1912) *MeddfStSk* No. 9.
SCHREINER, H. (1933) *FwCbl* **55**, 405.
SCHUBERT, A. (1939) *ThFJ* **90**, 821.
SCHULZ-BRÜGGEMANN (1947) Diss. Hanover–Münden 1946.
SCHWAPPACH, A. (1886) *AFJZ* **62**, 329.
— — (1889) *Wachstum u. Ertrag norm. Kiefernbestände* (Berlin).
— — (1890) as before: *Fichtenbestände* (Berlin).
— — (1893) as before: *Rotbuchenbestände* (Berlin).
— — (1902) *Wachst. u. Ertrag normal. Fichtenbestände i. Preußen* (Neudamm).
— — (1908) *Die Kiefer* (Neudamm).
— — (1911) *Die Rotbuche* (Neudamm).
— — (1920) *Unters. über d. Zuwachsleistungen v. Eichen-Hochwaldsbest.* 2nd ed. (Neudamm).
SEEBACH, CH. V. (1844) *Cotta-Album*, p. 231 (Breslau and Oppeln).
— — (1845) *Pfeils krit. Blätter* **21**, 141.
SEYBOLD, A. (1934) *Ber. d. D. Bot. Ges.*, p. 497.
— — (1942) (and WEISSWEILER), *Bot. Archiv* **43**, 267.
SIOSTRZONEK, E. (1958) *FwCbl* **77**, 193.
SONN, S. W. (1960) *Der Einfluß des Waldes auf den Boden.* Germ. edition (Jena).
SPEER, J. (1954) *Die Parität zwischen Landwirtschaft u. Forstwirtschaft.* Spec. No., *Landwirtschaftl. Woche, München.* (1959) *Die Preiskostenkalkulation i. d. Forstwirtschaft* (Munich).
— — (1960) Wald und Forstwirtschaft in der Industriegesellschaft. Munich Univ. lecture, new series No. 29 and *HoZbl* 1960, No. 138/9.
SPEIDEL, G. (1957) *Die rechnerischen Grundlagen d. Leistungskontrolle* (Frankfurt).
— — (1959) *AFJZ* **130**, 154.
STÅLFELT, M. G. (1925) *MeddfStSk* **21**, 181.

STREBEL, O. (1960) *FwCbl* **79**, 17.

TAMM, C. O. (1955) *MeddfStSk* **45**, No. 5.
— — (1956) *ibid.* **46**, No. 3.
THALENHORST, W. (1958) *Mitt. d. Nieders. V.A.* **21**.
TIRÉN, L. (1928) Einige Unters. über d. Schaftform, *MeddfStSk* **24**, No. 4.
— — (1929) Über Grundflächenberechnung und ihre Genauigkeit *ibid.* **25**, 229.
TISCHENDORF, W. (1925) *CfdfgF* **51**, 69, 217.
TOMA, G. T. (1940) *ZfFJ* **72**, 305, 379.
TOPCUOGLU (1940) *ThFJ* **91**, 485.
TRENDELENBURG, R. and MAYER-WEGELIN, H. (1955) *Das Holz als Rohstoff*, 2nd ed. (Munich).

VANSELOW, K. (1931) *Theorie u. Praxis d. natürl. Verj. i. Wirtschaftswald* (Neudamm).
— — (1937) *AFJZ* **113**, 33, 88, 114, 148.
— — (1941) *Einführung i. d. Forstl. Zuwachs- u. Ertragslehre* (Frankfurt).
— — (1942) (a) *FwCbl* **64**, No. 1/2; (b) *DDF* **24**, 261, 273.
— — (1943) (a) *FwCbl* **65**, 1; (b) *ibid.* **65**, 105; (c) *DDF* **25**, 289.
— — (1950) *FwCbl* **69**, No. 9.
— — (1951) (a) *FwCbl* **70**, 409; (b) *AFZ* **6**, No. 31/32.
— — (1956) *FwCbl* **75**, 193.
VATER, H. (1927) (and SACHSSE, H.) *Forstl. Anbauversuche, insbes. Düngungsversuche.* Publ. of Deutsch. Landwirtsch.-Ges. No. 352.

WAGENKNECHT, E. (1960) *MittStfBay* **31**, 252.
WAGNER, CH. (1923) (a) *Der Blendersaumschlag u. sein System*, 3rd ed. (Berlin); (b) *Die Grundlagen d. räumlichen Ordnung i. Walde*, 4th ed. (Berlin).
— — (1928) *Forsteinrichtung* (Berlin).
— — (1935) *Grundlegung einer forstlichen Betriebslehre* (Berlin).
WALTER, H. (1951) *Einführung i. d. Phytologie, III. Grundl. d. Pflanzenverbreitung*, Part I. Standortslehre (Stuttgart).
— — (1957) (and HABER) Ber. d. D. Bot. Ges., 275.
WEBER, H. W. (1929) *Das System der Forstwirtschaftslehre*, 2nd ed. (Giessen).
WEBER, R. (1881) *AFJZ* **57**, 1.
— — (1891) *Lehrb. d. Forsteinrichtung* (Berlin).
WECK, J. (1943) *DDF* **25**, 417.
— — (1944) *FA* **20**, 73.
— — (1947) *Forstl. Zuwachs- u. Ertragskunde*, 1st ed. (Radebeul).
— — (1950) *FwCbl* **69**, 584.
— — (1953) *AFZ* **8**, 39.
— — (1955) *Forstl. Zuwachs- u. Ertragskunde*, 2nd ed. (Radebeul and Berlin).
— — (1956) *FwCbl* **75**, 108.
— — (1957) *FA* **28**, 223.
WEHRMANN, J. (1956) *FwCbl* **75**, 357.

— — (1957) *MittStfBay* **29**, 62.
— — (1958) *Z. f. Pflanzenernährung* **84**, 271.
— — (1959) *FwCbl* **78**, 77.
WEIHE, J. (1955) *Das Wachstum d. Fichte nach d. Badischen Versuchsflächen* (Publications of Bad. Forstl. V.A., Freiburg).
— — (1958) *AFJZ* **129**, 233.
— — (1959) *ibid.* **130**, 11,161.
WEISE, W. (1880) *Ertragstafeln f. d. Kiefer* (Berlin).
WELLENHOFER, W. (1949) *Unters. über d. Ursache d. Eichenjahrringschwankungen usw.* (Diss. Munich, 1948.)
WICHT, CH. L. (1934) *Zur Methodik des Durchforstungsversuchs* (Tharandt).
WIEDEMANN, E. (1923) *Zuwachsrückgang u. Wuchsstockungen der Fichte*, 1st ed. (Tharandt).
— — (1925) *Die praktischen Erfolge des Kiefern-Dauerwaldes* (Brunswick).
— — (1926) *ZfFJ* **58**, 269.
— — (1927) *FwCbl* **49.**
— — (1928) *ZfFJ* **60**, 257.
— — (1930) (a) *FwCbl* **52**, 403; (b) *Anweisung f. d. Aufnahme u. Bearbeitung d. Versuchsflächen* (Neudamm).
— — (1931) *ZfFJ* **63**, 614.
— — (1933) *Deutsche Forstzeitg.* (1934) *ibid.*
— — (1936) *ZfFJ* **68**, 513.
— — (1937) *Die Fichte 1936* (Hanover).
— — (1939) *MittFuF* **10**, 3.
— — (1942) *MittFuF* **13**, No. 1.
— — (1943) (a) *ZfFJ* **75**, 227; (b) *AFJZ* **114**, 123.
— — (1948) *Die Kiefer* (Hanover).
— — (1949) *Ertragstafeln der wichtigen Holzarten* (Hanover).
— — (1950) *Ertragskundliche u. waldbauliche Grundlagen d. Forstwirtschaft*, 1st ed. (Frankfurt).
WIMMER, E. (1914) *Ertrags- u. Sortimentsunters. i. Buchenhochwald* (Karlsruhe).
WINDIRSCH, J. (1936) *ThFJ* **87**, 533.
WITTICH, W. (1934) *ZfFJ* **66**, 249.
— — (1935) *ibid.* **67**, 177.
— — (1938) *ibid.* **70**, 337.
— — (1939) *FA* **15**, 96.
— — (1942) *ZfFJ* **74**, Nos. 1/2, 7/8.
— — (1943) *FA* **19**, 1.
— — (1944) *ibid.* **20**, 110.
— — (1951) *FwCbl* **70**, No. 2.
— — (1952) *Der heutige Stand unseres Wissens vom Humus usw.* (Frankfurt).
— — (1953) *Schrift.—Reihe d. Forstl. Fak. Göttingen*, Vol. **9**, 7.
— — (1954) *FwCbl* **73**, 211.
— — (1955) *AFJZ* **126**, 109.
— — (1956) *FwCbl* **76**, 407.
— — (1957) *AFZ* **12**, 185.
— — (1958) (a) *AFZ* **13**, No. 10; (b) *Auswertg. v. Düngungsvers.* (Ruhr-Stickstoff, Bochum) p. 1.
WOELFLE, M. (1937) *FwCbl* **59**, 757.
— — (1954) *FwCbl* **73**, 158.

WOHLFARTH, E. (1935) *ZfFJ* **67**, 289, 344.
– – (1938) *AFJZ* **114**, 65, 102.

ZELLER, O. (1951) *Planta* **39**, 500.
ZIMMERLE, H. (1933) *Beiträge z. Biologie d. Kiefer i. Württemberg*, *MittWürttFA* **3**, 1.
– – (1936) (a) *MittWürttFA* **4**, No. 2, 5; (b) *ibid.* No. 2, 91; (c) *Silva* **24**, Nos. 6, 7, 8, 10, 39.
– – (1937) *Silva* **25**, Nos. 20 and 21.
– – (1938) (a) *AFJZ* **114**, 341; (b) *ibid.* 194.
– – (1939) *ibid.* **115**, 305.
– – (1940) *ibid.* **116**.
– – (1941) *ibid.* **117**, 85.
– – (1942) *ibid.* **118**, 32.
– – (1944) *ibid.* **120**, 29.
– – (1949) *Beiträge z. Biologie d. Fichte* (Stuttgart); (b) *FwCbl* **68**, 401.
– – (1951) *ibid.* **70**, 92.

– – (1952) Ertragszahlen f. Grüne Douglasie usw. i. Württemberg, *MittWürttFA* **9**, No. 2.
ZOEBELEIN, G. (1954) *Z. f. angew. Entomologie* **36**, 358.
– – (1956) *ibid.* **38**, 369.
– – (1957) *ibid.* **39**, 129; *FwCbl* **76**, 24.
ZÖTTL, H. (1957) *MittStfBay* **29**, 73.
– – (1958) (a) *Z. f. Pflanzenern.* **129**, 116; (b) *FwCbl* **77**, 1.
– – (1960) (a) *FwCbl* **79**, 72; (b) *ibid.* 221.
ZUNDEL, R. (1960) *Ertragskundl. Unters. i. zweialtrigen Best. usw.* Publ. of Landesforstverw. Baden-Württ. Vol. 6.
ZWÖLFER, W. (1952) *Verh. d. Ges. f. angew. Entomologie* **12**, 164.
– – (1953) *AFZ* **8**, 549.
– – (1957) *Z. f. angew. Entom.* **40**, 422.
ZYCHA, H. (1948) *FwCbl* **67**, 80.

INDEX

Acceleration of growth 233
Age
   actual 474
   breast-height 475
   cross-sectional 455
   final 473
   free-growing 454
   harvesting 444, 474
Age dependence 139
Age of assessment 168
Age of reference 168
Age phases, physiological 140
Amelioration 413
Annual ring indices 197
Annual rings 48–57
Annual shoots 39–41
Assimilation 10, 23, 36
   apparent 11
Assortment tables 70

Backman growth law 42
Band method of v. Baur 159
Bark thickness 73, 74
Basal area 101
   critical 229
   maximum 229
   mean 216
   optimum 229
Basal area increment 53, 149, 151
Basal area measurement 220
Basal area over a period 214
Beech 245–87
Beech characterization 245
Beech thinning and efficiencies 246–87
Biometrics 5
Biotypes 87
Branch respiration 37
Breeding 244, 488

Calculation methods 222
Caliper 220
Clay minerals 7
Climate and increment 196
Climate corrections 198
Compensation point 13
Competition 46
Control method 459
CO_2 14–18
Crop classification 96
Crop height, final 208

Crown 111
Crown canopy 101
Crown diameter 110
Crown efficiencies 119–39
Crown fullness ratio 112, 114
Crown maps 104, 105
Crown measures 111–13
Crown morphology 112
Crown part exposed to light 111, 112
Crown part in shade 111, 112
Crown projection 109
Crown size and efficiency 111, 130–2
Crown structure 111
Crown surface area 115
Crown volume 115

Degradation 8, 407
Degree of stocking 110
   natural critical 231
   optimum 459, 461
Diameter, the growth rhythm of the 51
Diameter distributions of stands 92–95
Diameter distributions of working sections 447–51
Diameter increment 51–56
Disengagement, degree of 107–8
Distribution, asymmetric 94–95

Economic forests, intensely managed 487
Edge effects 408–11
Eichhorn's rule 161
Establishment, methods of 338
Estimate of attained yield 168
Experimental layout 219
Experimental methods 219

Fertilizer treatment 413–27
Festmetres of felled timber 77
Festmetres of standing trees 77
Forest formations, types of 483
Forest organization 487
Form factor 64–69
Form factor measurement 222
Form height 151
Frequency distributions 92–95

Genetically fixed characteristics 85–87
Girth measuring 220
Ground coverage 101–11
Ground water level 408

Growing space   46, 101–11, 156, 365
Growing space index of v. Seebach   108
Growth acceleration   233
Growth-controlling mechanisms   85
Growth determinations   219
Growth law (Mitscherlich)   20–23
Growth laws   203
Growth patterns   203, 205
  comparative   187
Growth performance, comparative   194

Height
  final crop   208
  mean   143
  top   143
Height growth development   40–48
Height increment   40–48
Height measuring   221
Hohenadl's method   66, 67, 69, 491
Humus substances   7

Increment
  additive   346
  climate and   196
  current annual   80
  mean annual   80
  sectional area   53–57, 59–63
Increment determination   223
Increment efficiencies, comparative   187
Increment felling   184, 374
Increment reactions to thinning   227
Increment reduction   202
Increment reduction tables   187
Indicator method   160
Interest, accumulated   242

Larch   191, 358
Leaf efficiencies   30
Leaf quantities (areas)   31–33, 35, 115–17
Leaf respiration   36
Leaves in light   12
Leaves in shade   12
Light   11–13
Litter   347
Litter utilization   412

Mathematical statistics   5
Mixed stands   346–96
  basic problems of   348
  ratios of mixture in   347
  results in   348
  yield tables for   348

Natural forest stands   479–86
Needle quantities (weights)   31, 32, 38

Nominal area   108
Normal trend   176, 196
Norway spruce   287
Norway spruce characterization   287
Norway spruce thinning   290–323
Norway spruce thinning experiment at Bowmont   307
Nutrient media   9
Nutrient storage   9
Nutrient supplies   20–23

Oak   330–8
Oak characterization   330
Open-stand system   369–74
Overlapping of development   473, 474

Pathological influences   202
Perpetual forest   401
Photosynthetic effect   12
Physiological dependence, law of   21
Plant spacing   338
Plates, the phenomenon of   389
Podsolization   7
Poplar   195
Production and tree age   473
Production equation of Boysen-Jensen   34
Production spectra of Mar:Møller   36
Productive capacity   117
Projection ratio   109, 112
Proportionality limit   233, 389
Protective forests   486

Quality class, absolute   179
Quality class changes   176
Quality classification   158–86
  dynamic   180
  static   180

Radiation levels   117
Rapid growth management   313
  advantages and disadvantages of   320
Recruitment   459
Reduced length of harvested stems   236, 265
Relation
  auxiliary   161
  basic   160
  final   160
Reserves   127–9, 389, 391–401
Respiration   11, 15, 20, 23–26
  branch   37
  leaf   36
  root   15, 26
Respiration economy   25
Respiration loss   34–38
Revenue, gross (and net)   241

Root respiration   15, 26
Root system, dimensions of the   70–72
Rotation   436–54

Scots pine   323
Scots pine characterization   323
Scots pine reserves   391
Scots pine thinning   324–30
Seed development   201
Selection, group   467
Selection effects   244, 274, 282
Selection experiments   461–70
Selection stands   454
    height curves of   453
    production in   461
    quality classification in   454
Selective thinning   209
Silver fir characterization   366
Silver fir efficiencies   367, 368
Silvicultural treatments   297
Silvicultural units   208
Site quality   158
Sitka spruce   194
Social position   117
Soil biology   432
Soil degradation   8
Soil fauna   433
Soil respiration   11
Soil types   7
Solar radiation   11
Sowing efficiencies   339, 340
Spacing   338
    square   102, 103
    triangular   102, 103
Spread, degree of (crown)   112
Stages of development   480
Statistical shift   226
Steel tapes   220
Stem cross-sections   63
Stem form classes   87
Stem form theories   58–61
Stem number development   141
Stem of the future   277
Stem profile   57, 58, 60
Stem-wood   76
Sustained yield management   242

Taper (ratio $d_{1.3}/h$)   366, 457
Temperature   13
Thinning
    beginning of   217
    crown   212, 213
    low   212, 213
    selective   209

    the doctrine of (Schädelin)   284
    the kind of   213
Thinning frequency   217
Thinning grade   214
Thinning intensity   217
Thinning intervals   216, 218
Thinning reactions   222
Thinning severity   214
Thinning volume per cent   163
Timber, specific weight   78, 79
Timber dry weight   78, 79
Timber prices   240
Timber quality   240
Total crop yield   152, 165, 168
Transpiration   18–20, 27, 28
Tree classes
    by Kraft   84
    functional   89
    natural   83–87
    numerical   92
    technical   87
T-test   233
Twice-felled stands   369

Volume
    mean periodic   467
    units of   75–76
Volume increment   79–81, 149, 151, 152
Volume/weight relationships   78, 79

Water requirements   18
Water supply   172, 175, 176, 177
Wind effect   57
Wind pressure   59
Wind protection   17
Wood increment   201
Working plans   210, 211
Working sections   435

Yield, probable   168
    total crop   152, 165, 168
Yield changes   406
Yield classes   182
Yield deterioration   406
Yield factors   9
Yield level   167
Yield tables   164
    construction of   163, 185
    correction of   181
    general   181
Yield tables for spruce   172
Yield theory   3